ELECTROMAGNETIC THEORY

ELECTROMAGNETIC THEORY

Static Fields and Their Mapping

(formerly titled: *Electromagnetic Fields, Theory and Applications*)

ERNST WEBER

President, Polytechnic Institute of Brooklyn

Dover Publications, Inc., New York

Published in Canada by General Publishing Com-
pany, Ltd., 30 Lesmill Road, Don Mills, Toronto,
Ontario.
Published in the United Kingdom by Constable and
Company, Ltd., 10 Orange Street, London W.C.2.

This Dover edition, first published in 1965, is an
unabridged and corrected republication of the work
first published by John Wiley & Sons, Inc., in 1950
under the former title: *Electromagnetic Fields*, *Theory
and Applications*, *Volume 1—Mapping of Fields*. This
edition contains a new Preface by the author.

Library of Congress Catalog Card Number: 65-27006

Manufactured in the United States of America

Dover Publications, Inc.
180 Varick Street
New York, N. Y. 10014

To

CH. SONYA WEBER

whose unselfish and inspiring attitude

made this book possible

PREFACE TO THE DOVER EDITION

Static electric and magnetic force actions had been explored experimentally by C. Coulomb and A. Ampère, respectively, in great detail. The basic concepts of the theoretical formulation were developed by K. Gauss in analogy to gravitational force actions which also followed the inverse square law with respect to distance. It remained for M. Faraday, however, to evolve the concept of a continuous "field" underlying the force actions between charges and between magnets. In particular, his geometrical demonstrations of magnetic field patterns with iron filings caused J. Maxwell to conceive of potential fields, to portray the effect of matter upon fields by means of the material constants "permittivity" and "permeability" and to hypothesize the displacement current. Field theory became the capstone of continuum physics and has contributed an overwhelming variety of solutions to the potential equation.

In order to combine the emphasis on the basic aspects common to all potential fields with a comprehensive treatment of the available analytical and practical methods of field-plotting, this volume has been organized in a somewhat unconventional manner. Instead of the usual vertical division into electrostatics, magnetostatics, and electrokinetics, a horizontal division of the subject matter is used. Thus, all the physical relationships are established first, and the methods of actually obtaining static field distributions are demonstrated subsequently. This avoids considerable repetition and leads to a clearer understanding of the fact that methods of analysis are independent of the specific branch of application, and that nomenclature is frequently accidental and by no means the essence of knowledge. It is, of course, assumed that the reader possesses a general knowledge of the electromagnetic field as normally gained in a pertinent undergraduate course and that he is familiar with the principles of vector notation. To be sure, the field-mapping methods are generally formulated in specific coordinate systems as conditioned by the geometry of the fields studied; but the vector notation proves of definite advantage for the presentation of the basic relations in electric, magnetic, and other fields, as treated in the first three chapters.

Following the summary of the basic physical relations, the comparative physical quantities in six branches of physics and engineering are listed in table 9.1, which serves as the key for the translation of field solutions in any one branch into solutions of analogous problems in the other branches. Chapter 4 deals with the simple applications of the superposition principle, such as systems of point and line charges, line currents, and simple geometries of spatially distributed charges and currents. For more complicated geometries it is frequently—though not always—simplest to map the field distributions experimentally; the experimental methods that have been used successfully are described in Chapter 5, including the analogies utilized in the electrolytic trough. As alternatives to the experimental procedure, graphical and numerical field-plotting methods are taken up in Chapter 6 with emphasis on the practical phases of actual applications; rather extensive treatments are given of the uses of electrical and magnetic images and of inversion—methods which are not always sufficiently emphasized. Next, the use of analytic functions for the solutions of two-dimensional field problems is shown in Chapter 7, and in particular the extremely powerful methods of "conjugate" functions and of conformal mapping, which are amply demonstrated. Finally, Chapter 8 gives the mathematical treatment of three-dimensional field problems, involving by necessity a thorough discussion of orthogonal coordinate systems that is supported by many illustrations which—it is hoped—will make it easier to visualize clearly the geometrical aspects.

In order to aid a teacher in organizing the material into feasible courses, several suggestions are offered in line with courses which have been taught by the author. For the first part of a course on electromagnetic theory dealing with static fields one might combine Chapters 1 and 2 and section 8 of Chapter 3 with selected examples from Chapters 4 and 6 and section 25 of Chapter 7. For a one-semester course in applications of functions of a complex variable one might take the material of Chapter 7, sections 25 to 28. Again, for a course in classical boundary value problems dealing with the potential equation, one might combine section 9 with the two-dimensional applications in section 29 and Chapter 8 on three-dimensional applications. To satisfy individual requirements, still other combinations are possible.

This book's enduring usefulness may result partially from its quite extensive references bearing on many specific subjects and extending the illustrations of many methods far beyond the necessarily limited list of examples that could be treated or summarized in one volume. It is for this reason that I am particularly indebted to Dover Publications for the reprinting of this volume, which affords me the opportunity to correct the few errors that unfortunately escaped detection in the first edition.

ERNST WEBER

Brooklyn, New York
April, 1965

CONTENTS

ELECTROMAGNETIC
THEORY

NOTES FOR THE READER

The symbols of field quantities are tabulated in Appendix 1.

To transform the relations from the rationalized MKS unit system to other unit systems, consult Appendix 2.

A brief review of vector analysis is given in Appendix 3.

Equations are numbered consecutively in each section; references to equations in different sections carry the section number, thus (5·4) means equation (4) in section 5.

The Bibliography in Appendix 4 lists only books to which several references are made in the text; such references, e.g. Attwood,[A2] p. 243, give the page and the author, the superscript indicating number 2 of section A of the Bibliography.

1. THE ELECTROSTATIC FIELD

1. FUNDAMENTAL RELATIONS
IN THE ELECTROSTATIC FIELD

From primitive observations, electrostatics divides all materials into only two groups, conductors and insulators. The first group is endowed with infinite mobility of electric charges such that any redistribution occurs in an unobservably short time. The second group has zero mobility of electric charges; any redistribution occurs in an uninterestingly long time. Admittedly, this is a radical division, but it leads to a much simpler theory of the electrostatic field than would be possible otherwise. In addition, the results are of direct practical value, and deviations in specific cases can readily be indicated.

The basic quantitative relationship of electrostatics is Coulomb's law of force action between two charges Q_1 and Q_2,

$$F_e = \frac{1}{4\pi\varepsilon} \cdot \frac{Q_1 Q_2}{r^2} \tag{1}$$

The charges are assumed to be confined to very small regions (point charges) so that the distance r can be identified as the distance between centers, and ε is the absolute dielectric constant of the homogeneous infinitely extended medium in which the force F_e is measured; one usually expresses $\varepsilon = \varepsilon_v \varepsilon_r$, where ε_v is the absolute dielectric constant of free space (vacuum) (see Appendix 2 for unit relations). The relative dielectric constant ε_r is the numeric value generally found in the tables of material constants. Throughout this volume, only *isotropic* dielectric media will be considered, so that ε is always assumed to be independent of direction.

1

The study of electrostatics, then, is primarily concerned with the equilibrium distribution of charges on the various conductors comprising a particular system, under the influence of this Coulomb force.   If the charge Q_2 is very small, so that it causes a negligible and only local distortion of the field of charge Q_1, it can be used as a *probe* for the exploration of the force field of charge Q_1.   From (1), the limit value for vanishing Q_2

$$\lim_{Q_2 \to 0} \frac{F_e}{Q_2} = E_1 = \frac{1}{4\pi\varepsilon} \frac{Q_1}{r^2} \tag{2}$$

is then interpreted as the electric intensity or *field strength* of charge Q_1.   In the case of a single positive point charge, the field strength E has radial, outward direction, in vector notation (see Appendix 3 for a brief review of vector analysis)

$$\mathbf{E}_1 = \frac{1}{4\pi\varepsilon} \frac{Q_1}{r^3} \mathbf{r} \tag{3}$$

where $\mathbf{r}/r$ serves to indicate the radial direction.   In the case of any general distribution of a total charge Q, one can subdivide it into small elements Q_α, consider each to be a point charge, and by use of the principle of superposition obtain the resultant field vector $\mathbf{E}$ at any point P

$$\mathbf{E} = \frac{1}{4\pi\varepsilon} \sum_{\alpha=1}^{n} \frac{Q_\alpha}{r_\alpha{}^3} \mathbf{r}_\alpha \tag{4}$$

where the $\mathbf{r}_\alpha$ are the radius vectors from the charges Q_α to the point P.

If one places a very small charge $\overline{Q}$ into the electric field of any number of charges Q_α, and if one is permitted to disregard the effect of $\overline{Q}$ upon the charge distribution of the Q_α, then such a small charge is again called a probe charge, since it can well serve to probe or explore the electric field of the charge assembly by means of the force action upon it, which is given by (2) as, $\overline{Q}\mathbf{E}$.   Left free to move, at very low speed, this probe charge will trace the direction of the vector $\mathbf{E}$ in space and the path described is called a *field line* or also line of force; it has the vector $\mathbf{E}$ everywhere as tangent.   Defining the path element as $\mathbf{ds}$, its components dx, dy, dz must be proportional to those of $\mathbf{E}$, so that

$$\frac{dx}{E_x} = \frac{dy}{E_y} = \frac{dz}{E_z} \tag{5}$$

which is the differential equation of the field lines. Since for any point charge the field lines diverge radially for positive sign and converge radially for negative sign, there can be no closed field lines.

Carrying a small charge Q_2 over any finite path $\overline{P_1 P_2}$ within

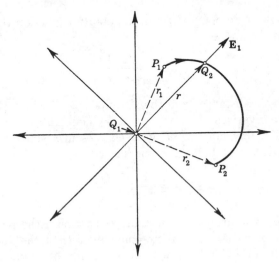

Fɪɢ. 1·1   Electrostatic Field of a Single Point Charge.

the field of a single point charge located at the origin as in Fig. 1·1 requires the work

$$W = \int_{P_2}^{P_1} \mathbf{F}_o \cdot \mathbf{ds} = Q_2 \int_{P_2}^{P_1} \mathbf{E} \cdot \mathbf{ds} \tag{6}$$

However, $\mathbf{E}$ has only radial direction, so that $\mathbf{E} \cdot \mathbf{ds} = E\,dr$ and hence with the use of (2)

$$W = Q_2 Q_1 \frac{1}{4\pi\varepsilon} \left(\frac{1}{r_2} - \frac{1}{r_1} \right)$$

The work is thus independent of the path; it depends only on the end points, and is therefore zero for a closed path. One can immediately generalize this fact because of (4) and characterize the electrostatic field as a *conservative* field. This means also, as seen from (6), that the line integral of the vector $\mathbf{E}$ vanishes for every closed path; all field lines emanate from, and terminate on, charges.

On the other hand, a line integral is independent of the path if the integrand represents a complete differential. This requires that the components of **E** can be identified as the derivatives of a single, scalar function Φ, the *electrostatic potential*. Vectorially,

$$\mathbf{E} = -\operatorname{grad} \Phi = -\nabla\Phi \tag{7}$$

and for the single point charge the potential function becomes at once from the above

$$\Phi = \frac{Q}{4\pi\varepsilon} \cdot \frac{1}{r} \tag{8}$$

where r is the distance from the charge center. Since (7) defines only the derivatives of Φ, any arbitrary constant could be added in (8). For any number of point charges in a single medium ε, superposition again holds and one has

$$\Phi = \frac{1}{4\pi\varepsilon} \sum_{\alpha=1}^{n} \frac{Q_\alpha}{r_\alpha} \tag{9}$$

subject to some arbitrary constant. Obviously, the scalar summation involved in (9) is more convenient than the vector sum required in (4). The surfaces obtained for constant values of potential are called *equipotential surfaces* and are equally as characteristic for the field structure as the field lines; in fact, they form with the latter an orthogonal system of surfaces and lines. The objective of *field mapping* is precisely the evaluation of this orthogonal field geometry in quantitative terms.

Returning to the concepts of conductors and insulators in the ideal sense, it must be clear at once that conductors can have charges only on the surface and must have constant potential throughout their interior; any potential variation would cause a field vector and, therefore, a force action until a surface charge distribution is established which maintains constant potential. Conversely, any charge in the interior of the conductor would be a source of field lines which could be maintained only by a potential difference. Any conductor surface is, therefore, an equipotential surface, and the field lines terminate perpendicularly to it.

An insulator or dielectric, on the other hand, will normally not carry any charges at all; it will serve primarily to separate charged conductors. In certain instances, space charges produced by thermionic or other emission, by glow discharges, or by arcs can exist within insulators. Assume again a single point charge Q in a homogeneous dielectric; then (2) will give the field strength as depending on the dielectric constant ε. However, the quantity $\varepsilon E = D$ is independent of the dielectric and appears as density of the charge were it distributed uniformly over the surface of a sphere of radius r. It is designated as a vector called *dielectric flux density* (or electric displacement),

$$\mathbf{D} = \varepsilon \mathbf{E} \tag{10}$$

for homogeneous dielectrics for which ε is a constant. Again generalizing for many point charges, the integral of $\mathbf{D} \cdot \mathbf{n}$ over any closed surface S gives then the sum of all charges contained within this surface (Gauss's dielectric flux theorem),

$$\iint_S \mathbf{D} \cdot \mathbf{n} \, dS = \Sigma Q_\alpha \tag{11}$$

no matter what their distribution. For a continuous space charge distribution of finite volume density ρ, the right-hand side of (11) is better written as the integral over the volume τ bounded by the closed surface S. Transforming also the left-hand surface integral, one has then

$$\iiint (\mathrm{div}\ \mathbf{D}) \, d\tau = \iiint \nabla \cdot \mathbf{D} \, d\tau = \iiint \rho \, d\tau$$

Applying this relation to very small dimensions one concludes that

$$\mathrm{div}\ \mathbf{D} = \nabla \cdot \mathbf{D} = \rho \tag{12}$$

or any space charge is a source or sink of the vector $\mathbf{D}$ independent of the dielectric medium.

In isotropic dielectrics, with no space charge, div $\mathbf{D} = 0$ and the vectors $\mathbf{E}$ and $\mathbf{D}$ have the same direction according to (10), so that the field lines of the vector $\mathbf{E}$ can also be interpreted as *dielectric flux lines*, being tangential to the vector $\mathbf{D}$ at every point. Since the total dielectric flux coming from a charge Q is numerically equal to the charge, one can conceive of a chosen number of *flux lines* to represent the charge value. In the case of several charges, the flux lines will then quantitatively represent the dielectric flux distribution. For conductors of arbitrary shape in a uniform dielectric, **D** is normal to the surface and its value is identical with the surface density of charge,

$$D \equiv D_n = \sigma \tag{13}$$

This follows from (11) since no electric field can exist within the conductor. The flux lines bounding a finite surface element δS which carries a charge $\sigma \, \delta S = \delta Q$ form a *flux tube* which will lead to an element $\delta S'$ on another conductor where it delimits a charge $(-\delta Q) = \sigma' \, \delta S'$. These flux tubes are a valuable aid in the visualization of the field geometry if no space charge is present (see Fig. 3·1).

2· ANALYTICAL THEORY OF THE ELECTROSTATIC FIELD

On the basis of section 1, the general problem of electrostatics can be formulated as the evaluation of the field distribution in dielectrics and of the surface charge distribution on conductors subject to certain known potential or field strength values designated as boundary conditions. Actually, potential values as such are arbitrary, as pointed out in section 1; only potential differences can be measured, so that, to any solution of the electrostatic potential function, an arbitrary constant could be added. Usually, one chooses some reference conductor such as ground to be of zero potential in order to simplify numerical computations.

As already indicated, solution of electrostatic field problems usually becomes more convenient with the use of the scalar electrostatic potential. As defined in (1·7), the electric field strength **E** can be expressed as the negative gradient of the potential. Introducing this into relation (1·10) and then substituting into (1·12), one has

$$\nabla \cdot \mathbf{D} = -\nabla \cdot (\varepsilon \nabla \Phi) = \rho \tag{1}$$

or also [see Appendix 3, (21)]

$$\nabla \Phi \cdot \nabla \varepsilon + \varepsilon \nabla^2 \Phi = -\rho \tag{1a}$$

This represents the most general differential equation for an inhomogeneous isotropic dielectric, wherein the variation of ε must be known. Though this general case has little practical value, it readily permits specialization for several important cases.

Special Cases of the Electrostatic Problem. *a.* If the dielectric is homogeneous (ε = cons), and without space charge, the differential equation (1) becomes *Laplace's equation*, or simply the *potential equation*

$$\nabla^2 \Phi = 0 \tag{2}$$

This special case is the most important one and admits quite readily of analytical, graphical, as well as experimental, solutions; most of the mapping methods pertain to it.

If one considers a single dielectric bounded entirely by conductor surfaces with charge distributions σ, it is possible to conceive of the individual surface charge elements $\sigma\, dS$ as point charges in the sense of (1·9) and to write at once a formal solution of (2) in the form of the integral

$$\Phi = \frac{1}{4\pi\varepsilon} \iint \frac{\sigma}{r}\, dS \tag{3}$$

which has to be extended over all the conductor surfaces. Since on conductor surfaces, as seen from the dielectric, $\sigma = D_n = \varepsilon E_n$ in accordance with (1·13), one can write (3) also in the form

$$\Phi = \frac{1}{4\pi} \iint \frac{E_n}{r}\, dS = \frac{-1}{4\pi} \iint \frac{\partial \Phi}{\partial n}\, \frac{dS}{r} \tag{3a}$$

which shows that the entire potential distribution is determined by the knowledge of the normal potential gradient on the conductor surfaces! A potential problem in which the values of the normal component of the field gradient are given on the bounding conductor surfaces is called a *boundary value problem of the second kind*, and (3a) represents the explicit solution for the special case that $E_n \neq 0$. Though (3) and (3a) are formal expressions of great value in the analytical theory of the electrostatic field, as for example in general existence proofs of solutions in potential theory, they do not have comparable practical value because boundary values are rarely specified in the above manner.

However, (3a) points out that Laplacian potential functions have exceptional qualities of regularity. Indeed, any function $\Phi(x, y, z)$ which has continuous second order derivatives in x, y, and z that satisfy the Laplace equation (2) is called a *harmonic function* within the region where that is true. Harmonic functions can, therefore, always be interpreted as potential solutions, and any potential solution must be a harmonic function or a finite or even infinite sum of harmonic functions. Moreover, such functions can be expanded near any point within the region of their definition into convergent power series, which characterizes them as *analytic functions*, so that the Laplace equation (2) can have only *analytic solutions!* It is this great regularity of behavior which has led to the various powerful methods of potential theory; for mathematical details see Kellogg.[C10]

b. If the dielectric is homogeneous (ε = cons), but with space charge, the differential equation (1a) reduces to

$$\nabla^2 \Phi = -\frac{\rho}{\varepsilon} \tag{4}$$

which is called *Poisson's equation.* This type of differential equation finds its most useful application in vacuum tube or gaseous discharge problems. A formal solution of it is represented by the superposition of a volume integral over all space charge elements $\rho \, d\tau$ conceived as point charges upon any solution of Laplace's equation, for example in the form (3) with the known surface charge distribution σ

$$\Phi = \frac{1}{4\pi\varepsilon} \iiint_\tau \frac{\rho}{r} \, d\tau + \frac{1}{4\pi\varepsilon} \iint \frac{\sigma}{r} \, dS \tag{5}$$

where r is the distance from the point at which Φ is being computed to the charge elements. Though (5) can be evaluated in some very simple cases, in most instances that is not possible. If the space charge density ρ is given as an explicit function of the space coordinates, then the solution is found best as the superposition of a Laplacian potential function and a particular integral of the inhomogeneous differential equation. In the practically important problems, however, the space charge density ρ is a function of the potential itself, so that (4) becomes a non-linear differential equation; these problems will not be considered further since their scope goes far beyond conventional potential theory.

c. If the dielectric is inhomogeneous and without space charge, the general differential equation (1a) reduces to

$$\varepsilon\nabla^2\Phi + \nabla\varepsilon \cdot \nabla\Phi = 0 \tag{6}$$

which can be solved in simpler cases if the variation of ε is given.

This differential equation is of importance in cable problems where the dielectric might be subjected to temperature gradients causing a variation of the dielectric constant, as well as in certain capacitance measurements where humidity and pressure variations might cause a variation of the dielectric constant.

The Boundary Conditions of the Electrostatic Field. As shown in section 1, all conductor surfaces in an electrostatic field must be equipotential surfaces; the specification of the potential values on the conductors, therefore, constitutes a convenient set of boundary conditions in the case of a single dielectric. Problems of this type are generally designated as *boundary value problems of the first kind*. Instead of the potential values, one could also assign the total charge values for the conductors, or give potential values for some and total charge values for the remaining conductors.

As pointed out above in connection with (3a), knowledge of the normal potential gradient on the boundaries of the electrostatic field region also defines the potential distribution uniquely except for an additive constant Φ_0 which can be interpreted as an absolute reference potential and which, for convenience, can be chosen as zero. *Boundary value problems* which specify the normal gradient value over the boundary surface of the field region under consideration are said to be *of the second kind*. Instead of normal gradient values, one could also specify charge densities on conductor surfaces.

The specification of potential values over certain areas of the boundary surface of the field region under consideration and of normal gradient values over the other areas leads to a *boundary value problem of the mixed kind;* though these are infrequent in purely electrostatic field problems, they arise often in connection with stationary current flow and similar flow problems (see section 9).

If several different dielectrics are present, then it is necessary to solve the differential equation (1a) (or the pertinent special forms) for each individual dielectric. In addition to the above boundary conditions on the conductor surfaces, continuity conditions at the boundary surfaces of any two dielectrics have to be satisfied in order to link all individual solutions so as to form the complete solution of the electrostatic field distribution.

Application of Gauss's dielectric flux theorem (1·11) to the small cylinder of height $dh \to 0$ enclosing the charged surface element dS

in Fig. $2 \cdot 1$, which might be the boundary surface between two different dielectrics, leads to

$$\iint \mathbf{D} \cdot \mathbf{n} \, dS = D_{n2} \, dS_2 - D_{n1} \, dS_1 = \sigma \, dS$$

In the limit of vanishing dh

$$D_{n2} - D_{n1} = \sigma \tag{7}$$

which is one general boundary condition for dielectrics. Usually,

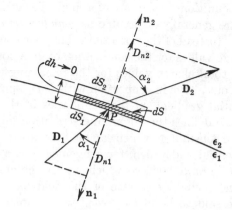

FIG. $2 \cdot 1$ Boundary Condition for the Dielectric Flux Density.

no surface charge exists, so that continuity of the normal component of the dielectric flux density is required.

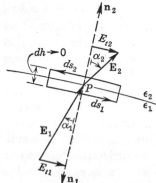

The existence of the scalar potential function Φ in $(1 \cdot 7)$ was inferred from the fact that the line integral of the electric field strength $\mathbf{E}$ vanishes for any closed path. If this relation is applied to a boundary surface of two dielectrics and choosing the path of integration as shown in Fig. $2 \cdot 2$, one immediately obtains as $dh \to 0$

$$E_{t1} = E_{t2} \tag{8}$$

FIG. $2 \cdot 2$ Boundary Condition for the Electric Field Strength.

the second general boundary condition. E_t stands for the field components parallel to the boundary surface at the point P.

A dielectric completely surrounded by other dielectrics must satisfy, therefore, boundary conditions involving only the derivatives of the potential function. If no surface charge exists, the combination of the two boundary conditions (7) and (8) leads to

$$\frac{E_{t2}}{E_{n2}} = \frac{\varepsilon_2}{\varepsilon_1} \cdot \frac{E_{t1}}{E_{n1}}$$

or

$$\tan \alpha_1 = \frac{\varepsilon_1}{\varepsilon_2} \tan \alpha_2 \tag{9}$$

if the angles of the field vectors with the normals to the boundary surface are designated by α_2 and α_1, respectively. Relation (9) is analogous to Snell's law of refraction in optics and is frequently called the law of refraction of the electrostatic field lines. It is of particular value in the graphical field plotting methods.

Electric Polarization. The characterization of a dielectric medium by the constant ε is satisfactory as long as no inquiry is made into the structural aspects of the medium which might be responsible for ε. To obtain a hypothetical concept of the nature of a dielectric, one can separate the dielectric flux density $(1 \cdot 10)$ into two components, one which could be thought of as existing in free space, the other as the particular modification caused by dielectric matter, namely,

$$\mathbf{D} = \varepsilon_0 \mathbf{E} + (\varepsilon - \varepsilon_0)\mathbf{E} = \varepsilon_0 \mathbf{E} + \mathbf{P} \tag{10}$$

where the quantity $\mathbf{P}$ is designated as *electric polarization*.

The effect of this separation upon the differential equation for the potential in a uniform dielectric is obtained by using (10) in $(1 \cdot 12)$:

$$\operatorname{div} \mathbf{D} = \rho = \varepsilon_0 \operatorname{div} \mathbf{E} + \operatorname{div} \mathbf{P}$$

Introducing $\mathbf{E} = -\nabla \Phi$ from $(1 \cdot 7)$

$$\rho = -\varepsilon_0 \nabla^2 \Phi + \operatorname{div} \mathbf{P}$$

one has also

$$\nabla^2 \Phi = -\frac{1}{\varepsilon_0} (\rho - \operatorname{div} \mathbf{P})$$

The dielectric can therefore be interpreted as a fictitious space charge distribution of volume density $\rho' = -\operatorname{div} \mathbf{P}$ existing in free space. If one excludes any real space charge by setting $\rho = 0$, then the uncharged dielectric medium can be represented only by a distribution of very small dipoles (see section 10), quadripoles, etc., which for small finite volume elements always have zero total charge, but which produce locally very strong dielectric flux densities. Without an externally applied electric field, it is assumed that these elemental units which are generally identified as molecules have random orientation so that over finite small volume elements also $\mathbf{P} = 0$. The application of a static electric field causes orientation of the dipoles and appearance of $\mathbf{P}$. Obviously, without *first* defining the underlying structure, $\mathbf{P}$ cannot be evaluated.

If one considers, then, a uniform dielectric of volume τ and constant ε in free space exposed to an electric field $\mathbf{E}_0$, one can represent the dielectric by the same volume τ filled with fictitious space charge $\rho' = -\operatorname{div} \mathbf{P}$. Since the actual structure can only include satiated charge complexes like dipoles, there remains on the surface of the volume τ a layer of "bound" charge with a density σ' which can be defined from the continuity condition (7) if combined with (10),

$$D_{n2} - D_{n1} = \sigma = \varepsilon_0(E_{n2} - E_{n1}) + P_{n2} - P_{n1}$$

As seen from (3a), the normal component E_n on conductors, or correspondingly the difference of the normal components in the two adjoining dielectrics, defines the potential values; thus, with the above,

$$E_{n2} - E_{n1} = \frac{1}{\varepsilon_0}[\sigma - (P_{n2} - P_{n1})] = \frac{1}{\varepsilon_0}(\sigma + \sigma') \quad (12)$$

and $\sigma' = -(P_{n2} - P_{n1})$. In the absence of true charge, the total contribution to the resultant potential existing outside or inside the dielectric is therefore similar to (5)

$$\Phi' = \frac{1}{4\pi\varepsilon_0}\iiint \frac{\rho'\,d\tau}{r} + \frac{1}{4\pi\varepsilon_0}\iint \frac{\sigma'\,dS}{r} \quad (13)$$

Obviously, $\mathbf{P}$ must depend on $\mathbf{E}_0$, the impressed field; if this field $\mathbf{E}_0$ is not rigidly fixed, but subject to modification by the presence of the dielectric, then mere superposition does not hold and (13) is only a first step in the solution.

3. ENERGY AND FORCES IN THE ELECTROSTATIC FIELD

For any finite assemblage (or system) of electrical charges, the total algebraic sum can be either zero or different from zero. In the first case, the system is called a *complete system*, all the field lines terminate on charges within the system, no field lines go into infinity, and the total dielectric flux through any closed surface surrounding the system is zero. In the second case, the system is incomplete in finite space; however, one can assume any very large spherical surface as carrying the opposite and equal of the resultant charge of the finite system since the total dielectric flux through any closed surface surrounding the system will be equal to the charge enclosed. The system together with the closed surface then will again be complete, and the field lines going into "infinity" are usually identified with stray capacitances.

The Ideal Condenser. The simplest complete system is that of two conductors in infinite space with equal and opposite charges. If the potential difference between the conductors is given, $V_{12} = \Phi_1 - \Phi_2$, with $\Phi_1 > \Phi_2$, and if the charges on the conductors are $Q_1 > 0$, and $Q_2 = -Q_1$, then the *capacitance* of the system is defined as the ratio

$$C = \frac{Q_1}{V_{12}} = \frac{Q_1}{\Phi_1 - \Phi_2} \tag{1}$$

This capacitance is a purely geometric characteristic of the electrostatic field and its distribution, and is indicative of the linear relationship between the field quantities.

The arrangement, called a "condenser," stores an electrostatic field energy equal to the work required to build up the charges on the conductors. Since the transfer of a charge element dQ requires an amount of work given by $(1 \cdot 6)$ and $(1 \cdot 8)$,

$$dW = (\Phi_1 - \Phi_2)\, dQ \tag{2}$$

the total work becomes with (1) above

$$W = \int_{Q=0}^{Q=Q_1} \frac{Q}{C}\, dQ = \frac{1}{2} \frac{Q_1^2}{C}$$

and therefore the field energy

$$W_e = \frac{1}{2} \frac{Q_1^2}{C} = \frac{1}{2} Q_1 V_{12} = \frac{1}{2} C V_{12}^2 \tag{3}$$

In this expression, all quantities are integral quantities, directly amenable to measurement.

The Influence of Ground. Generally, the concept of the ideal condenser is abstract because of the inevitable surroundings which will exert influence upon the field distribution. Consider first the simplest case, the influence of ground upon the charge distribution on two conductors. Obviously, if the ground is assumed, as is usual in electrostatic problems, to be an ideal conductor of poten-

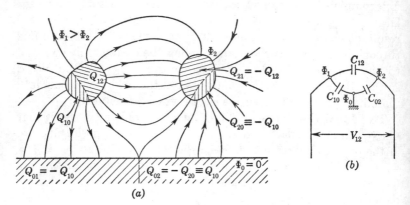

FIG. 3·1 The Influence of Ground upon the Electrostatic Field of Two Conductors.

tial zero (see beginning of section 2), charges will be induced in it, and field lines will span between ground and the other two conductors. Each conductor, therefore, will carry a total charge which will be bound partially by the other two conductors (see Fig. 3·1a). For conductor 1, for example, the charge will be $Q_1 = Q_{10} + Q_{12}$. Of course, the concept of *ground* could be replaced by that of a very large closed shield representing the inevitable surroundings and making the system a complete one.

One can now define only capacitance coefficients (or *partial capacitances* or also *direct capacitances* as defined by Campbell— see footnote 2, p. 17) such as

$$\frac{Q_{10}}{\Phi_1 - \Phi_0} = C_{10}, \qquad \frac{Q_{12}}{\Phi_1 - \Phi_2} = C_{12}, \qquad \frac{Q_{02}}{\Phi_0 - \Phi_2} = C_{02} \quad (4)$$

and because of the indicated charge values in Fig. 3·1a, one will immediately conclude that $C_{01} = C_{10}$, $C_{02} = C_{20}$, $C_{12} = C_{21}$, or that the "matrix" of possible capacitance coefficients

$$\begin{vmatrix} 0 & C_{01} & C_{02} \\ C_{10} & 0 & C_{12} \\ C_{20} & C_{21} & 0 \end{vmatrix}$$

is symmetrical about the main diagonal.   Physically, only $\binom{3}{2} =$ $\dfrac{3!}{2!\,(3-2)!} = 3$ independent capacitance coefficients[1] exist; this corresponds to the circuit equivalent of three condensers as shown in Fig. 3·1b.

The total charge on conductor 1 can now readily be expressed as the sum of the partial charges bound by all possible potential differences from conductor 1 to the other two conductors, namely,

$$Q_1 = Q_{10} + Q_{12} = C_{10}(\Phi_1 - \Phi_0) + C_{12}(\Phi_1 - \Phi_2) \qquad (5)$$

and the algebraic sign of the partial charge is that of the potential difference.

The total field energy stored in the electrostatic field becomes the sum total of that of the three individual condensers, namely,

$$W_e = \tfrac{1}{2}\,C_{10}V_{10}{}^2 + \tfrac{1}{2}\,C_{12}V_{12}{}^2 + \tfrac{1}{2}\,C_{02}V_{02}{}^2$$
$$= \tfrac{1}{2}\,Q_{10}V_{10} + \tfrac{1}{2}\,Q_{12}V_{12} + \tfrac{1}{2}\,Q_{02}V_{02} \qquad (6)$$

Systems of Conductors in a Homogeneous Dielectric. Assume a system of n conductors in a uniform, homogeneous dielectric with ground as the $(n+1)$st conductor with index 0.   The matrix of capacitance coefficients $C_{\alpha\beta}$ will now have $(n+1)$ rows and columns and be a direct extension of that given for two conductors and ground.   The total number of different capacitance coefficients is now $\dfrac{(n+1)!}{2!\,(n-1)!} = \dfrac{n(n+1)}{2}$ with all $C_{\alpha\alpha} = 0$, and the total charge on any one conductor in the system can be found by the superposition of the products of all the mutual capacitance

---

[1] The number is given as the combination of n different things taken r at a time without reference to their order; this is $_nC_r = \dfrac{n!}{r!\,(n-r)!} = \binom{n}{r}$, or the number of *combinations;* see Eshbach: *Handbook of Engineering Fundamentals*, p. 2-21; John Wiley, New York, 1936.

coefficients and the respective potential differences,

$$Q_\alpha = \sum_{\beta=0}^{n} C_{\alpha\beta}(\Phi_\alpha - \Phi_\beta), \qquad \alpha = 0, 1, 2, \cdots, n \qquad (7)$$

in direct analogy to (5). This expression also shows how the mutual capacitance coefficients of a system can be determined experimentally by means of ballistic galvanometers. The charges are measured after a known potential difference has been impressed between one conductor and ground to which all the remaining conductors are connected. Starting with conductor 1, and taking the ground potential $\Phi_0 = 0$, the charge values will be from (7)

$$Q_1 = \sum_{\beta=0}^{n} C_{1\beta}\Phi_1; \; Q_\alpha = -C_{\alpha1}\Phi_1 \qquad \text{for } \alpha = 0, 2, 3, \cdots, n$$

Measurement of the $n + 1$ charges (after disconnecting from ground so as to avoid charge redistribution in the system) gives $(n + 1)$ capacitance coefficients. Repetition of the procedure with rotational selection of conductors 2, 3, $\cdots$, etc., will give all other capacitance coefficients.

The total electrostatic energy of the system is again the sum of the field energies of all individual partial condensers. Because of the fact that the matrix terms to the right of the main diagonal comprise all the different capacitance coefficients, one can write this sum as

$$W_e = \frac{1}{2} \sum_{\alpha=0}^{n} \sum_{\beta=\alpha+1}^{n} Q_{\alpha\beta}(\Phi_\alpha - \Phi_\beta) = \frac{1}{2} \sum_{\alpha=0}^{n} \sum_{\beta=\alpha+1}^{n} C_{\alpha\beta}(\Phi_\alpha - \Phi_\beta)^2 \quad (8)$$

This relation is most useful as it contains only measurable quantities and can be directly applied to engineering problems.

In quasi-electrostatic fields, with potentials applied to the conductors, which are sinusoidally varying in time, the charges will also vary sinusoidally. Since the time rate of change of a charge is equivalent to a current, one obtains by differentiation of (7) with respect to time the concept of partial charging currents,

$$I_\alpha = \frac{dQ_\alpha}{dt} = \sum_{\beta=0}^{n} C_{\alpha\beta} \frac{d}{dt}(\Phi_\alpha - \Phi_\beta) = \sum_{\beta=0}^{n} I_{\alpha\beta} \qquad (9)$$

The charging currents $I_{\alpha\beta}$ can be measured very readily, and thus, with known applied potentials, an easy experimental determination of the capacitance coefficients is possible.[2] The procedure is quite similar to that outlined above.

Maxwell's Coefficients of Induction and of Potential.
For some applications it is convenient to reformulate the linear relationship between charges and potential differences, as given in (7), as relations between charges and individual conductor potentials, even though these potential values are not absolutely known. Thus, (7) can be rewritten

$$Q_\alpha = \left(\sum_{\beta=0}^{n} C_{\alpha\beta} \right) \Phi_\alpha + \sum_{\beta=0}^{n} (-C_{\alpha\beta}) \Phi_\beta$$

$$\equiv \sum_{\beta=0}^{n} k_{\alpha\beta} \Phi_\beta, \qquad \alpha = 0, 1, 2, \cdots, n \qquad (10)$$

where the $k_{\alpha\beta}$ are the coefficients of induction originally defined by Maxwell,[A17] Vol. I, p. 108.   From (10) one can take the relations

$$k_{\alpha\alpha} = \sum_{\beta=0}^{n} C_{\alpha\beta} = C_\alpha,$$

$$k_{\alpha\beta} = -C_{\alpha\beta}, \qquad \alpha = 0, 1, 2, \cdots, n \qquad (10a)$$
$$\scriptstyle (\beta \neq \alpha)$$

The $k_{\alpha\alpha}$ are the coefficients of self-induction, or the self-capacitances of the conductors, whereas the $k_{\alpha\beta}$ are the coefficients of mutual induction and always have a negative sign because they characterize induced charge values.

Because the system is complete, the total charge on ground (or on the enclosing shield) must be given by

$$Q_0 = - \sum_{\alpha=1}^{n} Q_\alpha$$

Introducing here Q_α from (10) and also using (10) with $\alpha = 0$,

$$Q_0 = \sum_{\beta=0}^{n} k_{0\beta} \Phi_\beta = - \sum_{\alpha=1}^{n} \left(\sum_{\beta=0}^{n} k_{\alpha\beta} \Phi_\beta \right)$$

one can express the coefficients of induction between ground and the n conductors

$$k_{0\beta} = - \sum_{\alpha=1}^{n} k_{\alpha\beta}$$

[2] K. W. Wagner, *E.T.Z.*, **33**, 635 (1912); G. A. Campbell, *Bell System Techn. Jl.*, **1**, 18 (1922); also in *Collected Papers by G. A. Campbell*, p. 169; American Telephone and Telegraph Company, New York, 1937.

The system (10) contains, therefore, only n unknown charges but $(n + 1)$ unknown potentials. However, absolute values of potentials are unknowable, so that one usually introduces here $\Phi_0 = 0$ and redefines the potentials Φ_α as potential differences to ground. This reduces (10) to

$$Q_\alpha = \sum_{\beta=1}^{n} k_{\alpha\beta}\Phi_\beta, \qquad \alpha = 1, 2, \cdots, n \tag{11}$$

with $\dfrac{n}{2}(n + 1)$ different coefficients of induction because $k_{\alpha\beta} = k_{\beta\alpha}$.

The system (11) can readily be inverted, i.e., the potentials can be expressed in terms of the charges

$$\Phi_\alpha = \sum_{\beta=1}^{n} s_{\alpha\beta}Q_\beta, \qquad \alpha = 0, 1, 2, \cdots, n \tag{12}$$

where the $s_{\alpha\beta}$ are the coefficients of potential originally defined by Maxwell,[A17] Vol. I, p. 108. The coefficient systems $k_{\alpha\beta}$ and $s_{\alpha\beta}$ are mutually related as coefficients of systems of linear equations; they are best expressed by means of determinants

$$k_{\alpha\beta} = (-1)^{\alpha+\beta}\frac{M_{\alpha\beta}(s)}{\Delta(s)}, \qquad s_{\alpha\beta} = (-1)^{\alpha+\beta}\frac{M_{\alpha\beta}(k)}{\Delta(k)} \tag{13}$$

where the $\Delta(s)$ and $\Delta(k)$ are the complete coefficient determinants of the $s_{\alpha\beta}$ and $k_{\alpha\beta}$, and where the $M_{\alpha\beta}$ are the respective minors obtained from the Δ by cancelling the αth row and βth column.

One can also express the electrostatic field energy of this complete system in terms of the potential and charge values. Increasing the charge value of the αth conductor at potential Φ_α by bringing a small increment dQ_α from zero potential requires a work according to (2) of value $dW_\alpha = \Phi_\alpha\,dQ_\alpha$. Applying small charge increments to all conductors of the system by taking them from zero potential gives

$$dW_e = \sum_{\alpha=1}^{n} \Phi_\alpha\,dQ_\alpha \tag{14}$$

or with (12)

$$\begin{aligned} dW_e &= \sum_{\alpha=1}^{n}\left(\sum_{\beta=1}^{n} s_{\alpha\beta}Q_\beta\right)dQ_\alpha \\ &= \sum_{\beta=1}^{n}\left(\sum_{\alpha=1}^{n} s_{\alpha\beta}\,dQ_\alpha\right)Q_\beta = \sum_{\beta=1}^{n} Q_\beta\,d\Phi_\beta \end{aligned} \tag{15}$$

The two forms (14) and (15) are summations over the same range and can therefore be combined to give

$$dW_e = \frac{1}{2} \sum_{\alpha=1}^{n} [\Phi_\alpha \, dQ_\alpha + Q_\alpha \, d\Phi_\alpha] = \frac{1}{2} \sum_{\alpha=1}^{n} d(\Phi_\alpha Q_\alpha)$$

so that

$$W_e = \frac{1}{2} \sum_{\alpha=1}^{n} \Phi_\alpha Q_\alpha \qquad (16)$$

By means of (10) and (11) one can readily show the identity with relation (8). On the other hand, using (10) or (12), one also has

$$W_e = \frac{1}{2} \sum_{\alpha=1}^{n} \sum_{\beta=1}^{n} k_{\alpha\beta} \Phi_\alpha \Phi_\beta = \frac{1}{2} \sum_{\alpha=1}^{n} \sum_{\beta=1}^{n} s_{\alpha\beta} Q_\alpha Q_\beta \qquad (17)$$

Integral Forms for Electrostatic Energy. In more general cases of systems of conductors in a space with various insulating media as well as space charges, integral relations for the total energy can be developed. On the basis of (14) one can define for a space charge $dQ = \rho \, d\tau$, and for a surface charge $dQ = \sigma \, dS$, and thus replace the summation in (16) by integrations:

$$W_e = \frac{1}{2} \iiint \Phi\rho \, d\tau + \frac{1}{2} \iint \Phi\sigma \, dS \qquad (18)$$

to be taken over the entire field space and over all conductor surfaces. Φ is the local value of the electrostatic potential. If one knows the charge and potential distributions, it is thus fairly easy to compute the total electrostatic energy. For a system of conductors in a homogeneous dielectric without space charge, this expression reduces obviously to (16) since the conductor potentials are constant.

In the specific case of a finite system of conductors within a single uniform dielectric bounded by a very large spherical surface, the surface integral of $\left(\varepsilon\Phi \frac{\partial\Phi}{\partial n} \right)$ taken over the entire dielectric can be transformed by Green's theorem (see Appendix 3),

$$\iint \left(\varepsilon\Phi \frac{\partial\Phi}{\partial n} \right) dS = \iiint [\varepsilon\nabla\Phi \cdot \nabla\Phi + \varepsilon\Phi\nabla^2\Phi] \, d\tau \qquad (19)$$

into a volume integral throughout the dielectric. Because at very large distance $\Phi \to 0$ as $1/r$, and $\partial\Phi/\partial n \to 0$ as $1/r^2$, the surface integral will vanish for the very large sphere and leave only the integrals over the conductor surfaces with normals pointing into these conductors. Introducing

$$-\nabla\Phi = \mathbf{E}, \qquad -\varepsilon\nabla\Phi = \mathbf{D}, \qquad \nabla^2\Phi = -\frac{\rho}{\varepsilon}$$

and reversing the normal direction to be outward with respect to the conductors, one obtains

$$\iint \Phi D_n \, dS = \iiint \mathbf{E}\cdot\mathbf{D} \, d\tau - \iiint \Phi\rho \, d\tau$$

Since $D_n = \sigma$ on the conductor surfaces, comparison with (18) leads at once to the alternative form for the electrostatic field energy

$$W_e = \frac{1}{2} \iiint \mathbf{E}\cdot\mathbf{D} \, d\tau \qquad (20)$$

where the integral has to be extended over the entire space occupied by the electrostatic field. This form permits, according to Maxwell's point of view, the interpretation as if the field energy be distributed throughout space with a local density $\frac{1}{2}\mathbf{E}\cdot\mathbf{D}$, entirely determined by the field vectors $\mathbf{E}$ and $\mathbf{D}$; the hypothetical nature of this interpretation has to be kept in mind, however.

It can be shown[3] that equation (20) holds for any electrostatic system, whatever the nature and number of different dielectrics may be, as long as the vectors $\mathbf{E}$ and $\mathbf{D}$ satisfy all the boundary conditions and $\mathbf{E} = -\text{grad }\Phi$ in each medium.

Forces in a System of Conductors. Assuming first an ideal condenser with charge, potential, and energy relations given by (1) and (3), one can consider two specific cases of mechanical action, the one in which the charges are kept constant, and the other in which the potentials are kept constant. The first case arises when the conductors, after receiving their charges, are isolated from the source; any decrease of their effective distance expressed as an increase of the capacitance will reduce the potential difference and, therefore, *decrease* the stored energy. This means that the conductors, if left free to move, will tend to convert field energy into mechanical work by an attractive force supplied by the system; conversely, an external force acting to increase the

[3] See references Livens[A15] and Stratton[A23] in Appendix 4.

distance will also increase the potential difference and the field energy. The second case above arises if the two conductors remain connected to a source of constant potential difference; any decrease of their effective distance will now increase the charge accumulation and therefore *increase* the field energy. This means, however, that the source has to supply not only this increase in field energy but also the mechanical work needed to move the conductors with respect to each other; by the law of conservation of energy this mechanical work is equal to the increase in field energy, since for a freely movable conductor it would be supplied by the system itself out of its field energy.[4]

If now an isolated *system of rigid conductors* is given with known charge values, the required force or torque to cause any change of a geometric positional element $\delta\eta$ (linear or angular displacement) of any conductor can be calculated by the principle of virtual work, expressing the rate of mechanical work as the negative rate of change of the stored potential energy W_e. For fixed charge values one uses best the second form of (17) and obtains directly for the rate of work done by the system

$$\frac{\partial W_{\mathrm{mech}}}{\partial \eta} = -\left(\frac{\partial W_e}{\partial \eta}\right)_{Q_\alpha = \mathrm{cons}} = -\frac{1}{2}\sum_{\alpha=0}^{n}\sum_{\beta=0}^{n} Q_\alpha Q_\beta \frac{\partial s_{\alpha\beta}}{\partial \eta} \quad (21)$$

which represents a force action in the direction of $\delta\eta$ if $\delta\eta$ is a linear displacement, or a torque if $\delta\eta$ is an angular increment. If $\partial W_e/\partial \eta$ is positive, external forces or torques have to deliver work (negative); if $\partial W_e/\partial \eta$ is negative, the electrostatic system converts part of the field energy into mechanical work (positive). Using any other expression for the electrostatic field energy and observing the condition of fixed charge values, one will obtain the same result (21).

On the other hand, if the potentials of a system of conductors remain fixed by permanent connections of the conductors to energy sources and a change $\delta\eta$ of a geometrical positional element η (distance or angle) takes place, then in order to maintain these potentials, energy W_s (positive) has to be supplied by the sources at the rate

$$\frac{\partial W_s}{\partial \eta} = +2\left(\frac{\partial W_e}{\partial \eta}\right)_{\Phi_\alpha = \mathrm{cons}} = +\sum_{\alpha=0}^{n}\sum_{\beta=0}^{n} \Phi_\alpha \Phi_\beta \frac{\partial k_{\alpha\beta}}{\partial \eta} \quad (22)$$

[4] For detail illustrations see Attwood,[A2] p. 191.

of which one half is used to cover the increase in field energy and the other half to cover the rate of work needed to produce the change $\delta\eta$. If $\partial W_e/\partial\eta$ is negative, then $-\partial W_s/\partial\eta$ indicates the rate of energy delivered back to the source. The actual force or torque producing $\delta\eta$ is, of course, the same as in (21), since the same initial potential-charge relations are presumed, so that

$$\frac{\partial W_{\text{mech}}}{\partial\eta} = \frac{1}{2}\frac{\partial W_s}{\partial\eta}$$

or also

$$\left(\frac{\partial W_e}{\partial\eta}\right)_{\Phi_\alpha = \text{cons}} = -\left(\frac{\partial W_e}{\partial\eta}\right)_{Q_\alpha = \text{cons}} \tag{23}$$

An alternative form to (22) is obtained by using expression (8) for the electrostatic field energy,

$$\frac{1}{2}\frac{\partial W_s}{\partial\eta} = +\frac{\partial W_{\text{mech}}}{\partial\eta} = +\frac{1}{2}\sum_{\alpha=0}^{n}\sum_{\beta=\alpha+1}^{n}(\Phi_\alpha - \Phi_\beta)^2\frac{\partial C_{\alpha\beta}}{\partial\eta} \tag{24}$$

which involves the more commonly used mutual capacitance coefficients; the signs of W_s as source energy and W_{mech} as mechanical work of the system are the same as in (21) and (22). Electrostatic instruments relying upon force actions between suitably arranged fixed and movable conductors present a wide field of pertinent practical applications. In many instances, simplifying approximations are possible by inspection of the actual field distribution.

Stresses in the Electrostatic Field. As visualized by Faraday and analytically formulated by Maxwell, the force action in the electrostatic field can be directly related to the field lines. Thus, one can introduce a stress per unit area of magnitude $\frac{1}{2}\mathbf{E}\cdot\mathbf{D}$ in the direction of the field lines upon a surface element taken perpendicular to the field lines, and a pressure per unit area of the same magnitude perpendicular to the field lines upon a surface element parallel to the field lines. This imagined system of forces accounts for Coulomb's force law and permits ready evaluation of force actions on the boundary surfaces of different media.

In the special case of a conductor, the vector $\mathbf{E}$ is always perpendicular to the surface of the conductor, so that there will be only a normal stress per unit area of magnitude $f_n = \frac{1}{2}ED$, the same value as the local density of the electrostatic energy stored in the field.   Obviously, there will be no resulting force in the case of spheres and cylinders with uniform charge distribution.

For a boundary surface between two insulators, the normal force per unit area will be given by the sum of the differences of normal stress and normal pressure on the two sides of the boundary surface.   One thus has (without surface charge)

$$f_n = -\frac{1}{2}(E_{1n}D_{1n} - E_{2n}D_{2n}) + \frac{1}{2}(E_{1t}D_{1t} - E_{2t}D_{2t})$$
$$= \frac{1}{2}(\varepsilon_1 - \varepsilon_2)\mathbf{E}_1 \cdot \mathbf{E}_2 \qquad (25)$$

if use is made of the boundary conditions $(2 \cdot 7)$ and $(2 \cdot 8)$.   This force urges medium 1 towards 2, and the total force is readily found by the proper surface integral.

These forms do not take into account electrostriction, the property of certain dielectric materials to expand or contract in an electric field.   A rather complete account of the more advanced theory is found in the references Livens[A15] and Stratton[A23], Appendix 4.

4· CRITICAL FIELD VALUES

One of the most obvious objectives in electrostatic design is to obtain forms of insulators and electrodes which will withstand all the electrical stresses that sound operation and occasional fault may impose.   In order to decide upon the reliability and factor of safety from this point of view, any design must be checked with respect to criteria pertaining to the critical values of electric field strength and dielectric losses.   For uniform field distributions as exist between plane electrodes, more or less definite values of breakdown field strength can be found experimentally; table $4 \cdot 1$ gives a summary of these values for a number of gases, liquids, and solids of general interest.   For non-uniform field distributions, the field strength values—though significant—are not by themselves decisive criteria of breakdown.   Theories have been developed, however, which attempt the formulation of generally useful criteria and which take the homogeneous field usually as the starting point. It will, therefore, be of interest to summarize briefly the relationships established for the occurrence of ionization, corona, and breakdown of the various insulating materials.

TABLE 4·1

DIELECTRIC PROPERTIES OF INSULATORS*

Material	Relative Dielectric Constant (ε_r)	Dielectric Breakdown Strength† kv/cm	Volume Resistivity, ohm cm	Surface Resistivity† (at 30% relative humidity), ohm/square§
Vacuum	1.0	—	—	—
Gases				
Air (normal conditions)	1.00059	30	—	—
Hydrogen (H_2)	1.00026	26	—	—
Liquids				
Carbon tetrachloride	2.21	660	—	—
Paraffin oil	—	180	10^{16}	—
Petroleum	2.1	—	10^{16}	—
Transformer oil (mineral)	2.5	100 to 160	10^{14}	—
Turpentine	2.2	110 to 160	—	—
Water, distilled	76	—	10^6	—
Solids				
Asbestos (paper 0.12 cm thick)	2.7	42	1.6×10^{11}	—
Asphalt (petroleum)	3.1	140	6.1×10^{14}	—
Bakelite, wood-molding mixture	4.5 to 5.5	177 to 216	1×10^{12}	3×10^{12}‖
Celluloid, clear (0.025 cm thick)	6.8 to 7.3	120 to 280	2×10^{10}	8×10^{10}
Ebonite	2.5	600	10^{16}	—
Fiber, vulcanized, all colors	5	50 to 100	5 to 20×10^9	3×10^{10}

Glass, light flint	7		10^{15}	—
hard crown	7 to 9	300	10^{15}	—
plate	5.5 to 9.1	300	2×10^{13}	3×10^{13}
Pyrex	4.5	900	10^{14}	—
Gutta percha	3 to 4	80 to 200	10^{15}	—
Jute, impregnated	3 to 4	12		
Lava	—	30 to 100	2×10^{10}	6×10^{11}
Mica (0.06 cm thick)	5 to 7	210 to 280	0.04 to 200 $\times 10^{15}$	2×10^{13}
Micarta	4.1	—	10^{11}	—
Paper, dry Manila	2.6	87	5×10^{4}	—
impregnated	3.5	150		
Paraffin (parowax)	1.9 to 2.6	115	1×10^{16}	1.5×10^{16}
Polystyrene	2.55	200	1×10^{16}	—
Porcelain	4.4	80 to 135	3×10^{14}	4×10^{13}
Pressboard, oiled (0.158 cm thick)	5.0	292		—
varnished (0.158 cm thick)	3	155		
Quartz (fused)	5	300	10^{16}	3×10^{12}‖
Rosin	2.5	—	5×10^{16}	8×10^{14}
Rubber, hard	2 to 3.5	700	1×10^{18}	6×10^{15}
Shellac	3.0 to 3.7	120 to 350	1×10^{16}	2×10^{14}
Slate	6.6 to 7.4	13 to 30	1×10^{8}	2×10^{8}
Wood, maple (paraffined)	4	46 to 60	3×10^{10}	1×10^{12}

* Partially taken from Eshbach: *Handbook of Engineering Fundamentals*, p. 12-60; partially from Attwood,[A2] p. 63. For a rather complete tabulation of dielectric constants and loss factors over wide frequency ranges see *Tables of Dielectric Materials*; published by Laboratory for Insulation Research, M.I.T., Vol. I, 1944, Vol. II, 1945, Vol. III, 1948.

† In uniform electrostatic field; approximate values only.

‡ Measured on surface of insulator between parallel conductor edges.

§ Resistance between two parallel sides of a square, measured directly in ohms.

‖ Values at 50 per cent relative humidity from *Handbook of Chemistry and Physics*; Chemical Rubber Publ. Co., Cleveland, Ohio.

Vacuum. The most ideal insulator is true vacuum which, entirely devoid of electricity as well as of matter, is subject neither to ionization nor to breakdown. There are, however, the possibilities of electric and thermionic emission of electrons or ions from the surfaces of the surrounding conductors[1] and insulators. According to Schottky's theory,[2] the purely electrostatic removal (cold emission) of an electron from the metal should require a field strength at the surface of the metal of about 10^8 volt/cm, a tremendously high value. Experimental evidence of cold emission[3] indicates qualitative agreement; quantitative relations are, however, very difficult to establish on account of the extreme sensitivity of the measurements to contamination of the vacuum by gas absorbed in the metal surface.[4]

Thermionic emission of electrons from a metal surface requires a thermal energy larger than a critical value called the "work function," which depends on the location of the electron within the metal. If, therefore, a metal is heated in vacuum, a current will be observed whose saturation value depends on the absolute temperature of the metal.[5]

In general, breakdown of vacuum as an insulator will be caused by the simultaneous action of thermionic and electric field emission; the latter will be usually small, except where inhomogeneities or improper design may raise the local field strength to excessive values.[6]

Gases. Even under normal conditions, air, the most natural insulator, shows a fairly constant ion content with slight local

---

[1] See the excellent summary, "Electron Emission," by J. W. McNall, in *Industrial Electronics Reference Book*, Chapter 2; John Wiley, New York, 1948.

[2] W. Schottky, *Zeits. f. Physik*, **14**, p. 63 (1923); R. H. Fowler and L. W. Nordheim, *Proc. Royal Soc.*, (A) **119**, p. 173 (1928).

[3] For example, R. A. Millikan and C. C. Lauritsen, *Phys. Rev.*, **33**, p. 598 (1929); F. Rother, *Ann. d. Physik*, **81**, p. 317 (1926); A. J. Ahearn, *Phys. Rev.*, **44**, p. 277 (1933); C. M. Slack and L. F. Ehrke, *Jl. Appl. Phys.*, **12**, p. 165 (1941).

[4] A. J. Ahearn, *Phys. Rev.*, **50**, p. 238 (1936); E. W. Müller, *Zeits. f. Physik*, **106**, p. 541 (1937).

[5] O. W. Richardson: *The Emission of Electricity from Hot Bodies;* Longmans Green, New York, 1916; A. L. Reimann: *Thermionic Emission;* John Wiley, New York, 1934; T. J. Jones: *Thermionic Emission;* Methuen, London, 1936.

[6] H. W. Anderson, *Trans. A.I.E.E.*, **54**, p. 1315 (1935); discussion **55**, p. 831 (1936).

variations. Because of the normal process of recombination, one must assume a definite and constant rate of ion production; measurements have shown this to be approximately[7]

Over land	8.1 to 9 ions/cm³/sec
Over sea	4.3 "
In brick buildings	12 to 14 "

The causes for this ionization are various; they may be radium emanation or γ-radiation from the interior of the earth, or they may be cosmic radiation from the universe. An electric field will, therefore, act to accelerate these ions or electrons and cause additional ionization. As long as the rate of recombination equals the rate of ion production, a stable condition will persist. On the other hand, if this equilibrium is disturbed by a sudden increase of the electric field, by strongly ionizing impurities, or by any other factors increasing the rate of ionization, a discharge current will form with dark glow, possibly leading to corona and eventual breakdown.

For a plane, uniform condenser with distance d between the electrodes, J. S. Townsend[8] found that, if α be the rate of ionization (i.e., the number of ion pairs created by an ion moving over a unit path) for negative ions or electrons, and β that for positive ions, the ionization current density J can be related to the saturation current density J_S that exists before ionization takes place by

$$J = J_S \frac{(\alpha - \beta)\varepsilon^{(\alpha-\beta)d}}{\alpha - \beta\varepsilon^{(\alpha-\beta)d}} \tag{1}$$

Infinite current or breakdown will then occur when the denominator becomes zero, or

$$\alpha\varepsilon^{-\alpha d} = \beta\varepsilon^{-\beta d} \tag{2}$$

Now, the rate of negative ionization, α, can be shown to depend primarily upon the free path of the electrons and the field strength.[9] Since the free path is inversely proportional to the pressure of the gas, one can deduce the semiempirical formula

$$\frac{\alpha}{P} = A \exp\left(-\frac{B}{E/P}\right) \text{ ion pairs/cm} \tag{3}$$

[7] McLennan, *Phil. Mag.*, **24**, p. 520 (1912); see also Schumann,[B37] p. 8 and Thomson and Thomson,[B40] p. 156.

[8] J. S. Townsend, in *Handbuch der Radiologie*, Vol. 1, 1919; see also Schumann,[B37] Cobine,[B33] and particularly Maxfield and Benedict,[B36] p. 277.

[9] For measurements see F. H. Sanders, *Phys. Rev.*, **44**, p. 1020 (1934).

in which the constants A and B can be determined experimentally for all gases. For air the numerical values are[10] $A = 13.2$, $B = 0.278$, if P is given in millimeters of mercury, and E in kilovolts/centimeter. On the other hand, ionization by positive ions takes place only close to the cathode surface, so that it is better described by a surface ionization number γ.[11] The breakdown criterion (2) for plane electrodes can therefore be written in the more practical form

$$Pd = \frac{1}{(\alpha/P)} \ln \left(1 + \frac{1}{\gamma} \right) \tag{4}$$

where P is the pressure of the gas in millimeters of mercury, and d the distance of the electrodes in centimeters; (α/P) is given by (3), and $\ln \left(1 + \dfrac{1}{\gamma} \right)$ is shown in Fig. 4·1 as a function of P/E. Relation (4) permits the general evaluation of either the breakdown field strength E or the critical distance d for *plane electrodes* with satisfactory results. Table 4·1 gives measured values of the breakdown strength for plane electrodes for several gases.

On the basis of Townsend's theory and a very great number of experimental data, W. O. Schumann[B37] was able to deduce a valuable and completely general empirical criterion for breakdown valid also for non-uniform field distributions. He found that the integral of α, the rate of negative ionization along any field line in a given field configuration, must be less than a constant value to insure stable operation. Application of this criterion to several simple electrode configurations has given results[12] in excellent agreement with experimental data. For practical numerical computations, especially in studying the influence of various geometric parameters of the electrode arrangement, this criterion can be used for normal pressure and temperature in the simplified form[13]

$$\int_a^{a'} (E - E_0)^2 \, dx \leqslant K \tag{5}$$

[10] Knoll, Ollendorff, and Rompe,[B34] see Table g29, p. 70; see also curve in "Electrical Conduction in Gases," by D. E. Marshall, Chapter 4 in *Industrial Electronics Reference Book;* John Wiley, New York, 1948.

[11] W. Schottky, *Zeits. f. Physik*, **14**, 63 (1923); Maxfield and Benedict,[B36] p. 292.

[12] D. W. Ver Planck, *Trans. A.I.E.E.*, **60**, p. 99 (1941); J. G. Hutton, *Trans. A.I.E.E.*, **66**, p. 1674 (1947).

[13] B. Davis, *Proc. A.I.E.E.*, **33**, p. 528 (1914).

where $E_0 = 24.5$ kv/cm, $K = 47.6$ (kv)^2/cm, and E is measured in kilovolts/centimeter. The integration has to be performed only over that part $\overline{aa'}$ of the "most dangerous" field line, for which $E \geqslant E_0$. The accuracy of the numerical results is quite

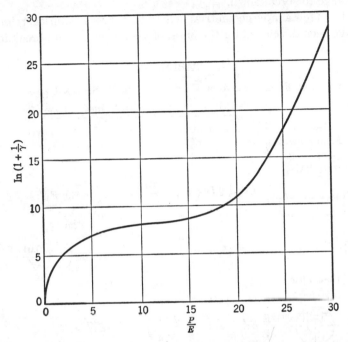

FIG. 4·1 Plot of the Function $n\left(1 + \dfrac{1}{\gamma}\right)$ against P/E. P = pressure in millimeter of mercury; E = field strength in kilovolts per centimeter. (Redrawn by permission from *Gasentladungstabellen*, by M. Knoll, F. Ollendorff, and R. Rompe; J. Springer, Berlin, 1935.)

satisfactory for most practical purposes, especially since all measurements of dielectric strength are subject to a modifying factor of probability, explained by Rogowski[14] as the sudden change from lower to higher current densities in the conducting path preparing the breakdown of a gas. Using the criterion (5), one would plot as abscissa the distance along a field line chosen so as to give the largest contribution to the integral, then plot

[14] W. Rogowski, *Arch. f. Elektrot.*, **26**, p. 643 (1932); see also G. L. Nord, *Trans. A.I.E.E.*, **54**, p. 955 (1935).

$(E - E_0)^2$ as ordinates, and integrate over the area to the point where this curve intersects the axis of abscissa. If this is done for various voltage values, interpolation will lead to the voltage which satisfies equality in (5) and thus constitutes the critical voltage for breakdown.

For a few simple geometries in air, more direct empirical relations have been developed for the onset of visual corona and breakdown.

TABLE 4·2

CRITICAL FIELD STRENGTH VALUES OF AIR IN SIMPLE GEOMETRIES

Critical Field Strength Values (kv/cm) for

Electrode Arrangement	Visual Corona (E')	Sparkover (E'')
Two Parallel Like Wires	$E_1' = 29.8 \left(1 + \dfrac{0.301}{a} \right)$	$\dfrac{2c}{a} < 30,\ E_1'' = E_1'$ $\dfrac{2c}{a} \geqslant 30,\ E_1'' =$ $30 \left(1 + \dfrac{0.01}{\sqrt{a}} \cdot \dfrac{2c}{a} \right)$
Concentric Cylinders	$E_1' = 31 \left(1 + \dfrac{0.308}{\sqrt{a}} \right)$	$E_1'' = E_1'$
Two Like Spheres	$E_1' = 27.2 \left(1 + \dfrac{0.54}{\sqrt{a}} \right)$	$s < 0.54\sqrt{a},\ E_1'' > E_1'$ $0.54\sqrt{a} < s < 2a,$ $E_1'' = E_1'$

Table 4·2 summarizes these criteria for air as given by Peek[B15] for normal atmospheric conditions. If the field strength at the point 1 of the electrode arrangement reaches the value corresponding to E_1' in the table, visual corona must be expected, and if it reaches a value corresponding to E_1'', sparkover must be expected; for spheres with spacing $s > 2a$, the sparkover occurs at the same critical field strength E_1' as for $s = 2a$.

If a solid insulator (porcelain, glass) is used in conjunction with air, its surface is boundary surface of two media of considerably different dielectric constants.   The evaluation of the distribution of the electrostatic field is then more complex, and the additional danger of flashover[15] occurs, i.e., breakdown of the air between the electrodes along the surface of the solid insulator.   This danger is most pronounced if the field lines are parallel to the boundary surface.[16]   It is, therefore, advisable, in combinations of air and solid insulators, to design the boundary surfaces so that the field lines are perpendicular to these boundary surfaces, at least in the proximity of the metal conductors.

Though most relations have been deduced specifically for air, they are valid for all gases in the same manner except for an appropriate change of the constants (see Knoll-Ollendorff-Rompe[B34]).

Liquids.   If a steady potential difference is applied to a liquid or solid insulator, a current will result which is very small in good insulators and becomes fairly large in poor insulators.   Obviously, then, there is no strictly electrostatic field, but rather a combination of the electrostatic and the electric conduction fields, which will slightly modify the analytic solution of the potential distribution.   For low voltages, however, especially in the range in which the insulators are being used in electrical apparatus, this distortion of the true electrostatic field is small and can be neglected. At higher potential differences the resulting distortions become important and determine the behavior of the insulator.

A closer investigation of the current shows that shortly after a d-c voltage has been applied to an insulator, the current will decrease at first fairly rapidly and practically exponentially; further decrease is slower and a definite final value is reached only after considerable time.[17]   To explain the observed time variation of the current, several theories have been advanced; the most plausible one, which has been confirmed by experiments on liquid

---

[15] See Pool[B15]; I. I. Torok and W. G. C. Ramberg, *Trans. A.I.E.E.*, **48**, p. 239 (1929); Schwaiger[B17].

[16] C. V. Fields and C. L. Caldwell, *Trans. A.I.E.E.*, **65**, p. 656 (1946); W. W. Pendleton, *Trans. A.I.E.E.*, **66**, p. 1324 (1947).

[17] J. B. Whitehead and R. Marvin, *Trans. A.I.E.E.*, **48**, p. 299 (1929); J. B. Whitehead, *Trans. A.I.E.E.*, **50**, p. 692 (1931); A. F. Joffé, *Ann. d. Physik*, **72**, p. 461 (1923); H. Schiller, *Zeits. f. techn. Physik*, **6**, p. 589 (1925); *Arch. f. Elektrot.*, **17**, p. 600 (1927); H. Schiller, *Ann. d. Physik*, **83**, p. 137 (1927); A. Gemant, *E.T.Z.*, **54**, p. 468 (1933); also Gemant[B14].

and solid insulators, assumes a progressive establishment of space charge near the electrodes so that the potential distribution becomes distorted. A stable condition is reached when the local ionization and the local reaction of the space charge are in equilibrium. This effect is known as *polarization* and gives rise to the so-called *absorption current*. One would expect this polarization to decay after the external potential difference has been removed, so that a similar component of the discharge current should be measured. Although many solids indeed show a release of the total collected charge, giving the impression of a *reversible* absorption current, most of the common liquids as well as a number of solids return less charge than they receive, and show the characteristics of a *non-reversible* absorption current. This is explained by an electrolytic *cleaning-up* process; it is assumed that during the charging period the space charges reach a saturation value, regular electrolysis sets in, and the electrolytic products are dissipated, thus purifying the insulator and rendering it of higher dielectric strength.

The final current is due either to occasional free electrons (present from some external cause of ionization, as X-rays or cosmic rays), or to partial internal dissociation producing ions (partial electrolysis caused by inhomogeneities). It is very characteristic of the electrolytic type of conductivity in liquid and solid insulators that the equivalent conductivity increases with the temperature and causes higher losses at high temperatures, a fact which is important in electrical design. It can be explained by the increased thermal agitation, causing a higher rate of dissociation which finally can result in actual decomposition.[18]

As in gases, so also in liquids, there will always be present an initial ionization caused by extraneous sources. A strong electrostatic field will maintain and increase this ionization by collision of the swiftly moving positive or negative ions with the molecules and atoms of the liquid. Ionization by collision is usually accompanied by luminosity (corona), since the occasional recombination of an electron and a positive ion releases the ionization energy in the form of infrared or even visual radiation. Experiments on oil by Gemant[19] demonstrate the scintillations by photographic record in an electrophotograph. The rate of ioniza-

---

[18] J. B. Whitehead and E. E. Miner, *Phys.*, **6**, p. 380 (1935); J. B. Whitehead and B. P. Kang, *Jl. Appl. Phys.*, **11**, p. 596 (1940).

[19] A. Gemant, *Zeits. f. techn. Physik*, **9**, p. 398 (1928) and **13**, p. 184 (1932).

tion, at lower field strength at least, seems to be proportional to the field strength,[20]

$$\alpha = C(E - E_0) \qquad (6)$$

where E_0 is the lower limit of field strength required for ionization, and C is a constant depending upon shape and spacing of the electrodes. For sufficiently high field strengths, ionization by collision increases very rapidly, "avalanche"-like, and can reach a stable condition by forming a space charge close to the anode, as was verified experimentally by Gemant.[21]

If the ionization becomes progressive, the conductivity might increase without limit and breakdown might occur. A general direct criterion for this stability of ionization is not known, although it seems well established that the building up of the space charge is a main contributory factor to the final breakdown of a liquid. A criterion developed by Dreyfus[22] for sharp-edged copper electrodes states that, in order to avoid breakdown, the integral along any field line of the field strength from the electrode with the highest field strength to the point a where the field strength falls below the asymptotic value for plane electrodes of large spacing must be less than a critical voltage characteristic for the liquid, namely,

$$\int_1^a E_s \, ds < V_{\text{crit}} \qquad (7)$$

Although this criterion is based upon the electrostatic field distribution and, therefore, does not take into account the space charge reaction, it implies the general experience that not the local field strength, but, rather, a field zone, is characteristic for the electrical stability. Without a specific knowledge of the value V_{crit}, relation (7) will primarily lead to the formulation of the dependence of breakdown upon the shape and spacing of the electrodes. A few critical measurements will then rapidly lead to a knowledge of V_{crit} for the specific material and configuration, making a general design criterion possible.

All practical insulating liquids have a certain content of moisture

[20] A. Nikuradse, *Ann. d. Physik*, **13**, p. 851 (1932); see also Gemant[B14], p. 122.

[21] A. Gemant, *Phys. Zeits.*, **30**, p. 33 (1929); J. Slepian, *Electr. World*, **91**, p. 761 (1928); J. B. Whitehead, *Electr. World*, **94**, p. 1083 (1929).

[22] L. Dreyfus, *Arch. f. Elektrot.*, **13**, p. 121 (1924).

and air, each acting in a different manner to reduce the dielectric strength of the liquid. Since water has a very high dielectric constant, small droplets will polarize and move into the densest region of the electrostatic field; if there are many small droplets of water, they may form dielectric bridges from one electrode to the other,[23] which, of course, is equivalent to breakdown on account of the much higher conductivity of water as compared with other liquids.

Air inclusions tend to ionize very rapidly[24] because the low dielectric constant of air causes a very high local field strength. As foci of progressive ionization, they not only can spread an avalanche of ions through the liquid, but also cause local heating and distortion of the field distribution, as well as initiate chemical changes,[25] which reduce considerably the dielectric strength of the insulating liquid.

Solids. In solid insulators the problem of ionization is essentially identical with that of electrical breakdown, since any appreciable ionization will be progressive. However, the breakdown of a solid insulator can be described as electric or thermic according to the prevailing characteristics summarized below.

Breakdown of solids is	
purely electric	purely thermal
if the breakdown voltage is	
highly dependent	not dependent
on inhomogeneities in the electrostatic field	
little dependent	extremely dependent
on temperature	
little dependent	highly dependent
on the conductivity of the insulator	
little dependent	extremely dependent
on the duration of voltage application	

[23] See references on high-voltage cables, particularly Dunsheath[B4].

[24] F. W. Peek, *Gen. Elec. Rev.*, **18**, p. 821 (1915); A. Gemant, *Wiss. Veröff. a. d. Siemens-Konzern*, **7**, part 2, p. 305 (1929); P. Dunsheath, *Jl. I.E.E.*, **73**, p. 321 (1933).

[25] J. Slepian, *Electr. World*, **91**, p. 761 (1928); J. B. Whitehead, *Electr. World*, **94**, p. 1083 (1929).

The theory of thermal breakdown is based on the thermal instability of certain inhomogeneities in the insulator in which heat is generated by the dielectric losses at a larger rate than can be transferred by the insulator to its surroundings. A first approximation assumed a conducting canal of inhomogeneities[26] through the insulator, from which heat was transferred to the electrodes only; a more complete treatment assumed an infinitely extended homogeneous thin insulator with heat conduction to the electrodes only, whereby the electrodes might have equal or different temperatures and thus impose a temperature gradient upon the insulator.[27] The resulting formulas for the highest permissible voltage applied to an insulating plate give proportionality with the thickness for high field strengths, and values independent of thickness for fairly low values of field strengths. A very large number of experimental data check the quantitative results of the theory.[28] For applied a-c voltages, secondary effects have to be considered also, such as variation of the apparent conductivity,[29] non-linearity in current voltage relations, and periodic dielectric losses which are independent of temperature.

The theory of electric breakdown is based on a mechanical breakdown of the crystal structure caused by excessive local field strengths. Since the ideal crystal structure did not give satisfactory results,[30] the hypothesis of inhomogeneities was introduced, especially the assumption of fine cleavage openings in the crystal. This assumption led to rather satisfactory values for the electrical breakdown voltage[31] and its variation with the thickness of the substance. One can conclude from many experiments on typically inhomogeneous crystals that there is a definite breakdown field strength which is a reproduceable constant of the material and is of the order of 2 to 5×10^5 volts/cm for porcelain and sodium chloride, respectively.

[26] K. W. Wagner, *Trans. A.I.E.E.*, **41**, p. 288 (1922).

[27] W. Rogowski, *Arch. f. Elektrot.*, **13**, p. 153 (1924); Th. Kármán, *Arch. f. Elektrot.*, **13**, p. 174 (1924), V. Fock, *Arch. f. Elektrot.*, **19**, p. 71 (1927); P. H. Moon, *Trans. A.I.E.E.*, **50**, p. 1008 (1931).

[28] L. Inge, N. Semenoff, and A. Walther, *Zeits. f. Physik*, **32**, p. 273 (1925); same, *Arch. f. Elektrot.*, **17**, p. 433 (1926); Schwaiger[B17]; V. M. Montsinger, *Trans. A.I.E.E.*, **54**, p. 1300 (1935).

[29] T. W. Dakin, *Trans. A.I.E.E.*, **67**, p. 113 (1948).

[30] W. Rogowski, *Arch. f. Elektrot.*, **18**, p. 123 (1927); A. Smekal, *Arch. f. Elektrot.*, **18**, p. 525 (1927); see also Schwaiger[B17].

[31] G. E. Horowitz, *Arch. f. Elektrot.*, **18**, p. 535 (1927).

For entirely homogeneous crystals and amorphous substances an ionization theory similar to Townsend's theory for gases was developed by Joffé[32] and shows satisfactory agreement with experimental tests. The breakdown field strength in this case is higher, but still a constant for the substance, and of the order of 1 to 3×10^6 volts/cm for glass[33] and quartz, respectively.

Since test data on breakdown of solid dielectrics always show a considerable spread, probability considerations have been introduced in order to predict with reasonable safety breakdown of large area samples from tests on comparatively small samples.[34]

PROBLEMS

1. Find a charge arrangement which produces the potential distribution
$$\Phi = \frac{Q}{4\pi\varepsilon} \frac{\exp (-r/a)}{r} \; ; \text{ is the solution unique? } \text{ (Stratton,}^{A\,23}\text{ p. 162.)}$$

2. Demonstrate the validity of $(2 \cdot 3)$ and $(2 \cdot 3a)$ by means of Green's theorem (Appendix 3). Hint: take in Green's theorem Φ as $1/r$ and exclude $r = 0$ by a very small sphere, counting its surface as one part of the boundary surface of the uniform dielectric.

3. Extend the demonstration in 2 to the validity of $(2 \cdot 5)$. What restrictions must be placed upon the space charge density ρ?

4. Compute the electric field inside and outside a sphere of radius a which is uniformly polarized. The electric field causing the polarization **P** is homogeneous throughout space (assume free space), has the same direction as **P**, and has value E_0. Establish the equivalence with a uniform dielectric sphere in the homogeneous field $\mathbf{E}_0$ (see section 21) and find the equivalent relative dielectric constant of the sphere in terms of E_0 and P.

5. A sphere of radius a in free space carries on its surface a double layer of electric charge, i.e., it has on the two faces of its boundary surface equal and opposite charge densities σ. What is the potential outside and inside the sphere? Hint: consider the radial distance between the charge densities as δa and very small compared with all finite distances; introduce the solid angle $d\Omega$ subtended by a surface element dS at the point of observation P.

6. Demonstrate that the potential of a double layer of charge density σ, small surface δS, and charge separation δa is given in free space by $\delta\Phi = \sigma \, \delta a \, \delta\Omega/4\pi\varepsilon_v$, where $\delta\Omega$ is the solid angle subtended by the surface δS at the point of observation. Apply this as approximation to the potential of a parallel

---

[32] A. Joffé, J. Kurchatoff, and K. Sinjelnikoff, *Publ. of M.I.T.*, No. 117, Vol. 62, 1927.

[33] N. D. Kenney, A. M. Luery, and J. D. Moriaty, *Trans. A.I.E.E.*, **51**, p. 404 (1932).

[34] M. C. Holmes, *Jl. Franklin Inst.*, **211**, p. 777 (1931); L. R. Hill and P. L. Schmidt, *Trans. A.I.E.E.*, **67**, p. 442 (1948).

plate condenser at very large distances from it. Show the analogy to the electric dipole in section 10. Show that the potential difference between the faces of the double layer is given by $\Phi_1 - \Phi_2 = \sigma\, \delta a/\varepsilon_v$.

7. What is the maximum charge that a smooth conducting sphere of radius a can hold in air under normal conditions without exhibiting corona effects?

8. Accepting a stress per unit area of magnitude $\frac{1}{2}\mathbf{E}\cdot\mathbf{D}$ in the direction of the electric field lines, show that two like charges of opposite sign attract each other in accordance with Coulomb's law $(1\cdot1)$. Hint: utilize the symmetry of the field distribution; see also section 10.

9. Accepting a pressure per unit area of magnitude $\frac{1}{2}\mathbf{E}\cdot\mathbf{D}$ normal to the direction of the field lines, show that two like charges of same sign repel each other in accordance with Coulomb's law $(1\cdot1)$. Hint: utilize the symmetry of the field distribution; see also section 10.

10. Given a fixed system of n conductors and ground (or grounded enveloping shield) in a single, uniform dielectric, assume that potentials Φ_α are applied to the individual conductors with respect to ground and that charges Q_α are measured. If then potentials Φ_α' are applied, charges Q_α' will result whereby $\sum_\alpha Q_\alpha\Phi_\alpha' = \sum_\alpha Q_\alpha'\Phi_\alpha$ (Green's reciprocation theorem). Prove this relation; utilize $(3\cdot11)$ or $(3\cdot12)$.

11. In order to determine the charge induced by an electron in one of the electrodes of a vacuum tube, one can apply Green's reciprocation theorem from the preceding problem to the following two conditions: (a) all electrodes are grounded except the one in question, to which voltage V is applied with respect to ground and a small conducting but uncharged sphere is placed at the position of the electron; (b) all electrodes are grounded, and the electron charge e is applied to the small conducting sphere. Show that the induced charge on the electrode in question is $Q' = -e\Phi/V$, where Φ is the potential existing under (a) on the small sphere. Apply this to a plane parallel diode. Apply it to a coaxial cylindrical diode.

12. The *uniqueness theorem* states that the potential function as a harmonic function is uniquely determined within a closed, regular region τ of a dielectric by its values on the boundary surface of this region. Prove this by applying Green's theorem (Appendix 3) to the difference of two potential functions $\Phi_1 - \Phi_2$, each function satisfying the Laplacian (or Poisson) differential equation and taking on the same value Φ_0 on the boundary surface.

13. Extend the proof in problem 12 to a finite number of finite conductor surfaces embedded in a homogeneous and isotropic dielectric of infinite extent without space charge.

14. The potential function Φ as a harmonic function is uniquely defined (except for an additive constant) within a closed, regular region τ of a dielectric by the values of its normal derivative on the boundary surface. Prove this, following the outline given in problem 12.

15. Extend the proof in problem 14 to a finite number of finite conductor surfaces embedded in a homogeneous and isotropic dielectric of infinite extent without space charge.

16. Extend the proof in problem 14 to a finite number of finite conduc-

tors embedded in several different dielectric media without space charge. (Smythe,[A22] p. 57.)

17. In an electrostatic field, the electric charges on fixed conductors embedded in an isotropic dielectric of fixed ε are so distributed over their surfaces that the electrostatic field energy is a minimum (Thomson's theorem). Prove this by applying (3·20) to two different sets Φ, $\mathbf{E}$, $\mathbf{D}$ and Φ', $\mathbf{E}'$, $\mathbf{D}'$, satisfying div $\mathbf{D}$ = div $\mathbf{D}'$ = ρ, and maintaining the same total charge on each conductor; the first set as electrostatic field solution must satisfy in addition curl $\mathbf{E}$ = 0, or $\mathbf{E}$ = $-\nabla\Phi$ and Φ = cons on all conductors. Hint: take the difference of the respective field energies and demonstrate it as an essentially positive quantity. (Abraham—Becker,[A1] p. 89.)

18. The electrostatic potential cannot have a maximum or a minimum value at any point of the field free of electric charge. (Observe that analytic functions satisfy an analogous condition; see section 25). Demonstrate this by application of (1·11). (Smythe,[A22] p. 13.)

19. Earnshaw's theorem asserts that an electric charge, subject only to electric forces, cannot be in stable equilibrium. Demonstrate this by means of the proof for 18. (Smythe,[A22] p. 13.)

20. Demonstrate that the introduction of an uncharged conductor into an electrostatic field produced by a system of conductors with fixed charges decreases the field energy. Hint: use a similar approach to that in problem 17 with both field sets corresponding to true electrostatic fields but extended over slightly different volumes. (Stratton,[A23] p. 117.)

21. Compute the potential distribution everywhere in free space produced by a uniform space charge distribution confined to a sphere of radius a. Can one define a capacitance of this sphere?

22. Demonstrate that for a homogeneous sphere of radius a, the ratio of surface potential to total charge is independent of the manner in which the charge is distributed radially throughout the sphere (assuming that the charge density is only a function of the radius and that the dielectric constants ε_i and ε_o for inside and outside medium, respectively, are constant).

23. Two conductors above ground and isolated from it form a condenser. If a potential difference $V = \Phi_1 - \Phi_2$ is applied between them, what are the individual potentials to ground in terms of Maxwell's potential coefficients? In terms of the capacitance coefficients?

24. Two conductors above ground are connected and have a potential difference V applied between them and ground. What are the individual charges collected on these conductors in terms of Maxwell's potential coefficients? In terms of the capacitance coefficients?

25. Given two conductors 1 and 2 above ground, three measurements are made: (a) voltage V is applied between 2 and ground with 1 isolated and charge Q_2 is registered; (b) 2 is disconnected and left isolated, V is applied between 1 and ground, and charge Q_1' is registered; (c) 1 is now disconnected and left isolated, V is again applied between 2 and ground, and the new charge Q_2'' is registered. Taking ground at zero potential, find all the potential coefficients in terms of the charges. Find all the capacitance coefficients. Find the induced potential values in the three experiments.

2. THE MAGNETOSTATIC FIELD

5. FUNDAMENTAL RELATIONS
IN THE MAGNETOSTATIC FIELD

Although the magnetic effects were studied first in connection with natural ores and loadstones, the basic relations can be more readily formulated quantitatively by studying the magnetic effects produced by steady current flow.   In this sense, then, Ampère's law of force action between currents becomes the basis of magnetostatics comparable in importance to the Coulomb law of electrostatics.   Indeed, Ampère's law is most suitable to point out the basically different physical aspects of the magnetostatic field; in its simplest form for two parallel currents it defines an attractive or repulsive force of value[1]

$$F_m = \frac{\mu}{2\pi} \frac{I_1 I_2}{r} l \tag{1}$$

where conventionally the positive sign is chosen for like currents which attract each other; it is well to observe that this is contrary to the convention established for the force between two electric charges.   In using (1), the currents are assumed to be confined to very thin wires parallel over the length l which itself is large compared with the distance r between the centers of the wires; μ is the absolute permeability of the homogeneous, infinitely extended medium in which the force F_m is measured (see Appendix 2 for unit relations).   One usually expresses $\mu = \mu_v \mu_r$, where μ_v is the absolute permeability of free space (vacuum), and μ_r the

---

[1] See the interesting account by A. M. Ampère, *Ann. de chimie et de phys.*, **15**, pp. 59, 170 (1820).

relative permeability; the latter is the numeric value generally found in the tables of material constants. The basic arrangement in this magnetic force experiment is essentially two-dimensional, and the interacting currents are parallel vectors in space; this explains the presence of the factor 2π [as compared with 4π in $(1\cdot1)$ for the truly three-dimensional case] and explains the variation with inverse distance (as compared with inverse square of distance in the Coulomb law). Throughout the book, only isotropic magnetic media will be considered, so that μ can always be assumed to be independent of direction.

If the current I_2 is very small, so that it causes a negligible and only local distortion of the field of current I_1, it can be used as a *probe* for the exploration of the force field created by current I_1. From (1), the limit value for vanishing I_2 and unit length

$$\lim_{I_2 \to 0} \frac{F_m}{I_2 l} = \frac{\mu}{2\pi} \frac{I_1}{r} = B_1 \qquad (2)$$

should be interpreted as the magnetic field strength[2] of the very long line current I_1; actually, it is more usually called *magnetic flux density*. As a vector, its direction is normal to both the current vector $\mathbf{I}_1$ and the radius vector $\mathbf{r}$ from the current to the point P (see Fig. $5\cdot1$) and forms with these in the order given a right-handed orthogonal triplet. One can, therefore, also write vectorially

$$\mathbf{B} = \frac{\mu}{2\pi} \frac{1}{r^2} \mathbf{I} \times \mathbf{r} \qquad (3)$$

where $\mathbf{r}/r$ serves to indicate the radial direction. For the single line current, this will define the vector $\mathbf{B}$ everywhere tangential to circles with O as centers. The vector character has been associated here and throughout this section directly with the current because of the very small cross-section of the conductor; more precisely, one could introduce a separate unit vector to emphasize the current as scalar cross-sectional integral of current density as is done in the next section.

---

[2] That the vector $\mathbf{B}$ enters into all force relations of the magnetic field has been repeatedly pointed out in some of the advanced books on electromagnetic theory; see Livens[A15] and Stratton[A23] in the reference list of Appendix 4, also R. W. King: *Electromagnetic Engineering*, Vol. I; McGraw-Hill, New York, 1945.

Now, quite differently from the electrostatic case, the force action of the field $\mathbf{B}_1$ upon current $\mathbf{I}_2$ is actually perpendicular to both these vectors and forms an orthogonal triplet with them in the right-handed order $\mathbf{I}_2$, $\mathbf{B}_1$, $\mathbf{F}_m$, so that vectorially one can write for (1) with (2) if one refers the action to unit length

$$\mathbf{f}_m = \mathbf{I}_2 \times \mathbf{B}_1 \tag{4}$$

leading to attraction along the center line if both currents have the *same* direction, and to repulsion if they flow in opposite directions.

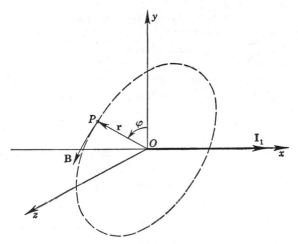

Fig. 5·1   Magnetic Field of a Single Line Current.

Instead of analogy between electrostatics and magnetostatics one finds here a strong difference which is, of course, related to the fact that charges are scalar quantities, whereas currents are space vectors; charges are centers of convergence or divergence of electrostatic field lines, whereas currents are axes of circulation of magnetic field lines.

Moving the small current $\mathbf{I}_2$ very slowly parallel to itself over a path $P_1 P_2$ in the field of the current $\mathbf{I}_1$, while maintaining $\mathbf{I}_2$ and its source constant, requires the work

$$W = \int_{P_1}^{P_2} \mathbf{F}_m \cdot \mathbf{ds} = l \int_{P_1}^{P_2} \mathbf{I}_2 \times \mathbf{B}_1 \cdot \mathbf{ds} \tag{5}$$

The length l could be interpreted as vector in the same direction as I_2, so that one can rewrite (5) as

$$W = I_2 \int_{P_1}^{P_2} \mathbf{1} \times \mathbf{B}_1 \cdot \mathbf{ds} = I_2 \Phi_m \tag{6}$$

where Φ_m is defined as the magnetic flux

$$\Phi_m = \int_{P_1}^{P_2} \mathbf{ds} \times \mathbf{1} \cdot \mathbf{B}_1 = \iint B_n \, dS \tag{7}$$

through the area described by the motion of the conductor. This magnetic flux vanishes for any closed surface, which is demonstrated in the simplest manner by integrating (3) over the surface of a sector of a cylindrical annulus. Thus, the field is of the conservative type; motion over any closed path must give zero result for work done.

If, however, the magnetic flux through any (reducible) closed surfaces vanishes, then the vector $\mathbf{B}$ cannot have any sources or sinks, or

$$\nabla \cdot \mathbf{B} = \text{div } \mathbf{B} = 0 \tag{8}$$

For a system of n parallel line currents of very great length in an infinite insulating medium the resultant vector $\mathbf{B}$ can readily be evaluated by means of superposition of the individual current contributions I_α from (3)

$$\mathbf{B} = \frac{\mu}{2\pi} \sum_{\alpha=1}^{n} \frac{1}{r_\alpha^2} I_\alpha \times \mathbf{r}_\alpha \tag{9}$$

where the $\mathbf{r}_\alpha$ are the perpendicular vectors from the line currents to the point of observation P. Such a system is, of course, two-dimensional in nature, i.e., the field distribution is the same in any plane orthogonal to the system. If one then defines *field lines* as the curves which have at every point the vector $\mathbf{B}$ as tangent, one has

$$\frac{dy}{B_y} = \frac{dx}{B_x} \tag{10}$$

as the differential equation for the two-dimensional case. Since the field lines circle around the conductors, and since the vector $\mathbf{B}$ has no divergence, there will be *only closed field lines*.

Most materials have a permeability close to that of free space; *diamagnetic* materials have permeabilities slightly smaller, weakly *paramagnetic* materials have permeabilities slightly larger, than that of free space. There is, however, a very important group of metals and their alloys which have very high permeabilities. Since iron is the outstanding representative of this group, they have been referred to as *ferromagnetic;* recently, certain alloys of weakly paramagnetic metals have been found also to possess high permeabilities. This whole group will, therefore, be designated better as *strongly paramagnetic.*

For many practical purposes of field mapping, it appears desirable to consider a sharp distinction between highly magnetic and non-magnetic materials and to assume an infinite value of permeability for the first group, and the value for free space for the second group which combines both the diamagnetic and weakly paramagnetic materials. This seems the much more advisable, because all the highly magnetic materials show strong non-linearity of the relation between H and B, (the so-called saturation effects) and, additionally, exhibit strong influence of the past magnetic history of the particular sample, making it well-nigh impossible to treat these materials analytically.

6. ANALYTICAL THEORY OF THE MAGNETOSTATIC FIELD

The general magnetostatic problem is the evaluation of the magnetic field distribution produced by given configurations of the electric current. The magnetic field itself is characterized by the vector **B**, which has physical properties quite different from those of the corresponding vector **E** of the electrostatic field. In this book no attempt will be made to treat the non-linear aspects of magnetic phenomena.

The Magnetostatic Potential. As shown in section 5 and indicated in Fig. 5·1, the magnetic field lines of a single very long line current are circles. The line integral of the vector **B** along a circular field line of radius r is, therefore, using (5·2),

$$\int_C \mathbf{B} \cdot \mathbf{ds} = \frac{\mu}{2\pi} \int_{\phi=0}^{2\pi} \frac{I_1}{r} r \, d\phi = \mu I_1 \tag{1}$$

and, indeed, any other simply reducible (see Appendix 3) path linking with the current will give the same result; the vector **B** is thus of the rotational (circuital) type. Since the line integral does not vanish, one cannot introduce a general scalar function as correlated potential function. If, however, a closed path C'

is chosen which does not encircle the current, the line integral along C' does vanish.   One can thus rescue the scalar potential concept if one makes sure by proper choice of a "barrier" surface that no possible path of integration can link with the current.   For a partial current loop this barrier surface is indicated in Fig. $6\cdot1$; it is prohibited ever to cross this double surface.   All the field lines are then conceived to "start" at the side of higher potential value and to terminate at the side of the lower potential value.

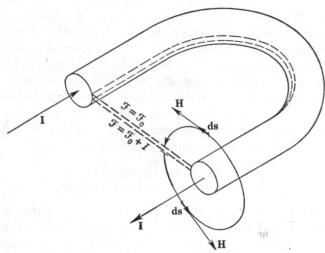

FIG. $6\cdot1$ Barrier Surface of the Magnetostatic Potential $\mathcal{F}$.

In introducing thus a restricted definition of a scalar potential, one might as well take cognizance of the fact that the line integral (1) depends on the magnetic characteristic of the medium, namely, the permeability μ.   It is convenient, then, to define a new vector

$$\mathbf{H} = \frac{1}{\mu}\,\mathbf{B} \tag{2}$$

usually called the *magnetizing force* (though it certainly is not a force and not even directly responsible for mechanical force actions) or *magnetic intensity*.   With this definition, (1) becomes

$$\int_C \mathbf{H}\cdot\mathbf{ds} = I \tag{3}$$

where I stands for the entire current flow *through* the closed path C.

(Frequently one writes the right-hand side as NI and means the total number of turns, each carrying the same current I.)

In regions outside of currents and properly provided with barrier surfaces over all current loops, one can then define

$$\mathbf{H} = -\operatorname{grad} \mathcal{F} = -\nabla \mathcal{F}, \qquad \int_1^2 \mathbf{H} \cdot \mathbf{ds} = \mathcal{F}_1 - \mathcal{F}_2 \qquad (4)$$

where $\mathcal{F}$ is the magnetostatic potential analogous to Φ, the electrostatic potential, defined by $(1 \cdot 7)$. The magnetostatic potential difference $(\mathcal{F}_1 - \mathcal{F}_2)$ is frequently called *magnetomotive force* or mmf in analogy to the electrostatic use; for singly closed line integrals of the type (1), this mmf becomes identical with the total current linked by the closed path. Its value is independent of the path if it links the current only once or if it is replaced by a line integral with terminal points on the two sides of the barrier surface.

Because of $(5 \cdot 8)$ and (2) and (4) above, one can now deduce

$$\nabla \cdot \mathbf{B} = -\nabla \cdot (\mu \nabla \mathcal{F}) = 0 \qquad (5)$$

or also

$$\nabla \mathcal{F} \cdot \nabla \mu + \mu \nabla^2 \mathcal{F} = 0 \qquad (5a)$$

This represents the most general differential equation for inhomogeneous media, wherein the variation of μ must be known. (Only the case of magnetically isotropic media is treated here, other media being omitted as beyond the scope of this monograph.) Comparison with $(21a)$ indicates the close analogy between $\mathcal{F}$ and the electrostatic potential Φ in media without space charge.

For magnetically homogeneous media the permeability is constant, and $(5a)$ reduces to the *Laplace equation*

$$\nabla^2 \mathcal{F} = 0 \qquad (6)$$

which is identical with $(2 \cdot 2)$ for the electrostatic potential and, as there, is the most important case admitting readily of analytical, graphical, as well as experimental, solutions; most of the mapping methods pertain to it. Any solution of (6) must again be a harmonic function, and must be analytic—just as the electrostatic potential function in section 2—in the regions outside of the current-carrying conductors and the properly constructed barrier surfaces. Unlike the electrostatic case, however, a formal solution cannot be given readily in terms of surface or volume integrals of physically observable magnetic distribution functions.

The Boundary Conditions of the Magnetostatic Field.
Assuming a boundary surface between two magnetically different

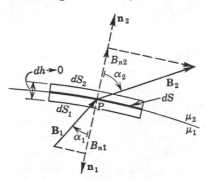

materials as indicated in Fig. 6·2, one can apply the relation (5·7) to the closed surface presented by the very small cylinder of height $dh \to 0$. One obtains

$$\iint \mathbf{B} \cdot \mathbf{n} \, dS$$
$$= B_{n2} dS_2 - B_{n1} \, dS_1 = 0$$

and in the limit for vanishing dh,

$$B_{n2} = B_{n1} \qquad (7)$$

FIG. 6·2   Boundary Condition for the Magnetic Flux Density.

This states that the normal component of the magnetic flux density is continuous through *any* boundary surface.

The application of (3) to a very small rectangular path of integration across the boundary surface as indicated in Fig. 6·3 leads to

$$\int_C \mathbf{H} \cdot \mathbf{ds} = H_{t_1} ds_1 - H_{t_2} ds_2 = \mathbf{J} \cdot \mathbf{dh} \times \mathbf{ds} \qquad (8)$$

if H_t designates the tangential component, and if one disregards the contributions of the normal components of H because $dh \to 0$. The right-hand side is again the total current flow *through* the closed path C and will vanish as dh is made to vanish unless the current density in the boundary surface itself is infinitely large. In the latter case, one defines

$$\lim_{dh \to 0} (\mathbf{J} \, dh) = \mathbf{K} \qquad (9)$$

as density of the *current sheet*, a concept analogous to surface charge density and particularly convenient in simplifying the description of distributed windings in machines, thin inductance coils, and the like.   With the concept (9), the second general boundary condition becomes

$$H_{t_1} - H_{t_2} = K_p \qquad (10)$$

where K_p is the component normal to H_t in the boundary surface.

In magnetostatic problems, the boundary conditions usually pertain to the field vectors and only rarely involve given values of the magnetostatic potential; they appear therefore frequently in the form of *general boundary value problems*. For $K = 0$, in

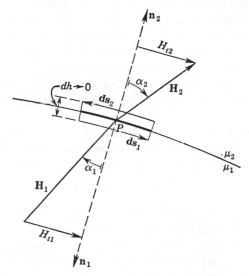

Fig. 6·3 Boundary Conditions for the Magnetizing Force.

the absence of a current sheet along the boundary surface, one can combine (7) and (10) by taking the ratios on both sides,

$$\frac{B_{n2}}{H_{t2}} = \frac{B_{n1}}{H_{t1}}$$

If one introduces the respective permeabilities and the angles α_1, α_2 of the field vectors with the surface normals, one obtains

$$\tan \alpha_1 = \frac{\mu_1}{\mu_2} \tan \alpha_2 \tag{11}$$

the *law of refraction* of magnetostatic field lines. This is of particular value for graphical field plotting.

If one applies the law of refraction to a boundary surface between a highly magnetic and a non-magnetic material of permeabilities μ_1 and μ_2 respectively, $\left(\dfrac{1}{\mu_1} \tan \alpha_1\right)$ will be a very small quantity for practically all angles α_1 less than $\pi/4$. This means, in turn, that tan α_2 and, therefore, α_2 will be very small, or the field lines in the non-magnetic material will be nearly perpendicular to the surface of the highly magnetic material. In practical problems one frequently assumes then the surfaces of highly magnetic materials as equipotential surfaces for which $\mathcal{F} = \text{cons}$, much like the conductor surfaces in electrostatics. This is further supported by the fact that the contribution of a highly magnetic material to the line integral (3) is very slight for reasonable values of flux densities. One thus can formulate certain magnetostatic problems as boundary value problems of the first kind and directly substitute electrostatic problems, for which solutions might already be known.

The Magnetic Vector Potential. Since the vector **B** cannot have sources or sinks under any conditions, it is possible (see Appendix 3) to associate with it a *vector potential* **A** such that

$$\nabla \times \mathbf{A} = \text{curl } \mathbf{A} = \mathbf{B} \tag{12}$$

This vector potential can, in turn, be related to current density **J** if one rewrites (3) in terms of surface integrals. The line integral can be transformed by Stokes's theorem (see Appendix 3), and the current I through the closed curve C can be defined as the flux of the current density vector **J**,

$$\iint (\text{curl } \mathbf{H}) \cdot d\mathbf{S} = \iint \mathbf{J} \cdot d\mathbf{S}$$

Because this relation to Stokes's theorem holds for any simple reducible surface S, the integrands themselves must be equal, giving with (12)

$$\text{curl } \mathbf{H} = \mathbf{J} = \nabla \times \left(\frac{1}{\mu} \nabla \times \mathbf{A} \right) \tag{13}$$

or also for general inhomogeneous media (non-isotropic media will again be considered beyond the scope of this monograph),

$$- \nabla \times \mathbf{A} \times \nabla \left(\frac{1}{\mu} \right) + \frac{1}{\mu} \nabla \times \nabla \times \mathbf{A} = \mathbf{J} \tag{14}$$

Comparing this vector differential equation with the scalar potential equations $(2 \cdot 1)$ and $(6 \cdot 5)$, one appreciates all efforts to define, even though for limited use only, the magnetostatic potential $\mathcal{F}$.

Of course, for homogeneous media (14) reduces to

$$\nabla \times \nabla \times \mathbf{A} = \mu \mathbf{J} \qquad (15)$$

the vector equivalent of Poisson's equation (2·4). If we now select the Cartesian coordinate system, because it is the only one in which the three unit vectors are completely symmetrical, each of constant magnitude and direction, we can interpret

$$\nabla \times \nabla \times \mathbf{A} = \nabla(\nabla \cdot \mathbf{A}) - (\nabla \cdot \nabla)\mathbf{A} \qquad (16)$$

where $\nabla \cdot \nabla = \nabla^2$ is the usual Laplacian operator. It is customary at this point to stipulate

$$\nabla \cdot \mathbf{A} = \text{div } \mathbf{A} = 0 \qquad (17)$$

because $\mathbf{A}$ is only mathematically defined, not measurable as a physical quantity and, in fact, only known through its coordinate derivatives by (12). The condition (17) essentially amounts to adjustment of $\mathbf{A}$ by addition of the gradient of an arbitrary scalar function Ψ; this does not affect the relation (12) since $\nabla \times \nabla \psi \equiv 0$.

With (16) and (17), the basic differential equation for the vector potential becomes in the Cartesian coordinate system

$$\nabla^2(\mathbf{i}A_x + \mathbf{j}A_y + \mathbf{k}A_z) = -\mu(\mathbf{i}J_x + \mathbf{j}J_y + \mathbf{k}J_z) \qquad (18)$$

simply a set of three independent scalar potential equations of the Poisson type. Each one of these can now be treated exactly like (2·4), and the formal solution results

$$\mathbf{A} = \mathbf{i}A_x + \mathbf{j}A_y + \mathbf{k}A_z = \frac{\mu}{4\pi} \iiint \frac{\mathbf{J}}{r} d\tau + \frac{\mu}{4\pi} \iint \frac{\mathbf{K}}{r} dS \qquad (19)$$

where $\mathbf{J}$ is the cross-sectional density and $\mathbf{K}$ the current sheet density; this integral expression can, of course, again be used independently of the particular coordinate system. For given current distributions in an infinite medium of constant permeability, one can therefore find the vector potential by direct integration (see Figs. 6·4 and 6·5) inside the current-carrying conductors as well as outside. One can also find solutions by superposition of the solution of the homogeneous vector differential equation and any particular integral of the inhomogeneous one. It must be borne in mind that (18) holds only in the Cartesian system; in any other coordinate system one must return to the more general form (15) as also emphasized in Appendix 3. Since the vector potential equation (15) is not generally separable with respect to the components in non-Cartesian coordinates, the

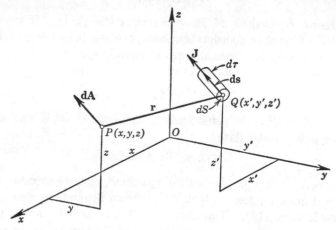

FIG. 6·4 Vector Potential Produced by Current Filament of Volume Distribution.

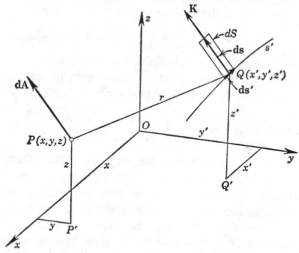

FIG. 6·5 Vector Potential Produced by Current Filament of a Current Sheet.

integral solutions (19) are of particular significance. For general methods of treating the form (15) see Smythe,[A22] p. 260.

If there are several magnetically different media, one has to find analytic solutions of the Poisson equations (18), or more generally of (15) for each medium independently, derive the field vectors **B** and **H**, and satisfy the boundary conditions (7) and (10). Because of the formal analogy between (19) and the scalar integral expression (2·5), one can readily formulate the boundary conditions for the vector potential itself as requiring the continuity of both the normal and the tangential components

$$A_{n_1} = A_{n_2}, \qquad A_{t_1} = A_{t_2} \tag{20}$$

This follows from the fact that the scalar potential function is continuous everywhere except at a layer of dipoles, across which it assumes a finite discontinuity; similarly, (20) will hold at all boundary surfaces except where the equivalent of a magnetic dipole layer exists.

Current Filaments. In many applications, it is possible to define the volume elements $d\tau$ in (19) as thin filaments parallel to the direction of the current density **J**, namely $d\tau = d\mathbf{S} \cdot d\mathbf{s}$, where both $d\mathbf{S}$ and $d\mathbf{s}$ point in the direction of **J** and where $d\mathbf{S}$ defines a surface element normal to **J**, whereas $d\mathbf{s}$ is the filament length. Without current sheets, the solution (19) can thus be written by interchanging the positions of **J** and $d\mathbf{s}$

$$\mathbf{A} = \frac{\mu}{4\pi} \iiint \mathbf{J} \cdot d\mathbf{S} \frac{d\mathbf{s}}{r}$$

If then the cross section of the conductor is very small compared with any distance r from the point of observation P (see Fig. 6·4), one can further evaluate the cross-section integral giving the total current I, and one has

$$\mathbf{A} = \frac{\mu}{4\pi} I \oint \frac{d\mathbf{s}}{r} \tag{21}$$

a much simpler line integral indicating that the elemental contribution to the vector potential gives a vector $d\mathbf{A}$ in the same direction as the filament. One must expect, of course, that $A \to \infty$ as one comes very close to the filamentary conductor.

The form (21) lends itself readily to the direct evaluation of the magnetic flux density **B**. With the curl operation applied to both sides, it can be taken under the integral sign because all quantities are continuous,

$$\mathbf{B} = \nabla \times \mathbf{A} = \frac{\mu}{4\pi} I \oint \nabla \times \frac{d\mathbf{s}}{r}$$

Now ∇ means differentiation with respect to (x, y, z), whereas the integration variables are (x', y', z') and $\mathbf{ds}$ contains only the latter set. Thus

$$\nabla \times \frac{\mathbf{ds}}{r} = \nabla \left(\frac{1}{r} \right) \times \mathbf{ds} = + \, \mathbf{ds} \times \frac{\mathbf{r}}{r^3}$$

One thus obtains the generalized form of the law of *Biot and Savart*

$$\mathbf{B} = \frac{\mu}{4\pi} I \int \frac{\mathbf{ds} \times \mathbf{r}}{r^3} \qquad (22)$$

As with the vector potential, so also with the magnetic flux density: as one approaches the filament, B will become infinite. The expressions (21) and (22) can therefore be well used to find the field quantities at some distance from the conductors considered as filaments, but one cannot actually admit zero cross section.

Flux Linkages. In a formal manner, one can get the total magnetic flux through a closed filament loop C produced by its own current with (12) as

$$\Phi_m = \iint_S \mathbf{B} \cdot \mathbf{dS} = \iint (\nabla \times \mathbf{A}) \cdot \mathbf{dS} = \int_C \mathbf{A} \cdot \mathbf{ds} \qquad (23)$$

the line integral of the vector potential extended over the loop. For a filament of zero cross section this expression will have little value, since $A \to \infty$ along the path of integration. If, on the other hand, one admits the finite cross section of the real conductor then the flux concept becomes indefinite, at least in the form given in (23).

However, for a finite cross section or a current sheet one can compute the vector potential $\mathbf{A}$ according to (19) anywhere in space with finite values. If one now subdivides the current flow into filaments $J \, dS$ as in Fig. 6·4 or $K \, ds'$ as in Fig. 6·5 and computes for each one the flux according to (23), the integrals over the respective cross sections will then constitute the magnetic *flux linkages* Λ in the two cases

$$\Lambda = \frac{1}{I} \iint J \left(\int_C \mathbf{A} \cdot \mathbf{ds} \right) dS \quad \text{or} \quad \frac{1}{I'} \int K \left(\int_{C'} \mathbf{A} \cdot \mathbf{ds} \right) ds' \qquad (24)$$

where the inner integral remains a function of the location of the filaments within the conductors. The division by the respective currents I and I' is necessary to restore proper dimension, since (24) really signifies an average value of the magnetic flux.

In a similar manner, the flux of the vector **B** through the filament loop C can be used for the inner integral in (24), if **B** itself is the total flux density produced by the conductor of finite cross section. This requires return to the more general solution (19) for the vector potential and application of the curl operation to it. As done in the derivation of (22), one can take $\nabla \times$ under the integral sign and apply it to $(1/r)$ only, since neither the vector densities **J** and **K** nor the elements $d\tau$ and dS depend on the coordinates of the point of observation where **B** is evaluated. Thus, one has

$$\mathbf{B} = \frac{\mu}{4\pi} \iiint \frac{\mathbf{J} \times \mathbf{r}}{r^3}\, d\tau + \frac{\mu}{4\pi} \iint \frac{\mathbf{K} \times \mathbf{r}}{r^3}\, dS \tag{25}$$

where, of course, $\mathbf{r}/r$ can be replaced by the unit vector in the direction of $\mathbf{r}$.

Magnetization. The characterization of a magnetic medium by the constant μ is satisfactory as long as no inquiry is made into the structural aspects of the medium that might be responsible for μ. To obtain a hypothetical concept of the nature of a magnetic material, one can separate in the magnetic intensity **H** the contribution which can be thought of to exist in free space from that thought to be caused by the presence of the magnetic material. Unlike the electrostatic case, however, one has here

$$\mathbf{H} = \frac{1}{\mu_0}\mathbf{B} - \left(\frac{1}{\mu_0} - \frac{1}{\mu}\right)\mathbf{B} = \frac{1}{\mu_0}\mathbf{B} - \mathbf{M} \tag{26}$$

in accordance with (21), where in most instances $\mu > \mu_0$, but where occasionally $\mu < \mu_0$ (diamagnetic substances). Since **B** defines the directly observable force actions, it is **H** that logically carries the influence of the medium; **M** is designated the *magnetization* or magnetic polarization analogous to **P**, the electric polarization (see section 2).

The effect of this separation upon the differential equation for the magnetostatic potential function $\mathcal{F}$ in a uniform magnetic medium is obtained by taking the divergence of (26) and observing (5·8)

$$\operatorname{div} \mathbf{H} = -\operatorname{div} \mathbf{M}$$

so that from (4) one has at once

$$\nabla^2 \mathcal{F} = \operatorname{div} \mathbf{M} \tag{27}$$

or the magnetization vector provides a source field for the magnetostatic potential, much as div **P** provides for the electrostatic potential Φ in $(2 \cdot 11)$. The magnetic material can therefore be interpreted as a fictitious distribution of volume density of magnetism $\rho_m' = -$div **M** existing in free space. Since there is no observable free magnetic quantity, ρ_m' can only mean a distribution of very small dipoles (see section 13) which for small finite volume elements always represents zero total magnetism, but which produces locally very strong magnetic intensities. These dipoles are equivalent to very small current loops which are assumed to have random orientation when no external magnetic field is applied, so that over finite small volume elements also **M** = 0. The application of a static magnetic field causes successive orientation[1] of small domains of dipoles and appearance of **M**. Obviously, without *first* defining the underlying structure, **M** cannot be evaluated.

If one considers, then, an isotropic magnetic material of volume τ and constant μ in free space and exposed to a magnetic field **B₀**, one can represent this material by the same volume τ filled with fictitious magnetism of density $\rho_m' = -$div **M**. The orientation of the dipoles caused by **B₀** will also leave on the surface of the volume τ an extra field which appears to come from a fictitious surface density of magnetism σ_m'. This can be defined from the normal components of the magnetic intensity **H** in the same manner as the electrostatic field gradient **E** defines the fictitious surface charge of polarization, since the normal component of the gradient completely specifies the potential distribution as shown in $(2 \cdot 3a)$. From (26) one has, observing (7),

$$H_{n2} - H_{n1} = -(M_{n2} - M_{n1}) = \sigma_m' \qquad (28)$$

The total contribution to the resultant magnetostatic potential existing outside or inside the material is, therefore, in analogy to $(2 \cdot 13)$,

$$\mathcal{F}' = \frac{1}{4\pi} \iiint \frac{\rho_m'}{r} \, d\tau + \frac{1}{4\pi} \iint \frac{\sigma_m'}{r} \, dS \qquad (29)$$

Obviously, **M** must depend on **B₀**, the impressed field, so that (29) is only a formal solution in the general case.

[1] F. T. Bitter: *Introduction to Ferromagnetism;* McGraw-Hill, New York, 1937; S. R. Williams: *Magnetic Phenomena;* McGraw-Hill, New York, 1931.

The separation (26) of the contributions to the magnetic intensity can be used also with the vector potential **A** from (12) and (19). Applying the curl operation $\nabla\times$ to (26), one has with (14)

$$\text{curl } \mathbf{H} = \mathbf{J} = \frac{1}{\mu_0} \nabla\times\mathbf{B} - \nabla\times\mathbf{M}$$

so that with (12) one obtains

$$\nabla\times\nabla\times\mathbf{A} = \nabla\times\mathbf{B} = \mu_0\mathbf{J} + \mu_0 \text{ curl } \mathbf{M} \tag{30}$$

Comparison with (15) shows at once that the effect of the magnetic medium can be represented as an equivalent current density $\mathbf{J}' = \text{curl } \mathbf{M}$, distributed throughout the volume of the magnetic material. The interchange between ρ_m', the volume density of magnetism in the magnetostatic potential field, and the current density $\mathbf{J}'$ in the vector potential field illustrates once more the ready conversion of the respective concepts.

Considering as before an isotropic magnetic material of volume τ and constant μ in free space and exposed to a magnetic field $\mathbf{B}_0$, one can represent this material by the same volume τ filled with fictitious current flow of density $\mathbf{J}' = \text{curl } \mathbf{M}$. For a formal solution one can then use (19), in which $\mu\mathbf{J}$ is to be replaced by $\mu_0\mathbf{J}'$ as indicated by (30) and where $\mu\mathbf{K}$ must be replaced by the surface discontinuity of the tangential components of **B** in accordance with condition (10). From (26) one has

$$H_{t_2} - H_{t_1} = \frac{1}{\mu_0} (B_{t_2} - B_{t_1}) - (M_{t_2} - M_{t_1})$$

$$= \frac{1}{\mu_0} (B_{t_2} - B_{t_1}) - K'$$

and since no real current sheet density exists, the left-hand side must be zero. This leads, therefore, to the fictitious current sheet density $\mathbf{K}'$ and thus to

$$\mathbf{A}' = \frac{\mu_0}{4\pi} \iiint \frac{\mathbf{J}'}{r} \, d\tau + \frac{\mu_0}{4\pi} \iint \frac{\mathbf{K}'}{r} \, dS \tag{31}$$

as the total contribution of the material to the resultant vector potential existing outside or inside the magnetic material. Again, $\mathbf{J}'$ and $\mathbf{K}'$ must depend on $\mathbf{B}_0$, so that (31) can only represent a formal solution in the general case where the magnetic material can react upon the impressed field, $\mathbf{B}_0$. If one can assume con-

stant magnetization **M** throughout the volume τ, then (31) reduces
to the surface integral; a magnetized cylinder can therefore be
considered the equivalent of a thin cylindrical coil carrying current
of sheet density **K′**. The direction of **K′** is such that from its
vector tip the difference $M_{t2} - M_{t1}$, if positive, has counterclockwise direction.

7· ENERGY AND FORCES
IN THE MAGNETOSTATIC FIELD

Considering any system of steady current distributions, then the
algebraic sum total of currents through a very large cross-sectional
surface (plane or curved in space) can be zero or different from
zero. In the first case, the system is called a *complete system*, and
all the currents flow in closed loops and permit definitions of
fluxes and energies in finite terms; the second case presumes as
part of the system wires of infinite length with no return, a
physically impossible arrangement which will not be considered
further.

As emphasized previously, only linear relationships between
currents and magnetic fields will be considered here; in all the
following relations, μ will therefore be assumed independent of
the current. The extension to the non-linear relationship in an

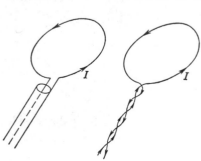

elementary manner is readily
possible and is given in
Attwood[A2]; however, the evaluation of the non-linear field
distributions is extremely difficult.

The Single Current Loop.
The simplest complete current
system is a single current loop
of simple geometry and arbitrary conductor cross section.
Since current has to be supplied by a source, it is neces-

FIG. 7·1   Single Current Loop, Idealized.

sary to effect an arrangement which minimizes the magnetic field
of the leads, as for example twisting of bifilar wires or a coaxial
cable as indicated in Fig. 7·1 in simple line drawing.

The magnetic flux linkages are given by either expression in
(6·24) and are proportional to the loop current I because of the

linear relation (6·21) between current and vector potential. The ratio

$$\frac{\Lambda}{I} = L \tag{1}$$

is called the *inductance* of the loop and is a purely geometric characteristic of the magnetic field and its distribution. One can actually give an explicit integral form if he observes that in (6·24) the two successive integrations are performed in mutually perpendicular directions and can therefore be combined into a volume or a surface integral, respectively, over the conductor

$$\Lambda = \frac{1}{I} \iiint \mathbf{J} \cdot \mathbf{A} \, d\tau \quad \text{or} \quad \frac{1}{I} \iint \mathbf{K} \cdot \mathbf{A} \, dS \tag{2}$$

Since **A** is itself given as an integral over the same cross section by (6·19), one has

$$L = \frac{\mu}{4\pi I^2} \iiint \mathbf{J} \cdot \left[\iiint \frac{\mathbf{J}}{r} \, d\tau \right] d\tau \quad \text{or}$$

$$\frac{\mu}{4\pi I^2} \iint \mathbf{K} \cdot \left[\iint \frac{\mathbf{K}}{r} \, dS \right] dS \tag{3}$$

Knowing the current distribution, one can therefore directly evaluate the inductance of the loop.

This loop is capable of storing a magnetic field energy equal to the work required to build up the magnetic field. Assuming a small virtual displacement δs of the loop, and applying it first to one of its filaments exposed to a field **B**, one obtains with adaptation of (5·6) for the virtual work on this filament

$$\delta W = (J \, dS)\delta\Phi_m \quad \text{or} \quad (K \, ds')\delta\Phi_m$$

where $\delta\Phi_m$ is the flux through the small area covered by the filament in its translation δs. For the virtual work on the total loop one has to integrate over the conductor cross section and has

$$\delta W = I\delta\Lambda \tag{4}$$

utilizing (6·24). If the magnetic field is produced by the current of the loop itself, then $\delta\Lambda$ can be produced only by a variation of the current with time so that one must introduce the induction law and account for the losses. The total magnetic field energy, however, can be evaluated from (4), so that with (1), barring any deformation,

$$W_m = \int_{I=0}^{I} IL \, \delta I = \tfrac{1}{2}LI^2 = \tfrac{1}{2}I\Lambda = \frac{1}{2L}\Lambda^2 \qquad (5)$$

quite analogous to the electrostatic relations in (3·3). Again as there, all the quantities are integral quantities and are amenable to measurement.

Two Current Loops. If two current loops with currents I_1 and I_2 are in close proximity, magnetic flux of one will link with the other. Computed anywhere in space, the expression for the resultant vector potential **A** will contain one term dependent on I_1 and another depending on I_2 in accordance with the superposition principle of linear forms. The flux linkages for the two loops will then be of the form

$$\left. \begin{aligned} \Lambda_1 &= L_1 I_1 + L_{12} I_2 \\ \Lambda_2 &= L_2 I_2 + L_{21} I_1 \end{aligned} \right\} \qquad (6)$$

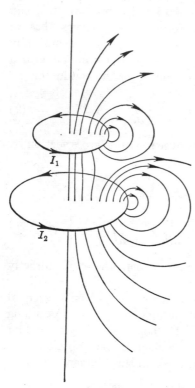

FIG. 7·2   Resultant Magnetic Field of Two Current Loops.

One designates L_1 and L_2 as self-inductances of the two loops and $L_{12} = L_{21} = M$ as their mutual inductance. These inductances are defined by (3) if one sets formally $\mathbf{J} = \mathbf{J}_1 + \mathbf{J}_2$ and identifies the resulting four terms as the appropriate self and mutual inductances. L_{12} and L_{21} are identical because their definitions differ only by the interchange in the order of integration. To emphasize the partial linkage, one can rewrite the pair of relations (6) in the form

$$\left. \begin{aligned} \Lambda_1 &= (L_1 - M)I_1 + M(I_1 + I_2) \\ \Lambda_2 &= (L_2 - M)I_2 + M(I_1 + I_2) \end{aligned} \right\} \qquad (7)$$

and define $(L_1 - M) = S_1$, $(L_2 - M) = S_2$, as primary and secondary leakage inductance, respectively, considering the arrangement as the prototype of a two-winding transformer. $M(I_1 + I_2) = \Lambda_m$ is then called the usefully linked flux, or main flux linkage.

For the simple case of two circular loops, Fig. 7·2 might represent a typical resultant field distribution for assumed current values I_1 and I_2. It is quite customary to take the field lines closing around only one conductor as representing the leakage flux lines of (7) and to take the lines passing through both loops as representing the main flux lines of (7). This interpretation is, however, incorrect,[1] since the geometry of the field lines at every point depends on both currents simultaneously, as does the vector potential; a few graphs would readily bear out that for different current ratios the resultant field distribution changes little whereas the flux contributions in (7) change rapidly. In order to restore correlation between field distribution and the

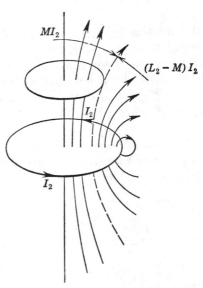

FIG. 7·3   Interaction of Two Current Loops.

flux linkages according to (7), one must consider one current at a time, as for example I_2 in Fig. 7·3, and relate it to the second equation of (7).

The total magnetic field energy in the system is given by the sum of the two loop energies

$$W_m = \tfrac{1}{2}I_1\Lambda_1 + \tfrac{1}{2}I_2\Lambda_2 = \tfrac{1}{2}L_1I_1{}^2 + MI_1I_2 + \tfrac{1}{2}L_2I_2{}^2 \quad (8)$$

The center term is the mutual energy. Its value can be computed readily even if the loops degenerate into current filaments, since

---

[1] E. Weber, "What is Leakage?" *Elektrot. und Masch.*, **48**, p. 943 (1930); also *E.T.Z.*, **51**, pp. 1221 and 1267 (1930).

the contribution to the vector potential by one filament is, according to (6·21),

$$\mathbf{A}_1 = \frac{\mu}{4\pi} I_1 \int \frac{d\mathbf{s}_1}{r}$$

whereas the flux through the second filament is by (6·23)

$$\Phi_{12} = \int_{C_2} \mathbf{A}_1 \cdot d\mathbf{s}_2 = MI_1 \tag{9}$$

the integral being taken over the second filament. The self-energies can, however, be computed only for volume or surface distributions of currents.

It should be noted that L_1 and L_2, the self-inductances, are quite independent of the presence of the other loop. This will be so in all cases where the current distribution is assumed to be known.

System of Loops in Homogeneous Medium. The generalization from two loops to n loops is now readily made. The flux linkages for loop α will be

$$\Lambda_\alpha = \sum_{\beta=1}^{n} L_{\alpha\beta} I_\beta, \qquad \alpha = 1, 2, \cdots, n \tag{10}$$

and the total magnetic field energy becomes

$$W_m = \frac{1}{2} \sum_{\alpha=1}^{n} I_\alpha \Lambda_\alpha = \frac{1}{2} \sum_{\alpha=1}^{n} \sum_{\beta=1}^{n} L_{\alpha\beta} I_\alpha I_\beta \tag{11}$$

a quadratic function of the loop currents. Since $L_{\alpha\beta} = L_{\beta\alpha}$, there will be $n(n+1)/2$ different inductance values.

The force or torque action in such a system caused by any change of a geometric element $\delta\eta$ (linear or angular displacement) can be calculated by the principle of virtual work. According to (4), the mechanical work δW can be expressed directly as the change of the magnetic field energy $I\delta\Lambda$ for a single filament. For fixed current values in the system (11), one has then for the mechanical action the positive rate of magnetic field energy

$$\frac{\partial W_{\text{mech}}}{\partial \eta} = + \frac{\partial W_m}{\partial \eta} = + \frac{1}{2} \sum_{\alpha=1}^{n} \sum_{\beta=1}^{n} I_\alpha I_\beta \frac{\partial L_{\alpha\beta}}{\partial \eta} \tag{12}$$

whereas in the electrostatic case the negative rate of energy has to be taken as seen in (3·26). This is related to the fact that currents of opposite sign repel each other, and that magnetic field energy has kinetic rather than potential character.

Integral Forms of Magnetostatic Energy. The magnetic field energy for a finite system of loops of arbitrary individual cross sections in a homogeneous medium can be expressed either by (11) or, introducing the expressions (2) for the flux linkages, also as

$$W_m = \frac{1}{2} \iiint \mathbf{A} \cdot \mathbf{J} \, d\tau + \frac{1}{2} \iint \mathbf{A} \cdot \mathbf{K} \, dS \qquad (13)$$

where the integrals have to be extended over all the current loop volumes and current loop sheets of the system. The form of (13) can readily be compared with the analogous electrostatic energy expression (3·18), where scalar potential and scalar densities take the place of the corresponding vectors in (13). The vector potential itself is obtained by (6·19), quite analogous to the expression for the scalar potential (2·5).

By means of the vector analogue of Green's theorem [Appendix 3, (32)], one can transform (13) into a very simple volume integral. Let in the theorem $\mathbf{V} = \mathbf{W} \equiv \mathbf{A}$, the vector potential, and observe

$$\nabla \times \mathbf{A} = \mathbf{B}, \qquad \nabla \times \nabla \times \mathbf{A} = \mu \mathbf{J}$$

and multiply by $1/2\mu$; then it yields

$$\frac{1}{2\mu} \iiint \mathbf{B}^2 \, d\tau - \frac{1}{2} \iiint \mathbf{A} \cdot \mathbf{J} \, d\tau = \frac{1}{2\mu} \iint (\mathbf{A} \times \mathbf{B}) \cdot d\mathbf{S} \qquad (14)$$

The surface integral is to be taken over the infinite sphere bounding the medium and all current loop sheets which represent internal boundary surfaces for the medium. The volume integrals are to be taken over all space within this very large sphere, whereby the second one will contribute only at places where $\mathbf{J} \neq 0$.

Since, however, $B \to 0$ as $1/r^2$, and $A \to 0$ as $1/r$, at very large distance from the finite loop system, the surface integral can be restricted to the current loop sheets. On these, A and B_n will be continuous, whereas H_t will have a discontinuity according to (6·10) of value K, the current sheet density; integrating over the surface of the sheet, therefore, only H_t will contribute

$$\iint (\mathbf{A} \times \mathbf{B}) \cdot d\mathbf{S} \to \iint (\mathbf{A} \cdot \mathbf{K}) \, dS$$

and by comparison with (13) one finds the alternative expression for the magnetic field energy

$$W_m = \frac{1}{2} \iiint \mathbf{H} \cdot \mathbf{B} \, d\tau = \frac{1}{2\mu} \iiint B^2 \, d\tau \qquad (15)$$

to be taken over all space. This form again permits, according to Maxwell's point of view, the interpretation as if the field energy were distributed through space with a local density $\frac{1}{2}\mathbf{H} \cdot \mathbf{B}$, entirely determined by the field vectors. This expression can be shown to be valid for any magnetostatic system in which there are no permanent magnets.

Stresses in the Magnetostatic Field. As in the electrostatic field, so here in the magnetostatic field Faraday's visualization of force action as associated with the configuration of field lines was formulated by Maxwell, who introduced a stress per unit area of magnitude $\frac{1}{2}HB$ in the direction of the field lines, and a pressure per unit area of the same magnitude perpendicular to the field lines upon a surface element parallel to the field lines. This imagined system of forces accounts for Ampère's force law and permits evaluation of force actions on the boundary surfaces of different magnetic materials. Thus, the force normal to a boundary surface urging medium 1 towards medium 2 will be (without current sheet) the difference of the normal stresses plus the difference of the normal pressures on the two sides of the boundary surface:

$$f_n = -\tfrac{1}{2}(H_{1n}B_{1n} - H_{2n}B_{2n}) + \tfrac{1}{2}(H_{1t}B_{1t} - H_{2t}B_{2t})$$

Because of the continuity of B_n and H_t across the boundary, one can transform this into

$$f_n = -\frac{1}{2}\left(\frac{1}{\mu_1} - \frac{1}{\mu_2}\right)B_n{}^2 + \frac{1}{2}\,(\mu_1 - \mu_2)H_t{}^2$$

$$= \frac{1}{2}\,(\mu_1 - \mu_2)\mathbf{H}_1 \cdot \mathbf{H}_2 \qquad (16)$$

These forms do not take into account the secondary effects of magnetostriction and do not apply strictly for ferromagnetic materials. A rather complete account of the more advanced theory is given in the references Livens[A15] and Stratton,[A23] Appendix 4.

PROBLEMS

1. The barrier surface in Fig. 6·1 has a magnetostatic potential difference $\mathcal{F}_1 - \mathcal{F}_2 = I$ between its faces. Show that it can be interpreted, therefore, as a fictitious magnetic shell (magnetic double layer) of moment $I = \sigma_m \, \delta a$ per unit area, where σ_m is the fictitious magnetic charge density and δa the very small charge separation. Hint: refer to problem 6 of chapter 1 and use (6·4).

2. Demonstrate the uniqueness theorem for the magnetostatic potential function of any number of current loops in free space, each loop furnished with an appropriate barrier surface. Hint: note the preceding problem and apply the method of problem 12 in chapter 1.

3. Compute the magnetic field inside and outside a uniformly magnetized sphere of radius a. The magnetic field causing the magnetization $\mathbf{M}$ is homogeneous throughout space (assume free space), has the same direction as $\mathbf{M}$, and has value B_0. Establish the equivalence with a uniform magnetic sphere in the homogeneous field $\mathbf{B}_0$ and find the equivalent relative permeability of the sphere in terms of M and B_0 (see problem 4 in chapter 1).

4. The measurement of the force action between the near ends of two long bar magnets leads to "Coulomb's force law for magnetic poles." Show that this law must have the form $F_m = \mu Q_{m1} Q_{m2}/4\pi r^2$, where Q_m are the magnetic quantities measuring the pole strengths, μ the absolute permeability of the medium in which the measurement is made, and r the center distance of the magnetic poles. Hint: deduce the concept of "field strength" as in Coulomb's law for electric charges and observe (5·4) as well as problem 1 above; see also magnetic dipole in section 13.

5. Demonstrate that the formal solution (6·19) satisfies the condition (6·17) for finite distributions of $\mathbf{J}$ and $\mathbf{K}$.

6. Give the derivation of (6·25) from the formal solution (6·19) for the vector potential.

7. In a region free of current flow and bounded by a closed surface S, the vector potential is uniquely defined by its values on the boundary surface; demonstrate the uniqueness theorem for the vector potential. Hint: apply the vector analogue to Green's theorem (Appendix 3) with $\mathbf{P} = \mathbf{Q} = \mathbf{A} - \mathbf{A}'$, where $\mathbf{A}$ and $\mathbf{A}'$ are two different solutions each satisfying the differential equation $\nabla \times \nabla \times \mathbf{A} = 0$ and the boundary condition. (Stratton,[A23] p. 256.)

8. Accepting a stress per unit area of magnitude $\frac{1}{2}\mathbf{H} \cdot \mathbf{B}$ in the direction of the magnetic field lines, show that two parallel like currents flowing in the same direction attract each other in accordance with Ampère's law (5·1). Hint: utilize the symmetry of the field distribution.

9. Accepting a pressure per unit area of magnitude $\frac{1}{2}\mathbf{H} \cdot \mathbf{B}$ normal to the direction of the field lines, show that two parallel like currents flowing in opposite directions repel each other in accordance with Ampère's law (5·1). Hint: utilize the symmetry of the field distribution.

10. Given a fixed system of n conductor loops in a homogeneous and isotropic medium, assume that currents I_α are flowing in the individual loop and that flux linkages Λ_α are measured. If then new currents I_α' are flowing, the corresponding flux linkages Λ_α' are related by $\sum_{(\alpha)} I_\alpha \Lambda_\alpha' = \sum_{(\alpha)} I_\alpha' \Lambda_\alpha$ (analogue

to Green's reciprocation theorem; see problem 10 in chapter 1). Prove this relation; utilize (7·10).

11. Find the expression for the torque exerted upon a single plane filament loop of current I in a uniform magnetic field $\mathbf{B}_0$ if the plane of the loop makes the angle θ with the direction of $\mathbf{B}_0$. Express the relation in vectorial form by introducing the magnetic moment of the equivalent magnetic shell.

12. Find the general expressions for the force and the torque exerted upon a small circular filament loop of current I in a non-uniform magnetic field $\mathbf{B}$. Using the concept of the equivalent magnetic shell, convert the expressions into vectorial form; compare with the analogous electric dipole problem in section 10.

13. Find the force action between two identical filament loops of opposite current $\pm I$, if they are placed parallel to each other at very small distance δa. Observe the direction of the force and compare with the analogous electrostatic problem of two charged conducting loops.

14. Any filament loop of current I can be represented as a network of elementary filament loops, the contour of each of which carries the same current I. The force on each elementary loop of area dS is given by $\mathbf{dF}$ as found in problem 12. Demonstrate that the total force upon the actual loop can also be expressed by $\mathbf{F} = I \oint \mathbf{dl} \times \mathbf{B}$, where $\mathbf{dl}$ is the vector line element of the loop. (Smythe,[A22] p. 276.)

15. On the basis of the experimentally confirmed force action (5·4) one can assume the force on any element $I\,\mathbf{dl}$ of a filament loop to be given by $\mathbf{dF} = I\,\mathbf{dl} \times \mathbf{B}$. Using this, demonstrate the validity of (7·4) for a finite current loop of finite cross section S. Hint: divide the current volume into filaments $\mathbf{J}\,dS$.

16. Formulate the general boundary conditions pertaining to the normal and tangential derivatives of the vector potential, excluding the possibility of a magnetic shell in the boundary surface.

17. Formulate the boundary condition for the magnetic vector potential if the boundary surface is a magnetic shell of moment $\mathbf{m}_1$ per unit area.

18. The magnetic forces act to increase the magnetic field energy as shown in (7·12), so that the latter is frequently interpreted as analogous to kinetic energy; considering it as potential energy, one must define it by $U = -W_m$. Show by means of Faraday's law of induction $V = -\delta\Phi_m/\delta t$ that the work done in a small actual (not virtual) displacement of a single filament loop, keeping the current I constant, is exactly compensated by the energy furnished by the supply voltage; the total work done on the circuit is thus zero. (Stratton,[A23] p. 119.)

19. Show that a freely movable filament loop carrying current I will be in stable equilibrium in a magnetic field if the loop links the greatest possible magnetic flux.

20. Given two filament loops carrying currents I_1 and I_2 in arbitrary relative position and with individual supply voltages V_1 and V_2. If the two loops attract each other and if the currents are kept constant, show that one half of the energy supplied by the sources is used for the mechanical work. Note problem 18. (Smythe,[A22] p. 306.)

21. Find the vector potential and magnetic field produced by a plane current sheet of infinite extent with uniform parallel current flow of density $\mathbf{K}$.

22. Find the magnetic field in an infinite plane slab of magnetic material with permeability μ_2 if on its two faces thin current sheets are applied carrying currents of densities $\pm\mathbf{K}$ in opposite directions. Find the field outside the slab if the permeability there is μ_1.

23. Find the magnetic field far from a thin cylindrical bar magnetized uniformly parallel to its axis if the radius is a and the length $2l$. Define its magnetic moment and show the equivalence to a bar magnet.

24. Demonstrate that for finite current distributions (7·4) can also be expressed as the volume integral of $\mathbf{H} \cdot \delta\mathbf{B}$. Hint: use the first form of (7·2) with fixed current value; observe (6·13) and $\nabla \times \delta\mathbf{A} = \delta\mathbf{B}$.

25. Show that in ferromagnetic materials the hysteresis loss per cycle and per unit volume can be represented by the integral $-\displaystyle\int \mathbf{M} \cdot d\mathbf{B}$ taken over one complete cycle of magnetization.

3. GENERAL FIELD ANALOGIES

8. THE ELECTRIC CURRENT FIELD

Chapter 1 has dealt with the electrostatic field in insulators (dielectrics). In conductors, the presence of a constant electric field causes a continuous migration of charges, usually electrons in metals, and ions in electrolytes. The flow rate of charges or the *current*

$$I = \frac{dQ}{dt} \tag{1}$$

as measured through a stationary surface has the characteristics of the flow of an incompressible fluid, namely, that neither source nor sink can exist within the fluid itself. In terms of the density of the flow through unit area, designated by the vector $\mathbf{J}$, incompressibility means

$$\iint_S \mathbf{J} \cdot \mathbf{n} \, dS = 0 \tag{2}$$

or in accordance with Gauss's theorem (see Appendix 3)

$$\operatorname{div} \mathbf{J} = \nabla \cdot \mathbf{J} = 0 \tag{3}$$

For stationary currents, Ohm's law expresses the experimental fact that the potential difference $\Phi_1 - \Phi_2$ (voltage) applied at the ends of a long conductor is proportional to the resulting current within the conductor,

$$\Phi_1 - \Phi_2 = V_{12} = RI \tag{4}$$

with R defined as resistance. For long conductors (wires) of uniform cross section S, the resistance is simply related to the geometry,

$$R = \frac{l}{\gamma S} \tag{5}$$

where γ is the uniform conductivity of the material and l the length of the conductor. This experimental fact can be translated into

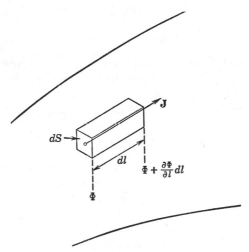

Fig. 8·1 Differential Form of Ohm's Law.

a vector relationship by considering a volume element in an extended conductor of arbitrary shape. Referring to Fig. 8·1, the elemental potential difference in the direction of current flow can be found by a Taylor series approximation as $-(\partial\Phi/\partial l)\,dl$, the current of the element as $J\,dS$, and the resistance from (5) as $\frac{1}{\gamma}(dl/dS)$. Thus, (4) leads to

$$-\frac{\partial\Phi}{\partial l}\,dl = \frac{dl}{\gamma\,dS}\,J\,dS \tag{6}$$

or in general vector relation

$$-\text{grad }\Phi = -\nabla\Phi = \frac{1}{\gamma}\mathbf{J} \tag{7}$$

This can be readily verified by writing (6) for the three orthogonal directions of a coordinate system and taking the vector sum.

The negative gradient of the electric potential Φ can be defined as the electric field strength **E** within conductors in the same manner as within dielectrics by (1·7), and one obtains

$$\mathbf{J} = \gamma \mathbf{E} \tag{8}$$

the differential form of Ohm's law. Combining (7) with (3) yields, then,

$$\nabla \cdot \mathbf{J} = -\nabla \cdot (\gamma \nabla \Phi) = 0$$

or also

$$\nabla \Phi \cdot \nabla \gamma + \gamma \nabla^2 \Phi = 0 \tag{9}$$

the general differential equation for an inhomogeneous conductor, wherein the variation of γ must be known. (Only the case of isotropic conductors is treated here.)

For homogeneous media, γ will be a constant and (9) reduces to *Laplace's equation*

$$\nabla^2 \Phi = 0 \tag{10}$$

identical with (2·2) for the electrostatic field in homogeneous dielectrics. In a boundary value problem of the first kind with only two prescribed boundary potential values of a single medium (see section 2), the solution for the electric field strength **E** will be identical, therefore, whether this single medium be a dielectric or a conductor; in the first case, which is the ideal condenser of section 3, the electric vector **E** will be responsible for a dielectric flux density $\mathbf{D} = \varepsilon \mathbf{E}$, whereas in the second case, it will be responsible for a current density $\mathbf{J} = \gamma \mathbf{E}$. The total dielectric flux between the two boundary potentials will be

$$\iint \mathbf{D} \cdot d\mathbf{S} = \varepsilon \iint \mathbf{E} \cdot d\mathbf{S} = C(\Phi_1 - \Phi_2)$$

whereas the total current flow for the conducting medium is

$$\iint \mathbf{J} \cdot d\mathbf{S} = \gamma \iint \mathbf{E} \cdot d\mathbf{S} = \frac{1}{R}(\Phi_1 - \Phi_2)$$

so that for the *same* geometry one has

$$CR = \frac{\varepsilon}{\gamma} \tag{11}$$

Solving a condenser problem in electrostatics, one can immediately obtain the resistance between the same electrodes by application of (11).

The Boundary Conditions of the Electric Current Field.

If several different conducting media are present, then it is necessary to solve the differential equation (10), or the more general form (9), for each individual conductor and to link these solutions by continuity conditions along the boundary surfaces.

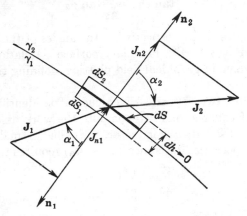

FIG. 8·2 Continuity of Current Flow across a Boundary Surface between Two Conductors.

The basic condition (2), if applied to a small cylinder of height $dh \to 0$, as indicated in Fig. 8·2, leads at once to

$$\iint \mathbf{J} \cdot \mathbf{n} \, dS = J_{n2} \, dS_2 - J_{n1} \, dS_1 = 0$$

In the limit for vanishing dh

$$J_{n2} = J_{n1} \tag{12}$$

which is one general boundary condition and states the continuity of current flow across a boundary surface under stationary conditions.

From the fact that the electric field strength is derived from the scalar potential Φ in the same manner as in electrostatics, one can deduce as in (2·8)

$$E_{t2} = E_{t1} \tag{13}$$

the second general boundary condition. E_t is the respective field component tangential to the boundary surface.

The combination of the two conditions (12) and (13) leads to

$$\frac{E_{t_2}}{E_{n_2}} = \frac{\gamma_2}{\gamma_1} \frac{E_{t_1}}{E_{n_1}}$$

or

$$\tan \alpha_1 = \frac{\gamma_1}{\gamma_2} \tan \alpha_2 \tag{14}$$

if α_1 and α_2 designate, respectively, the angles of the field vectors with the normals to the boundary surface. Relation (14) is of particular value in graphical field plotting, defining the refraction of field lines.

Dissipation into Heat. Since current is identified with the migration of charges, one can compute the work associated with current flow through a conductor. Moving a small charge dQ through the potential difference $(\Phi_1 - \Phi_2)$ requires the work

$$dW = (\Phi_1 - \Phi_2) \, dQ$$

as indicated in (3·2). The time rate of work, or power, can be expressed with (1) as

$$P = \frac{dW}{dt} = V_{12}I = RI^2 \tag{15}$$

if one also utilizes Ohm's law (4). This power must be expended to maintain the current flow through the conductor, and it appears as heat created by the "resistance" to the migration of the elementary charges. The experimental proof was given by Joule, and (15) is usually called *Joule's law.*

One can readily express (15) in terms of the characteristic field vectors if he applies this relation to the volume element shown in Fig. 8·1. With the resistance and current values as defined for (6), one has for the power loss in the volume element

$$dP = \frac{dl}{\gamma \, dS} (J \, dS)^2 = \frac{1}{\gamma} J^2 \, d\tau = \mathbf{E} \cdot \mathbf{J} \, d\tau \tag{16}$$

and therefore for the total power dissipated in a conductor

$$P = \iiint \mathbf{E} \cdot \mathbf{J} \, d\tau \tag{17}$$

which is valid for all media, even for non-isotropic media. This form permits the interpretation as if the dissipation would take place with a volume density $\mathbf{E} \cdot \mathbf{J}$, entirely determined by the field vectors $\mathbf{E}$ and $\mathbf{J}$; the hypothetical nature of this interpretation has to be kept in mind, however.

Concept of the Semiconductor or Semidielectric. Though for purposes of analysis it is convenient to admit only two classes of media, namely, ideal dielectrics and pure conductors, many materials exhibit a significant combination of both characteristics; such materials are then called semiconductors or semidielectrics, depending upon the characteristic one wishes to stress.

The electric field distribution in semidielectrics is found by solving the Laplace differential equation for the potential Φ and satisfying all the boundary conditions. However, the field vector $\mathbf{E}$ now causes simultaneously electrostatic polarization and conduction current, so that

$$\mathbf{D} = \varepsilon\mathbf{E}, \qquad \mathbf{J} = \gamma\mathbf{E} \tag{18}$$

both apply. At the boundary surface of two semiconductors the conditions (12) and (13) have to be satisfied; the current flow *must* be continuous, since otherwise unlimited accumulation of charge would occur, contrary to the condition of stationary flow. Because of the existence of $\mathbf{D}$, the respective boundary condition (2·7)

$$D_{n2} - D_{n1} = \sigma \tag{19}$$

also must be satisfied, i.e., a surface charge density σ *must* appear of value

$$D_{n2} - D_{n1} = \left(\frac{\varepsilon_2}{\gamma_2} - \frac{\varepsilon_1}{\gamma_1}\right) J_n \tag{20}$$

obtained by combination of (18) and (12). Only if by chance

$$\frac{\varepsilon_2}{\gamma_2} = \frac{\varepsilon_1}{\gamma_1}$$

will this surface charge disappear.

9· OTHER PHYSICAL FIELDS

The concept of a stationary field occurs in several other branches of physics and engineering, such as aerodynamics and hydrodynamics, conduction of heat, and gravitational theory.[1] As far as

[1] E. Weber, "Mapping of Fields," *Electr. Eng.*, **53**, p. 1563 (1934). See also list of references in Appendix 4, C.

TABLE

Quantity	Electrostatic Field	Magnetostatic Field
Potential function	Φ, electrostatic potential	$\mathcal{F}$, magnetostatic potential
Potential difference	$\Phi_1 - \Phi_2 = \int_1^2 E_s \, ds = V$, voltage (electromotive force)	$\mathcal{F}_1 - \mathcal{F}_2 = \int_1^2 H_s \, ds$, magnetomotive force
Equipotential surface	$\Phi = $ cons (conductor surfaces)	$\mathcal{F} = $ cons (usually iron surfaces)
Potential gradient	$\mathbf{E} = -\mathrm{grad}\ \Phi$, electric field strength	$\mathbf{H} = -\mathrm{grad}\ \mathcal{F}$, magnetizing force
Characteristic constant of medium	ε, absolute dielectric constant	μ, absolute permeability
Associated field vector	$\mathbf{D} = \varepsilon\mathbf{E}$, dielectric flux density (displacement vector)	$\mathbf{B} = \mu\mathbf{H}$, magnetic flux density (magnetic induction)
Flux of the associated vector	$\psi = \int D_n \, dS$, dielectric flux	$\Phi_m = \int B_n \, dS$, magnetic flux
Total flux*	$\oint D_n \, dS = Q$, electric charge within S	$\oint B_n \, dS = 0$
Divergence of associated field vector	div $\mathbf{D} = \rho$, space charge density	div $\mathbf{B} = 0$
Basic differential equation of the potential function	$\nabla^2\Phi = -\rho/\varepsilon$	$\nabla^2\mathcal{F} = 0$
Field transmittance	$C = \psi/(\Phi_1 - \Phi_2) = \psi/V$, capacitance	$\mathcal{P} = \Phi_m/(\mathcal{F}_1 - \mathcal{F}_2)$, permeance

* Total flux is defined as the integral over a closed surface.

9·1

IN SCALAR POTENTIAL FIELDS

Electric Current Field	Stationary Temperature Field	Fluid Dynamic Field	Gravitational Field
Φ, electric potential	T, temperature	Φ, velocity potential	U, Newton's potential (force function)
$\Phi_1 - \Phi_2 = \int_1^2 E_s\, ds = V$, voltage (electromotive force)	$T_1 - T_2 = \int_1^2 U_s\, ds$, temperature difference	$\Phi_2 - \Phi_1 = \int_1^2 v_s\, ds$, potential difference	$U_2 - U_1 = \int_1^2 g_s\, ds$, potential difference
$\Phi = $ cons (electrode surfaces)	$T = $ cons, isotherms	$\Phi = $ cons (equipotential surfaces)	$U = $ cons
$\mathbf{E} = -\text{grad } \Phi$, electric field strength	$\mathbf{U} = -\text{grad } T$, temperature gradient	$\mathbf{v} = +\text{grad } \Phi$, velocity	$\mathbf{g} = +\text{grad } U$, gravitational acceleration
γ, electric conductivity	k, thermal conductivity	ρ, mass density (incompressible)	$\gamma = 1/G$, reciprocal of gravitation constant G
$\mathbf{J} = \gamma\mathbf{E}$, current density	$\mathbf{J} = k\mathbf{U}$, heat power flow density	$\mathbf{F} = \rho\mathbf{v}$, flow rate density	$\mathbf{f} = \gamma\mathbf{g}$, gravitational mass vector
$I = \int J_n\, dS$, electric current	$Q = \int J_n\, dS$, heat power flow	$Q = \int F_n\, dS$, flow rate	$\Phi = \int f_n\, dS$, flux of gravitational mass vector
$\oint J_n\, dS = 0$	$\oint J_n\, dS = H$, heat power within S	$\oint F_n\, dS = E$, efflux	$\oint f_n\, dS = -4\pi M$, M mass within S
div $\mathbf{J} = 0$	div $\mathbf{J} = h$, space density of heat sources	div $\mathbf{F} = e$, space density of efflux	div $\mathbf{f} = -4\pi\rho$, ρ mass density
$\nabla^2\Phi = 0$	$\nabla^2 T = -h/k$	$\nabla^2\Phi = +e/\rho$	$\nabla^2 U = -4\pi G\rho$
$G = I/(\Phi_1 - \Phi_2) = I/V$, conductance	$G = Q/(T_1 - T_2)$, thermal conductance	$G = Q/(\Phi_2 - \Phi_1)$, hydraulic conductance	

the phenomena admit the definition of scalar potential functions, their mathematical treatment is much alike; this makes it possible to deduce analogies and to translate solutions from any one field into any other field of applications. In this manner, though this book is primarily concerned with electric and magnetic fields, the solutions given can readily be interpreted for applications to other field problems.

In order to assist in this translation, table 9·1 presents a survey of a number of branches of physics which admit of a unified mathematical treatment, utilizing the field concept. Each one of the branches of physics is characterized by a *fundamental scalar* satisfying the Poisson or Laplace differential equation, and a *derived field vector* which is defined as the (positive or negative) gradient of that scalar. As the table outlines in detail, there are additional analogous concepts for each branch, and the quantities in any one column can be considered entirely equivalent to the respective quantities (in the same line), for example, of the electrostatic field. It is necessary only to study in detail the solution of a problem in one branch in order to be able to predict for every other branch the similar solution with proper transposition of terms.

The column of table 9·1 headed *Electrostatic Field* presents a summary of the relations discussed in section 2; the column headed *Magnetostatic Field* summarizes the relations discussed in section 6; and the column headed *Electric Current Field* summarizes the relations discussed in section 8. The relations presented in the other columns will now be briefly discussed in order to provide a better understanding of the terminology.

Stationary Temperature Field.[2] Under stationary conditions, the flow of heat power is very similar to the stationary flow of electric current in conductors. Heat power will always flow from points of higher temperature to points of lower temperature; it can, therefore, be characterized by a vector density **J** which is measured in power per unit area. The vector **J** must, of course, point into the direction of greatest temperature fall; it is indeed proportional to the temperature gradient,

$$\mathbf{J} = -k \text{ grad } T = -k \ (\nabla T) \tag{1}$$

[2] See references in Appendix 4, C, b. For analogies to electrical problems see M. Avrami and V. Paschkis, *Trans. A.I.C.E.*, **38**, p. 631 (1942).

where k is the thermal conductivity of the conductor. Again, under stationary conditions, heat power can neither accumulate nor vanish locally (unless there are extraneous sources of heat). The flux integral of $\mathbf{J}$ over a closed surface must, therefore, be zero, and the vector $\mathbf{J}$ itself cannot have any divergence,

$$\text{div } \mathbf{J} = \nabla \cdot \mathbf{J} = 0 \tag{2}$$

Combination of (1) and (2) leads at once to the Laplacian differential equation

$$\nabla^2 T = 0 \tag{3}$$

pointing to temperature T as the scalar function analogous to the electrostatic potential Φ. A usual problem in heat conduction assumes certain metallic surfaces as *isothermal*, i.e., of constant temperature, and endeavors to find the total heat power flow from high temperature T_1 to low temperature T_2 through the thermal insulation between the metals. This is a boundary value problem of the first kind, exactly like current flow between two equipotential surfaces. If one defines the total power flow

$$Q = \iint J_n \, dS \tag{4}$$

through the cross section S, one can then evaluate a *thermal resistance*

$$R_{\text{th}} = \frac{T_1 - T_2}{Q} \tag{5}$$

and measure[3] it in *thermal ohms* (actually °C/watt in the Giorgi system). The reciprocal quantity, thermal conductance,[4] is included in table 9·1.

In many thermal problems relating to natural cooling of bodies by radiation, convection, and conduction of heat to the ambient medium, the boundary condition on the cooling surface defines the heat transfer to the ambient in terms of Newton's condition

$$-k\left(\frac{\partial T}{\partial n}\right)_i = \alpha_t(T_i - T_a) \tag{6}$$

---

[3] C. Hering, *Metal. and Chem. Engg.*, **9**, p. 13 (1911); *Electrical Engineers' Handbook, Electric Power*, edited by H. Pender, W. A. Del Mar, and K. McIlwain, p. 14-193; John Wiley, New York, 1936.

[4] More generally used and measured in watt/°C or Btu/°F; see W. H. McAdams: *Heat Transmission;* McGraw-Hill, New York, 1942.

Here, T_i is the temperature and $(\partial T/\partial n)_i$ its normal derivative on the boundary surface but within the cooling body; T_a is the ambient temperature (assumed constant); and α_t is the heat transfer coefficient.   Since T_a is constant, one can introduce the temperature rise above ambient

$$\theta = T - T_a \tag{7}$$

as main variable, rather than the absolute temperature values. This changes (3) to

$$\nabla^2 \theta = 0 \tag{8}$$

with the boundary condition on the cooling surface

$$-k\left(\frac{\partial \theta}{\partial n}\right) = \alpha_t \theta \tag{9}$$

This type of problem, usually referred to as a boundary value problem of the *third kind*, has no analogue in the electric or magnetic fields; therefore, no direct solutions will be given here.

Finally, there are thermal problems, of considerable importance for electrical design, in which distributed heat sources occur. The computation of the temperature rise of electrical conductors which carry current belongs in this group.   Here, the flow vector **J** has as source the Joule heat h created by the electric current in unit volume; thus,

$$\text{div } \mathbf{J} = \nabla \cdot \mathbf{J} = h \tag{10}$$

and the combination with (1) leads now to

$$\nabla^2 T = -\frac{h}{k}, \tag{11}$$

a Poisson differential equation of the same type as the electrostatic space charge equation (2·4).

Fluid Dynamic Fields.[5]   The flow of incompressible fluids and gases without internal friction is, in first approximation, again very similar to the electric current flow.   (Historically, the laws of electric current flow were patterned after the relations of fluid flow.)

The flow density through unit area is defined at any point in space as the product of mass density ρ and velocity **v** of the fluid

$$\mathbf{F} = \rho \mathbf{v} \tag{12}$$

[5] See references in Appendix 4, C, c.

For an incompressible fluid with no sources or sinks, the total flux through a closed surface must vanish, i.e., the vector $\mathbf{F}$ cannot have a divergence

$$\text{div } \mathbf{F} = \nabla \cdot \mathbf{F} = 0 \tag{13}$$

This relation becomes in Cartesian coordinates

$$\frac{\partial}{\partial x}(\rho v_x) + \frac{\partial}{\partial y}(\rho v_y) + \frac{\partial}{\partial z}(\rho v_z) = 0$$

and is the well-known equation of continuity. If the fluid is also homogeneous, so that ρ is everywhere the same, one has from (13)

$$\text{div } \mathbf{v} = \nabla \cdot \mathbf{v} = 0 \tag{14}$$

In irrotational flow, defined by

$$\text{curl } \mathbf{v} = \nabla \times \mathbf{v} = 0 \tag{15}$$

one can introduce a scalar potential function. It is customary to define a *velocity potential* Φ, such that velocity becomes the *positive* gradient

$$\mathbf{v} = +\text{grad } \Phi = +\nabla\Phi \tag{16}$$

and to consider the flow density vector $\mathbf{F}$ as an associated vector. The combination of (13) with (16) leads then at once to the Laplace differential equation for the velocity potential

$$\nabla^2\Phi = 0 \tag{17}$$

For fluid flows bounded by solid guides, the boundary conditions are quite analogous to those of the electric current flow, namely, the normal component of $\mathbf{F}$ must vanish on the walls. The lines to which the velocity vector $\mathbf{v}$ is everywhere tangential are called *stream lines;* they form with respect to the equipotential surfaces an orthogonal system of gradient lines.

If sources or sinks are included in the field region, then the total flux of vector $\mathbf{F}$ through a closed surface inclosing a source becomes the efflux E

$$\oint \mathbf{F} \cdot d\mathbf{S} = E \tag{18}$$

and locally the divergence of $\mathbf{F}$ will not vanish. As in the electrostatic case, the potential equation then becomes the Poisson type

$$\nabla^2 \Phi = + \frac{e}{\rho} \qquad (19)$$

where e is the volume density of the efflux E. Usually, one assumes point or line sources, introducing them as singularities in the same manner as point charges and line charges in electrostatics.

Incompressible fluid motion can also include rotation about an axis or about a solid body. In this case, curl $\mathbf{v}$ is still zero at every point, but the line integral of the vector $\mathbf{v}$ inclosing the axis of rotation is obviously not zero. This is exactly analogous to the magnetic field of line currents treated in section 6. As indicated there, one can salvage the concept of the scalar potential function by appropriately defining barrier surfaces as double layers of sources and sinks; no path of integration can penetrate this layer. One will proceed in a similar manner in fluid dynamics, defining the circulating flow also as *vortex flow*. General solutions in fluid dynamics consist, therefore, of a superposition of electrostatic and magnetostatic field solutions.

Gravitational Fields.[6] The basic theory of electrostatic and magnetostatic phenomena was developed by Gauss in analogy to the gravitational theory,[7] since all three rested upon force actions varying as the inverse square of the distance. One usually writes the attractive force between two masses m_1 and m_2

$$F = G \frac{m_1 m_2}{r^2} \qquad (20)$$

where G is the universal gravitational constant, of value 6.664×10^{-11} m^3/kg sec^2 in the MKS system of units. Similarly to the point charge in electrostatics (section 1), one can let m_2 be a probe mass of vanishing dimensions and deduce a field strength $\mathbf{g}$, or the gravitational acceleration, as

$$\mathbf{g} = \lim_{m_2 \to 0} \frac{\mathbf{F}}{m_2} = -G \frac{m_1}{r^3} \mathbf{r} \qquad (21)$$

$\mathbf{g}$ is quite analogous to field strength $\mathbf{E}$ in $(1 \cdot 3)$, except for the

---

[6] See references in Appendix 4, C, d.

[7] K. F. Gauss: "General Theorems Concerning Attractive and Repulsive Forces Varying as the Inverse Square of the Distance" (original title in Latin), 1826; see *Collected Works*.

negative sign in direction, which is occasioned by the fact that all masses have the same sign and attract, whereas like charges repel each other. The vector **g** defines the *force lines* as everywhere tangential to **g**, giving thus a direct visualization of the gravitational force field.

As for any conservative force, the line integral of **F** over a closed path must vanish, which infers the existence of a scalar potential function U such that

$$\mathbf{g} = +\text{grad } U = +\nabla U \tag{22}$$

Now, for a single mass point m_1 with its radial force lines, one can form the flux of **g** through a concentric spherical surface, and one obtains with (21)

$$\oint g_n \cdot dS = -G4\pi m_1 \tag{23}$$

It is customary to absorb the universal factor G in the associated vector

$$\mathbf{f} = \frac{1}{G}\,\mathbf{g} \tag{24}$$

and thus obtain generally for the flux of this new vector

$$\oint f_n \, dS = -4\pi M \tag{25}$$

where M is the total mass within the closed reducible surface of integration. By Gauss's theorem one can deduce from (25)

$$\text{div } \mathbf{f} = \nabla \cdot \mathbf{f} = -4\pi\rho \tag{26}$$

if ρ is the mass density of any arbitrary spatial distribution. This relation is again quite analogous to $(1 \cdot 12)$, except for the negative sign.

The combination of (22) with (24) and (26) leads to

$$\nabla^2 U = -4\pi G\rho \tag{27}$$

the Poisson equation of the gravitational potential function valid within regions occupied by distributed mass. Outside of masses, (27) reduces, of course, to the Laplacian differential equation. Electrostatic problems can, therefore, very readily be interpreted as gravitational problems and vice versa.

PROBLEMS

1. The electric resistance of a volume element is frequently written in the form $dR = dl/\gamma\, dS$. Why should this form be deprecated? How must it be interpreted and used in order to yield correct results?

2. Prove that the electric current density in a given conductor distributes itself so that the joule loss or dissipation into heat is a minimum. Hint: assume two sets of current densities $\mathbf{J} = \gamma\mathbf{E}$, $\mathbf{J}' = \gamma\mathbf{E}'$, both satisfying the condition of zero divergence to prevent accumulation of charge; the first set satisfies additionally $\mathbf{E} = -\operatorname{grad}\phi$. (See also Smythe, [A22] p. 228.)

3. Since the electric current field can be derived from a Laplacian potential function, the uniqueness of the potential solution can be demonstrated in the same manner as in electrostatics. Formulate the theorem corresponding to problem 12 in chapter 1 for a conductor and prove it.

4. Formulate the uniqueness theorem for a conductor corresponding to the analogous theorem for a dielectric defined in problem 14 in chapter 1 and prove it.

5. If one defines conductance G as the inverse of resistance R, $(8\cdot11)$ can be written $(C/\varepsilon) = (G/\gamma)$. Introduce and define conductance coefficients for a system of perfectly conducting electrodes within a homogeneous isotropic medium of conductivity γ in analogy to the capacitance coefficients defined in $(3\cdot7)$; show how they can be determined by simple measurements.

6. Derive a lumped resistance analogue to an electrostatic problem of n conductors embedded in a uniform dielectric; note the preceding problem.

7. Derive the analogue to Green's reciprocation theorem in problem 10, chapter 1, for a system of perfectly conducting electrodes within a homogeneous and isotropic medium of conductivity γ.

8. The integral expression $(8\cdot17)$ for dissipated power in a conductor of arbitrary shape is analogous to $(3\cdot20)$ for the electrostatic field energy. Convert it into the form $P = I^2R$ by means of Green's theorem, Appendix 3.

9. Demonstrate that any assumed current distribution for a fixed total current in a conductor leads to a higher resistance than the current distribution that follows from the solution of Laplace's equation $(8\cdot10)$.

10. Demonstrate that the introduction of a perfectly conducting element of volume τ_0 into a conductor of conductivity γ decreases the resistance. Hint: assume two sets $\mathbf{J} = \gamma\mathbf{E}$ and $\mathbf{J}' = \gamma\mathbf{E}'$ derived from complete solutions of the respective Laplacian differential equations, the first set giving Φ for the original volume τ, the second set giving Φ' for the volume $(\tau - \tau_0)$; note the similarity to problem 20 in chapter 1.

11. Since the temperature field in a region without sources is a solution of the Laplacian differential equation, its uniqueness can be demonstrated in the same manner as in electrostatics. Formulate the theorem corresponding to problem 12 in chapter 1 for a finite regular region τ in a uniform thermal medium and prove it.

12. Formulate the uniqueness theorem for the temperature field in a thermal medium corresponding to the analogous theorem for a dielectric defined in problem 14 of chapter 1 and prove it.

13. The heat exchange by conduction in a single thermal medium between several sources, each of different uniform surface temperature T_α, can be rep-

resented by thermal conductance coefficients in analogy to the capacitance coefficients defined in $(3 \cdot 7)$; introduce and define these coefficients and show how they can be determined by simple measurements.

14. Derive a lumped resistance analogue to the thermal system described in the preceding problem.

15. Extend the proof in problem 12 to a finite number of finite heat sources, each with a different uniform fixed temperature T_α along its surface, embedded in a homogeneous and isotropic thermal medium of infinite extent in which no generation of heat takes place.

16. Extend the proof in problem 15 to a finite number of finite heat sources embedded in several different thermal media in which no generation of heat takes place; consider the boundary conditions at all interfaces of the thermal media as the analogues to $(8 \cdot 12)$ and $(8 \cdot 13)$.

17. Since the velocity potential in a region without sources is a solution of the Laplacian differential equation, its uniqueness can be demonstrated in the same manner as in electrostatics. Formulate the theorem corresponding to problem 13 in chapter 1 for a finite regular region τ in an incompressible fluid and prove it.

18. The flow of an incompressible fluid between several sources and sinks of different but individually constant values of velocity potentials Φ_α can be represented by hydraulic conductance coefficients in analogy to the capacitance coefficients defined in $(3 \cdot 7)$; introduce and define these coefficients; derive the analogue in terms of lumped electrical resistances.

19. Formulate the uniqueness theorem for the flow pattern of an incompressible fluid corresponding to the analogous theorem for a dielectric defined in problem 14 of chapter 1, and prove it.

20. Find the gravitational potential distribution everywhere in space produced by a sphere of uniform mass density ρ and of radius a.

21. Find the gravitational potential distribution everywhere in space produced by a sphere of total mass M of radius a, and with a density $\rho(r)$ which is only a function of the radial distance. Demonstrate that the potential external to the sphere is the same as if the mass M were concentrated at the center of the sphere (point mass). Check the analogous results for electric charges.

22. Derive for the gravitational potential the integral expression analogous to $(2 \cdot 5)$ for the electrostatic field. Demonstrate the validity by means of Green's theorem from Appendix 3; observe the analogous problems 2 and 3 in chapter 1.

23. Find the gravitational potential distribution everywhere in space produced by a sphere of radius a which is composed of two hemispheres of different mass densities ρ_1 and ρ_2.

24. Deduce the general boundary conditions for the vector $\mathbf{f}$ of the gravitational field defined by $(9 \cdot 24)$ and $(9 \cdot 26)$.

4· FIELDS OF SIMPLE GEOMETRIES

Many of the very simple field solutions are also given in the elementary textbooks and treatises. For the sake of completeness, mention will be made of these simple cases with references to the appropriate literature.

10· SYSTEMS OF POINT CHARGES

The single point charge produces radial field lines with a field vector

$$\mathbf{E} = \frac{1}{4\pi\varepsilon} \frac{Q}{r^3} \mathbf{r} \tag{1}$$

as originally deduced from Coulomb's law in section 1. Of course, both this field vector and the associated potential

$$\Phi = \frac{1}{4\pi\varepsilon} \frac{Q}{r} \tag{2}$$

take on infinite values as $r \to 0$ so that strictly no physical reality can be attached to this concept of "point charge." However, the vanishing dimension eliminates the problem of charge distribution and thus makes readily possible the evaluation of field distributions for systems of point charges by direct superposition of the individual contributions.

Two Point Charges. Assume two point charges of values Q_1 and Q_2; the resultant field vector is the vector sum

$$\mathbf{E} = \frac{1}{4\pi\varepsilon}\left(\frac{Q_1}{r_1{}^3}\mathbf{r}_1 + \frac{Q_2}{r_2{}^3}\mathbf{r}_2\right) \tag{3}$$

where $\mathbf{r}_1$ and $\mathbf{r}_2$ are the radius vectors from the respective charges

82

to the point of observation P. Since the field distribution must be symmetrical about the line connecting the charges, it is convenient to choose a cylindrical coordinate system as in Fig. 10·1

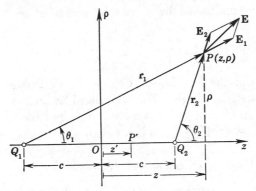

FIG. 10·1   Two Point Charges.

with its z-axis through the charges and with $\rho = (x^2 + y^2)^{\frac{1}{2}}$ as the perpendicular distance from it.

The *field lines* are then defined in accordance with (1·5) by

$$\frac{dz}{E_z} = \frac{d\rho}{E_\rho} \qquad (4)$$

The radius vectors are

$$\mathbf{r}_1 = \mathbf{u}_z(z + c) + \mathbf{u}_\rho\rho, \qquad \mathbf{r}_2 = \mathbf{u}_z(z - c) + \mathbf{u}_\rho\rho \qquad (5)$$

with $\mathbf{u}_z$ and $\mathbf{u}_\rho$ as unit vectors in the respective directions. Introducing (3) into (4) and omitting the factor $1/4\pi\varepsilon$ since it cancels out yield

$$\frac{dz}{Q_1 \dfrac{z + c}{r_1{}^3} + Q_2 \dfrac{z - c}{r_2{}^3}} = \frac{d\rho}{Q_1 \dfrac{\rho}{r_1{}^3} + Q_2 \dfrac{\rho}{r_2{}^3}}$$

Crosswise multiplication and collection of terms with the same $r_\alpha{}^3$ in the denominator lead to

$$\frac{Q_1}{r_1{}^3} [\rho \, dz - (z + c) \, d\rho] + \frac{Q_2}{r_2{}^3} [\rho \, dz - (z - c) \, d\rho] = 0 \qquad (6)$$

But

$$d\left(\frac{z \pm c}{\rho}\right) = \frac{1}{\rho^2} [\rho \, dz - (z \pm c) \, d\rho]$$

so that (6) becomes also

$$Q_1 \frac{\rho^2}{r_1^3} d\left(\frac{z+c}{\rho}\right) + Q_2 \frac{\rho^2}{r_2^3} d\left(\frac{z-c}{\rho}\right) = 0 \qquad (7)$$

which, when multiplied by ρ, can be identified as the complete differential of

$$Q_1 \frac{z+c}{r_1} + Q_2 \frac{z-c}{r_2} = k \qquad (8)$$

the integral of the field lines. Choice of the constant k leads to the individual field lines. For the actual evaluation of the field lines, this can be changed to a more convenient form by observing that $\cos\theta_1 = (z+c)/r_1$ and $\cos\theta_2 = (z-c)/r_2$, so that (8) becomes

$$Q_1 \cos\theta_1 + Q_2 \cos\theta_2 = k \qquad (9)$$

Starting with a particular point P in the z-ρ-plane, one can measure the angles θ_1 and θ_2 and thus determine k; one can then follow the field line through P by choosing different values of θ_1 and by computing the necessary angles θ_2 from (9) for the specific k. Intersection of the radius vectors will give the successive points of the field line.

The equipotential lines in the z-ρ-plane are directly given by

$$\Phi = \frac{1}{4\pi\varepsilon}\left(\frac{Q_1}{r_1} + \frac{Q_2}{r_2}\right) \qquad (10)$$

Assuming a specific value of the potential Φ and choosing a distance r_1, one can compute the necessary distance r_2 as

$$r_2 = \frac{Q_2}{4\pi\varepsilon\Phi - Q_1/r_1} \qquad (11)$$

Thus, individual points along the equipotential line can readily be constructed. Obviously, the family of the equipotential lines and that of the field lines must be mutually orthogonal at all points, which usually is a welcome check.

Good graphs of equipotential and field lines for $Q_1 = -Q_2$ and $Q_1 = +Q_2$, respectively, can be found in Attwood,[A2] Figs. 1·22 to 1·24; in Jeans,[A10] Figs. 17 and 15, 16; in Harnwell,[A9] Figs. 1·23 and 1·22; in Ramsay,[A21] pp. 36 and 37; and in Smythe,[A22] Figs. 1·08a and 1·08b. In both charge arrangements, there is also symmetry about the plane $z = 0$ of Fig. 10·1. For like charges, the equipotential surfaces close to the charges are almost spheres, become pear-shaped, merge into an hour-glass shape, and finally approximate spheres again but with centers at 0, as the values Φ decrease in (10). For opposite charges, the equipotential surfaces close to the charges are also almost spheres, then become pear-shaped but with the pointed sections outward; the plane perpendicular to and bisecting the center line is also an equipotential surface.

One finds also graphs of charge arrangements $Q_1 = -4Q_2$ in Jeans,[A10] Figs. 19, 20; in Maxwell[A17] as an excellent plate at the end of the book; and in Ramsay,[A21] p. 38; of $Q_1 = 2Q_2$ and $Q_1 = -2Q_2$ in Attwood,[A2] Figs. 1·25 and 1·27, respectively; and of $Q_1 = +4Q_2$ again as an excellent plate in Maxwell.[A17] In all cases of unequal charge values, one finds a *singular point* on the axis at which the electric field **E** vanishes, or, since along the axis only E_z can exist, where $E_z = 0$. For a point P', Fig. 10·1,

$$r_1 = c + z', \qquad |r_2| = c - z'$$

and, therefore, at this point, using (3) and (5),

$$4\pi\varepsilon E_z = Q_1 \frac{1}{(c + z')^2} - Q_2 \frac{1}{(c - z')^2} \tag{12}$$

For $E_z = 0$ one can solve the quadratic form and obtain

$$z' = (\eta \mp \sqrt{\eta^2 - 1})\, c \tag{13}$$

with the definition

$$\left.\begin{aligned} \eta &= \frac{Q_1 + Q_2}{Q_1 - Q_2} \text{ for like charges} \\ \eta &= \frac{Q_1 - Q_2}{Q_1 + Q_2} \text{ for opposite charges} \end{aligned}\right\} \quad |Q_1| > |Q_2| \tag{14}$$

The upper sign in (13) holds for like charges where $z' < c$, whereas the lower sign holds for opposite charges where $z' > c$; in the case $|Q_1| < |Q_2|$ one can use the same definitions of η but must reverse the signs of the square root in (13). At the singular points, no force action can take place on a probe charge located there; however, it is easily shown, as in Jeans,[A10] that these are points of unstable equilibrium, no stable equilibrium being possible in a purely electrostatic force field (Earnshaw's theorem, see

Smythe[A22]). Actually, for two positive charges the field vector along the axis points from both directions towards the singular point, whereas perpendicular to the axis it points radially out; for two negative point charges just the reverse is true. For two opposite charges, the singular point always occurs on the side of the smaller charge; if this is the positive one, then the field vector behaves as in the case of two positive charges; if it is the negative one, then the field vector behaves as in the case of two negative charges. From this, one deduces that the potential must have a saddle point. This means that the potential goes through a minimum along the axis if the field vectors there point towards the singular point, and simultaneously it goes through a maximum in the direction normal to the axis. The reverse is true if the field vectors along the axis point away from the singular point.

Conducting Planes and Point Charges. The field distribution of two point charges of equal magnitude and opposite sign, as pointed out above, includes the plane of symmetry between the point charges as an equipotential surface. Conversely, then, one concludes that the field between a conducting plane and a point charge must be the same as between two equal point charges of opposite sign separated by double the distance between plane and given point charge; the generalized utilization of such analogies is called the method of images[1] and will be more extensively treated in section 21. For the particular case of a conducting plane, Fig. 10·2 indicates the field distribution in front of the conducting plane as one half of the field between the given charge $+Q$ and the *image* $-Q$. The potential distribution in the right-hand half space is given by

$$\Phi = \frac{Q}{4\pi\varepsilon}\left(\frac{1}{r} - \frac{1}{r'}\right) + \Phi_0 \qquad (15)$$

where Φ_0 is an arbitrary constant available to adjust the absolute potential of the conducting plane. Along the plane $z = 0$, the field vector has the value

$$E = E_z = -\frac{Q}{4\pi\varepsilon}\frac{2h}{r^3} \qquad (16)$$

The negative sign defines the direction into the conducting plane,

---

[1] W. Thomson: *Papers on Electrostatics and Magnetism*, p. 73; Macmillan, London, 1872; first published in *Cambridge and Dublin Math. Jl.*, 1848.

and $r^2 = h^2 + \rho^2$, where ρ is the normal distance from the z-axis. The induced charge density on the plane is given by

$$\sigma = D_{z/x=0} = -\frac{Q}{2\pi}\frac{h}{r^3} \tag{17}$$

and the integral over the entire plane $z = 0$ is readily shown to be $-Q$. Rather complete treatment of this and similar uses dis-

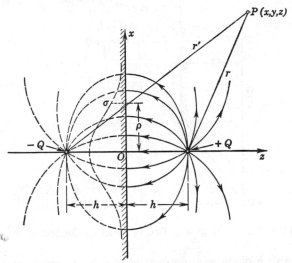

Fig. 10·2   Conducting Plane and Point Charge.

cussed below is found in Bennett and Crothers,[A3] p. 184; in Jeans,[A10] p. 185; in Mason and Weaver,[A16] pp. 109–112; in Maxwell,[A17] Vol. I, p. 252, etc.; and in Ramsay,[A21] p. 116, etc.

The force action on the given charge Q caused by its own inducing action upon the conducting plane can readily be computed as the force between it and its image,

$$F = \frac{1}{4\pi\varepsilon}\frac{Q^2}{(2h)^2} \tag{18}$$

It is this force action which has to be overcome in the emission of electrons (where signs are just reversed) from metal surfaces by either thermionic or field forces; it was first introduced as *image force* by W. Schottky[2] in the computation of the *work function*

[2] W. Schottky, *Zeits. f. Physik*, **14**, p. 63 (1923); see also A. L. Reimann: *Thermionic Emission;* John Wiley, New York, 1934.

of electrons.   Obviously, this image force can have significance only for distances from the metal surface, for which it appears approximately like a mathematical plane.

The extension to a point charge in a metallic corner as shown in Fig. 10·3 is straightforward.   In order to make the intersecting

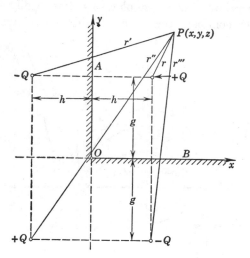

FIG. 10·3   Point Charge and Two Intersecting Conducting Planes.

planes A and B of the same potential, it is necessary to place three image charges as indicated.   The resultant potential at a point P will then be

$$\Phi = \frac{Q}{4\pi\varepsilon}\left(\frac{1}{r} - \frac{1}{r'} + \frac{1}{r''} - \frac{1}{r'''}\right) + \Phi_0 \qquad (19)$$

Obviously, the induced charge distribution will have two maxima, one on each plane almost opposite the location of Q and slightly shifted away from the corner.   The total charges on planes A and B are, respectively,

$$Q_A = -\frac{2}{\pi}Q\tan^{-1}\frac{g}{h}, \qquad Q_B = -\frac{2}{\pi}Q\tan^{-1}\frac{h}{g} \qquad (20)$$

and the sum total is again $-Q$.   The force action, too, can be found by superposition of all three image forces.   Actually, this example is only a special case of the more general one of two metallic planes intersecting ·at an angle π/n, where n be any arbitrary integer; the number of image charges is then $(2n - 1)$, symmetrically located along the circle through the given charge. If n is not an integer, an infinite number of images results (see section 26).

Sphere and Point Charge.   The equipotential surfaces of two point charges with opposite signs always include one sphere surrounding the smaller charge. This can be seen from (10) and Fig. 10·1 if one takes $\Phi = 0$, yielding

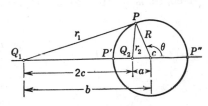

$$\frac{r_2}{r_1} = -\frac{Q_2}{Q_1} = \alpha \qquad (21)$$

which defines a spherical surface.   Referring to Fig. 10·4,

FIG. 10·4   Point Charge and Sphere.

then, one can readily determine the radius R by selecting points P' and P'' for which, respectively,

$$\left(\frac{r_2}{r_1}\right)' = \frac{R - a}{b - R}, \qquad \left(\frac{r_2}{r_1}\right)'' = \frac{R + a}{b + R} \qquad (22)$$

Equating these expressions gives for the sphere

$$R^2 = ab, \qquad \alpha = -\frac{Q_2}{Q_1} = \sqrt{\frac{a}{b}} \qquad (23)$$

One can solve for the location and radius of the sphere also directly in terms of the charge ratio α and the distance $2c$ between the charges,

$$a = 2c\,\frac{\alpha^2}{1 - \alpha^2}, \qquad b = 2c\,\frac{1}{1 - \alpha^2}, \qquad R = 2c\,\frac{\alpha}{1 - \alpha^2} \qquad (24)$$

wherefrom $a < b$, if $\alpha < 1$, i.e., the sphere surrounds the smaller charge.

Reversing the process, one can define the field distribution between a grounded sphere of radius R and a point charge Q_1 as described by the field between two point charges of values Q_2 and Q_1, where Q_2 as the *image* of Q_1 with respect to the surface of the sphere, has the value

$$Q_2 = -\frac{R}{b}Q_1 \qquad (25)$$

and is located on the axis at $a = R^2/b$ from the center of the sphere towards Q_1.   Figure $10 \cdot 5$ thus illustrates the field distribution for a charge $+Q$ located at a distance equal to the radius R from the surface of the sphere; in this case, the image charge is $-\frac{1}{2}Q$ according to (25) and is located at $a = R/2$ to the left of C, the center of the sphere.   The singular point of vanishing field strength is located at $z' = (3 + \sqrt{8})c$ in accordance with (13)

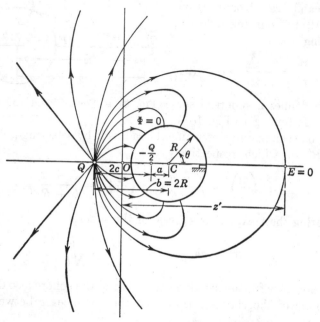

FIG. $10 \cdot 5$ Field Lines between Point Charge and Sphere for $b = 2R$.

and (14), whereby $2c = b - a = \frac{3}{2}R$ is the distance between the given point charge and its image.   Good treatments of this and similar problems are found in Attwood,[A2] pp. 153–156; in Jeans,[A10] p. 189; in Mason and Weaver,[A16] p. 112; in Maxwell,[A17] Vol. I, p. 245; in Ramsay,[A21] p. 117; in Smythe,[A22] p. 114; and in Stratton,[A23] p. 201.

From the resultant potential distribution

$$\Phi = \frac{Q}{4\pi\varepsilon}\left(\frac{1}{r_1} - \frac{R}{b}\frac{1}{r_2}\right) \tag{26}$$

obtained by combining (25) and (10), one can also obtain the charge distribution on the surface of the sphere, expressed in terms of the angle θ

$$\sigma = \varepsilon E = -\frac{Q}{4\pi} \cdot \frac{b^2 - R^2}{R(b^2 + R^2 + 2Rb \cos \theta)^{3/2}} \qquad (27)$$

Integrated over the sphere, this gives exactly $Q_2 = -(R/b)Q$ in accordance with (25). Maximum and minimum charge densities are found for $\theta = \pi$ and $\theta = 0$, respectively, and their ratio becomes

$$\frac{\sigma_{\max}}{\sigma_{\min}} = \left(\frac{b + R}{b - R}\right)^3 \qquad (28)$$

Even for $b = 10R$, this will still be $(11/9)^3 = 1.82$, indicating the strong local field concentration caused by point charges in three-dimensional geometries.

If the sphere is not grounded, but carries an arbitrary charge Q' with a corresponding potential value different from zero, one can use direct superposition of the radial field of another point charge $Q'' = \left(Q' + \dfrac{R}{b} Q_1\right)$ located at the center of sphere. The total potential anywhere in space will then be the combination of (26) and of the potential produced by Q'', namely,

$$\Phi = \frac{Q_1}{4\pi\varepsilon}\left(\frac{1}{r_1} - \frac{R}{b}\frac{1}{r_2}\right) + \frac{1}{4\pi\varepsilon}\left(Q' + \frac{R}{b} Q_1\right)\frac{1}{r} \qquad (29)$$

where Q_1 is the value of the external point charge, r_1 and r_2 are as indicated in Fig. 10·4, and r is the distance from the center of the sphere. On the surface of the sphere, this gives now the potential

$$\Phi_0 = \frac{1}{4\pi\varepsilon}\left(Q' + \frac{R}{b} Q_1\right)\frac{1}{R} \qquad (30)$$

which, of course, could be prescribed instead of the charge Q'. The charge density on the surface of the sphere is the superposition of (27) and of the uniform density $Q''/4\pi R^2$ produced by Q''.

For the special case that the sphere is insulated, its charge must remain zero, $Q' = 0$, so that $Q'' = (R/b)Q_1$. The surface charge is partly negative—opposite the positive point charge Q_1—and partly positive.[3] One can readily find the angle θ_0 which separates

[3] See Attwood,[A2] p. 154, and Ramsay,[A21] p. 117.

these two zones, by putting the resultant charge density equal to zero, resulting in

$$\cos \theta_0 = -\frac{1}{2\alpha} \{1 + \alpha^2 - (1 - \alpha^2)^{\frac{3}{2}}\} \qquad (31)$$

with $\alpha = \sqrt{a/b} = R/b$ from (23). For small values of α, the binomial expansion of the second term yields the very simple form $\cos \theta_0 \approx -\frac{5}{6}\alpha$, or $\theta_0 \approx 94°13'$. As the point charge recedes, the angle θ_0 defining the neutral zone approaches 90°.

The Electric Dipole. If two equal charges of opposite sign approach each other indefinitely without merging, then r_1 and r_2 in Fig. 10·1 can be closely approximated by the radius vector from the center 0 and, with reference to Fig. 10·6,

$$\frac{1}{r_1} - \frac{1}{r_2} \to \frac{1}{r - l/2 \cos \theta} - \frac{1}{r + l/2 \cos \theta} \to \frac{l \cos \theta}{r^2} \qquad (32)$$

Thus, the potential function (10) becomes

$$\Phi = \frac{Q}{4\pi\varepsilon} \frac{l \cos \theta}{r^2} = \frac{1}{4\pi\varepsilon} \frac{1}{r^3} \mathbf{p} \cdot \mathbf{r} \qquad (33)$$

if one defines

$$\mathbf{p} = Q\mathbf{l} \qquad (34)$$

as the *dipole moment*, a vector pointing out of the positive charge along the axis of the dipole. The field vector $\mathbf{E}$ follows in the spherical coordinate system from (33) directly as [Appendix 3, (38)]

$$E_r = -\frac{\partial \Phi}{\partial r} = \frac{p}{4\pi\varepsilon} \cdot \frac{2 \cos \theta}{r^3}, \qquad E_\theta = -\frac{1}{r}\frac{\partial \Phi}{\partial \theta} = \frac{p}{4\pi\varepsilon} \frac{\sin \theta}{r^3} \qquad (35)$$

Unlike a point charge, the dipole has an almost entirely local influence, its field lines concentrate between the two charges, and the field vector $\mathbf{E}$ decreases with the third power of the distance. Figure 10·6 indicates also the field distribution, where the field lines are defined by

$$\frac{dr}{E_r} = \frac{r\,d\theta}{E_\theta}$$

which, upon integration, gives

$$r = k \sin^2 \theta \qquad (36)$$

where k is an arbitrary constant defining any individual field line. The equipotential surfaces are, from (33),

$$r^2 = \left(\frac{p}{4\pi\varepsilon\Phi}\right) \cos\theta \qquad (37)$$

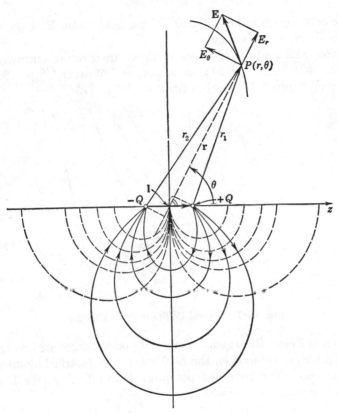

FIG. 10·6 Field Distribution of an Electric Dipole. Solid lines = field lines; dashed lines = equipotential lines.

Choosing a set of values for θ, one thus computes the set of r values defining the locus points for any constant value of Φ.

In a uniform electric field $\mathbf{E}_0$, the dipole does not experience a resultant force; however, a torque

$$\mathbf{T} = \mathbf{p} \times \mathbf{E}_0 \qquad (38)$$

will be exerted, trying to align the dipole moment $\mathbf{p}$ with the electric field line through its center. This property is utilized in the visualization of electric field lines by means of small crystallic needles (see section 16). In a non-uniform field, there will also be a resultant force action of value

$$\mathbf{F} = (\mathbf{p} \cdot \nabla)\mathbf{E} \tag{39}$$

since only the vectorial difference of the field vector $\mathbf{E}$ at the ends of the dipole can contribute.

Good treatments of the electric dipole are given in Harnwell,[A9] p. 60; in Jeans,[A10] p. 51; in Mason and Weaver,[A16] p. 18; in Smythe,[A22] pp. 6–10; and in Stratton,[A23] p. 175.

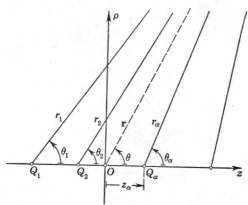

FIG. 10·7   Several Collinear Point Charges.

Several Point Charges. If several point charges are arranged along a line, or *collinearly*, the field will be symmetrical about the line as axis. The resultant potential Φ and field vector $\mathbf{E}$ are readily found by superposition

$$\Phi = \frac{1}{4\pi\varepsilon} \sum_{(\alpha)} \frac{Q_\alpha}{r_\alpha}, \qquad \mathbf{E} = \frac{1}{4\pi\varepsilon} \sum_{(\alpha)} \frac{Q_\alpha}{r_\alpha^{\,3}} \mathbf{r}_\alpha \tag{40}$$

The general evaluation of field lines is readily possible in the same manner as for two point charges. Following (4) with the two components of $\mathbf{E}$ taken from (40) as sums (see also Fig. 10·7), one can deduce a relation like (6) by again collecting terms with the same $r_\alpha^{\,3}$, namely,

$$\sum_{(\alpha)} Q_\alpha \frac{\rho^2}{r_\alpha^{\,3}} d\left(\frac{z - z_\alpha}{\rho}\right) = 0 \tag{41}$$

Integration yields then

$$\sum_{(\alpha)} Q_\alpha \cos \theta_\alpha = k \tag{42}$$

the equation of the field lines. The practical use of this equation is, however, rather limited, so that field distributions are actually found by graphical means; see for example Attwood[A2] for $(+Q, -\frac{1}{2}Q, -\frac{1}{2}Q)$, Fig. 1·26, and for $(+Q, -Q, +Q, -Q)$, Fig. 1·28.

At large distances, the potential function of these collinear point charges can be expressed in terms of the quantities r, θ, the coordinates of the point P with respect to the arbitrary origin 0. One has, for large values r, approximately

$$r_\alpha = r\left[1 - 2\frac{z_\alpha}{r}\cos\theta + \left(\frac{z_\alpha}{r}\right)^2\right]^{\frac{1}{2}} \approx r\left[1 - \frac{z_\alpha}{r}\cos\theta\right] \tag{43}$$

so that (40) becomes

$$\Phi \approx \frac{1}{4\pi\varepsilon r}\sum_{(\alpha)} Q_\alpha\left(1 + \frac{z_\alpha}{r}\cos\theta\right) \tag{44}$$

If one now chooses the origin 0 so that with respect to it $\sum_{(\alpha)} Q_\alpha z_\alpha = 0$, i.e., so that it is identical with the *center of gravity* of the point charges, then the potential can be simplified to

$$\Phi \approx \frac{1}{4\pi\varepsilon r}\sum_{(\alpha)} Q_\alpha \tag{45}$$

Thus, at large distances, the potential of the collinear charges can be found as that of a single point charge equal to the sum total of all charges Q_α, and located at the center of gravity which can be determined in the conventional manner with respect to an arbitrary origin by

$$z_g = \frac{\sum_{(\alpha)} z_\alpha Q_\alpha}{\sum_{(\alpha)} Q_\alpha} \tag{46}$$

where the z_α are measured from the origin with proper algebraic sign. If the $\sum_{(\alpha)} Q_\alpha = 0$, then no center of gravity exists; one can, however, find the two centers of gravity, one for all positive charges and the other for all negative charges and show that equal and opposite point charges $\sum Q^+ = -\sum Q^-$, located at the respective centers of gravity, represent a dipole which approximates the actual field at large distances.

For any arbitrary complex of point charges, (40) will still hold, but no general solution of field lines can be given. An excellent graph of three charges (+15, −12, +20) is found in plate IV of

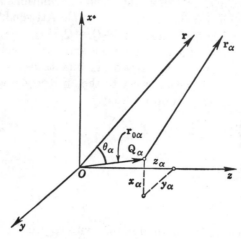

FIG. 10·8   Typical Geometric Relations for Space Arrangement of Point Charges.

Maxwell.[A17]   At large distances from the complex, the potential in (40) can again be expressed most simply in terms of the center of gravity of the point charges, since from Fig. 10·8

$$r_\alpha = r\left[1 - 2\frac{r_{0\alpha}}{r}\cos\theta_\alpha + \left(\frac{r_{0\alpha}}{r}\right)^2\right]^{1/2} \approx r\left[1 - \frac{r_{0\alpha}}{r}\cos\theta_\alpha\right] \quad (47)$$

and thus

$$\Phi \approx \frac{1}{4\pi\varepsilon r}\sum_{(\alpha)} Q_\alpha\left(1 + \frac{r_{0\alpha}}{r}\cos\theta_\alpha\right)$$

However, θ_α, as the angle between two vectors from the origin, follows the composition of the respective direction cosines,[4] so that

$$\cos\theta_\alpha = \frac{x_\alpha}{r_{0\alpha}}\frac{x}{r} + \frac{y_\alpha}{r_{0\alpha}}\frac{y}{r} + \frac{z_\alpha}{z_{0\alpha}}\frac{z}{r}$$

[4] See for example: Eshbach, *Handbook of Engineering Fundamentals*, p. 2-71; John Wiley, New York, 1936.

Choosing the reference point 0 such that with reference to it

$$\sum Q_\alpha x_\alpha = \sum Q_\alpha y_\alpha = \sum Q_\alpha z_\alpha = 0$$

then one obtains (45) again with the same interpretation. The center of gravity with respect to an arbitrarily chosen origin has then the coordinates[5]

$$x_g = \frac{\sum x_\alpha Q_\alpha}{\sum Q_\alpha}, \qquad y_g = \frac{\sum y_\alpha Q_\alpha}{\sum Q_\alpha}, \qquad z_g = \frac{\sum z_\alpha Q_\alpha}{\sum Q_\alpha} \qquad (48)$$

11· QUASI POINT CHARGES

The concentration of the electric charge in a mathematical point is a matter of computational convenience; nothing is changed as far as the outside field is concerned if one assumes a small, finite radius a of the charge and a distribution either uniformly over the surface with the density $\sigma = Q/4\pi a^2$, or uniformly over the volume, with the density $\rho = 3Q/4\pi a^3$. In either case, the potential on the surface of the sphere has now associated with it a definite value obtained from (10·2) by putting $r = a$

$$\Phi_s = \frac{Q}{4\pi\varepsilon a} \qquad (1)$$

The ratio of the charge to its potential can be defined as the capacitance of the sphere,

$$C = \frac{Q}{\Phi_s} = 4\pi\varepsilon a \qquad (2)$$

and is directly proportional to the radius of the sphere. Since the potential vanishes as $r \to \infty$, one can also consider this as capacitance to an infinitely large sphere, in the sense of an ideal condenser.

For many practical purposes one can treat widely separated charges as point charges in order to obtain the overall field distribution in mathematically simple form by direct superposition. Yet, close to the charges one can avoid the excessive values of potential and field strength, normally associated with the concept of the point charge, by defining quasi point charges, i.e., small but finite charged spheres.

[5] See Attwood,[A2] pp. 42-43.

Two Quasi Point Charges. The potential anywhere in space surrounding two small spheres with $Q_1 = -Q_2 = Q$ and with $a_1 \ll 2c$, $a_2 \ll 2c$ (see Fig. 11·1) is approximately that of two point charges located at the centers of the spheres. Thus, in accordance with (10·10),

$$\Phi(P) \doteq \frac{Q}{4\pi\varepsilon}\left(\frac{1}{r_1} - \frac{1}{r_2}\right) \tag{3}$$

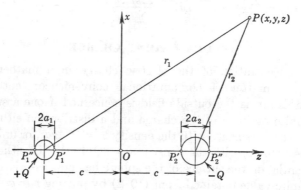

FIG. 11·1   Two Small Spheres as Quasi Point Charges.

On the surfaces of the two spheres, one has, respectively,

$$r_1 = a_1, \quad r_2 \approx 2c, \quad \Phi_1 \approx \frac{Q}{4\pi\varepsilon}\left(\frac{1}{a_1} - \frac{1}{2c}\right) \tag{4}$$

$$r_1 \approx 2c, \quad r_2 = a_2, \quad \Phi_2 \approx \frac{Q}{4\pi\varepsilon}\left(\frac{1}{2c} - \frac{1}{a_2}\right) \tag{5}$$

so that the potential difference becomes

$$V_{12} = \Phi_1 - \Phi_2 \approx \frac{Q}{4\pi\varepsilon}\left(\frac{1}{a_1} + \frac{1}{a_2} - \frac{1}{c}\right) \tag{6}$$

One can thus define the capacitance between these spheres as

$$C = \frac{Q}{\Phi_1 - \Phi_2} \approx \frac{4\pi\varepsilon}{\dfrac{a_1 + a_2}{a_1 a_2} - \dfrac{1}{c}} \approx 4\pi\varepsilon\,\frac{a_1 a_2}{a_1 + a_2} \tag{7}$$

For equal radii, the capacitance reduces to one half that of a single sphere, so that one can interpret this as a series combination of the capacitance of sphere 1 to the infinite sphere and from there to sphere 2.

Though one would construct the field picture exactly in accordance with section 10 for two point charges, the assumption of finite radii permits the evaluation of capacitance coefficients which would be manifestly impossible for point charges. In order to determine the error of (4) and (5) one might observe that this system can be described in terms of Maxwell's potential coefficients given in (3·12), namely,

$$\Phi_1 = S_{11}Q_1 + S_{12}Q_2$$
$$\Phi_2 = S_{21}Q_1 + S_{22}Q_2 \tag{8}$$

from where, by comparison with (4) and (5),

$$S_{11} = \frac{1}{4\pi\varepsilon a_1}, \qquad S_{12} = S_{21} = \frac{1}{4\pi\varepsilon 2c}, \qquad S_{22} = \frac{1}{4\pi\varepsilon a_2} \tag{9}$$

For example, the contribution of charge Q_2 to potential Φ_1 actually varies from a maximum at point P_1' to a minimum at point P_1'' (see Fig. 11·1). Thus, actually,

$$\frac{1}{2c + a_1} < 4\pi\varepsilon S_{12} < \frac{1}{2c - a_1} \tag{10}$$

constitute the limits of variation. For equal and opposite charges, and for values $(a_1/c) \leqslant 0.2$, one finds a resultant maximum potential variation of $+1$ per cent to -1.1 per cent referred to the median potential value computed with $S_{12} = 1/4\pi\varepsilon 2c$. The approximations are, therefore, quite satisfactory as long as $2c$ is larger than ten times the radius of the larger sphere.

For the evaluation of the charge distribution on the sphere a_1, one can also use the relations from section 10 on sphere and point charge. Thus, a charge Q_2, taken as a point charge, induces on the grounded sphere a_1 a charge

$$Q_2' = -\frac{a_1}{2c} Q_2 = -\alpha_1 Q_2 \tag{11}$$

where the notation of (10·25) has been translated into the appropriate one indicated by Fig. 11·1. The distribution over the sphere a_1 causes a charge density given by (10·27) with θ replaced by $(\pi - \theta)$ because the inducing point charge is to the right; again translating, this becomes in first approximation

$$\sigma_1' = - \frac{Q_2}{4\pi a_1^2} \alpha_1 \frac{1 - \alpha_1^2}{[1 + \alpha_1^2 - 2\alpha_1 \cos \theta]^{\frac{3}{2}}}$$

$$\approx - \frac{Q_2}{4\pi a_1^2} \alpha_1 (1 + 3\alpha_1 \cos \theta) \quad (12)$$

where $\alpha_1 = a_1/2c$, and where the binomial expansion was invoked. Since the sphere a_1 is not grounded, but rather carries a total charge Q_1, one has to locate at its center another charge

$$Q_1'' = Q_1 - Q_2' = Q_1 + \alpha_1 Q_2$$

which is uniformly distributed over the sphere's surface with density $\sigma_1'' = Q_1''/4\pi a_1^2$. The total charge density becomes, then,

$$\sigma_1 = \sigma_1' + \sigma_1'' = \frac{Q_1}{4\pi a_1^2} - \frac{Q_2}{4\pi a_1^2} 3\alpha_1^2 \cos \theta \quad (13)$$

The integral over the total sphere gives Q_1, as required; the second term is the non-uniformity caused by the proximity of Q_2. The effect of Q_2 depends upon (α_1^2); for $Q_1 = \pm Q_2$ and $\alpha_1 = 0.1$ (the limit of the approximate treatment), the charge density has maximum deviations of ± 3 per cent from uniformity.

To get the charge distribution on sphere a_2, one would reverse the process and obtain

$$\sigma_2 = \frac{Q_2}{4\pi a_2^2} + \frac{Q_1}{4\pi a_2^2} 3\alpha_2^2 \cos \theta \quad (14)$$

where θ is always counted counterclockwise from the positive z-axis.

Obviously, the field distribution between two small spheres as in Fig. 11·1 is symmetrical about the y-z-plane. One can, therefore, use the lower half of the arrangement to simulate half spheres in conductive ground (or electrolyte) and evaluate the resistance between them as a simple grounding problem. Using relation (8·11), one has at once from (7) for the half space

$$R = \frac{\varepsilon}{\gamma C/2} = \frac{1}{2\pi\gamma} \cdot \frac{a_1 + a_2}{a_1 a_2} \quad (15)$$

The stream lines of the electric current in the earth are identical with the electrostatic field lines, and the current densities on the spheres can be evaluated from the charge densities (13) and (14).

Conducting Planes and Quasi Point Charges. The same approximate treatment is applicable to a single small spherical charge of radius a at a distance $h > 5a$ from a perfectly conducting plane. By the principle of images (see section 10 and Fig. 10·2) one can replace the effect of the plane by a like sphere at distance $2h$ with opposite charge. With $a_1 = a_2 = a$, (7) will give the capacitance of two equal spheres; observing that the potential difference between the two spheres must be halved to maintain the same potential value on the plane, one obtains

$$C = 4\pi\varepsilon a \tag{16}$$

for the capacitance between sphere and plane. The distribution of the resulting field and of the induced charge density in the plane can be obtained in the same manner as for the point charge and plane (see section 10); the mechanical force can be found by (10·18). The charge distribution on the sphere itself is obtained from (14) with $Q_1 = -Q_2 = Q$ and omission of all indices, as

$$\sigma = \frac{Q}{4\pi a^2}\,(1 - 3\alpha^2\cos\theta) \tag{17}$$

where $\alpha = a/2h$ in appropriate modification.

This treatment can, of course, be extended to all cases where the solution for point charges has previously been given in section 10.

For two quasi point charges opposite a conducting plane, as shown in Fig. 11·2, one can readily substitute the appropriate images and find the resultant potentials as

$$\Phi_1 = \frac{1}{4\pi\varepsilon}\left(\frac{1}{a_1} - \frac{1}{2h_1}\right)Q_1 + \frac{1}{4\pi\varepsilon}\left(\frac{1}{r_{12}} - \frac{1}{r_{12}'}\right)Q_2 \tag{18}$$

$$\Phi_2 = \frac{1}{4\pi\varepsilon}\left(\frac{1}{r_{12}} - \frac{1}{r_{12}'}\right)Q_1 + \frac{1}{4\pi\varepsilon}\left(\frac{1}{u_2} - \frac{1}{2h_2}\right)Q_2 \tag{19}$$

where

$$r_{12} = [(2c)^2 + (h_2 - h_1)^2]^{\frac{1}{2}}, \qquad r_{12}' = [(2c)^2 + (h_2 + h_1)^2]^{\frac{1}{2}} \tag{20}$$

The factors to Q_1 and Q_2 can be identified by (3·12) or also (8) above as the Maxwell potential coefficients $S_{\alpha\beta}$ for the two quasi point charges in the presence of the conducting plane. If now

$Q_1 = -Q_2 = +Q$, so that the two charges represent a condenser arrangement in the presence of ground, then their capacitance can easily be computed from

$$\Phi_1 - \Phi_2 = \frac{Q}{4\pi\varepsilon}\left[\left(\frac{1}{a_1} + \frac{1}{a_2} - \frac{2}{r_{12}}\right) - \left(\frac{1}{2h_1} + \frac{1}{2h_2} - \frac{2}{r_{12}'}\right)\right] \quad (21)$$

Comparison of this form with (6) readily indicates that the second

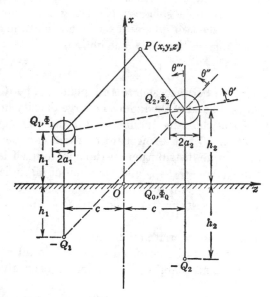

FIG. 11·2　Two Quasi Point Charges above Ground.

parenthesis stands for the influence of ground upon the capacitance of the two spheres. Again, the induced charge distribution on the conducting plane can be found by treating $+Q$ and $-Q$ as actual point charges; similarly, mutual force actions can be evaluated.

In order to obtain the total charge distribution on one sphere, say a_2, one can use the superposition one by one of the effects of each of the other point charges. Thus, the effect of the actual charge $+Q$ is again given by the second term in (14) with $Q_1 = Q$, but with θ' counted from the center line as indicated in Fig. 11·2. For the effect of the image of $+Q$ one would count θ'' from the diagonal center line as indicated in Fig. 11·2, and, finally, for the image of $-Q$ one introduces θ'''. The resultant charge distribution becomes, therefore,

$$\sigma_2 = \frac{Q}{4\pi a_2{}^2}\left[1 - 3\left(\frac{a_2}{2h_2}\right)^2 \cos\theta''' - 3\left(\frac{a_2}{r_{12}}\right)^2 \cos\theta'\right.$$
$$\left. + 3\left(\frac{a_2}{r_{12}'}\right)^2 \cos\theta''\right] \quad (22)$$

Sphere and Quasi Point Charge. In a very similar manner, the results of the section on point charge and sphere can be modified to allow for a finite, though small, radius a_1 of the quasi point charge and thus permit definition of capacitance coefficients.

Thus, for the grounded sphere of arbitrary radius R in Fig. 10·4, one can replace the effect on the sphere of a point charge of value $Q_2 = -(R/b)Q_1$ and located at a distance $2c = b - (R^2/b)$ from Q_1. The potential on a_1 must now be

$$\Phi_1 = \frac{Q_1}{4\pi\varepsilon}\left(\frac{1}{a_1} - \frac{R}{b}\frac{1}{2c}\right)$$

so that the capacitance of the small sphere a_1 in the presence of the grounded sphere becomes

$$C = \frac{Q_1}{\Phi_1} = \frac{4\pi\varepsilon a_1}{1 - \dfrac{a_1}{b}\dfrac{R/b}{1 - (R/b)^2}}$$
$$\approx 4\pi\varepsilon_1 a_1\left[1 + \frac{a_1}{b}\frac{R/b}{1 - (R/b)^2}\right] \quad (23)$$

Since the limitation $a_1/(b - R) \geqslant 0.1$ seems appropriate (a little more severe than for two point charges), it appears that the increase in capacitance is limited to less than 5 per cent. The charge distribution on the small sphere a_1 can be found from (13) by replacing Q_2 and $2c$ according to the definitions above.

In the general case of any arbitrary charge Q_s on the large sphere, the general potential distribution is given by (10·29). One can readily deduce the potential value on the small sphere a_1, by letting $r_1 = a_1$, $r_2 = 2c$, $r = b$, and also $Q' = Q_s$. This leads after ordering to

$$\Phi_1 = \frac{1}{4\pi\varepsilon}\left[\frac{1}{a_1} - \frac{R}{b}\left(\frac{1}{2c} - \frac{1}{b}\right)\right]Q_1 + \frac{1}{4\pi\varepsilon}\frac{1}{b}Q_s \quad (24)$$

whereas the potential of the large sphere is directly from (10·30)

$$\Phi_s = \frac{1}{4\pi\varepsilon}\frac{1}{b}Q_1 + \frac{1}{4\pi\varepsilon}\frac{1}{R}Q_s \tag{25}$$

Again, (24) and (25) define Maxwell's potential coefficients in accordance with (8); from these, one can, of course, compute the induction and capacitance coefficients in accordance with (3·13) and (3·11).

If the two charges are equal and opposite, $Q_1 = -Q_s = Q$, then the spheres form a condenser of direct capacitance

$$C = \frac{Q}{\Phi_1 - \Phi_s} = \frac{4\pi\varepsilon}{\left[\dfrac{1}{a_1} + \dfrac{1}{R}\left(1 - \dfrac{(R/b)^4}{1 - (R/b)^2}\right) - \dfrac{2}{b}\right]} \tag{26}$$

which for small values (R/b) at once approaches (6), the capacitance of two small spheres with the appropriate changes in notation.

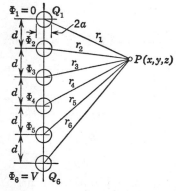

Several Collinear Quasi Point Charges. If several small spheres of radius a are arranged collinearly with equal spacings $d > 10a$, the potential distribution can readily be found as that of point charges at the centers of the spheres (see Fig. 11·3). For n spheres there are n charges and n potential values, so that a total of n quantities must be prescribed to permit evaluation of the other n unknowns.

FIG. 11·3 Several Collinear Quasi Point Charges.

One practical case is obtained by assuming the first sphere grounded, $\Phi_1 = 0$, the last one carrying the total voltage $\Phi_n = V$, and the $(n-2)$ spheres in between with floating potentials, i.e., insulated so that $Q_2 = Q_3 = \cdots Q_{n-1} = 0$. The charges Q_1 and Q_n are then related to the given potential values by the simple forms

$$\Phi_1 = S_{11}Q_1 + S_{1n}Q_n = 0 \tag{27}$$

$$\Phi_n = S_{n1}Q_1 + S_{nn}Q_n = V \tag{28}$$

since no other charges exist. In a manner similar to two quasi point charges, the potential coefficients are

$$S_{11} = S_{nn} = \frac{1}{4\pi\varepsilon a}, \qquad S_{1n} = S_{n1} = \frac{1}{4\pi\varepsilon(n-1)d} \qquad (29)$$

The charges become, if one observes $(S_{11}S_{nn}) \gg S_{1n}{}^2$,

$$Q_n = +4\pi\varepsilon aV, \qquad Q_1 = -4\pi\varepsilon a\frac{a}{(n-1)d}V \qquad (30)$$

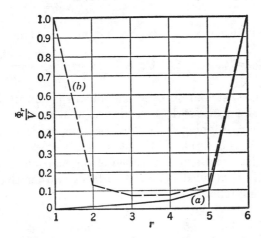

Fɪɢ. 11·4 Distribution of Induced Potentials over Six Insulated Collinear Quasi Point Charges: (a) one end grounded, (b) symmetrical distribution.

and the floating potentials

$$\Phi_r = S_{r1}Q_1 + S_{rn}Q_n = V\frac{a}{d}\left[\frac{1}{n-r} - \frac{1}{(n-1)(r-1)}\right] \qquad (31)$$

for all values $r = 2, 3, \cdots, (n-1)$. The distribution for a series of $n = 6$ spheres is shown as line (a) in Fig. 11·4 for $a/d = 0.1$; obviously, there is little difference from the free potential distribution of a single point charge located at the center of Q_n even though the actual field picture would be very complex. F. Ollendorff[1] has used this simplified field picture as a model to approximate the field distribution about a chain of high-voltage suspension insulators, assuming the metal cap of the uppermost insulator (next to the cross arm) to have ground potential, and the metal

[1] F. Ollendorff, *Arch. f. Elektrot.*, **16**, p. 261 (1927); **17**, pp. 79 and 242 (1927).

suspender of the lowest one (connected to the conductor) to have line potential. He also computed the potential distribution over the surface of an insulator, which checked satisfactorily with measured values.

If one assumes the potentials $\Phi_1 = \Phi_n = V$, and again insulated spheres in between with $Q_2 = Q_3 = \cdots Q_{n-1} = 0$, then (27) and (28) will lead to

$$Q_1 = Q_n = \frac{V}{S_{11} + S_{1n}}$$

and for the induced potentials one finds in accordance with (31)

$$\Phi_r = (S_{r1} + S_{rn})\, Q_1 = V \frac{a}{d}\, \frac{(n-1)}{(n-r)(r-1)} \tag{32}$$

This potential distribution over the spheres is shown as line (b) in Fig. 11·4 for $a/d = 0.1$; as expected, it is a symmetrical distribution, again dropping sharply between the outermost members of the chain. This emphasizes that the greatest electrical stresses occur in the immediate neighborhood of the high-voltage terminal and that only controlled potential surfaces (rather than floating ones) can bring relief.

12· LINE CHARGES AND QUASI LINE CHARGES

For known distributions of charge along simple geometrical lines, it is possible to evaluate the potential distribution by the direct integration

$$\Phi = \frac{1}{4\pi\varepsilon} \int \frac{\lambda\, ds}{r} \tag{1}$$

where λ is the line charge density, ds the line element, and r the distance between the charge element and the point of observation P. Expression (1) is, of course, the limit of the sum (1·9) of the point charges ($\lambda\, ds$).

For practical applications it is disconcerting that the potential and field strength values at the charged line become infinitely high. One can, however, frequently approximate a given conductor geometry by quasi line charges; that is, one can compute the general field distribution in terms of charged *lines*, but then select an appropriate equipotential surface close to the charged line as a good representation of the actual given geometry. This provides for finite field values on the equipotential surface and permits evaluation of capacitance coefficients and charge densities.

Finite Straight Line; Rod Electrode. The finite straight line in Fig. 12·1 may carry a uniform charge distribution of

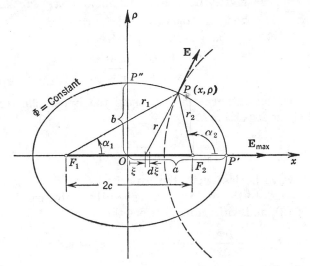

FIG. 12·1   Finite Straight Line with Uniform Charge Density.

density $Q/2c$. Because of axial symmetry, the integral (1) can be expressed

$$\Phi = \frac{1}{4\pi\varepsilon} \cdot \frac{Q}{2c} \int_{\xi=-c}^{\xi=+c} \frac{d\xi}{\sqrt{(x-\xi)^2 + \rho^2}}$$

$$= \frac{Q}{4\pi\varepsilon 2c} \ln \frac{(x+c) + r_1}{(x-c) + r_2} \tag{2}$$

with the notations from Fig. 12·1. The equipotential surfaces are confocal rotational (prolate) ellipsoids, with the fixed foci F_1 and F_2 at the ends of the charged line, which itself is a degenerate ellipsoid of vanishing minor axis. For larger distances, major and minor axes $2a$ and $2b$ become nearly equal; the equipotential surfaces approach spheres. The field lines are given by the orthogonal system of confocal hyperbolae. Details on the simpler computations, as well as related applications, are found in Abraham and Becker,[A1] p. 62; in Attwood,[A2] pp. 81–84; in Bennett and Crothers,[A3] p. 192; in Breisig,[A4] p. 77.

Since any equipotential surface can be taken as a new conductor surface, (2) gives also the potential distribution surrounding a *prolate ellipsoidal surface* with total charge Q at constant potential Φ_s. If one has given the major and minor axes $2a$, $2b$, then $c = \sqrt{a^2 - b^2}$; choosing point P on the surface of the ellipsoid, say at P'', then $x = 0$, $r_1 = r_2 = a$, and

$$\Phi_s = \frac{1}{4\pi\varepsilon} \frac{Q}{2c} \ln \frac{a+c}{a-c} \tag{3}$$

so that the capacitance follows, using the hyperbolic function instead of the logarithm,

$$C = 4\pi\varepsilon a \frac{c/a}{\tanh^{-1}(c/a)} \tag{4}$$

It will always be less than the capacitance of the sphere with diameter equal to the major axis. The field vector can be found by use of (2), and with simplifications this yields

$$E_x = -\frac{\partial \Phi}{\partial x} = +\frac{Q}{4\pi\varepsilon 2c} \frac{1}{\rho} (\sin \alpha_2 - \sin \alpha_1)$$

$$= \frac{Q}{4\pi\varepsilon 2c} \left(\frac{1}{r_2} - \frac{1}{r_1} \right) \tag{5}$$

$$E_\rho = -\frac{\partial \Phi}{\partial \rho} = +\frac{Q}{4\pi\varepsilon 2c} \frac{1}{\rho} (\cos \alpha_1 - \cos \alpha_2) \tag{6}$$

Though it is not possible to develop a simple general expression for the charge density on the ellipsoid here (see section 31 for that), the maximum and minimum values can readily be given. At P', with $r_1 = a + c$, $r_2 = a - c$, one obtains from (5)

$$\sigma_{\max} = \varepsilon E_x = \frac{Q}{4\pi b^2} \tag{7}$$

whereas at P'', with $\rho = b$, $\cos \alpha_1 = c/a$, $\cos \alpha_2 = -c/a$, it follows from (6)

$$\sigma_{\min} = \varepsilon E_\rho = \frac{Q}{4\pi ab} \tag{8}$$

so that the ratio of maximum to minimum charge density is

exactly the ratio of major to minor axis, a/b. This ratio also holds for the pertinent field gradients, so that the maximum dielectric stress must be expected at the apex of the major axis. Combining (7) with (4), one deduces

$$\sigma_{max} = \frac{\Phi_s}{b} \frac{c/b}{\tanh^{-1}(c/a)} = \frac{\Phi_s}{b} \cdot F \qquad (9)$$

where the factor F is a function of only $b/a = \beta$

$$\frac{1}{F} = \beta \frac{\tanh^{-1}\sqrt{1-\beta^2}}{\sqrt{1-\beta^2}} \qquad (10)$$

Figure 12·2 gives a graph of $1/F$; it indicates that, as the ratio β decreases, the gradient E_{max} increases very rapidly indeed.

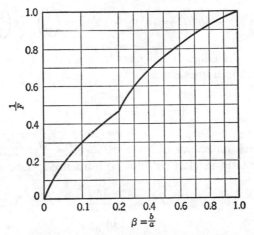

FIG. 12·2 Factor $1/F$ for the Maximum Field Gradient of the Ellipsoid in Fig. 12·1.

For a large ratio a/b, the ellipsoid can be made to approximate the shape of a cylindrical rod. Since no reasonable solution of the potential problem for a finitely long cylinder of non-vanishing diameter d and length l is known, it has become customary to substitute the ellipsoidal rod. For ratios $d/l < 0.1$, and choosing $2a = l$, $2b = d$, the approximation is valid

$$c = \sqrt{a^2 - b^2} \approx a\left[1 - \frac{1}{2}\left(\frac{b}{a}\right)^2\right]$$

Introducing this into (3) gives

$$\Phi_s = \frac{Q}{4\pi\varepsilon a}\ln\frac{2a}{b} \tag{11}$$

so that the capacitance of the rod-like antenna becomes

$$C' = \frac{2\pi\varepsilon l}{\ln\dfrac{2l}{d}} \tag{12}$$

This is designated C' because other choices of equivalent parameters are possible.   Instead of inscribing the ellipsoid, giving the
smallest equivalent, one could just circumscribe the rod with it,
giving the largest equivalent.   For fixed foci, one must have

$$(a'')^2 - (b'')^2 = (a')^2 - (b')^2 = \left(\frac{l}{2}\right)^2 - \left(\frac{d}{2}\right)^2$$

In addition, the ellipse must pass through $x = l/2 = a'$, $\rho = d/2$
$= b'$, so that in normal form

$$\left(\frac{a'}{a''}\right)^2 + \left(\frac{b'}{b''}\right)^2 = 1$$

The combination shows $a'' = a'\ \sqrt{2}$, $b'' = b'\ \sqrt{2}$, so that the
logarithmic term in (12) will not be influenced; however,

$$C'' = \frac{2\pi\varepsilon\sqrt{2}\ l}{\ln\dfrac{2l}{d}} \tag{13}$$

For practical purposes it might be most advisable to select an
average value between (12) and (13), such as $(1 + \sqrt{2})/2 \approx 1.2$,
and

$$C = \frac{2.4\pi\varepsilon l}{\ln\dfrac{2l}{d}} \tag{14}$$

The same solution can also be applied to all stationary flow
problems, such as current flow from a vertical grounding rod, as
in Fig. 12·3a, into the ground, or from a horizontal tube lying on

the surface of ground,[1] as in Fig. 12·3b. For the vertical rod one must take its length within ground as $l/2$ in order to have the surface of ground as plane of symmetry. In both cases, the vertical as well as the horizontal rod, only one half of the total space is

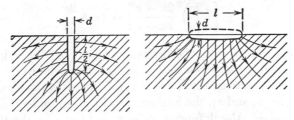

FIG. 12·3 Thin Ellipsoids as Grounding Rods: (a) vertical, (b) horizontal, arrangement.

occupied by the current flow; the resistance is therefore twice the value obtained from the capacitance expression (12), namely,

$$R = 2 \frac{\varepsilon}{\gamma C'} = \frac{1}{\gamma \pi l} \ln \left(\frac{2l}{d} \right) \tag{15}$$

Though the overall resistance is the same, the current distribution is, of course, quite different, and, in particular, the field gradient along the surface of the ground is much higher for the horizontal rod.

Finite Straight Line above Ground. The proximity of ground for a vertical, uniformly charged line of length $2c$ can be taken into account by the image line below ground. With the same axial symmetry as in Fig. 12·1, the integration (2) over both charged lines (actual and image) leads, with the designations in Fig. 12·4a, to

$$\Phi = \frac{1}{4\pi\varepsilon} \cdot \frac{Q}{2c} \left[\ln \frac{(x - h + c) + r_1'}{(x - h - c) + r_2'} \right.$$
$$\left. - \ln \frac{(x + h + c) + r_1''}{(x + h - c) + r_2''} \right] \tag{16}$$

The equipotential surfaces have a sort of oval shape and include, of course, the plane $x = 0$. For a thin rod of mean diameter d

[1] Ollendorff,[A18] p. 96; for a good summary of grounding problems see R. W. Ryder, *Jl. I.E.E.*, **95**, part III, p. 175 (1948); also R. Rüdenberg, *Electr. Engg.*, **64**, p. 1 (1945).

and length $l \gg d$, one can find the approximate capacitance, as influenced by ground, by evaluating (16) at $x = h$; this yields in the neighborhood of the charged line with ρ small in all radius vectors

$$\ln\left[\left(\frac{2c}{\rho}\right)^2 \frac{2h-c}{2h+c}\right] = 4\pi\varepsilon\Phi\,\frac{2c}{Q}$$

Specifically, for $2\rho = d$, the diameter of the rod, the value of Φ_s results, which is the potential on the surface of the rod. Putting $\rho = 0$ in (16), one can then solve that relation with the same potential value for x_2 and x_1, the intersection of the equipotential surface with the x-axis; the difference $x_2 - x_1 = l$ must be the length of the rod. As long as $(d/l) \ll 1$, one obtains in good approximation

$$C = \frac{Q}{\Phi_s} = \frac{2\pi\varepsilon l}{\ln\left(\dfrac{2l}{d}\sqrt{\dfrac{2H+l/2}{2H+3l/2}}\right)} \tag{17}$$

as the capacitance of a finite rod located perpendicular to a conducting plane. This becomes for $H \to \infty$, or for a single rod by itself, identical with (12); for $H \to 0$, one deduces

$$C = \frac{2\pi\varepsilon l}{\ln\left(\dfrac{2l}{d\sqrt{3}}\right)} \tag{18}$$

the capacitance of a vertical rod of potential Φ_s directly on the surface of the conducting plane of potential $\Phi = 0$, which gives the largest possible value. The capacitance between the two rods is one half the value resulting from (17), because the potential difference is $(2\Phi_s)$; one could also consider the two half spaces connected in series.

The charge density induced in the plane $\Phi = 0$ can be obtained from (5) with the potential solution (16). Along $x = 0$, only the component E_x exists, and, as seen from Fig. 12·4a, $r_1' = r_2'' = [H^2 + \rho^2]^{1/2}$, $r_1'' = r_2' = [(H+l)^2 + \rho^2]^{1/2}$, so that

$$\sigma = \varepsilon E_{x/x=0}$$

$$= -\frac{Q}{2\pi l}\left[\frac{1}{(H^2+\rho^2)^{1/2}} - \frac{1}{[(H+l)^2+\rho^2]^{1/2}}\right] \tag{19}$$

if one also uses $2c \approx l$. The maximum value obtains directly under the rod at $\rho = 0$,

$$\sigma_{\max} = - \frac{Q}{2\pi} \frac{1}{H(H+l)} \tag{20}$$

whereas for the single point charge above ground, (10·17) gave $\left(- \dfrac{Q}{2\pi} \dfrac{1}{h^2}\right)$. The variation with distance ρ is quite similar in both cases; the point charge, however, has a slightly stronger local

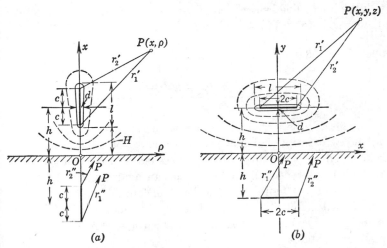

Fig. 12·4 Finite Rod above Ground: (a) vertical, (b) horizontal, arrangement.

effect, i.e., the induced charge density is slightly higher close to, and slightly lower far from, the point charge, than is the case for the charged finite rod.

The same solution can be applied to all flow problems, thermal, hydrodynamical, or electrical, by use of the general table 9·1. For example, the electrical resistance between two cylindrical electrodes of finite length is given by

$$R = 2 \frac{\varepsilon}{\gamma C} = \frac{1}{\gamma \pi l} \ln\left(\frac{2l}{d} \sqrt{\frac{2H + l/2}{2H + 3l/2}}\right) \tag{21}$$

where the factor 2 accounts for the potential difference $(2\Phi_s)$ between the rods.

Instead of a uniform charge distribution, one can also assume some arbitrary function $f(\xi)$ with

$$\frac{1}{2c} \int_{-c}^{+c} f(\xi)\, d\xi = 1$$

so that the total charge remains as Q. The evaluation of the resulting integral can be made simple with the proper choice of $f(\xi)$.

For a horizontal, uniformly charged straight line above ground, as in Fig. 12·4b, no axial symmetry will exist. The treatment with the image line below ground can be carried through in similar manner as before[2] and will yield

$$\Phi = \frac{1}{4\pi\varepsilon} \cdot \frac{Q}{2c} \left[\ln \frac{[(x+c)^2 + (y-h)^2 + z^2]^{1/2} + (x+c)}{[(x-c)^2 + (y-h)^2 + z^2]^{1/2} + (x-c)} \right.$$
$$\left. - \ln \frac{[(x+c)^2 + (y+h)^2 + z^2]^{1/2} + (x+c)}{[(x-c)^2 + (y+h)^2 + z^2]^{1/2} + (x-c)} \right] \quad (22)$$

which can also be written in terms of the radius vectors r_1', r_1'', r_2', and r_2'', except that now the coordinate z of the point P must be included. The equipotential surfaces close to the charged lines are slightly flattened ellipsoids which can again readily be taken to approximate a finite cylindrical rod of length l and diameter d as indicated in Fig. 12·4b. Evaluating (22) at $x = z = 0$ and in the neighborhood of the charged line with $y = h \pm \rho$, where ρ is small, one obtains

$$\ln \left[\left(\frac{2c}{\rho} \right)^2 \frac{(c^2 + 4h^2)^{1/2} - c}{(c^2 + 4h^2)^{1/2} + c} \right] = 4\pi\varepsilon\Phi \frac{2c}{Q}$$

Specifically, for $2\rho = d$, the diameter of the rod, the value Φ_s results, which is the potential on the surface of the rod. Putting $y = h$, $z = 0$ in (22), one can solve it with the same potential value Φ_s for the value x; this corresponds to the intersection of the equipotential surface with the line $y = h$ and defines the length $l/2$. As long as $(d/l) \ll 1$, one obtains in good approximation

$$C = \frac{Q}{\Phi_s} = \frac{2\pi\varepsilon l}{\ln \left(\dfrac{2l}{d} \dfrac{l}{4h} \left[\sqrt{1 + \left(\dfrac{4h}{l} \right)^2} - 1 \right] \right)} \quad (23)$$

[2] For a different approximation see F. L. ReQua, *Trans. A.I.E.E.*, **64**, p. 724 (1945).

as the capacitance of a finite rod parallel to a conducting plane. The capacitance between the two rods themselves will again be one half the value given by (23) because the total potential difference is $(2\Phi_s)$.

For a *very long rod* above ground such that $(4h/l) \ll 1$, expression (23) simplifies to

$$C = \frac{Q}{\Phi_s} = \frac{2\pi \varepsilon l}{\ln \dfrac{4h}{d}} \tag{24}$$

In this case (and this case only), it is possible to define a *capacitance per unit length* of the charged line or rod to ground

$$C_1 = \frac{2\pi \varepsilon}{\ln \dfrac{4h}{d}} \tag{25}$$

which is independent of the length of the rod.   This means that end effects become a negligible part of the electrical field configuration, so that for practical purposes the important region of the field between the two charged lines, or between line and ground, can be considered *two-dimensional*, depending only on the cross-sectional dimensions of the system and not on its length (see further below).

As in the other cases above, this solution can again be applied to all flow problems.   For example, one can consider the plane $x = 0$ as the surface of an electrolyte extending to $x > 0$ into which two electrodes are immersed, formed by the right halves of the rod and its "image."   The resistance between these electrodes can then be computed from (23) as

$$R = 4 \frac{\varepsilon}{\gamma C} = \frac{2}{\gamma \pi l} \ln \left(\frac{2l}{d} \frac{l}{4h} \left[\sqrt{1 + \left(\frac{4h}{l}\right)^2} - 1 \right] \right) \tag{26}$$

where the factor 4 accounts for current flow from only one half the total ellipsoidal surface (for $x > 0$) and for the potential difference $(2\Phi_s)$ between the rods.

Very Long Straight Line.   If one lets $c \to \infty$ in (2), he should obtain the potential function of a very long straight line. Obviously, unless one defines $Q/2c = \lambda$ as a finite charge per unit length, one could not attach much sense to $c \to \infty$; conversely,

$Q = 2c\lambda$ will itself become infinite with c, so that a truly infinitely long line represents difficulties of realization.[3]

Assuming axial symmetry and independence with respect to coordinate x (end effects are disregarded because of the great length), then one can more readily deduce the dielectric flux density **D** from the application of Gauss's theorem (1·11) to a concentric cylindrical surface of radius ρ and unit length

$$D_\rho = \frac{\lambda}{2\pi\rho} \qquad (27)$$

since the flux lines are radial. The potential can then be found by direct integration

$$\Phi = -\int_{\rho_1}^{\rho_2} E_\rho \, d\rho = +\frac{\lambda}{2\pi\varepsilon} \ln\left(\frac{\rho_1}{\rho}\right) \qquad (28)$$

This value is independent of the path of integration, and ρ_1 is a conveniently chosen reference point at which one assumes $\Phi = 0$. Such a compromise is customary, since the logarithmic potential function becomes infinite at both limits $\rho = 0$ and $\rho = \infty$. The equipotential surfaces are the concentric cylinders $\rho = $ cons; any one of these could be chosen as a conductor surface and be assigned a value Φ_0 which could be added on in (28). However, for the single conductor it is not possible to define a capacitance value because of the logarithmic nature of the potential variation.

Two Parallel Very Long Straight Lines. The resultant potential function of two parallel lines is simply the superposition

$$\Phi = \frac{\lambda_1}{2\pi\varepsilon} \ln\left(\frac{a_1}{r_1}\right) + \frac{\lambda_2}{2\pi\varepsilon} \ln\left(\frac{a_2}{r_2}\right)$$

where λ_1 and λ_2 are the linear charge densities, and a_1 and a_2 arbitrary constants corresponding to ρ_1 in (28). For equal and opposite charge densities, $\lambda_1 = -\lambda_2 = \lambda$, the expression can be simplified to

$$\Phi = \frac{\lambda}{2\pi\varepsilon} \ln\left(\frac{r_2}{r_1}\right) + \Phi_0 \qquad (29)$$

where r_1 and r_2 are the distances from the charged lines as indicated in Fig. 12·5. The arbitrary constant Φ_0 serves to adjust absolute potential values when desired. The equipotential surfaces are

[3] See Attwood,[A2] p. 76; Kellogg,[C10] p. 62; and Smythe,[A22] p. 62.

given by $r_2/r_1 = k'$: they are the family of excentric cylinders with their axes M parallel to the line charges in the x-z-plane in Fig. 12·5; the field lines are given by $\phi_2 - \phi_1 = k''$: they are the orthogonal family of circles passing through the line charges and have their centers N along the y-z-plane in Fig. 12·5. Details of the computations and graphical field pictures are given in many books, such as Attwood,[A2] pp. 85–88; Bennett and Crothers,[A3] p. 140; Jeans,[A10] p. 195; Küpfmüller,[A14] pp. 70–76; Mason and

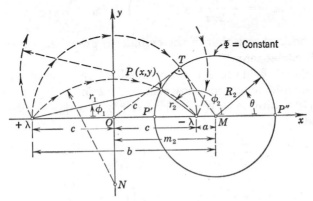

Fɪɢ. 12·5 Two Parallel Very Long Straight Lines with Equal and Opposite Charges.

Weaver,[A16] p. 136; Ramsay,[A21] pp. 41, 140; Bewley,[D1] p. 43; and practically all references listed in Appendix 4, B, a and 4, B, b.

Cylinder and Parallel Straight Line. Since the equipotential surfaces of two parallel straight lines are circular cylinders, (29) must also describe the potential distribution between a finite cylinder of radius R_2 in Fig. 12·5 and a line charge $(+\lambda)$. The cylinder will carry the total charge $(-\lambda)$ per unit length and will have a potential defined by the special values of r_2 and r_1 along its surface. Thus, for the point P',

$$r_1' = c + (m_2 - R_2), \qquad r_2' = c - (m_2 - R_2) \qquad (30)$$

where m_2 is the distance of the axis of the cylinder from the origin O. From the triangle OMT in Fig. 12·5, one also takes

$$R_2{}^2 = m_2{}^2 - c^2 = (m_2 + c)(m_2 - c) = ba \qquad (31)$$

a relationship which permits interpretation of the line charge $(-\lambda)$

as the *image* of the line charge $(+\lambda)$ with respect to the cylinder R_2. The relation (31) defines the location of $(-\lambda)$ when R_2 and b are given, or, conversely, locates the center of R_2 with respect to the two equal and opposite line charges. With (30) and (31), the general form (29) yields now

$$\Phi_{(R_2)} = -\frac{\lambda}{2\pi\varepsilon} \ln\left[\frac{m_2}{R_2} + \sqrt{\left(\frac{m_2}{R_2}\right)^2 - 1}\right] + \Phi_0$$

$$= -\frac{\lambda}{2\pi\varepsilon} \cosh^{-1}\left(\frac{m_2}{R_2}\right) + \Phi_0 \qquad (32)$$

Φ_0 can be so chosen that, if the cylinder is grounded, its potential value becomes zero.

The electric field vector can most readily be computed in the Cartesian coordinate system chosen in Fig. 12·5. Using the general form (29) with $r_1 = [(x + c)^2 + y^2]^{\frac{1}{2}}$, $r_2 = [(x - c)^2 + y^2]^{\frac{1}{2}}$, one finds

$$E_x = -\frac{\partial\Phi}{\partial x} = +\frac{\lambda}{2\pi\varepsilon}\left(\frac{x + c}{r_1^2} - \frac{x - c}{r_2^2}\right) \qquad (33)$$

$$E_y = -\frac{\partial\Phi}{\partial y} = -\frac{\lambda}{2\pi\varepsilon}\, y\left(\frac{1}{r_2^2} - \frac{1}{r_1^2}\right) \qquad (34)$$

The maximum field strength will certainly exist along the x-axis between the cylinder R_2 and the line charge $(+\lambda)$. Because of $y = 0$, only E_x will exist there and, in accordance with the assumed charges, will point in the positive x-direction

$$E_x = +\frac{\lambda}{2\pi\varepsilon}\left(\frac{1}{c - x} - \frac{1}{c + x}\right) = \frac{\lambda}{\pi\varepsilon}\frac{c}{c^2 - x^2}$$

On the line charge, where $x \to (-c)$, the field strength will approach infinite value as expected; on the cylinder, the maximum value will be

$$(E_{R_2})_{\max} = \frac{\lambda}{2\pi\varepsilon}\frac{1}{R_2}\frac{1 + \alpha}{1 - \alpha} \qquad (35)$$

where $\alpha = R_2/b$. For $\alpha \to 0$, this becomes consistent with (27).

By means of a transformation of coordinates from (x, y) to (r, θ), with the axis of the cylinder R_2 as center,

$$x = m_2 + r\cos\theta, \qquad y = r\sin\theta$$

one can evaluate $E_r = -(\partial\Phi/\partial r)$ from (29) and obtain the induced surface charge density on the cylinder (negative, because E_r is directed towards the surface of the cylinder),

$$\sigma = \varepsilon E_{r/\hat{r}=R_2} = -\frac{\lambda}{2\pi R_2}\frac{1-\alpha^2}{1+\alpha^2+2\alpha\cos\theta} \qquad (36)$$

The maximum exists at P' for $\theta = \pi$, the minimum at P'' for $\theta = 0$, and their ratio is

$$\frac{\sigma_{\max}}{\sigma_{\min}} = \left(\frac{1+\alpha}{1-\alpha}\right)^2 = \left(\frac{b+R_2}{b-R_2}\right)^2 \qquad (37)$$

It is significant to compare this result with that for point charge and sphere in section 10 and to observe the larger inhomogeneity in the latter case.

If the cylinder R_2 is *insulated*, then it cannot acquire any resultant charge. The placement of a line charge $(+\lambda)$ into the axis of the cylinder contributes a constant potential on its surface as well as an additional uniform charge density $\sigma' = \lambda/2\pi R_2$, but reduces the total charge to zero. The resultant charge density will be negative closest to the inducing line charge $(+\lambda)$, and positive on the opposite side. The neutral zone exists where $(-\sigma) = \sigma'$, which gives with (36) the value $\cos\theta_0 = -\alpha$. For $\alpha = 0.1$, one finds $\theta_0 = 95°44'$; the neutral zone moves rapidly to larger angles θ as α increases.

Two Parallel Cylinders with Equal and Opposite Charges. Selecting any two cylinders from the family of the equipotential surfaces, they can at once be considered as carrying opposite and equal charges and as forming a condenser. If one cylinder is outside the other as in Fig. $12\cdot6a$, and R_1, R_2, D are the given parameters, one must first locate the equivalent line charges. From the triangles OP_1M_1 and OM_2P_2 one takes the relations

$$m_1{}^2 = c^2 + R_1{}^2, \qquad m_2{}^2 = c^2 + R_2{}^2 \qquad (38)$$

so that

$$m_1{}^2 - m_2{}^2 = (m_1 + m_2)(m_1 - m_2) = R_1{}^2 - R_2{}^2$$

Defining $R_1/D = \eta_1$, $R_2/D = \eta_2$, and observing $(m_1 + m_2) = D$, one readily finds

$$m_1 = \frac{D}{2}[1 + (\eta_1{}^2 - \eta_2{}^2)], \qquad m_2 = \frac{D}{2}[1 - (\eta_1{}^2 - \eta_2{}^2)] \qquad (39)$$

so that the origin O can be located.   Combining now (38) and (39), one also obtains

$$2c = D[1 - 2(\eta_1^2 + \eta_2^2) + (\eta_1^2 - \eta_2^2)^2]^{1/2} \qquad (40)$$

The potential values on the two cylinders can be computed from

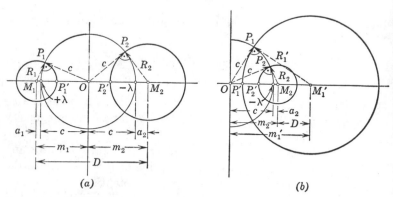

(a)   (b)

FIG. 12·6   Two Parallel Cylinders: (a) one outside the other, (b) one inside the other.

the general form (29) in the same manner as indicated for (32) whereby for the point P_1' on cylinder R_1

$$(r_1')_1 = c - (m_1 - R_1), \qquad (r_2')_1 = c + (m_1 - R_1)$$

whereas for the point P_2' on cylinder R_2

$$(r_1')_2 = c + (m_2 - R_2), \qquad (r_2')_2 = c - (m_2 - R_2)$$

The potential on R_1 is positive, that on R_2 negative, so that the capacitance per unit length becomes[4]

$$C_1 = \frac{\lambda}{\Phi_{R_1} - \Phi_{R_2}} = \frac{2\pi\varepsilon}{\left[\cosh^{-1}\dfrac{m_1}{R_1} + \cosh^{-1}\dfrac{m_2}{R_2}\right]} \qquad (41)$$

The charge distribution on each cylinder is given by the properly modified form (36), using for the cylinder R_2 the value $\alpha_2 = R_2/b_2 = R_2/(c + m_2)$, and for the cylinder R_1 the value $\alpha_1 = R_1/b_1 = R_1/(c + m_1)$.

[4] A. E. Kennelly, *Proc. Am. Phil. Soc.*, **48**, p. 142 (1909); also *Electr. World*, **56**, p. 1000 (1910); C. L. Dawes, *Phys.*, **4**, p. 81 (1933); also many of the references in Appendix 4, A; and Schwaiger,[B17] p. 68.

If the cylinders have *equal radii*, $R_1 = R_2 = R$, then (39) indicates $m_1 = m_2 = D/2$, the capacitance takes the much simpler form

$$C_1 = \frac{\pi\varepsilon}{\cosh^{-1}\dfrac{D}{2R}} \tag{42}$$

and charge and field distributions are perfectly symmetrical.

Finally, if one of the cylinders encloses the other, as in Fig. 12·6b, relations (38) are still valid, but now $(m_1' - m_2) = D$, so that

$$m_1' = \frac{D}{2}[(\eta_1'^2 - \eta_2^2) + 1], \qquad m_2 = \frac{D}{2}[(\eta_1'^2 - \eta_2^2) - 1] \tag{43}$$

This locates the origin O to the left of the cylinders; the value for c remains the same as in (40) and locates the line charge $(-\lambda)$. The potentials on the cylinders are evaluated as above for (41). Selecting P_1' and P_2' as indicated in Fig. 12·6b leads to the capacitance per unit length

$$C_1 = \frac{\lambda}{\Phi_{R_1'} - \Phi_{R_2}} = \frac{2\pi\varepsilon}{\left[\cosh^{-1}\dfrac{m_2}{R_2} - \cosh^{-1}\dfrac{m_1'}{R_1'}\right]} \tag{44}$$

which increases beyond all limits as R_1' approaches R_2.

For *finite* but small *radii* of the two wires in Fig. 12·6a with the respective potentials Φ_1 and Φ_2, one can apply (29) to the surfaces of the wires with the approximations

$$r_1 = R_1, \qquad r_2 \approx 2c \approx D, \qquad \Phi_1 = \frac{\lambda}{2\pi\varepsilon}\ln\frac{D}{R_1} + \Phi_0 \left.\begin{array}{c}\\\\\\\\\end{array}\right\}$$

$$r_1 \approx 2c \approx D, \qquad r_2 = R_2, \qquad \Phi_2 = \frac{\lambda}{2\pi\varepsilon}\ln\frac{R_2}{D} + \Phi_0 \tag{45}$$

so that the capacitance per unit length follows at once

$$C_1 = \frac{\lambda}{\Phi_1 - \Phi_2} = \frac{\pi\varepsilon}{\ln\dfrac{D}{\sqrt{R_1 R_2}}} \tag{46}$$

Actually, of course, the potential contribution of conductor **2** over the surface of conductor **1** is not quite constant; the approximations in (45) for Φ_1 and Φ_2 are accurate to better than ± 1 per cent if $D/R \geqslant 10$, which is generally true for aerial transmission systems of parallel wires. The same result is obtained from (41), if one lets η_1 and η_2 in (39) and (40) become very small. The charge distribution can still be evaluated from (36); if $\alpha^2 \ll 1$, the simpler expression

$$\sigma \approx \pm \frac{\lambda}{2\pi R} \left(1 - \frac{2R}{D} \cos \theta \right) \tag{47}$$

may be used for either R_1 or R_2.

Conducting Plane and Parallel Straight Line or Cylinder. The effect of the conducting plane upon the field distribution of a single very long straight line of charge density $(+\lambda)$ can again be replaced by that of the *image* of the straight line, so that the problem reduces to the case of two parallel very long straight lines (see references, p. 116) and the potential is given by (29), where Φ_0 is now the potential of the plane.[5] The charge induced on the plane can be found from (33) if one uses the notation of Fig. 12·5, as

$$\sigma = \varepsilon E_x = -\frac{\lambda}{2\pi\varepsilon} \frac{2c}{c^2 + y^2} \tag{48}$$

The negative sign arises from the fact that the field strength is directed towards the plane.

For a thin wire, the relations (45) and (46) are valid with $R_1 = R_2$. The capacitance per unit length of the wire with respect to the conducting plane (for example, ground) becomes from (46)

$$C_1 = \frac{2\pi\varepsilon}{\ln \dfrac{D}{R}} \tag{49}$$

where the factor 2 accounts for one half of the potential difference $(\Phi_1 - \Phi_2)$ between wire and plane. For the charge distribution on the wire one can use (47) if $D/R \geqslant 10$. For a cylinder of larger radius, the precise form (42) must be used for the capacitance per unit length, again inserting the factor 2 as in (49). Obviously, the charge distribution on the conducting plane will always be

[5] For an interesting application to heat flow problems in connection with the "heat pump" see Ch. H. Coogan, *Paper* No. 3, Engg. Exp. Station, Univ. of Conn., June 1948.

given by (48) since the equivalent line charge and its image do not change.

If the charged line is parallel to the edge of two intersecting conducting planes, the same considerations apply as in the analogous case for point charges treated in section 10; the number of necessary images is always equal to $(2n - 1)$ if the planes intersect at an angle π/n and n is an integer.

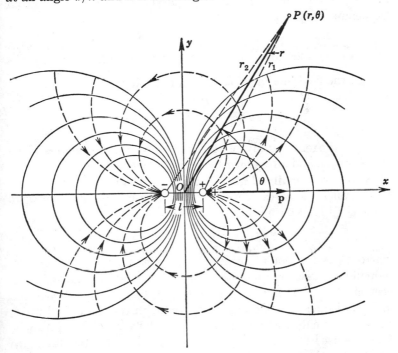

Fig. 12·7　Dipole Line (Small but Finite Spacing).

Dipole Line. If the distance $2c = l$ between the two charged lines becomes infinitesimally small, then the potential function (29) can be approximated (see Fig. 12·7), with $r_1 \simeq r - (l/2)\cos\theta$, $r_2 \approx r + (l/2)\cos\theta$, by

$$\Phi = \frac{\lambda}{2\pi\varepsilon}\ln\left(1 + \frac{l}{r}\cos\theta\right) \approx \frac{\lambda}{2\pi\varepsilon}\frac{l\cos\theta}{r} \tag{50}$$

or, defining the dipole moment of the two lines as a vector,

$$\mathbf{p} = \lambda \mathbf{l} \tag{51}$$

along the axis of the dipole and out of the positive charged line, also

$$\Phi = \frac{1}{2\pi\varepsilon r^2} \, \mathbf{p} \cdot \mathbf{r} \tag{52}$$

The equipotential surfaces are cylinders with their axes parallel to the dipole line in the x-z-plane and all passing between the charged lines (see Fig. 12·7). The field vector **E** is given [Appendix 3, (38)] by

$$E_r = -\frac{\partial \Phi}{\partial r} = \frac{\lambda}{2\pi\varepsilon} \frac{l}{r^2} \cos\theta, \qquad E_\theta = -\frac{1}{r}\frac{\partial\Phi}{\partial\theta} = \frac{\lambda}{2\pi\varepsilon}\frac{l}{r^2}\sin\theta \tag{53}$$

so that the field lines are found by integrating

$$\frac{dr}{r \, d\theta} = \frac{E_r}{E_\theta} = \cot\theta$$

as the orthogonal family of circles $\sin\theta = kr$ with centers along the y-z-plane and all passing through the z-axis.

System of Parallel Thin Wires above Ground.   In a system of n parallel thin wires above ground as in Fig. 12·8, one can write the general relationship in accordance with (3·12)

$$\Phi_\alpha = s_{\alpha 1}\lambda_1 + s_{\alpha 2}\lambda_2 + \cdots + s_{\alpha n}\lambda_n \tag{54}$$

where Φ_α is the potential of the αth wire, $\lambda_1, \lambda_2, \cdots, \lambda_n$ are the individual line charge densities, and $s_{\alpha\beta}$ are the mutual potential coefficients which include the effect of the image. When the mutual distances are all large compared with the radii of all wires, these coefficients can readily be obtained by similar approximations, as used for (45). Thus, the effect of wire β and its image upon wire α is given by (29)

$$s_{\alpha\beta}\lambda_\beta = \frac{\lambda_\beta}{2\pi\varepsilon} \ln \frac{r_{\alpha\beta}'}{r_{\alpha\beta}} \tag{55}$$

where $r_{\alpha\beta}'$ is the distance from center of wire α to center of the *image* of β, whereas $r_{\alpha\beta}$ is the center distance of the two wires directly. For the self-coefficient one has

$$s_{\alpha\alpha}\lambda_\alpha = \frac{\lambda_\alpha}{2\pi\varepsilon} \ln \frac{2h_\alpha}{R_\alpha} \tag{56}$$

where h_α is the height above ground, $2h_\alpha$ the distance to the image of wire α, and R_α its radius. All the potential coefficients can readily be computed if the geometry is completely given.

By (3·13) and (3·11) one can also compute the mutual capacitance coefficients which, however, are always rather complicated expressions, since they must involve the complete determinant of the potential coefficients as well as the pertinent minors; in general,

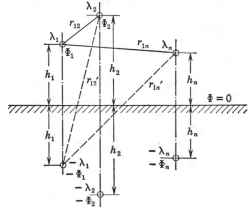

Fig. 12·8   System of Parallel Thin Wires above Ground.

no simplifications can be permitted. For two wires above ground forming a transmission system with $\lambda_1 = -\lambda_2 = \lambda$, one obtains, with the designations of Fig. 12·8 for the capacitance per unit length in the presence of ground,

$$C_1 = \frac{\lambda}{\Phi_1 - \Phi_2} = \frac{1}{s_{11} + s_{22} - s_{12} - s_{21}} = \frac{2\pi\varepsilon}{\ln\left(\dfrac{r_{12}^2}{R_1 R_2} \cdot \dfrac{4h_1 h_2}{r_{12}^2 + 4h_1 h_2}\right)} \quad (57)$$

Many special applications are found in the references listed in Appendix 4, B, a, as well as in Ollendorff,[A18] pp. 123–143.

Circular Ring of Charge. For a total charge Q uniformly distributed over a circular ring of radius a, the line density will be $Q/2\pi a$, and the potential is obtained by direct integration as in (1). Referring to Fig. 12·9, one can choose the point of observation $P(\rho, z)$ along the x-z-plane because of the axial symmetry. One then has the line element $ds = a\, d\phi$ and thus

$$\Phi = \frac{1}{4\pi\varepsilon}\frac{Q}{2\pi a}\int_{\phi=0}^{2\pi}\frac{a\, d\phi}{[(\rho - a\cos\phi)^2 + (a\sin\phi)^2 + z^2]^{1/2}}$$

Introducing the change of variables (Ollendorff,[A18] p. 101–104),

$$\cos \phi = 2 \sin^2 \beta - 1, \qquad d\phi = -2 \, d\beta$$

the integral reduces to the normal form

$$\Phi = \frac{Q}{4\pi\varepsilon} \cdot \frac{2}{\pi} \cdot \frac{1}{[(\rho + a)^2 + z^2]^{1/2}} \int_0^{\pi/2} \frac{d\beta}{[1 - k^2 \sin^2 \beta]^{1/2}} \quad (58)$$

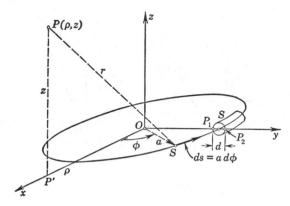

FIG. 12·9 Circular Ring of Charge.

of the complete elliptic integral[6] of the first kind $F\left(\dfrac{\pi}{2}, k\right) = K(k)$
with the modulus

$$k^2 = \frac{4\rho a}{(\rho + a)^2 + z^2} \quad (59)$$

A different treatment with an expansion into an infinite series of Legendre polynomials is given in Smythe,[A22] p. 137.

Along the axis $\rho = 0$, so that $k^2 = 0$, and since $K(0) = \pi/2$, one has

$$\Phi_{\rho=0} = \frac{Q}{4\pi\varepsilon} \frac{1}{\sqrt{a^2 + z^2}} \quad (60)$$

a result that can be obtained more simply by direct integration.

---

[6] See Jahnke and Emde: *Tables of Functions;* reprinted by Dover Publications, New York, 1943; originally published by B. G. Teubner, Leipzig, 1938. This reference contains also extensive tables and graphs of elliptic integrals and functions.

The field strength along the axis is

$$E_{z/\rho=0} = \frac{Q}{4\pi\varepsilon} \cdot \frac{z}{(a^2 + z^2)^{3/2}} \tag{61}$$

and has a maximum value at $z = a/\sqrt{2}$. Attwood,[A2] p. 65, gives a simple treatment and graph of the field distribution.

In order to permit a definition of capacitance, one has to substitute again a quasi line charge, i.e., admit a small but finite diameter $d \ll a$ of the charge distribution as indicated at S in Fig. 12·9. On the surface of this thin toroid k^2 approaches unity, so that it is more convenient to use the complementary modulus $k'^2 = 1 - k^2$, for which one obtains with (59)

$$k'^2 = 1 - k^2 = \frac{(\rho - a)^2 + z^2}{(\rho + a)^2 + z^2} \approx \left(\frac{d}{4a}\right)^2 \tag{62}$$

since the numerator is exactly the equation of the small cross-sectional circle; the simplification in the denominator is based on $\left(a - \dfrac{d}{2}\right) < \rho < \left(a + \dfrac{d}{2}\right)$ and $d \ll a$. The complete elliptic integral $K(k)$ can be expressed[7] in ascending powers of k'^2; using only the first term, $K(k) \approx \ln (4/k') = \ln (16a/d)$, and (58) becomes

$$\Phi_s \approx \frac{Q}{4\pi\varepsilon} \cdot \frac{2}{\pi} \cdot \frac{1}{2a} \ln \frac{16a}{d} \tag{63}$$

so that the capacitance of the thin circular ring of charge follows as

$$C = \frac{Q}{\Phi_s} = 4\pi\varepsilon \frac{\pi a}{\ln (16a/d)} \tag{64}$$

an approximation to better than 2 per cent for $d/a \leqslant 0.1$. Further details must be left for section 33, dealing with toroidal coordinates.

Circular Ring of Charge above Ground. The effect of ground can readily be replaced by that of the *image* ring of charge below ground, as indicated in Fig. 12·10. The potential value anywhere in space is the difference of two expressions obtained from (58), one with z replaced by $(z - h)$ and representing the contribution of the actual charged line; the other with z replaced

[7] Jahnke and Emde, *loc. cit.*, p. 73.

by $(z + h)$ and representing the contribution of the image. Thus

$$\Phi = \frac{Q}{4\pi\varepsilon} \frac{2}{\pi} \left\{ \frac{K(k_1)}{[(\rho + a)^2 + (z - h)^2]^{\frac{1}{2}}} \right.$$

$$\left. - \frac{K(k_2)}{[(\rho + a)^2 + (z + h)^2]^{\frac{1}{2}}} \right\} \quad (65)$$

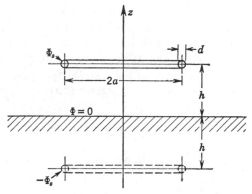

FIG. 12·10   Circular Ring of Charge above Ground.

where again $K(k_1)$ and $K(k_2)$ are the complete elliptic integrals of the first kind with

$$\left. \begin{array}{l} k_1{}^2 = \dfrac{4\rho a}{(\rho + a)^2 + (z - h)^2} \\[3mm] k_2{}^2 = \dfrac{4\rho a}{(\rho + a)^2 + (z + h)^2} \end{array} \right\} \quad (66)$$

From (65) one can also evaluate the field vector **E** by direct differentiation. In particular, one obtains for the charge density induced in the surface of ground for $z = 0$:

$$\sigma = \varepsilon E_{z/z=0} = - \frac{Q}{4\pi} \cdot \frac{2}{\pi} \frac{2h}{[(\rho + a)^2 + h^2]^{\frac{3}{2}}}$$

$$\left[K(k) - \frac{4\rho a}{(\rho - a)^2 + h^2} B(k) \right] \quad (67)$$

where $B(k)$ is the complete elliptic integral

$$B(k) = \int_0^{\pi/2} \frac{\cos^2\beta \, d\beta}{[1 - k^2 \sin^2 \beta]^{\frac{1}{2}}}$$

and where the modulus k is either k_1 or k_2 from (66) with $z = 0$. The expression (67) gives the charge distribution as a function of ρ and shows maximum value close to $\rho = a$, and a minimum at $\rho = 0$ of value

$$\sigma_{\rho=0} = -\frac{Q}{4\pi} \frac{2h}{(a^2 + h^2)^{3/2}}$$

For large values of h, this density becomes identical with the maximum density induced by a point charge at height h above ground as seen from (10·17).

The potential on the surface of the ring can be found by superposition as the sum of (63) and of the contribution of the image according to (58) if one replaces $\rho \approx a$, $z \approx 2h$. Thus,

$$\Phi_s = \frac{Q}{4\pi\varepsilon} \frac{2}{\pi} \left[\frac{1}{2a} \ln \frac{16a}{d} - \frac{1}{[(2a)^2 + (2h)^2]^{1/2}} K(k) \right] \qquad (68)$$

where now k^2 follows from (59) for the same values ρ and z

$$k^2 \approx \frac{4a^2}{(2a)^2 + (2h)^2} = \frac{1}{1 + (h/a)^2} \qquad (69)$$

From (68), the capacitance with respect to the image is directly $C = Q/\Phi_s$, whereas the capacitance to ground must be twice this value because only one half the potential difference exists between ring and ground.

13· LINE CURRENTS AND QUASI LINE CURRENTS

For currents concentrated in mathematical lines, the magnetic field **B** can be evaluated either by direct integration in accordance with (6·22)

$$\mathbf{B} = \frac{\mu}{4\pi} I \oint \frac{d\mathbf{s} \times \mathbf{r}}{r^3} \qquad (1)$$

or from the vector potential **A**, which itself is found by the line integral (6·21), namely,

$$\mathbf{A} = \frac{\mu}{4\pi} I \oint \frac{d\mathbf{s}}{r}, \qquad \mathbf{B} = \text{curl } \mathbf{A} \qquad (2)$$

In either case, only closed line integrals have physical significance, since steady currents can be maintained only in closed circuits.

Because of the concentration of the current in a mathematical line, both the vector potential **A** and the magnetic flux density **B** approach infinite values as one approaches the current line; this has also been pointed out in section 6. In order to avoid these infinite values, one usually substitutes quasi line currents, i.e., one admits finite and usually circular cross sections which are small compared with all other physical dimensions of the system. Within the conductor one assumes uniform current distribution and the same permeability μ as the surrounding medium, usually air.

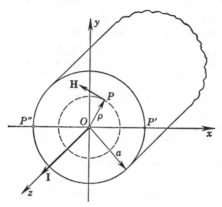

FIG. 13·1   Representative Cross Section of Quasi Line Current.

Proximity of Quasi Line Current.   If one concentrates on the immediate neighborhood of a straight conductor of small circular cross section with radius a, one may disregard the magnetic field effects of any other current carrying parts of the system if they are far removed; indeed, one can consider the piece of quasi line current as taken from a very long straight wire and consider it entirely by itself. Assume, as indicated above, uniform current density and therefore circular magnetic field lines concentric with the axis of the conductor, as in Fig. 13·1. Application of the line integral (6·3) to a field line within the conductor gives

$$2\pi\rho H_\phi' = \left(\frac{\rho}{a}\right)^2 I, \qquad H_\phi' = I\,\frac{\rho}{2\pi a^2} \qquad (3a)$$

whereas the same line integral along a field line outside the conductor gives

$$2\pi\rho H_\phi'' = I, \qquad H_\phi'' = \frac{I}{2\pi\rho} \qquad (3b)$$

On the surface of the conductor, continuity of H_ϕ is satisfied; it reaches there its largest value.

Since the magnetic intensity H_ϕ'' outside the wire decreases as $1/\rho$, the external magnetic flux linked with the total current over a length l of the wire

$$\Phi_m'' = \mu l \int_{\rho=a}^{\rho} H_\phi'' \, d\rho = \frac{\mu}{2\pi} lI \ln \frac{\rho}{a}$$

has no physical meaning unless the upper limit has a definite finite value. This serves to emphasize that only closed current loops can have physical significance, even though one has already avoided the infinities caused by line currents.

The necessity of considering only closed current loops brings with it the fact that the field as found in (3) will actually never exist in and near quasi line currents; there will strictly always be distortion caused by other parts of the system. If, however, the radius a is small enough, the actual field lines within the conductor will be so close to concentric circles that one can retain (3a) as a first-order approximation. This gives, then, for the internal magnetic field energy per unit length from (7·15)

$$W_{m1}^{(i)} = \frac{\mu}{2} \int_{\rho=0}^{\rho=a} \left(\frac{\rho}{2\pi a^2}\right)^2 I^2 2\pi\rho \, d\rho = \frac{1}{2} I^2 \frac{\mu}{8\pi} \qquad (4)$$

This yields by definition (7·5) the internal inductance per unit length

$$L_{i1} = \frac{\mu}{8\pi} \qquad (5)$$

independent of the radius of the conductor and the simplest expression obtainable for any shape of cross section.

Rectangular Current Loop. For a current loop of conductors of small cross section in the shape of the rectangle in Fig. 13·2 and fed in a manner as indicated in Fig. 7·1, one can evaluate the vector potential at a point $P(x, y, z)$ by performing the integration prescribed by (2) along the axis of the wire. Because the direction of **A** is the same as that of the element **ds**, one will generally have at P the component A_x contributed by the loop sides of length $2a$, and the component A_y by the loop sides of length $2b$. Therefore,

$$A_x = \frac{\mu}{4\pi} I \left[\int_{s=-a}^{s=+a} \frac{ds}{r'} - \int_{s=+a}^{s=-a} \frac{ds}{r'''} \right] \tag{6}$$

where

$$(r')^2 = (x - s)^2 + (y + b)^2 + z^2;$$

$$(r''')^2 = (x - s)^2 + (y - b)^2 + z^2 \tag{7}$$

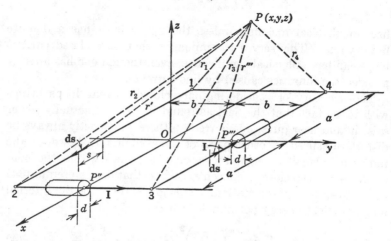

FIG. 13·2   Rectangular Current Loop.

The integrals are of elementary type and lead to

$$A_x = \frac{\mu}{4\pi} I \ln \left(\frac{r_1 + a + x}{r_2 - a + x} \cdot \frac{r_3 - a + x}{r_4 + a + x} \right) \tag{8}$$

where r_1, r_2, r_3, and r_4 are the distances from the point P to the individual vertices of the rectangle, respectively. Along the center plane $y = 0$, one has $r_1 = r_4$, and $r_2 = r_3$, so that $A_x = 0$. In similar manner, one finds

$$A_y = \frac{\mu}{4\pi} I \ln \left(\frac{r_2 + b + y}{r_3 - b + y} \cdot \frac{r_4 - b + y}{r_1 + b + y} \right) \tag{9}$$

From these expressions for the components of the vector potential one can readily deduce the field components by the second relation (2),

$$B_x = -\frac{\partial A_y}{\partial z}, \quad B_y = +\frac{\partial A_x}{\partial z}, \quad B_z = \frac{\partial A_y}{\partial x} - \frac{\partial A_x}{\partial y} \quad (10)$$

The indicated differentiations are very easily performed, since they are all of the type

$$\frac{\partial}{\partial u} \ln (r + k) = \frac{1}{r + k} \frac{\partial}{\partial u} (r + k) = \frac{u}{r(r + k)}$$

where u is either $(x \pm a)$, $(y \pm b)$, or z but is never contained in k. In the plane of the rectangle, $B_x = B_y = 0$ and

$$B_z = \frac{\mu}{4\pi} I \sum_{(\alpha)} (-1)^\alpha \frac{x_\alpha + y_\alpha - r_\alpha}{x_\alpha y_\alpha}, \qquad \alpha = 1, 2, 3, 4 \quad (11)$$

with $x_1 = x_4 = (x + a)$, $x_2 = x_3 = (x - a)$; $y_1 = y_2 = y + b$, $y_3 = y_4 = y - b$; and $r_\alpha = [x_\alpha^2 + y_\alpha^2]^{1/2}$. Obviously, B_z becomes infinitely large on the conductor loop.

In order to obtain the total inductance of the loop, the magnetic field is divided into external and internal regions. One computes the external magnetic flux as that fully linked with the loop current, which for small cross section is given by the integral

$$\Phi_m{}'' = \int_{x=-a+\frac{d}{2}}^{x=+a-\frac{d}{2}} dx \int_{y=-b+\frac{d}{2}}^{y=+b-\frac{d}{2}} B_z \, dy$$

where the limits are the innermost points of the loop conductor, as for example P'' and P''' in Fig. 13·2. Division by current I yields the external inductance

$$L_{\text{ex}} = \frac{2\mu_{\text{ex}}}{\pi} \left\{ 2\sqrt{a^2 + b^2} + a \ln \left(\frac{8a}{d}\right) + b \ln \left(\frac{8b}{d}\right) \right.$$

$$- 2(a + b) - a \ln \left(1 + \sqrt{1 + \left(\frac{b}{a}\right)^2}\right) \quad (12)$$

$$\left. - b \ln \left(1 + \sqrt{1 + \left(\frac{a}{b}\right)^2}\right) \right\}$$

To this one has to add the internal inductance, which with (5) is simply

$$L_i = 2(2a + 2b) L_{i_1} = \frac{\mu_i}{2\pi} (a + b)$$

where μ_i is the absolute permeability of the conductor material.

One can, of course, also evaluate the magnetic field directly by application of (1) rather than first determining the vector potential as in (2). Frequently, however, the integrations involved in (2) are simpler to perform than those in (1), and the differentiations are readily carried through. For a finite length of a straight wire, the computations of the magnetic field are given in many elementary books such as Attwood,[A2] p. 276, who also applies the results to a rectangular loop; Bennett and Crothers,[A3] p. 424; and Cullwick,[A6] p. 184. More general treatments are found in Hague,[B44] and particularly in Grover.[B43] It is important to observe that *inductance of a piece of wire* not forming a closed loop has *no meaning*, since the definition of external inductance rests upon that of magnetic flux through a defined area, and the current linking it.

Two Long Parallel Straight Line Currents. In transmission line problems, the approximate rectangular loops formed by the parallel wires permit the assumption $2a \gg 2b$, so that the contributions of the two small sides can be disregarded. Actually, in (8) one can approximate for $|x| \ll a$,

$$r_1 = [(x + a)^2 + (y + b)^2 + z^2]^{1/2} \approx + a\sqrt{1 + \left(\frac{\rho_1}{a}\right)^2}$$

where $\rho_1 = [(y + b)^2 + z^2]^{1/2}$ is the normal distance of P from the left wire; analogously one finds r_4 with $\rho_2 = [(y - b)^2 + z^2]^{1/2}$ taking the place of ρ_1. As a becomes *very* large, but $|x|$ remains small compared with a, the ratio $\dfrac{r_1 + a + x}{r_4 + a + x} \to 1$. On the other hand,

$$r_2 = [(x - a)^2 + (y + b)^2 + z^2]^{1/2} \approx + a\sqrt{1 + \left(\frac{\rho_1}{a}\right)^2}$$

and analogously for r_3; here, however, $\dfrac{r_3 - a + x}{r_2 - a + x} \to \left(\dfrac{\rho_2}{\rho_1}\right)^2$, so that (8) takes the form

$$A_x = \frac{\mu}{4\pi} I \ln \frac{(y - b)^2 + z^2}{(y + b)^2 + z^2} = \frac{\mu}{2\pi} I \ln \frac{\rho_2}{\rho_1} \tag{13}$$

where ρ_2 and ρ_1 are the normal distances of P from the wires and are the same radii as are designated r_2 and r_1, respectively, in Fig. 12·5. The same approximations yield at once $A_y = 0$ in (9), so that the magnetic field becomes *two-dimensional*, independent of distance x. With (10) and (13) one derives

$$B_y = + \frac{\partial A_x}{\partial z} = \frac{\mu}{2\pi} I \left[\frac{z}{\rho_2{}^2} - \frac{z}{\rho_1{}^2} \right] ;$$

$$B_z = - \frac{\partial A_x}{\partial y} = \frac{\mu}{2\pi} I \left[\frac{y+b}{\rho_1{}^2} - \frac{y-b}{\rho_2{}^2} \right] \quad (14)$$

It should be emphasized that this requires $|x| \ll a$, or, physically, that one keeps very far from the ends of the transmission line.

The field configuration can easily be evaluated, since the field lines are defined by

$$\frac{dy}{dz} = \frac{B_y}{B_z} = \frac{\dfrac{\partial A_x}{\partial z}}{-\dfrac{\partial A_x}{\partial y}}$$

or also

$$\frac{\partial A_x}{\partial z} dz + \frac{\partial A_x}{\partial y} dy = dA_x = 0, \qquad A_x = \text{cons} \quad (15)$$

If the magnetic field is *two-dimensional*, then a single component of the vector potential exists, and the lines $A = \text{cons}$ become the field lines. For the two parallel line currents, (13) indicates for the field lines $\rho_2/\rho_1 = \text{cons}$, or the *same* condition as found for the equipotential surfaces of two parallel, very long and uniformly charged lines following (12·29). Thus, magnetic and electrostatic field lines are the mutually orthogonal families of circles in Fig. 12·5.[1] This is *not* true for finite cross sections of the wires, though for very small cross sections, or quasi line currents, it can be assumed as a reasonable approximation.

The external inductance for two wires of small diameters d_1 and d_2 is obtained per unit length from the flux, which can be evaluated best by use of (6·23) applied to the rectangle *abcd* in Fig. 13·3,

$$\Phi_m = \oint \mathbf{A} \cdot \mathbf{ds} = \frac{\mu}{2\pi} I \left[\ln \frac{2b - \dfrac{d_1}{2}}{\dfrac{d_1}{2}} - \ln \frac{\dfrac{d_2}{2}}{2b - \dfrac{d_2}{2}} \right] \quad (16)$$

---

[1] Also Attwood,[A2] p. 269, for further details.

so that

$$L_{\mathrm{ex1}} \approx \frac{\mu_{\mathrm{ex}}}{\pi} \ln \frac{4b}{\sqrt{d_1 d_2}} \qquad (17)$$

since both d_1 and d_2 must be small compared with $2b$ to justify the use of the field produced by line currents.

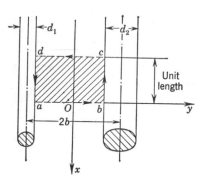

Fig. 13·3 External Flux of Two Long Parallel Quasi Line Currents.

The internal inductance is twice the value (5), once for each conductor. This same result is obtained by Smythe,[A22] p. 317, by using expression (7·13) for the field energy of two parallel conductors; the results are actually rigorous for any, even small, spacing $2b$ of the conductors as shown in (15·13).

Dipole Line Currents. If the distance $2b$ of the two parallel line currents decreases to very small values, one has the analogous case to that of the electrostatic dipole line. Again, one can then approximate as shown in Fig. 13·4 (analogous to Fig. 12·7)

$$\rho_1 \approx r + b \cos \phi, \qquad \rho_2 \approx r - b \cos \phi$$

so that the vector potential from (13) becomes, with $b \ll r$,

$$A_x = \frac{\mu}{2\pi} I \ln \frac{r - b \cos \phi}{r + b \cos \phi} \approx -\frac{\mu}{\pi} I \frac{b}{r} \cos \phi$$

The negative sign arises from the fact that the vector potential points in the same direction as the nearest current; for $y > 0$ and $z > 0$ the nearer current is in the negative direction in accordance with the Fig. 13·2, which underlies the expression (13). The magnetic field components are found as in (14) or, better, using the right-handed cylindrical coordinates r, ϕ, and x and Appendix 3, (37),

$$B_r = +\frac{1}{r} \frac{\partial A_x}{\partial \theta} = +\frac{\mu}{\pi} I \frac{b}{r^2} \sin \phi$$

$$B_\phi = -\frac{\partial A_x}{\partial r} = -\frac{\mu}{\pi} I \frac{b}{r^2} \cos \phi$$

The field lines are circles through the origin and are the orthogonal family to the electrostatic field lines if one considers the currents as representing electrostatically equal and opposite charged lines as in Fig. 12·7, but with reversed signs.

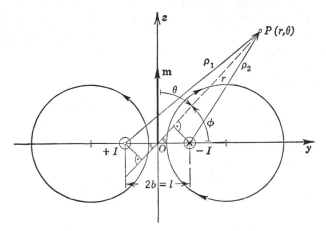

FIG. 13·4   Dipole Line Currents.

Changing to the complementary angle $\theta = \pi/2 - \phi$ permits the interpretation of A_x in terms of a vector product

$$\mathbf{A}_x = \frac{\mu}{2\pi} \frac{1}{r^2} \mathbf{m}_1 \times \mathbf{r} \tag{18}$$

where

$$\mathbf{m}_1 = I2b\mathbf{n} \tag{19}$$

is the magnetic dipole moment per unit length of the dipole current line, defined by the area of the loop per unit length times the current bordering it, and directed so that as seen from its tip the current flows counterclockwise.   The form (18) is very similar to the definition of the scalar electrostatic potential (12·52).   In fact, one could as well introduce the scalar magnetostatic potential function

$$\mathcal{F} = \frac{1}{2\pi} \frac{1}{r^2} \mathbf{m}_1 \cdot \mathbf{r}$$

from which the magnetic intensity components $\mathbf{H}_r$, $\mathbf{H}_\phi$ follow in exact analogy to the electrostatic field components (12·53).

Since the magnetic field components decrease as $1/r^2$, the dipole line currents represent a more local field than conductors with finite separation; use is made of this fact in bifilar windings.

Two Pairs of Long Parallel Line Currents. For each pair of parallel thin wires $1'2'$ and $1''2''$ (see Fig. 13·5) with currents I' and I'', respectively, the external vector potential is given by (13) and the respective self-inductance by (17), using the primed or the double-primed quantities from Fig. 13·5.

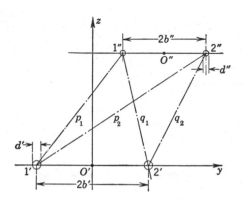

FIG. 13·5   Mutual Inductance of Two Pairs of Long Parallel Wires.

To obtain the mutual effect for thin wires, one can substitute in good approximation the total flux linked by the center filaments of the wires $1''2''$ and produced by the pair $1'2'$. Using the same method as in (16) and introducing the vector potential $A_x{'}$ from (13), with $\rho_2 = q_1$, $\rho_1 = p_1$ at the center of $1''$ and with $\rho_2 = q_2$, $\rho_1 = p_2$ at the center of $2''$, one has

$$\Phi_{\text{mutual}} = \frac{\mu}{2\pi} I' \left[\ln \frac{q_1}{p_1} - \ln \frac{q_2}{p_2} \right] = \frac{\mu}{2\pi} I' \ln \frac{q_1 p_2}{q_2 p_1} \qquad (20)$$

It is obviously possible to arrange the four wires in such a way that $q_1 p_2 = q_2 p_1$, so that no resultant mutual linkage exists, or that magnetic interference is avoided. Though this is feasible for rigid installations, the variable spacing of aerial transmission lines normally prevents utilization of this relation, and consequently recourse is taken to proper alternating transposition of the wires.[2]

[2] H. S. Osborne, *Trans. A.I.E.E.*, **37**, p. 897 (1918); Corbett,[B2] p. 30, and Appendices.

Relation (20) is then the basic relation for evaluating the "cross talk" or inductive interference of parallel pairs of thin wires.

The magnetic field lines are obtained from $A_x = $ cons, as in (15), where A_x is now the total vector potential at any point P in space,

$$A_x = \frac{\mu}{2\pi}\left[I' \ln \frac{\rho_2{}'}{\rho_1{}'} + I'' \ln \frac{\rho_2{}''}{\rho_1{}''} \right] \qquad (21)$$

with the ρ's designating the normal distances of the point P from the respective wires.   The geometry is very complex, depending on the current ratio in the two pairs of wires.

If linkage between the parallel wire pairs is desired, then (20) gives the useful mutual flux and the mutual inductance $M = \Phi_{\text{mutual}}/I'$, whereas the difference between self-inductance of one pair and this value M gives the leakage inductance in conformity with (7·7).

Systems of Long Parallel Straight Line Currents.   For any number n of parallel wires isolated from ground, the sum of all currents must be zero in order to constitute a physically possible system.   It now becomes necessary to distinguish between "wire currents" and "loop currents" in the sense that the former are the observed currents I_α in the individual wires, whereas the latter are the currents I_ν associated with the definition and measurement of flux linkages and therefore of inductances as in (7·10).   Since the inductances are geometric quantities, an accurate knowledge of the loop currents is not necessary for their evaluation;   any convenient temporary choice is satisfactory.   Thus, one can choose any four wires as a combination of two pairs and at once use the methods outlined above.

Since n wires can be arranged in $n' = \dfrac{n}{2}(n-1)$ different pairs or loops, and these n' loops again in $n'' = \dfrac{n'}{2}(n'-1)$ loop pairs, there will, in general, be $n'' = \tfrac{1}{8}(n+1)n(n-1)(n-2)$ different mutual loop inductances.   This number n'' includes loop pairs with one conductor in common, i.e., arrangements in three-conductor groups.   In Fig. 13·5, this latter case exists if $1''$ and $1'$ become identical and therefore $p_1 \rightarrow \dfrac{d'}{2}$, $q_1 \rightarrow \left(2b' - \dfrac{d'}{2} \right)$.

Thus, the mutual inductance is, from (20),

$$M = \frac{\mu}{2\pi} \ln \left(\frac{4b'}{d'} \cdot \frac{p_2}{q_2} \right) \tag{22}$$

where d' is the diameter of the common conductor.

In three-phase systems with $n = 3$ wires, $n' = 3$, and $n'' = 3$, there exist three loops and three mutual loop inductances, which in case of geometrical symmetry are identical and have $p_2 = q_2 = 2b'$. Many practical applications are found in Woodruff[B12] and Clarke.[B1]

With the same assumptions as discussed for two parallel straight line currents, the resultant external vector potential of the n wires can be written

$$A_x = -\frac{\mu}{2\pi} \sum_{\alpha=1}^{n} I_\alpha \ln \rho_\alpha \tag{23}$$

where the ρ_α are the normal distances from the point of observation P to the wire centers; the negative sign could be avoided by writing $\ln (1/\rho_\alpha)$ as in (13). The two-dimensional field distribution is again defined by (15), but its analytical interpretation is hardly feasible. The direct evaluation of the magnetic field has been shown in (5·9).

Circular Loop. Assume an ideal circular current produced by a wire loop with twisted leads as shown in Fig. 7·1, and disregard the effect of these leads. The circular current is then similar to the circular ring of charge in Fig. 12·9, and its vector potential can be found by direct integration

$$\mathbf{A} = \frac{\mu}{4\pi} I \oint \frac{d\mathbf{s}}{r}$$

$$= \frac{\mu}{4\pi} I \int_{\phi=0}^{2\pi} \frac{\mathbf{u}_1 a \sin \phi \, d\phi + \mathbf{u}_2 a \cos \phi \, d\phi}{[(\rho - a \cos \phi)^2 + (a \sin \phi)^2 + z^2]^{1/2}} \tag{24}$$

The first component is in the radial direction and is cancelled by the symmetrical element $(-\phi)$; the second component is tangential to the circle and, upon changing variables as in section 12 for the circular ring of charge, leads to

$$A_\phi = \frac{\mu}{2\pi\rho} I[(\rho + a)^2 + z^2]^{1/2} \left[(1 - \tfrac{1}{2} k^2) K(k) - E(k) \right] \tag{25}$$

where $K(k)$ and $E(k)$ are the complete elliptic integrals of first and second kinds,[3] respectively. The modulus k is the same as (12·59).

The magnetic field vector **B** is obtained by differentiation in the cylindrical coordinate system [Appendix 3, (37)]

$$B_\rho = -\frac{\partial A_\phi}{\partial z} = \frac{\mu}{2\pi} I \frac{z}{\rho} [(\rho + a)^2 + z^2]^{-\frac{1}{2}}$$
$$\left[-K(k) + \frac{a^2 + \rho^2 + z^2}{(a - \rho)^2 + z^2} E(k) \right] \tag{26}$$

$$B_z = \frac{1}{\rho}\frac{\partial}{\partial \rho}(\rho A_\phi) = \frac{\mu}{2\pi} I[(\rho + a)^2 + z^2]^{-\frac{1}{2}}$$
$$\left[+K(k) + \frac{a^2 - \rho^2 - z^2}{(a - \rho)^2 + z^2} E(k) \right]$$

with $B_\phi = 0$ because of the axial symmetry. The magnetic field lines are plane curves in the meridional planes and are defined by $B_\rho/B_z = d\rho/dz$, which leads with (26) to the total differential

$$\frac{\partial}{\partial \rho}(\rho A_\phi)\, d\rho + \frac{\partial}{\partial z}(\rho A_\phi)\, dz = d(\rho A_\phi) = 0$$

or to

$$(\rho A_\phi) = \text{cons} \tag{27}$$

as the simple *equation of field lines for axially symmetrical fields.* Thus, with (25), the field lines can be found numerically as oval-shaped closed curves surrounding the wire. A simple graph is given in Attwood, [2] p. 260; H. Lamb,[C22] p. 220, gives the analogous graph of a circular vortex line. Extensive tables of $(4\pi a B_z/\mu I)$ from (26) as functions of ρ/a and z/a have been computed by Blewett;[4] the Fig. 1 of this reference also gives graphs of the radial variation of B_z for three different values of z/a, which are utilized (same ref., p. 979) to locate two circular coils of different currents, such as to produce cancellation of their fields over a limited region, for use as flux coils in synchrotrons.

[3] See Jahnke and Emde: *Tables of Functions*, p. 73; reprinted by Dover Publications, New York, 1943.

[4] J. P. Blewett, *Jl. Appl. Phys.*, **18**, p. 968 (1947).

A general analytical treatment is given in Ollendorff,[A18] p. 111; in Smythe,[A22] pp. 266 and 270; and in Zworykin et al.,[B32] p. 472; the magnetic field B_z in the plane of the loop[5] where $z = 0$ is given in Cullwick,[A6] p. 140. Along the axis for $\rho = 0$, (26) reduces to

$$B_\rho = 0, \qquad B_z = \frac{\mu}{2} I \frac{a^2}{(a^2 + z^2)^{3/2}} \tag{28}$$

which can be found directly by use of (1); see Attwood,[A2] p. 226; Harnwell,[A9] p. 288; and Spangenberg,[B29] p. 400.

In order to evaluate the inductance of the loop, one has to admit a finite small diameter d, as in Fig. 12·9. The external inductance is then obtained by integration of A_ϕ along the innermost filament, for which $\rho = a - (d/2)$, $z = 0$, so that

$$L_{ex} = 2\pi\rho \frac{A_\phi}{I} = 2\mu a \left(1 - \frac{d}{4a}\right)\left[\left(1 - \frac{1}{2}k^2\right) K(k) - E(k)\right] \tag{29}$$

with k from (12·59) as

$$k = 2 \frac{\sqrt{a\left(a - \frac{d}{2}\right)}}{2a - \frac{d}{2}} \approx 1 - \left(\frac{d}{4a}\right)^2 \tag{30}$$

Since $d \ll a$, one changes advantageously to the complementary modulus k' as in (12·62); with $K(k) \approx \ln(4/k')$ as there, and $E(k) \approx 1$,[6] one obtains the much simpler expression (Smythe,[A22] p. 316; Ollendorff,[A18] p. 113)

$$L_{ex} \approx \mu a \left[\ln\left(\frac{16a}{d}\right) - 2\right] \tag{31}$$

The internal inductance is closely $(2\pi a)$ times the value given in (5).

Magnetic Dipole. For a very small circular loop, the denominator of (24) can be written

$$r_0 \left[1 - \frac{2a\rho}{r_0^2} \cos\phi\right]^{1/2}, \text{ if } r_0 = (\rho^2 + z^2)^{1/2} \gg a$$

The integral becomes, then, by expanding the square root bi-

---

[5] See also H. W. Reddick and F. H. Miller: *Advanced Mathematics for Engineers*, p. 137; John Wiley, New York, 1938.

[6] Jahnke and Emde, *loc. cit.*, p. 73.

nomially and taking the first two terms into the numerator,

$$A_\phi = \frac{\mu}{4\pi} I \int_{\phi=0}^{2\pi} \frac{a}{r_0} \cos \phi \left[1 + \frac{a\rho}{r_0^2} \cos \phi \right] d\phi \approx \frac{\mu a^2}{4r_0^2} I \frac{\rho}{r_0} \qquad (32)$$

Using spherical coordinates, $\rho/r_0 = \sin \theta$, and the magnetic field components are [Appendix 3, (41)]

$$\left. \begin{aligned} B_r &= \frac{1}{r \sin \theta} \frac{\partial}{\partial \theta} (A_\phi \sin \theta) = + \frac{\mu}{4\pi} a^2 \pi I \frac{2 \cos \theta}{r^3} \\ B_\theta &= - \frac{1}{r} \frac{\partial}{\partial r} (rA_\phi) = + \frac{\mu}{4\pi} a^2 \pi I \frac{\sin \theta}{r^3} \end{aligned} \right\} \qquad (33)$$

These magnetic field components have exactly the same form as the electric field components (10·35) describing the electric dipole, so that it is proper to identify the small circular current loop as the equivalent of the magnetic dipole, of *magnetic moment* $(a^2\pi I)$, which, as vector, points in the normal direction from which the current appears to flow counterclockwise,

$$\mathbf{m} = \mathbf{n}a^2\pi I \qquad (34)$$

The magnetic field lines are defined in accordance with (27) as

$$(\rho A_\phi) = \frac{\mu a^2}{4r_0} I \left(\frac{\rho}{r_0} \right)^2 = \frac{\mu}{4\pi} a^2 \pi I \frac{\sin^2 \theta}{r_0} = \text{cons}$$

which is identical with (10·36), indicating north and south magnetic quantities to be the equivalent of positive and negative charges (Fig. 10·6). One can, of course, now construct a scalar magnetic potential in analogy to (10·33), namely,

$$\mathcal{F} = \frac{\mu}{4\pi} (a^2\pi I) \frac{\cos \theta}{r_0^2} = \frac{\mu}{4\pi} \frac{1}{r^3} \mathbf{m} \cdot \mathbf{r} \qquad (35)$$

if one defines the magnetic moment as

$$\mathbf{m} = Q_m \mathbf{l} \qquad (36)$$

Q_m representing the magnetic north quantity, and $\mathbf{l}$ the center distance directed out of the north pole. Though this analogy is quite useful in certain respects, it is necessary to realize that magnetic quantity has not been perceptibly isolated and that its concept is a mathematical aid devoid of physical reality.

With the aid of the magnetic dipole concept one can also construct dipole layers as the equivalent of finitely large current loops. The alignment of the magnetic dipole in a uniform magnetic field B_0 is caused by a torque

$$\mathbf{T} = \mathbf{m} \times \mathbf{B}_0 \tag{37}$$

Good treatments of the magnetic dipole are given in Attwood,[A2] p. 219; in Smythe,[A22] p. 266; and in Stratton,[A23] p. 237.

Two Circular Loops. The magnetic effects of two circular loops are obtained by direct superposition of the individual vector potentials computed by (25) or of the magnetic fields computed by (26). The mutual linkage is readily obtained by application of (29), choosing A_ϕ as produced by one loop and integrating over the center line of the other loop.

For two coaxial circular loops, the computations are straightforward. If the loop radii are a' and a'' and their center distance h, then the mutual inductance is, from (25), with $\rho = a''$, $z = h$, and a replaced by a',

$$M = \mu\, 2\sqrt{a'a''} \cdot \frac{1}{k} \left[\left(1 - \frac{1}{2}\,k^2 \right) K(k) - E(k) \right] \tag{38}$$

where

$$k = 2\sqrt{a'a''}\, [(a' + a'')^2 + h^2]^{-\frac{1}{2}}$$

These forms,[7] as well as many others for arbitrary mutual location of circular loops,[8] are given in Grover,[B43] and in the form of series of Legendre polynomials also in Smythe,[A22] pp. 310–312. The mutual force action of coaxial loops is computed by Smythe,[A22] p. 277.[9] Simple field graphs are found[10] in Attwood,[A2] pp. 226 and 227.

14· SIMPLE SYSTEMS
OF DISTRIBUTED CHARGES

The simplest types of condenser arrangements are two parallel plates, two concentric cylinders, and two concentric spheres.

[7] S. Butterworth, *Phil. Mag.*, **31**, p. 4439 (1916); also *Scient. Papers Natl. Bur. of Stand.*, No. 320, 1918.

[8] See also *Proc. I.R.E.*, **32**, p. 620 (1944).

[9] For tabulated values, see Jahnke and Emde, *loc. cit.*, pp. 86–89.

[10] See also L. Fleischmann, *Arch. f. Elektrot.*, **21**, p. 31 (1929); Gianella, Revue gén. de l'élec., **22**, pp. 711 and 761 (1927).

Their treatment for a single dielectric is found in any of the references in Appendix 4, A; 4, B, a; and 4, B, b as for example in Attwood,[A2] pp. 68–78, and will, therefore, be very briefly summarized with the emphasis on the extensions to the less usual applications.

Parallel Plate Condenser. For infinitely large plates of potentials Φ_I and $\Phi_{II} < \Phi_I$ (see Fig. 14·1 with $\epsilon_1 = \epsilon_2$), the potential distribution must be linear in x and a homogeneous field gradient E exists,

$$\Phi = \Phi_I - \frac{x}{d}(\Phi_I - \Phi_{II}),$$

$$\text{(1)}$$

$$E_x = \frac{1}{d}(\Phi_I - \Phi_{II})$$

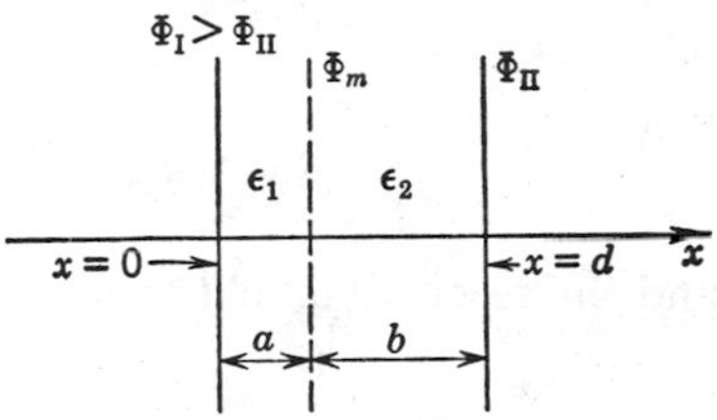

FIG. 14·1   Parallel Plate Condenser with Two Different Dielectrics.

Practical condensers are, of course, of finite size, so that field fringing would have to be taken into account (see section 27). However, if one surrounds the finite plates of arbitrary area S by

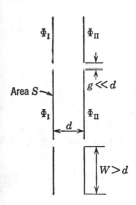

FIG. 14·2   Principle of Guard Rings for Parallel Plate Condenser.

guard rings of a width W considerably larger than the distance d and of the same potentials as the plates (see Fig. 14·2), then the field between the active condenser plates approximates the ideal plate condenser very closely as long as the gap $g \ll d$. In what follows, it will always be assumed that systems which would require infinite extension to be ideally simple are approximated by suitable guard arrangements. One can, of course, also assume one of the electrode potentials to be zero, which simplifies some of the expressions.

The ideal parallel plate condenser of finite area S and with a single dielectric of constant ϵ carries a total positive charge Q_I on plate I, which follows from the uniform charge density $\eta_I = +D_{x/x=0}$ with (1) as

$$Q_I = +\frac{\epsilon}{d}(\Phi_I - \Phi_{II})S \qquad \text{(2)}$$

The capacitance of the condenser is, therefore,

$$C = \frac{\varepsilon}{d} S \tag{3}$$

With *two different uniform dielectrics* separated by a plane parallel to the condenser planes, as shown in Fig. 14·1, the potential distribution in each dielectric is linear

$$\left.\begin{aligned} \Phi_1 &= \Phi_I - \frac{x}{a} (\Phi_I - \Phi_m) \\[2ex] \Phi_2 &= \Phi_m - \frac{x-a}{b} (\Phi_m - \Phi_{II}) \end{aligned}\right\} \tag{4}$$

and the respective field vectors are

$$E_{x1} = \frac{1}{a} (\Phi_I - \Phi_m), \qquad E_{x2} = \frac{1}{b} (\Phi_m - \Phi_{II}) \tag{5}$$

However, the potential value Φ_m is unknown and must be evaluated from the boundary conditions at the plane of separation in accordance with section 2. Continuity of the dielectric flux density (normal to the boundary surface) gives $\varepsilon_1 E_{x1} = \varepsilon_2 E_{x2}$, which leads with (5) to

$$\Phi_m = \frac{\varepsilon_1 b \Phi_I + \varepsilon_2 a \Phi_{II}}{\varepsilon_1 b + \varepsilon_2 a} \tag{6}$$

The significant and distressing aspect is the fact that the above boundary condition stipulates a higher field gradient for the dielectric material with lower constant ε (and generally lower dielectric strength) and vice versa, independent of the relative thicknesses. A slight air gap $a \ll b$ in series with a solid material will therefore be overstressed and will ionize if the field gradient in the solid is chosen as high as is permissible for it alone; the only recourse is the complete elimination of air and substitution by a good liquid insulator through some vacuum impregnation process; see Peek.[B15]

The charge on electrode I is again found from the uniform charge density $\eta_I = +D_{x1/x=0}$; the capacitance of the total condenser is then, with (5) and (6),

$$C = \frac{\varepsilon_1 E_{x1} S}{\Phi_I - \Phi_{II}} = \frac{\varepsilon_1 \varepsilon_2}{\varepsilon_1 b + \varepsilon_2 a} S = \frac{S}{\left(\dfrac{b}{\varepsilon_2} + \dfrac{a}{\varepsilon_1}\right)} \tag{7}$$

which can be interpreted as the series combination of the two partial condensers formed by assuming the boundary surface Φ_m to be a conducting surface. This is possible here because the surface happens to be equipotential. Should the boundary surface between the two dielectrics be of any arbitrary shape, then the field distribution would no longer be homogeneous and the potential function would become rather complex.

For $n > 2$ *dielectric slabs* with boundary surfaces parallel to the electrode surfaces, the same procedure can be followed; the capacitance can be given at once as the series combination of the n partial capacitances, since $\varepsilon_1 E_1 = \varepsilon_\alpha E_\alpha$, so that

$$\frac{1}{C} = \frac{1}{S} \sum_{\alpha=1}^{n} \frac{d_\alpha}{\varepsilon_\alpha} \qquad (8)$$

where d_α are the individual thicknesses, and ε_α the corresponding dielectric constants. The field strength in any one dielectric is found from (7) with (8)

$$E_\alpha = \frac{1}{\varepsilon_\alpha} (\Phi_I - \Phi_{II}) \left(\sum_{\alpha=1}^{n} \frac{d_\alpha}{\varepsilon_\alpha} \right)^{-1} \qquad (9)$$

and the potential value at any interface is the difference of Φ_I and $\sum d_\alpha E_\alpha$ up to that interface. The total sum $\sum_{\alpha=1}^{n} d_\alpha E_\alpha$ is, of course, the total potential difference.

In real dielectrics, where the electrical conductivities are not negligibly small, the boundary conditions require continuity of the current density, so that $\gamma_1 E_1 = \gamma_\alpha E_\alpha$ and the potential distribution is determined by the conductivities. There will then be surface charges on all the interfaces in accordance with (8·20).

Coaxial Cylinder Condenser. For infinitely long coaxial cylinders of potentials Φ_I and $\Phi_{II} < \Phi_I$, and of radii R_1 and R_2, respectively, and with a single dielectric, the potential varies logarithmically as for a single uniformly charged line in (12·28), so that

$$\Phi = \Phi_I - \frac{\ln r/R_1}{\ln R_2/R_1} (\Phi_I - \Phi_{II}), \qquad E_r = \frac{\Phi_I - \Phi_{II}}{r \ln R_2/R_1} \qquad (10)$$

Practical arrangements are, of course, of finite length, so that field fringing would have to be taken into account (see section 30). However, as in the parallel plate condenser, one can arrange guard electrodes—cylinders of same radii and same potentials spaced a gap $g \ll R_1$ from the test electrodes—which insure for these the ideal coaxial cylinder field; this procedure will be assumed throughout the remainder of this section, wherever precision requires it.

The ideal coaxial cylinder condenser of length L has a charge on the inner conductor $Q_I = 2\pi R_1 L D_{r=R_1}$, which gives with (10) a capacitance

$$C = \frac{Q_I}{\Phi_I - \Phi_{II}} = \frac{2\pi\varepsilon L}{\ln R_2/R_1} \tag{11}$$

Since the radial electric field strength is largest at the inner conductor, it represents the design criterion for test electrodes,[1] for coaxial cables, and for bushings; on the other hand, the outer radius R_2 defines the overall size. For a fixed value of R_2, the inner radius R_1 can be chosen so as to lead to the lowest possible value of $E_{r=R_1}$ by minimizing

$$E_{R_1} = \frac{\Phi_I - \Phi_{II}}{R_2} \cdot \frac{R_2/R_1}{\ln R_2/R_1} \tag{12}$$

with respect to the ratio $R_2/R_1 = \eta$. Actually,

$$\frac{d}{d\eta}\left(\frac{\eta}{\ln \eta}\right) = 0 \quad \text{for} \quad \eta = e \tag{13}$$

where $e = 2.718\cdots$ is the base of natural logarithms. Other considerations might alter slightly this optimum ratio, but few designs deviate significantly (see references in Appendix 4, B, a, and 4, B, b).

The stationary flow of heat between concentric cylinders of temperatures T_I and T_{II} also follows the relations (10) with appropriate use of the analysis pointed out in section 9. Thus, the total heat flow per unit length is given by

$$Q_{th} = \frac{2\pi k}{\ln R_2/R_1} (T_I - T_{II}) \tag{14}$$

where k is the thermal conductivity. In a cable in which the inner conductor carries a current I, and the outer conductor represents a protective sheath without current flow, Q_{th} must represent the heat generated by current I, or $Q_{th} = I^2 R$, where R is the electrical resistance of the inner conductor per unit length.

[1] Schwaiger,[B17] and A.S.T.M., *Tentative Standards for Oil Testing*, 1936.

If T_{II} is the given ambient temperature, and T_I selected as the maximum permissible temperature of the inner conductor in view of the adjacent insulation, one can deduce the maximum current rating I of the cable (the current-carrying capacity). The simultaneous electric and thermal stresses of the dielectric present the main problem in efficient cable design.

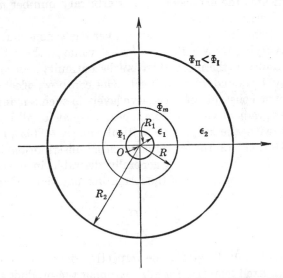

FIG. 14·3 Coaxial Cylinder Condenser with Two Different Dielectrics.

With *two different dielectrics* in concentric layers, as in Fig. 14·3, the potential distribution in each dielectric is given by (10) if appropriate substitutions are made for radii and potential values pertinent to the dielectric layers. The interface potential Φ_m is determined by the boundary condition $\varepsilon_1 E_1(r = R) = \varepsilon_2 E_2(r = R)$, or

$$\varepsilon_1 \frac{\Phi_I - \Phi_m}{R \ln R/R_1} = \varepsilon_2 \frac{\Phi_m - \Phi_{II}}{R \ln R_2/R}$$

which gives

$$\Phi_m = \frac{(\varepsilon_1 \ln R_2/R)\Phi_I + (\varepsilon_2 \ln R/R_1)\Phi_{II}}{\varepsilon_1 \ln R_2/R + \varepsilon_2 \ln R/R_1} \tag{15}$$

As in the plane case, the boundary condition dictates a discontinuity in radial electric field strength which tends to overstress electrically any air inclusions in bushings (see Peek,[B15] p. 316, and Karapetoff,[A11] p. 175). The overall capacitance of the condenser is the series combination of the partial capacitances of the two dielectric layers,

$$\frac{1}{C} = \frac{1}{2\pi L}\left(\frac{1}{\varepsilon_1}\ln\frac{R}{R_1} + \frac{1}{\varepsilon_2}\ln\frac{R_2}{R}\right) \tag{16}$$

which indicates the extension to any arbitrary number n of concentric dielectric layers.

As seen from (10), each dielectric layer has a non-uniform field gradient, varying from highest to lowest value in the ratio of the bounding radii; furthermore, there is a discontinuity at the interface imposed by the boundary conditions. One can, now, select the radii and dielectric constants of successive layers in such a manner that the largest gradient value becomes nearly equal for all layers and consistent with the respective critical values. This process of "uniformization" of the electric potential distribution is called *grading of insulation*[2] and is generally desirable in non-uniform fields for most efficient use of the insulating material. Combining (10) and (11), one has

$$E_r = \frac{Q_{\mathrm{I}}}{2\pi\varepsilon L r} \tag{17}$$

which holds in any layer for the respective dielectric constant ε, since Q_{I} is a fixed quantity for all. Keeping the product $\varepsilon \times r_{\min}$ for each layer to nearly the same value improves the electrical stress distribution markedly. As pointed out before, however, thermal considerations may force compromises which vary with the actual characteristics of insulators.

From (17), one can also deduce the principle of the condenser bushing[3] in which ε is kept constant, but where in the product (Lr) the length is stepped down inversely as the radius increases; this is achieved by means of auxiliary electrodes. Obviously, in the field distribution, fringing must be taken into account.

[2] H. S. Osborne: "Potential Stresses in Dielectrics," Dissertation at M.I.T., 1910; B. Hague, "Intersheath Stress," *Electrician*, **117**, pp. 161-163 (1936); Bennett and Crothers,[A3] p. 158; Schwaiger,[B17] p. 132; J. B. Whitehead, *Trans. A.I.E.E.*, **64**, p. 555 (1945).

[3] A. B. Reynders, *Jl. A.I.E.E.*, **28**, p. 209 (1909); C. L. Fortescue and J. E. Mateer, *Elec. Jl.*, **10**, p. 718 (1913); E. E. Spracklen, D. E. Marshall, and P. O. Langguth, *Trans. A.I.E.E.*, **47**, p. 684 (1928); H. J. Lingal, H. L. Cole, and T. R. Watts, *Trans. A.I.E.E.*, **62**, p. 269 (1943).

Concentric Sphere Condenser. For two ideally closed, concentric spheres of radii R_1 and R_2 and potentials Φ_I and $\Phi_{II} < \Phi_I$, the radial field distribution is essentially the same as for a single quasi point charge of section (11), so that with satisfaction of the boundary values

$$\left. \begin{array}{l} \Phi = \Phi_I - \dfrac{R_2}{R_2 - R_1}\left(1 - \dfrac{R_1}{r}\right)(\Phi_I - \Phi_{II}) \\[3mm] E_r = +\dfrac{R_1 R_2}{R_2 - R_1}\dfrac{1}{r^2}(\Phi_I - \Phi_{II}) \end{array} \right\} \tag{18}$$

In most practical cases, leads must be used to apply the potentials, and spacers are needed between the spheres to maintain concentricity; it is assumed that in first approximation at least these effects are negligible. It is also possible to use sections of spherical surfaces with appropriate guard surfaces as indicated for the cylindrical condenser.

The charge on the inner sphere is $Q_I = 4\pi R_1{}^2 D_{r=R_1}$, which gives with (18) the capacitance

$$C = 4\pi\varepsilon\frac{R_1 R_2}{R_2 - R_1} = 4\pi\varepsilon R_1 \frac{1}{1 - R_1/R_2} \tag{19}$$

For finitely closed surfaces, as for these concentric spheres, the capacitance value remains finite, even if the outer surface recedes to infinity. Since the radial electric field is strongest at the inner sphere, one can as for cylinders compute an optimum ratio R_2/R_1 for which the lowest value of $E_{r=R_1}$ exists with R_2 kept fixed. Minimizing

$$E_{R_1} = \frac{\Phi_I - \Phi_{II}}{R_2}\cdot\frac{\eta^2}{\eta - 1} \tag{20}$$

with respect to $\eta = R_2/R_1$ leads to

$$\frac{d}{d\eta}\left(\frac{\eta^2}{\eta - 1}\right) = 0 \quad \text{for} \quad \eta = 2 \tag{21}$$

with the optimum ratio of field strength values $E_{R_1}/E_{R_2} = (R_2/R_1)^2 = 4$. It is here, therefore, still more important than in cylindrical arrangements to introduce uniformization of the potential distribution. The processes are, of course, quite similar to the ones for coaxial cylinders except that it will rarely be possible to maintain the ideal condenser field.

15· SIMPLE SYSTEMS OF DISTRIBUTED CURRENTS

In many practical applications involving finite current densities, the permeability of the conductor can be assumed to be the same as that of the surrounding medium, usually air.   One can then evaluate by direct integration either the vector potential by $(6 \cdot 19)$ or the magnetic field by the generalized Biot-Savart law $(6 \cdot 22)$.

Single Long Conductor of Circular Cross Section.   Though this case was used in section 13, it is of value to set down the complete solution for later applications.   Assume for the moment a conductor of radius a and permeability μ_i and an external permeability μ_e; then the magnetic field vector is, from $(13 \cdot 3)$,

$$B_{\phi i} = + \frac{\mu_i}{4\pi} \frac{2r}{a^2} I, \qquad B_{\phi e} = \frac{\mu_e}{2\pi} \frac{1}{r} I \qquad (1)$$

if I is the total current uniformly distributed over the cross section, and r the variable distance from the axis.   Because of axial symmetry, the magnetic field lines are concentric circles, and the field depends only upon r.   It is desirable also to find the vector potential which can have only a component parallel to the current flow.

In cylindrical coordinates we have $B_\phi = - \dfrac{\partial A_z}{\partial r}$ from Appendix 3, (37), since all other components vanish.   One can, therefore, directly integrate and obtain

$$A_{zi} = - \frac{\mu_i}{4\pi} \left(\frac{r}{a}\right)^2 I + D_i, \qquad A_{ze} = - \frac{\mu_e}{2\pi} I \ln r + D_e \quad (2)$$

with D_i and D_e as integration constants.   The same result can be obtained by solution of the differential equation for the vector potential or by application of the integral $(6 \cdot 19)$, as in Smythe,[A22] p. 317, and Hague,[B44] p. 275.[1]   There is no unique way in determining the constants, since the general boundary conditions $(6 \cdot 7)$ and $(6 \cdot 10)$ apply only to the magnetic field.   Assuming continu-

---

[1] But see also discussion and correction: T. J. Higgins, *Electr. Engg.*, **59**, p. 246 (1940) and B. Hague, *Electr. Engg.*, **59**, p. 479 (1940).

ity of the vector potential according to $(6 \cdot 20)$, so that $A_{zi} = A_{ze}$ at $r = a$, one has from (2)

$$- \frac{\mu_i}{4\pi} I + D_i = - \frac{\mu_e}{2\pi} I \ln a + D_e \qquad (3)$$

Now, there is equally no reason why the additive constant D_i should contain μ_e, nor why D_e should contain μ_i, so that the most reasonable choice appears to be

$$D_i = \frac{\mu_i}{4\pi} I + A_0, \qquad D_e = \frac{\mu_e}{2\pi} I \ln a + A_0 \qquad (4)$$

where A_0 is an arbitrary constant which can as well be taken $A_0 = 0$ unless convenience suggests otherwise. One thus has (slightly at variance with above references)

$$A_{zi} = \frac{\mu_i}{4\pi} \left[1 - \left(\frac{r}{a} \right)^2 \right] I, \qquad A_{ze} = \frac{\mu_e}{2\pi} I \ln \frac{a}{r} \qquad (5)$$

The magnetic field lines are obtained by letting $A_z = \text{cons}$, which defines concentric circles inside and outside the conductor.

Two Parallel Long Conductors of Circular Cross Sections. Since normally no perceptible magnetic interaction of steady currents, disturbing the uniform current distributions, occurs, the individual solutions of the magnetic field for the single conductors can be superimposed everywhere in space. This is quite at variance with the electrostatic case and destroys many analogies.

Outside of both conductors the resultant magnetic field is (see Fig. $15 \cdot 1$) the vectorial combination of the individual fields given by (1) and in accordance with $(5 \cdot 3)$

$$\mathbf{B}'' = \frac{\mu}{2\pi} \left(\frac{1}{r_1^2} \mathbf{I}_1 \times \mathbf{r}_1 + \frac{1}{r_2^2} \mathbf{I}_2 \times \mathbf{r}_2 \right) \qquad (6)$$

i.e., it is the same as for two line currents concentrated *along the axes* of the conductors! For equal and opposite currents, therefore, the magnetic field lines outside the conductors will be the family of eccentric circles described in section 13; however, these field lines will now *not* be orthogonal to the electrostatic field lines, or be identical with the electrostatic equipotential lines, which are circles generated by two equivalent charged lines (see section 12) *not identical with the axes* of the conductors; see Attwood,[A2] p. 272. Only if the radii of the conductors are very small compared with distance can the approximation be made, identifying the magnetic field lines with electrostatic equipotential lines.

Within conductor 1, provided $\mu_1 = \mu_2 = \mu$, the resultant field is

$$\mathbf{B}_1' = \frac{\mu}{2\pi}\left(\frac{1}{R_1{}^2}\,\mathbf{I}_1{\times}\mathbf{r}_1 + \frac{1}{r_2{}^2}\,\mathbf{I}_2{\times}\mathbf{r}_2\right) \tag{7}$$

If the two currents are equal and opposite, so that $I_1 = -I_2 = I$,

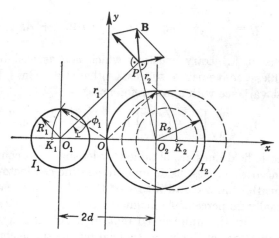

FIG. 15·1   Two Parallel Conductors of Circular Cross Sections.

there exists a point K_1 on the x-axis at which $B_1' = 0$, namely, at

$$\frac{\mu}{2\pi}I\left(\frac{r_1}{R_1{}^2} - \frac{1}{2d + r_1}\right) = 0, \qquad r_1 = \sqrt{d^2 + R_1{}^2} - d \tag{8}$$

as indicated in Fig. 15·1.   The point K_1 is called the *kernel* of conductor 1; it is also called the convergence center of the resultant field lines within conductor 1.   The geometry of the field lines is best obtained by means of the vector potential within 1, which follows from (5) as

$$A_{z1} = \frac{\mu}{2\pi}I\left\{\frac{1}{2}\left[1 - \left(\frac{r_1}{R_1}\right)^2\right] - \ln\frac{R_2}{r_2}\right\} \tag{9}$$

In the cylindrical coordinates r_1, ϕ_1 of conductor 1 one can express

$$r_2 = [(2d)^2 + r_1{}^2 - 4dr_1\cos\phi_1]^{\frac{1}{2}}$$

so that $A_{z1} = $ cons gives

$$-\left(\frac{r_1}{R_1}\right)^2 + \ln\left[1 + \left(\frac{r_1}{2d}\right)^2 - \frac{r_1}{d}\cos\phi_1\right] = \text{cons} \qquad (10)$$

taking all constant terms inclusive of $\ln(2d/R_2)$ on the right-hand side. Obviously, for $d \to \infty$, the concentric field lines of the single conductor result. If d is reasonably large, or also in the neighborhood of the kernel K_1, where r_1 is small, one can approximate $\ln(1 + u) \approx u$, and thus obtain from (10)

$$r_1{}^2\left[\frac{1}{R_1{}^2} - \frac{1}{(2d)^2}\right] + \frac{r_1}{d}\cos\phi_1 = \text{cons}$$

This is the equation of circles with centers at $\left[\dfrac{1}{2d}\Big/\left(\dfrac{1}{R_1{}^2} - \dfrac{1}{(2d)^2}\right)\right] \to \dfrac{R_1{}^2}{2d}$, which is the location of the kernel if one admits the same degree of approximation in (8). The magnetic field lines in conductor 1 (and similarly in conductor 2) start out, therefore, as circles near the kernel, then become deformed into oval-shaped curves, which, upon meeting the boundary surface, continue outside as eccentric circles. Figure 15·1 shows two accurately computed field lines as illustrations; Attwood[A2] gives other illustrations, pp. 272, 393.

The total inductance of two very long conductors forming a rectangular loop can be found per unit length by direct application of (7·1) and (7·2)

$$L_1 = \frac{\Lambda}{I} = \frac{1}{I^2}\left[\iint J_1 A_{z1}\, dS_1 + \iint J_2 A_{z2}\, dS_2\right] \qquad (11)$$

where $J_1 = +I/\pi R_1{}^2$ and $dS_1 = r_1\, dr_1\, d\phi_1$ are current density and cross-section element of conductor 1, and J_2, dS_2 correspondingly for conductor 2. If one observes (see No. 523 in B. O. Peirce: *A Short Table of Integrals*, Ginn & Co., Boston, 1929)

$$\int_0^\pi \ln\left[1 + \left(\frac{r_1}{2d}\right)^2 - \frac{r_1}{d}\cos\phi_1\right] d\phi_1 = 0 \qquad (12)$$

the integrations in (11) with (9) and its equivalent for conductor 2 are readily evaluated, leading to

$$L_1 = \frac{\mu}{\pi}\left[\ln\frac{2d}{\sqrt{R_1 R_2}} + \frac{1}{4}\right] \qquad (13)$$

which is identical with the form derived in section 13 as approximation for two wires at large distance $2d$. The exact form is given by Smythe,[A22] p. 318; Russel,[B11] p. 85, gives the corresponding expression for two parallel hollow cylindrical conductors. The appearance of the simple logarithmic terms in the final result led Maxwell[A17] to the definition of the "geometric mean distance" D of a finite cross section S from a point P

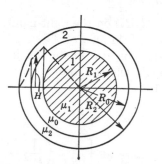

FIG. 15·2   Coaxial Cylindrical Conductors.

$$S \ln D = \iint (\ln r) \, dS \qquad (14a)$$

where r is the distance of the element dS from P, and the integration is performed over the entire cross section. The extension to the geometric mean distance of two areas S_1 and S_2 with respect to each other gives similarly

$$S_1 S_2 \ln D = \iint dS_2 \iint (\ln r) \, dS_1 \qquad (14b)$$

where r is now the mutual distance of the two section elements dS_1 and dS_2; these integrals can be related to inductance calculations.[2]   Because of (12), circular cross sections lead to particularly simple results.

Coaxial Cylindrical Conductors.   In order to provide a two-conductor system with no external magnetic effects, one can use a coaxial cable or pair of conductors, as shown in Fig. 15·2, carrying currents $I_1 = -I_2 = I$. The magnetic field within the inner conductor and between the two conductors is the same as given in (1) with appropriate changes in notation:

$$B_{\phi 1} = \frac{\mu_1}{4\pi} \frac{2r}{R_1{}^2} I, \qquad B_{\phi 0} = \frac{\mu_0}{2\pi} \frac{1}{r} I \qquad (15a)$$

The field in the outer conductor is

$$B_{\phi 2} = \frac{\mu_2}{2\pi r} \left[I - \frac{r^2 - R_0{}^2}{R_2{}^2 - R_0{}^2} I \right] = \frac{\mu_2}{2\pi} \frac{1}{r} \frac{R_2{}^2 - r^2}{R_2{}^2 - R_0{}^2} I \qquad (15b)$$

[2] See Woodruff[B12] and Clarke[B1].

reducing to zero at $r = R_2$; Fig. 15·2 indicates the variation of the field as a function of radius r.

The total inductance of the cable per unit length can best be computed from the magnetic field energy in terms of the field vectors as outlined in (7·15). Since $HB = (1/\mu)B^2$, one can use relations (15) directly for the respective zones and obtains the result

$$L_1 = \frac{2W_m}{I^2} = \frac{1}{2\pi}\left\{\frac{\mu_1}{4} + \mu_0 \ln \frac{R_0}{R_1}\right.$$

$$\left. + \frac{\mu_2}{R_2{}^2 - R_0{}^2}\left[\frac{R_2{}^4}{R_2{}^2 - R_0{}^2}\ln\frac{R_2}{R_0} - \frac{1}{4}(3R_2{}^2 - R_0{}^2)\right]\right\} \quad (16)$$

If $R_2 < 1.25R_0$, the contribution of conductor 2 can be approximated by $\mu_3\dfrac{R_2 - R_0}{3R_0}$; assuming also the permeabilities of all three regions to be the same, one has the much simpler form

$$L_1 = \frac{\mu}{2\pi}\left\{\frac{1}{4} + \ln\frac{R_0}{R_1} + \frac{R_2 - R_0}{3R_0}\right\} \quad (17)$$

as found in Breisig,[A4] p. 161; Russel,[B11] p. 83, derives the inductance of two coaxial hollow cylinders and then reduces to the solid inner conductor.[3]

Long Thin Rectangular Bars. For many practical applications it is permissible to approximate bus bars as very thin ribbons of rectangular cross section, as in Fig. 15·3; the advantage will be apparent in the next subsection, where the finite rectangular cross section will be treated. For infinitesimal thickness the current is distributed in a current sheet of uniform density $K_z = I/2h$ and the vector potential can be evaluated by the second part of (6·19),

$$A_z = \frac{\mu}{4\pi}\iint \frac{K_z}{r}\,dy'\,dz' \quad (18)$$

where $r = [x^2 + (y - y')^2 + (z - z')^2]^{\frac{1}{2}}$, y' varies over the width $2h$, and z' over the infinite length of the conductor. The integral in z' leads to $(-2\ln r')$, with r' the perpendicular distance of P from the filament dy' as in the case of the very long

---

[3] T. J. Higgins, *Trans. A.I.E.E.*, **64**, p. 385 (1945) gives an appraisal of existing literature.

straight line current (section 13); indeed, $(K_z \, dy')$ could have been considered directly as a straight filament. The further integration involves

$$\int \ln (x^2 + u^2) \, du = u \ln (x^2 + u^2) - 2u + 2x \tan^{-1} \frac{u}{x}$$

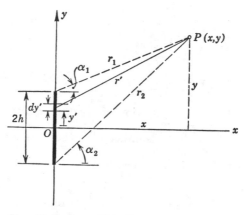

FIG. 15·3   Long Thin Rectangular Bus Bar.

with $u = (y - y')$. Introducing the lower limit $u_1 = y + h$ and the upper limit $u_2 = y - h$, one has

$$A_z = + \frac{\mu}{2\pi} \frac{I}{2h} \left\{ (y - h) \ln \frac{r_1}{h} - (y + h) \ln \frac{r_2}{h} + x(\alpha_1 - \alpha_2) \right\} \quad (19)$$

where r_1, α_1 and r_2, α_2 are the values designated in Fig. 15·3; the constant value $[4h(1 - \ln h)]$ has been added in the brackets in order to make $A_z = 0$ at $x = y = 0$, though this is strictly arbitrary. The vector potential is finite at all finite points, and $A_z =$ cons defines the magnetic field lines which are very nearly ellipses near the origin; they become practically circles far from the bar, because then $\alpha_1 \approx \alpha_2$, $r_1 \approx r_2 \approx r_0$, where r_0 is the distance of P from the origin.[4]

The magnetic field vector is obtained by differentiation of the vector potential, and, with the simplifying notation from Fig. 15·3,

[4] H. B. Dwight, *Electr. Rev.*, **70**, p. 1087 (1917); A. R. Stevenson and R. H. Park, *Gen. Elec. Rev.*, **31**, p. 159 (1928); also Hague,[B44] p. 283.

can be brought into the useful forms

$$B_x = -\frac{\partial A_z}{\partial y} = -\frac{\mu}{2\pi}\frac{I}{2h}\ln\frac{r_2}{r_1}$$

$$B_y = -\frac{\partial A_z}{\partial x} = +\frac{\mu}{2\pi}\frac{I}{2h}(\alpha_2 - \alpha_1)$$

(20)

These expressions can form the basis of graphical field analysis for two-dimensional fields (see section 20) and can readily be used for the evaluation of force actions between bus bars.[5]

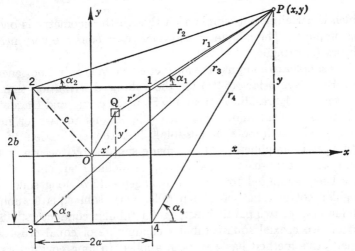

FIG. 15·4   Long Conductor of Rectangular Cross Section.

Long Conductors of Rectangular Cross Section. For finite rectangular cross section, as in Fig. 15·4, the vector potential A_z can be written

$$A_z = -\frac{\mu}{2\pi}\frac{I}{4ab}\iint \ln r'\, dx'\, dy'$$

where $r' = [(x - x')^2 + (y - y')^2]^{1/2}$, and the integration extends over the entire cross section; here, $I\,dx'\,dy'/4ab$ can be considered a straight filament in accordance with (13·23). The in-

[5] H. B. Dwight, *Electr. World*, **70**, p. 522 (1917); Stevenson and Park, *loc. cit.*; also Hague,[B44] p. 337; E. Weber, *Wiss. Veröff. a. d. Siemens-Konzern*, **8**, p. 166 (1929).

tegrations give,[6] with the designations of Fig. 15·4,

$$
\begin{aligned}
A_z = - \frac{\mu}{2\pi} \cdot \frac{I}{4ab} & \left\{ (x-a)(y-b) \ln \frac{r_1}{c} - (x+a)(y-b) \ln \frac{r_2}{c} \right. \\
& + (x+a)(y+b) \ln \frac{r_3}{c} - (x-a)(y+b) \ln \frac{r_4}{c} \\
& + \frac{1}{2} \left[(x-a)^2(\alpha_1 - \alpha_4) + (x+a)^2(\alpha_3 - \alpha_2) \right. \\
& \left. \left. + (y-b)^2 \cdot (\alpha_1 - \alpha_2) + (y+b)^2(\alpha_3 - \alpha_4) \right] \right\}
\end{aligned}
\tag{21}
$$

which is certainly not simple even though the geometry is one of the simplest. The magnetic field lines $A_z = $ cons are very nearly ellipses (see Hague,[B44] p. 281).

It is simpler to compute the magnetic field vector by the generalized Biot-Savart law (6.25) for the volume distribution than to differentiate A_z; results are found in Strutt, *loc. cit.*, and Hague[B44] Extension of field and inductance calculations to two or more rectangular conductors is possible,[7] but the evaluation of inductances is simplified—but not made simple—by the use of the geometric mean distances (GMD), as defined in (14), which have been computed for several arrangements of long solid rectangular conductors,[8] of two parallel very thin square tubular conductors,[9] of two parallel rectangular tubular conductors,[10] and also of two coaxial square tubular conductors of equal cross sections;[11] this method has also been applied to long conductors of structural shape.[12] By utilizing complex function theory, in particular some elements of conformal mapping, the multiple integrals in (14b) can be simplified.[13]

[6] M. Strutt, *Arch. f. Elektrot.*, **17**, p. 533, and **18**, p. 282 (1928); Hague,[B44] p. 280; A. H. M. Arnold, *Jl. I.E.E.*, **70**, p. 579 (1931).

[7] H. B. Dwight, *Elec. Jl.*, **16**, p. 255 (1919); Ed. Roth, *Revue gén. de l'elect.*, **44**, p. 275 (1938).

[8] E. B. Rosa, *Bull. Natl. Bur. of Stand.*, **3**, p. 1 (1907); T. J. Higgins, *Jl. Appl. Phys.*, **14**, p. 188 (1943); H. B. Dwight, *Trans. A.I.E.E.*, **65**, p. 536 (1946).

[9] H. B. Dwight and T. K. Wang, *Trans. A.I.E.E.*, **57**, p. 762 (1938).

[10] T. J. Higgins, *Trans. A.I.E.E.*, **60**, p. 1046 (1941).

[11] H. P. Messinger and T. J. Higgins, *Trans. A.I.E.E.*, **65**, p. 328 (1945).

[12] T. J. Higgins, *Trans. A.I.E.E.*, **62**, p. 53 (1943) and **65**, p. 893 (1946).

[13] T. J. Higgins, *Trans. A.I.E.E.*, **66**, p. 12 (1947).

The force actions between conductors of solid rectangular cross sections can be computed by direct integration of the forces between very thin rectangular bars,[14] as has been borne out by experimental measurements.[15] Similar computations were made for conductors of structural shape.[16]

Cylindrical Coils. Consider a helical current filament as shown in Fig. 15·5, starting at A in the x-z-plane and forming an integral number N of turns of radius a and pitch p. A point P on this helix is then defined by

$$x = a \cos \phi, \qquad y = a \sin \phi,$$

$$z = a\phi \tan \alpha$$

if ϕ is counted from A, and if $\tan \alpha = p/2\pi a$, with α the slope; the line element ds at P has the components

$$dx = -a \sin \phi \, d\phi,$$

$$dy = +a \cos \phi \, d\phi,$$

$$dz = a \tan \alpha \, d\phi$$

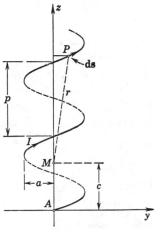

FIG. 15·5   Helical Current Filament.

In order to find the magnetic field at any point M on the axis, at a distance c from the origin in the plane of A, one best uses the generalized Biot-Savart law (6·22). For the axial component, observing that the radius vector $\mathbf{r}$ is directed from the current element to point M, this gives

$$B_z = \frac{\mu}{4\pi} I \int \frac{-y \, dx + x \, dy}{[x^2 + y^2 + (z-c)^2]^{3/2}}$$

$$= \frac{\mu}{4\pi} I \int_{\phi=0}^{\phi=N2\pi} \frac{d\phi}{a[1 + (\phi \tan \alpha - c/a)^2]^{3/2}} \qquad (22)$$

With the substitution $u = (\phi \tan \alpha - c/a)$, the integral can be easily evaluated. It simplifies further to use $p = 2\pi a \tan \alpha$, and

[14] O. R. Schurig and M. F. Sayre, *Jl. A.I.E.E.*, **44**, p. 365 (1925); also Hague,[B44] p. 338.

[15] C. J. Barrow, *Trans. A.I.E.E.*, **30**, p. 392 (1911).

[16] T. J. Higgins, *Trans. A.I.E.E.*, **62**, p. 659 (1943) and **63**, p. 710 (1944).

to measure the distance of M from the center of the helix as $b = (N/2)p - c$; the result is

$$B_z = \frac{\mu}{2}\frac{I}{p}\left[\frac{Np/2 + b}{[a^2 + (Np/2 + b)^2]^{1/2}} + \frac{Np/2 - b}{[a^2 + (Np/2 - b)^2]^{1/2}}\right] \quad (23)$$

At the center of the helix $b = 0$ and

$$B_{z0} = \frac{\mu}{2}\frac{NI}{[a^2 + (Np/2)^2]^{1/2}} = \mu\frac{I/p}{[1 + (2a/Np)^2]^{1/2}} \quad (24)$$

which reduces for an infinitely long coil to the uniform value $\mu I/p = \mu H_z$. The field along the axis has in the general case of the short coil also components in x- and y-directions and is not completely axially symmetrical because of the helical pitch. Smythe,[A22] p. 272, indicates the evaluation of these components;[17] more details are found in Grover[B43].

As $\alpha \rightarrow 0$, the pitch p also approaches zero. One can obtain, however, the field of a uniform cylindrical current sheet from (23), if one defines $Np/2 = l$ with $2l$ designating the length of the coil. Because of the symmetry, B_z is now the only component and (24) gives its value at the center of the helix as

$$B_z = \frac{\mu NI}{2(a^2 + l^2)^{1/2}} \quad (25)$$

For $l \gg a$, a long coil, this reduces to $B_{z0} = \mu NI/2a$, given in many references; for the simpler treatment, see Attwood,[A2] p. 263; Bennett and Crothers,[A3] p. 457; Mason and Weaver,[A16] p. 208; Maxwell,[A17] II, p. 310; Harnwell,[A9] p. 288; Cullwick,[A6] p. 142; and Stratton,[A23] p. 232.

For this latter case, particularly for closely wound cylindrical coils, inductance calculations have been made; they establish the linkage between one of the circular loops with another and integrate over the length of the coil, avoiding infinities by assuming finite, but small, radius of the wire. The integrals become elliptic, as in section 14, and can also involve Bessel functions. See Russell,[B11] pp. 108, 113, but particularly Grover[B43] and Rosa and Grover.[18] The same method is directly applicable to the computation of the mutual inductance and force actions of two

[17] See also A. Russell, *Proc. Phys. Soc. London*, **20**, p. 476 (1907).
[18] E. B. Rosa and F. W. Grover, *Bull. Natl. Bur. of Stand.*, **8**, p. 1 (1912).

very thin coaxial coils,[19] as well as to coils of rectangular cross section, either coaxial or parallel.[20] For a single coil of small but finite cross section, specific simplifications are possible in evaluating the magnetic field, which are valuable for search coils and similar applications.[21]

In some applications, particularly where magnetic effects are to be observed on particles or sample materials, it is important to have a closely uniform magnetic field over a given volume. One can compute, then, the necessary arrangement of windings of non-uniform coils.[22]

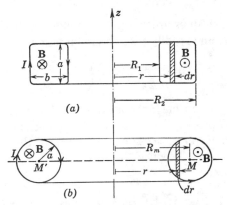

FIG. 15·6 Toroidal Coil: (a) rectangular cross section, (b) circular cross section.

Toroidal Coil. A toroidal core of magnetic material of permeability μ can be wound with wire ideally so that the winding represents a uniform current sheath circulating about the core in meridional planes as in Fig. 15·6. In this ideal case, the magnetic field is entirely confined within the core, the magnetic field lines are concentric circles about the z-axis, and each line links with the entire current volume, which might be called $2\pi R_1 K_1 = 2\pi R_2 K_2 = NI$, if there are N idealized turns each carrying the current I. The magnetic flux density is then, irrespective of the cross section

[19] T. H. Havelock, *Phil. Mag.*, (6), **15**, p. 332 (1908).

[20] H. B. Dwight: *Electrical Coils and Conductors, Their Characteristics and Theory*, McGraw-Hill, New York, 1945; see also Grover[B43] and Hak[B45].

[21] H. B. Dwight and G. O. Peters, *Trans. A.I.E.E.*, **63**, p. 684 (1944).

[22] L. W. McKeehan, *Rev. Scient. Instr.*, **7**, p. 150 (1936) and **19**, p. 475 (1948); J. Hak, *Arch. f. Elketrot.*, **30**, p. 736 (1936).

of the core, given by the value of its line integral along a circle

$$2\pi r B_\phi = \mu NI \tag{26}$$

This means that B_ϕ varies inversely as the distance from the z-axis so that the magnetic flux is not uniformly distributed over the cross section of the core.

For the rectangular cross section in Fig. $15 \cdot 6a$ one can find the flux linkages by direct integration in simple manner,

$$\Lambda = N \int_{R_1}^{R_2} B_\phi a \, dr = \frac{\mu}{2\pi} N^2 Ia \ln \frac{R_2}{R_1} \tag{27}$$

since all the field lines are completely linked with all the N turns. Dividing by I, one readily gets the inductance

$$L = \frac{\mu}{2\pi} N^2 a \ln \left(1 + \frac{b}{R_1}\right)$$

Only for $b \ll R_1$ can one approximate the logarithm by b/R_1 and thus express L proportionally to the cross-sectional area.

For the circular cross section in Fig. $15 \cdot 6b$, the integration is a little more involved because the height of the individual slice dr is variable, namely,

$$\Lambda = N \int_{R_m-a}^{R_m+a} B_\phi \, 2[a^2 - (R_m - r)^2]^{1/2} \, dr$$

Introducing (26) and taking the square root into the denominator by simply multiplying numerator and denominator by it give three terms which in the limits reduce to the simple form

$$\Lambda = \mu N^2 I [R_m - \sqrt{R_m{}^2 - a^2}] \tag{28}$$

if one observes $\sin^{-1}(1) = \pi/2$, $\sin^{-1}(-1) = -\pi/2$. Again, if $a \ll R_m$, one can approximate the bracket by $a^2/2R_m$, leading to proportionality with the cross-sectional area. These simple cases are also treated in Smythe,[A22] p. 288, and Russell,[B11] p. 71.

The inductance has also been computed for a core of rectangular cross section and a winding of variable and comparatively large thickness;[23] in this case the incomplete linkage of the field lines within the winding has to be taken into account, and the result is by no means brief though relatively simple.

[23] H. B. Dwight, *Trans. A.I.E.E.*, **64**, p. 805 (1945).

PROBLEMS

1. To evaluate the earth resistance between two ground electrodes a distance $2c$ apart one might replace the electrodes by semispheres of radius a_1 and a_2 as in Fig. 11·1, where the y-z-plane might represent the boundary between ground and air. Assuming uniform conductivity γ, find the amount of current between the electrodes from the surface to the variable depth h below ground along the x-y-plane. At what depth will the current have reached half of the total value?

2. Compute the amount of charge induced within a circular area of radius h of an infinite conducting plane by a point charge $+Q$ located at a distance h from the plane.

3. Find the field distribution and the induced charge densities for a point charge $+Q$ located midway between two conducting planes intersecting at an angle of $\pi/3$. Verify that each conducting plane will have induced in it $-Q/2$.

4. Compute the force exerted upon a point charge $+Q$ by an insulated sphere of radius R if the point charge is located at distance $b > R$ from the center of the sphere. What will be the force if the sphere carries a charge Q_1?

5. Find the force and torque upon an electric dipole located at a distance $b > R$ from the center of a grounded sphere, if (a) the dipole has its moment $\mathbf{p}$ directed along a radius vector from the center of the sphere; (b) the dipole moment is at right angle to the radius vector.

6. Verify the force action (10·39) upon an electric dipole in a non-uniform electric field; derive the torque exerted upon the dipole in a non-uniform electric field.

7. Find the charge density induced in an insulated sphere of radius R by an electric dipole located at $b > R$ from the center of the sphere, for the two principal directions of the dipole moment given in problem 5.

8. An electric dipole of moment $\mathbf{p}$ has its axis directed at an angle ψ against an infinite conducting plane. Find the charge density induced in the plane.

9. In problem 8, find the force and torque exerted upon the dipole.

10. Referring to Fig. 11·2, assume the small sphere of radius a_1 to have a voltage V applied between it and ground. Find the potential induced on the insulated small sphere of radius a_2 with respect to ground.

11. Assume the two small spheres in Fig. 11·2 to represent source and sink, respectively, for the flow of an incompressible fluid bounded by the y-z-plane. Compute the hydraulic resistance. Interpret the problem as a stationary electric current problem.

12. Find the approximate distribution of the induced charge on a small sphere of radius a located on the plane of symmetry between two orthogonally intersecting conducting planes and a distance $h > 5a$ from them. Show that the maximum density is greater by the factor $(\sqrt{2} - \frac{1}{2})$ than for a single plane at the same distance.

13. Assume three like small spheres of radius a located symmetrically with respect to each other at distances $h > 5a$. Compute the mutual capacitance coefficients. Find the approximate distribution of the induced charge density on each sphere.

14. The finite line in Fig. 12·1 carries a total charge Q distributed with a line density proportional to the absolute distance from the center of the line. Find the potential distribution in space. What are the potential values along $\rho = 0$? Find the equipotential lines at large distance from the charged line.

15. The finite line in Fig. 12·1 carries a charge distribution with a line density directly proportional to distance from the center, positive for $\xi > 0$ and negative for $\xi < 0$, so that the total charge is zero. Find the potential distribution in space. What are the potential values along $\rho = 0$? Find the equipotential lines at large distance from the charged line.

16. The finite uniformly charged line of Fig. 12·4b is parallel to two conducting planes which intersect orthogonally and is located in the plane of symmetry at a distance h from the planes. Determine the capacitance with respect to the conducting planes. Utilize (12·23).

17. Find the force exerted by the conducting plane (or ground) upon the uniformly charged line of Fig. 12·4b.

18. Why can the expression (3·20) for the electrostatic field energy not be applied to a single very long straight line carrying a uniform charge density λ?

19. What is the capacitance to ground of two identical parallel charged rods as in Fig. 12·4b, each carrying the charge $Q/2$ and both located at the same height h above ground? How does it differ from the capacitance of an identical single rod at the same height above ground?

20. Compute the force per unit length between two parallel infinitely long cylinders of radii R_1 and $R_2 < R_1$ with the distance $2c > (R_1 + R_2)$ between their axes. Show the simplifications if (a) $2c \gg (R_1 + R_2)$, or (b) $R_1 = R_2$, or (c) $R_1 = R_2$ and $2c \gg R_1$.

21. Find the potential distribution caused by a uniformly charged very thin circular disk of radius a.

22. An electrostatic voltmeter can be constructed based on the force action between two finite, charged cylinders enclosing each other. Find the force per unit length for the arrangement in Fig. 12·6b.

23. Of two semi-infinite coaxial cylinders of radii $R_1 > R_2$ the first extends from $z = 0$ to $z = -\infty$ and is fixed; the second extends from $z = -c$ to $z = +\infty$ and can move parallel to the axis. If the cylinders have potentials Φ_1 and Φ_2, compute the force action between them. Hint: use the principle of virtual work.

24. Three parallel very long wires of equal radii R are at the same height above ground. Find the capacitance coefficients for the wires if their distances $2c \gg R$.

25. Three parallel very long wires above ground form a three-phase transmission line. What conditions must be satisfied in order to permit the definition of a real capacitance per wire as the ratio of total charge per unit length of the wire to its phase voltage?

26. Find the potential distribution at very large distance from n parallel wires constituting a power transmission line system.

27. Find the average capacitance to ground of one wire of a transmission system, taking into account its sag between two support towers.

28. Find the capacitance between a small sphere of radius b located on the

center line of a thin circular ring of charge and this ring. Assume the circular loop as in Fig. 12·9 and the distance of the sphere as $z = h$.

29. Find the ratio of maximum to minimum charge density for the circular ring of charge in Fig. 12·9 with finite diameter of cross section d.

30. A circular loop of radius a carrying current I_1 is located midway between two parallel wires spaced $2c > 2a$ apart and can rotate about its diameter parallel to and in the same plane with the wires. Find the torque as a function of the angle between the plane of the loop and the plane of the wires if the wires carry currents $\pm I_2$. Which is the position of stable equilibrium?

31. Find the magnetic field distribution at large distance from n parallel wires, which form a complete transmission system. Demonstrate that the field can be approximated by that of an equivalent dipole line and give the location of the latter.

32. Give the magnetic field distribution far from the rectangular current loop in Fig. 13·2. Demonstrate the equivalence with the field of a magnetic dipole whose moment is $4abI$.

33. Find the inductance of a thin elliptical current loop of major and minor axis a and b, respectively, and of wire diameter $d \ll b$.

34. Find the mutual inductance between two parallel pairs of dipole line currents as a function of the angle between their respective planes.

35. Prove that there is no mutual inductance between two pairs of parallel line currents $\pm I_1$ and $\pm I_2$ spaced $2a$ and $2b$, respectively, and crossing orthogonally. Assume that the planes of the wire pairs intersect along a line parallel to the first pair and at a distance $2a$ from the nearer wire.

36. Demonstrate the equivalence of the circular current loop with a magnetic shell of dipole moment nI per unit area. Find the magnetic field of the magnetic shell and show the identity with (13·26).

37. Find the mutual inductance of two identical circular loops of radii a lying in parallel planes of small spacing $c \ll a$.

38. The space between two parallel conducting planes is filled with a dielectric whose dielectric constant varies linearly along the normal to the parallel planes from a minimum value ε_1 on Φ_1 to ε_2 on Φ_2. Find the capacitance per unit area of this condenser.

39. In a coaxial cylindrical system, the inner solid metal cylinder of radius R_1 is kept at temperature T_1 by joule heat from a continuous current; the outer metal cylinder (sheath) is kept at temperature T_2. Find the temperature distribution and the thermal resistance if the thermal conductivity of the insulation varies linearly from a larger value k_1 at R_1 to a smaller value k_2 at R_2.

40. A parallel plate condenser of spacing d between the conducting plates is filled with a medium of dielectric constant $\varepsilon = \varepsilon' + (\varepsilon_1 - \varepsilon') \cdot \exp(-x/d)$. Find the capacitance per unit area. Give the charge density for a potential difference $\Phi_1 - \Phi_2$ applied to the plates.

41. In a coaxial cylinder condenser two different imperfect dielectrics are used in concentric layers as in Fig. 14·3, where the inner layer has electrical conductivity γ_1 and the outer layer γ_2. Find the total current flow if a potential difference $\Phi_I - \Phi_{II}$ is applied. Find the potential distribution and the surface charges.

42. In a coaxial cable one increases the inductance in order to improve the transmission characteristics by wrapping a magnetic tape of high permeability upon the inner conductor. Assuming a uniform layer of permeability μ_2 and of thickness t on the inner conductor of radius R_1 in Fig. 15·2, what is the increase in inductance per unit length?

43. Wrapping a thin magnetic tape of high permeability μ_2 upon the two conductors of Fig. 15·1 with $R_1 = R_2$, what will be the approximate increase of inductance per unit length?

44. Two parallel identical, long thin rectangular bars (Fig. 15·3) are arranged in parallel planes. Find the force action between them if their distance is $c < 2h$.

45. Find the inductance of the two bars of problem 44.

46. Find the force action between the two parallel conductors of Fig. 15·1.

47. A thin flat pancake coil can be made in two layers so connected that the current flows in both layers in the same direction; the leads can then be ideally twisted so that the coil can be replaced by uniformly distributed circular currents. Find the magnetic field distribution of this pancake coil if the inner radius is R_1 and the outer radius R_2.

48. Find the mutual inductance of two parallel coaxial identical pancake coils as in problem 47 if their center distance is h.

5. EXPERIMENTAL MAPPING METHODS

The analytical expressions for the field quantities in simple geometries are fairly simple themselves, so that their use has become reasonably common. In many instances, they can be used as first or qualitative approximations for more complex field distributions. Where, however, quantitative values of greater accuracy are required, it becomes necessary to obtain solutions for the exact geometry with the attendant complications of analytical treatment. To escape the rigor of advanced mathematical methods, many experimental methods have been developed, in most instances for specific applications. These experimental methods are, of course, also of great value in aiding the visualization of field distributions and as checks on analytical solutions.

16· EXPERIMENTAL MAPPING OF ELECTROSTATIC FIELDS

For the quantitative mapping of electrostatic fields, it suffices to have a map either of the potential distribution or of the field lines. Two-dimensional geometries or those with axial symmetry are simplest to represent, because one single plane section gives all the information needed. For general three dimensional field distributions, one needs several to many plane sections and, in addition, a careful interpretation of the individual maps in order to conceive the actual field picture.

Mapping of Potential Distributions. By electrostatic induction, an isolated uncharged small metallic probe brought into an electrostatic field, as shown in Fig. 16·1, will experience a charge separation but retain zero resultant charge; it will also assume the local potential value that existed, before its insertion, or approximately the average value over its surface if its size cannot be disregarded.   Connecting an electrostatic voltmeter V to the probe, as shown in the dotted line, will place the capacitance C of the voltmeter in parallel with the capacitance C_{1p} existing between probe and conductor 1, draw off a considerable part of the negative induced charge of the probe, and leave it essentially positively charged, thus severely distorting the original field distribution and altering the local potential.   Opportunity must be

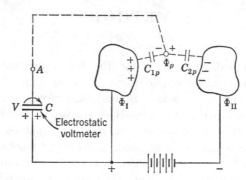

Fig. 16·1   Potential Measurement by Probe.

given, therefore, to expel the surplus positive charge, so that Φ_p is identical with the undisturbed local potential, before measurement can be made.   Then, with proper provision and with some experience, the probe can be moved so as to keep this potential constant; it will thus describe an equipotential surface.   Of course, the lead to the probe can itself act disturbingly; usually, local shielding of the lead with an isolated braid avoids any serious effects.

The simplest probe arrangement is the use of a small metal sphere and connection to ground at A so as to release some of the surplus induced charge; see Maxwell,[A16] I, p. 340.   Although the method is satisfactory to determine the relative potential at the particular point, it is not applicable when ground potential is used elsewhere in the system.   In such cases, one can use a small Bunsen burner as in Pohl,[A20] p. 65, whereby the flame acts as the probe and the hot gases provide an automatic dissipator of the free induced charge; the burner itself assumes the potential at the point at which it is located.   A similar principle is involved in the less convenient water-drop probe, in which water dripping continuously through a metal tube at a slow rate dissipates the surplus charge.[1] Care must be taken, by appropriately shielding the probe, to avoid field distortion by it.

Another type is the emission probe for fields in vacuum.[2] In this case a small metal plate, properly coated with emissive material, is used as probe, heated by a separate electric heating coil to a temperature high enough to cause thermionic emission and thus release the surplus induced charges. Since thermionic emission is primarily electronic, the electrostatic voltmeter of Fig. 16·1 must be connected to the negative conductor. This probe has been used extensively to explore the field distribution near electrodes, particularly grids, within vacuum envelopes or in gas discharges. Special vacuum-tight seals of simple construction must be provided to allow for adjustment of probe location. The practical use of this probe requires experience, since the emitted electrons may collect as space charge close to the metal probe and cause distortion, especially in regions of weak electric fields. Similarly, one must guard against the emitted charges condensing upon one of the main electrode surfaces and upon dielectric supports or the envelope, producing considerable distortion of the potential distribution. Measurements are somewhat slow, since it requires appreciable time for the thermionic probe to acquire the local potential.

For a coaxial cylindrical diode, the potential distribution has been measured with a very fine tungsten-wire probe parallel to the equipotential surfaces.[3] The anode is coated on its inner surface with a fluorescent substance (e.g., willemite) which glows under the bombardment of the electrons emitted from the cathode. If the probe wire has the same potential as local exists before insertion of the probe, the electron stream from the cathode remains uniform, and the anode illuminates uniformly; otherwise, the probe wire causes a shadow on the anode which is readily observable with open construction of the tube. Thus, the potential of the probe can be adjusted for disappearance of the anode

[1] C. H. Lees, *Proc. Royal Soc.*, **A91**, p. 440 (1915); also A. Wigand, *Ann. d. Physik*, **75**, p. 279 (1924), and **85**, p. 333 (1928).

[2] I. Langmuir, *Jl. Franklin Inst.*, **196**, p. 751 (1923); also N. Semenoff and A. Walther, *Zeits. f. Physik*, **17**, p. 67 (1923); A. Walther and L. Inge. *Zeits. f. Physik*, **19**, p. 192 (1923).

[3] D. E. Kenyon, *Rev. Scient. Instr.*, **11**, p. 308 (1940).

shadow. In a particular diode, the probe wire was strung in a pivoted frame, allowing exploration of the potential distribution under operating conditions. Comparison of the theoretical distribution for conditions of temperature limitation and space charge limitation with the measurements was satisfactory. This method can, of course, be used only where the potential distribution is constant along the length of the wire.

For low audiofrequencies, the ratio of the capacitances C_{1p} and C_{2p}, between the probe and the main electrodes, can be taken as

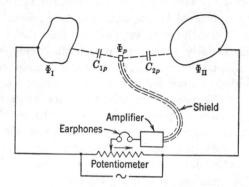

FIG. 16·2   Capacitance Probe for Potential Measurements.

a measure of the probe potential and directly indicated,[4] as shown in Fig. 16·2. The calibrated potentiometer is set to some definite ratio of its two resistance sections. Silence in the telephone of the amplifier circuit will occur if the probe is at a position so that the ratio of the two partial capacitances with respect to the two electrodes becomes equal to the resistance ratio of the potentiometer; to avoid extraneous influences, the lead to the probe must again be carefully shielded. For best sensitivity the capacity of the probe ought to be fairly large; this, however, must be reconciled with the fact that the probe itself must be small so as not to distort the field distribution. The frequency is advantageously chosen between about 500 and 1000 cycles per second, although with a proper amplifier even commercial power frequencies are employable.

For very high voltages the potential distribution over the surface of axially symmetrical insulators can be determined con-

[4] N. Semenoff and A. Walther, *Zeits. f. Physik*, **19**, p. 136 (1923).

veniently according to methods developed by A. Schwaiger,[B17] p. 184.[5]   A wire loop is placed around the insulator and a calibrated spark gap connected between this wire and the one electrode of the insulator; varying the spark gap setting or the potential applied to the insulator until breakdown occurs gives the potential difference between the wire (or the local point on the surface of the insulator) and the electrode.   If, on the other hand, the spark gap is connected between the wire loop and the center tap of a calibrated potentiometer, as in Fig. 16·3, a null method can

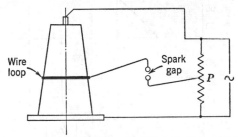

Fig. 16·3   Measurement of Potential Distribution with Spark Gap.

be arranged.   Thus, one can vary the potentiometer tap until the spark gap electrodes can be brought very close together without spark; the needed potentiometer setting indicates the value of the local potential.

Another method proposed by Schwaiger[B17] for extremely high voltages uses the principle of the electroscope.   Small cotton or silk fibers, or paper pieces, are fixed to an isolated wire loop on the insulator; if the voltage is applied to the insulator, the electrostatic forces will cause these fibers to make an angle with the insulator surface which can be observed with a telescope.   If the same angle is then reproduced with a known voltage applied to the wire probe, this voltage will indicate the local potential on the insulator surface.   For convenience and rapidity of measurements a number of exploring wire loops with indicators can be used simultaneously.

Utilization of Potential Maps.   The direct measurement of the potential distribution leads to a plot of the equipotential lines; in order to complete the field picture, it is then necessary to plot the field lines as the family of orthogonal curves.   No

---

[5] *Elektrot. und Masch.*, **37**, p. 569 (1919); also A. Fontvieille, *Revue gén. de l'élec.*, **10**, p. 599 (1921).

difficulty should be encountered if the equipotential lines originally were chosen close enough.

In order to obtain quantitative values for the field strength, it is best to plot on a separate graph as abscissa distances along a

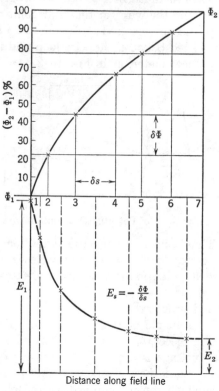

Fig. 16·4   Field Strength Distribution Obtained from Potential Graph.

particular field line (stretching this field line into a straight line), and as ordinate the observed potential values, as in Fig. 16·4. The approximate potential distribution is obtained by drawing a smooth curve through these distinct points.   Using $E = -(\delta\Phi/\delta s)$, the average value of the field strength can easily be computed for each of the intervals δs; in Fig. 16·4 these values are indicated at the center points of the intervals δs.   An approximate field strength distribution is obtained by again drawing a smooth line through these distinct points.   Extrapolation to the surfaces of the electrodes gives the approximate field strength values there.

Knowing the electric field strength distribution, one can easily obtain the displacement vector or dielectric flux density by simply multiplying the field strength values with the absolute dielectric constant of the medium.   This gives also the local charge densities on the surfaces of the conductors, since they are equal to the magnitudes of the displacement vector at the surface of the conductor.

Measurement of Surface Charge Distributions.   The local charge density on conductor surfaces can best be determined by direct contact of an isolated small metallic disk probe with the conductor surface, so that it assumes its potential and carries the local charge density according to the equilibrium distribution.   If, then, the probe is carefully removed perpendicular to the surface, the charge remaining on it is equal to the charge over the same area of the conductor, and division by this small area gives the charge density in good approximation.   Obviously, the accuracy will depend on the manipulation and on the relative size of the probe, as well as on its shape.

The most suitable form of probe is a small disk, preferably of the same local surface curvature as the conductor, and with an insulated handle.   The disadvantages of fitting and handling such probe are, however, considerable. Using, then, a small flat circular disk probe of radius r and thickness t, Maxwell,[A17] I, p. 344, derived the relation

$$\sigma = \sigma_m \left(1 + 8 \frac{t}{r} \ln \frac{8\pi r}{t} \right) \tag{1}$$

where σ_m is the measured and σ the true value of the surface charge density as corrected for the finite thickness of the probe.   For a small sphere of radius a as probe, Maxwell (*loc. cit.*) investigated the local field distortion produced if this small sphere be in contact with the surface of the conductor which has a radius of curvature b at the point of contact.   The local charge density σ follows from the measured charge q of the sphere as

$$\sigma = \frac{6b}{\pi a^2} q \tag{2}$$

The knowledge of the charge distribution on the surface of conductors is equivalent to knowledge of the dielectric flux density and thus of the field strength at the surface of the conductor.   The latter is of particular interest when predicting corona and break-down limits. The values of surface field strength obtained by direct measurement can be compared with the extrapolated values from the potential graph.

Mapping of Field Lines. Visual records of field line distributions are obtained in a simple manner by cutting the electrodes of tin foil, pasting them in proper relationship on smooth paper, and then pouring freshly powdered gypsum crystals on the paper; tapping the paper after the voltage has been applied to the tin foils will assist in having the needle-like gypsum particles arrange themselves in the direction of the field lines.[6] Instructive photographs of simple geometries are given in Pohl,[A20] Chapter II. Only fresh powder should be used because gypsum is hygroscopic. In similar manner, one can use cotton fibers,[7] small pieces of light paper, or small silk pieces as illustrated by Schwaiger,[B17] p. 184. Very interesting also is the use of $\frac{1}{2}$ per cent crystalline quinine sulphate in turpentine, leading to a sedimentation of the crystals along the field lines.[8] Here, the electrodes are metal pieces in a shallow tank.

Suspensions of short and coarse artificial silk fibers in carbon-tetrachloride have been used to get photographs of the entire field geometry on large-scale models.[9] Improved photographs were obtained with a tank illuminated from below and filled with two liquids, carbon tetrachloride and eocene, separated by gravity, with the silk fibers floating in the plane of separation, thus permitting a sharp focussing of the camera. It is important to select a proper voltage, since too high a voltage will cause the fibers to drift rather quickly.

For high voltages and any type of electric field with axial symmetry, a method developed by M. Toepler[10] is advantageous. The probe consists here of a small piece of straw about 1 in. long, provided with a steel needle axis of about $\frac{1}{2}$ in. suspended on a

[6] C. Fischer, *Phys. Zeits.*, **9**, p. 221 (1908).

[7] D. Robertson, *Edinburgh Proc.*, **22**, p. 361 (1889); A. Perrin, *Bull. Soc. Internationale des Electriciens*, **6**, p. 83 (1889).

[8] M. Seddig, *Phys. Zeits.*, **5**, p. 403 (1904); *Ann. d. Physik*, **11**, p. 815 (1903), where an excellent bibliography is given.

[9] R. H. George, K. A. Oplinger, and C. F. Harding, *Bull.* No. 29, Engg. Exp. Station, Purdue Univ., Lafayette, Ind., 1927.

[10] V. Regerbis, *E.T.Z.*, **46**, pp. 298, 336 (1925); this reference gives several excellent field picture reproductions and a good bibliography.

silk thread, so that the straw can rotate in a vertical plane as shown in Fig. 16·5 and assume the direction of the field line.   The projections of the various positions of the straw upon a meridional plane (most conveniently obtained by tracing with pencil the shadow produced by parallel light) give an array of field line elements which easily can be composed into complete field lines.   The advantage of the method is the rapidity with which the field line elements can be obtained, although the composition of the field picture requires experience.

With all the methods outlined above, one obtains only the geometry of the field lines and has to compute the values of the field strength by constructing the orthogonal potential lines and then using the same method, as shown in Fig. 16·4.

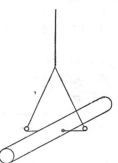

Fig. 16·5   Straw Probe for Field Mapping.

17· EXPERIMENTAL MAPPING OF MAGNETIC FIELDS

Many experimental methods have concentrated on the direct measurement of the magnetic field vector **B**, since the vector potential **A** is not in itself amenable to measurement, indeed, is not an observable physical quantity.   Since **B** can conveniently be measured directly in the ambient medium (in contrast to the electric field vector **E**), problems of coil design for desired field distributions, of core design in ferromagnetic circuits, and of proper linkage in coupled circuits have been solved frequently by the construction and extensive study of models as far as applicable. The unfortunate fact of variable permeability of most magnetic materials has made imperative field exploration for precise performance predictions.

Mapping of Field Vector B.   The most common method of measuring the field vector **B** is by means of a small search coil connected to a ballistic galvanometer by means of bifilar leads so as to avoid uncertain or variable magnetic linkage over part of the circuit.   In exploring magnetic fields of *permanent magnets*, the search coil is quickly removed from the test position 1 to a final position 2, and the maximum reading of the galvanometer is recorded as the integral of the electric current in the closed circuit. This current is given by $i = v/(R + R_g)$, where $v = -N(d\Phi_m/dt)$

is the induced voltage, and R and R_g are the coil and galvanometer resistances, respectively; N is the number of turns of the search coil, and Φ_m the average magnetic flux linked with a turn. The maximum deflection of the galvanometer records effectively

$$Q = \int_0^\infty i \, dt = -\frac{N}{R + R_g} \int_1^2 d\Phi_m = \frac{N}{R + R_g} (\Phi_{m1} - \Phi_{m2}) \quad (1)$$

if the time constant of the circuit is considerably smaller than that

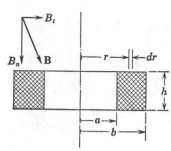

FIG. 17·1 Average Linkage of Search Coil in Magnetic Field.

of the galvanometer. If the coil is removed from the test position with flux Φ_{m1} to a position of zero magnetic field, then the galvanometer indicates directly the local component B_n normal to the coil area; if the coil can be flipped in place, then the galvanometer indicates $2B_n$. Assume, as in Fig. 17·1, that the coil is cylindrical of inner radius a, outer radius b, and height h; then the turns per unit area are given by $N/h(b - a)$; the average flux linkage for locally uniform field B_n is then

$$\Lambda = \frac{1}{N} \int_a^b (r^2 \pi B_n) \frac{N}{h(b - a)} h \, dr = \frac{\pi}{3} (b^2 + ab + a^2) B_n \quad (2)$$

so that one can also define an effective area $\pi/3(b^2 + ab + a^2)$ of the coil. Turning the coil in three mutually orthogonal directions, one can get the three coordinate system components of **B**. On the other hand, one can attempt to find the direction of maximum indication which is orthogonal to the field line at the point of measurement.

Of course, the coil area must be chosen small enough in order to justify the assumption of locally uniform fields. For electron optical systems, search coils as small as $2b = h = 0.04$ cm, $N = 100$ turns, with wire of 0.002-cm diameter, have been used[1] and dimensions of $2b = 0.1$ cm are rather frequent; usually, in electron lenses it is necessary only to measure the field along the axis of symmetry, so that the manipulation is simplified; see Appendix 4, B, c, and also section 30. For measurements on larger magnetic

[1] J. Dosse, *Zeits. f. Physik*, **117**, p. 437 (1941).

systems one chooses conveniently an effective area of 1 cm^2; then the flux value is identical with the value B_n in (2). In general, direct determination of the direction of field lines is not very satisfactory: it is usually more time consuming than measuring in three mutually orthogonal directions; on the other hand, the limited sensitivity of the ballistic galvanometer can introduce a serious error for low values of the field components. It is, therefore, advisable to check the field distributions by means of iron filings as indicated below.

In the case of *electromagnets*, it is not necessary to move the search coil; the excitation current of the magnet can be turned on or off (over a shunt resistance to avoid arcing). For smaller units, the excitation current can be reversed, leading then to twice the value of Q in (1), since $\Phi_{m2} = -\Phi_{m1}$. In a-c magnets, the search coil has induced in it an a-c current which can be amplified and read on a vacuum tube voltmeter or observed on an oscilloscope; calibration is usually necessary to minimize errors. However, in this case, the coil can readily be turned until maximum indication occurs, defining then the direction of the field lines in rather convenient manner.

To increase the sensitivity of the search coil arrangement in stationary magnetic fields, one can provide for rotation about an axis preferably normal to the direction of the field lines. The flux linkage then varies sinusoidally and causes an a-c current in the coil circuit, which can again be amplified electronically and read on a vacuum tube voltmeter. An interesting and very precise arrangement was used in the magnetic field measurements preliminary to the design of synchrotron magnets.[2] Two coils of $2b = 0.3$ cm were driven by the same lucite spindle at 1750 rpm, one exposed to the field to be measured, the other in the field of an auxiliary electromagnet with rotatable axis. The coils were connected in series opposition so that differential readings resulted which were minimized by rotating the auxiliary electromagnet. The output gave, then, the change in search coil field as compared with the fixed and opposing auxiliary coil field, and the angle of rotation of the magnet indicated the change in search coil field direction. Differential changes equivalent to 0.1 per cent of the field value could be measured reliably.

[2] W. C. Parkinson, G. M. Grover, and H. R. Crane, *Rev. Scient. Instr.*, **18**, p. 734 (1947).

An entirely different method of measuring **B** is by means of the change of electrical resistance which certain metals like bismuth, antimony, and tellurium experience in a magnetic field.[3] The largest effect is observed in bismuth; since it can be produced in thin wires and wound in spirals, it has been used most frequently,[4] though its characteristics are somewhat dependent on ambient factors such as temperature, stresses, and orientation. It is, therefore, advisable to calibrate these spirals before and after use in order to assure reliability of the measurement. Their very simple use as one arm of a Wheatstone bridge makes them valuable tools for quick surveys of relatively strong magnetic fields. A more elaborate and automatically temperature-compensated bridge-type flux meter has been developed by G. S. Smith.[5]

The use of the Hall effect in a small germanium probe for the measurements of medium-range magnetic fields has been described recently.[6]

Mapping of Magnetic Field Lines. For the study of the overall geometry of magnetic fields, which can be significantly represented in plane sections such as in two-dimensional geometries or geometries with axial symmetry, the use of iron filings on paper is indispensable. Excellent reproductions of simple fields are found in Pohl,[A20] Chapters I, III, and V.

To obtain a permanent record of the field lines, one can place a white carton coated with paraffin between heavy metal blocks constituting a model of the magnetic and conducting materials. Pouring the iron filings on the paraffin and letting them orient in the magnetic field, one can then heat the paraffin superficially so that the filings sink into its surface. This method has been extensively used for the study of magnetic field distributions in electrical machines[7] under varying conditions of excitation of pole and armature windings.

The iron filings give, of course, only the overall geometry of the

---

[3] L. L. Campbell: *Galvanomagnetic and Thermomagnetic Effects;* Longmans, Green, New York, 1923.

[4] G. Bublitz, *Arch. f. techn. Messen*, No. 83, V391-2, May 1938.

[5] *Electr. Engg.*, **56**, pp. 441, 475 (1937); also *Bull*. No. 103, Engg. Exp. Station, Univ. of Washington, Seattle, 1940.

[6] G. L. Pearson, *Rev. Scient. Instr.*, **19**, p. 263 (1948).

[7] E. Roth, *Bull. soc. franc. élec.*, **7**, p. 13 (1937); some reproductions in *Elektr. und Masch.*, **55**, p. 338 (1937).

field; they do not directly indicate the magnitude of the field vector **B**.   Since, however, outside of current-carrying conductors, the concept of the magnetostatic potential can be used, as shown in section 6, it is possible to construct the orthogonal equipotential lines.   For two-dimensional and axially symmetrical fields, one can then obtain quantitative values by using the same construction as is indicated in section 16 for the electrostatic field.   To ascribe definite values to the equipotential lines, one must be able to establish an absolute scale somewhere in the field, as needs to be done also in the graphical field plots explained in section 20 or in the experimental methods described below.

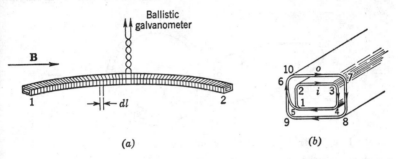

(a)   (b)

Fig. 17·2   Double-layer Coil for Measurement of Magnetostatic Potential Difference: (a) general view, (b) connection between layers at 1.

Measurement of Magnetostatic Potential Differences. With a specially constructed double-layer coil of considerable length l but very small cross section, as indicated in Fig. 17·2, one can measure the magnetostatic potential difference or magnetomotive force produced by an arbitrary conductor arrangement.[8] The inner layer is a continuous helical coil, wound from 2 towards 1, whereas the outer layer on the left-hand side is wound from 1 towards the center; Fig. 17·2b indicates the continuity of the wire from inner layer i to outer layer o.   The outer layer on the right-hand side is also wound from 2 towards the center, where the two ends serve as bifilar leads to a ballistic galvanometer.   If the two ends 1 and 2 touch, the coil forms geometrically a circular loop; however, there is no metallic contact between 1 and 2, and

  [8] W. Rogowski and W. Steinhaus, *Arch. f. Elektrot.*, **1**, p. 141 (1912); see also Pohl,[A20] Chapter IV, for excellent demonstrations of its uses; also Küpfmüller,[A14] p. 143.

any current in the circuit closed through the galvanometer flows in the two layers i and o in opposite directions, thus producing no net magnetic field.

If this coil is brought into the field of a current and the current is interrupted, the ballistic galvanometer will indicate the change in magnetic flux linked by the coil as in (1). If the number of turns per layer per unit length is n, then the coil length dl has a flux linkage

$$d\Lambda = SB_n 2n \ dl$$

where S is the average area of inner and outer coil section, and B_n the component of the magnetic field normal to the element dl.

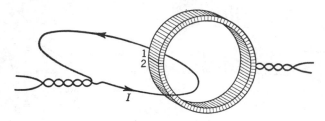

Fig. 17·3   Measurement of mmf Produced by Current Loop.

The ballistic galvanometer measures the total flux linkage or, in accordance with (1),

$$Q = -\frac{1}{R + R_g} \int_1^2 SB_n 2n \ dl = -\frac{2nS}{R + R_g} \int_1^2 \mathbf{B} \cdot \mathbf{dl}$$

$$= \frac{2nS}{R + R_g} \mu(\mathcal{F}_2 - \mathcal{F}_1) \quad (3)$$

where (6·4) has been introduced. Thus, this double-layer coil measures directly the magnetostatic potential difference, independent of its own shape, between any two points of space it is capable of reaching. Bending the coil into a circle linking it with a circular current loop, as in Fig. 17·3, still measures $(\mathcal{F}_2 - \mathcal{F}_1) = I$ the result of the line integral of $\mathbf{H}$ carried right to the barrier surface of Fig. 6·1, since the ends 1 and 2 of the coil do not make metallic contact. Of course, it is not permissible to bend the coil into a double loop circling the current I twice, since then it physically penetrates the barrier surface; this would void the uniqueness condition of potential values.

With one end kept fixed in space, the other coil end can be used to map the potential distribution relative to the first point and thus introduce the absolute scale needed for the quantitative interpretation of field line distributions (see above).

Measurement of Flux Linkage. In order to check linkage or leakage calculations, it is frequently desired to measure flux linkages. The most accurate results in circuits without iron are obtained by placing a fine wire as search coil right alongside the winding for which the linkage should be measured and using the ballistic galvanometer method, as for example for high-frequency alternators.[9] If iron is present, its saturation characteristics as well as eddy current effects have to be taken into account or at least qualitatively kept in mind.

In a-c magnetic circuits, the search coil can measure linkages under direct operating conditions, as for example in slots of electrical machines,[10] and it has been used as a voltmeter loop in high-voltage transformers after appropriate calibration.

18· UTILIZATION
OF FIELD ANALOGIES

As pointed out in Chapter 3, several other field phenomena besides electrostatics and magnetostatics show the same basic relationships between the characteristic field vectors, so that close analogies can be established, as summarized in table 9·1. Any solution for one of the field types can readily be translated into a solution for the other field types. In the experimental investigation, this permits welcome substitutions in instances where the original field is difficult, if not impossible, to explore.

Two-dimensional Current Flow. Current flow in thin plane conducting sheets (or uniform thin metallic films) is genuinely two-dimensional and can readily be used in accordance with section 8 to represent electrostatic or magnetostatic field distributions in geometries which over the center portions at least can be considered as two-dimensional (see specifically sections 12 to 15 for illustrations). As an example, take the dielectric field between two parallel cylindrical conductors within a grounded sheath, as in Fig. 18·1; assume also two different dielectrics, gutta-percha of

[9] N. M. Oboukhoff, *Engg. Exp. Station Publ.* No. 40, Oklahoma Agricultural and Mech. College, Stillwater, Oklahoma, June 1939.

[10] H. Rothert, *Arch. f. Elektrot.*, **32**, pp. 306 and 372 (1938).

relative dielectric constant $\epsilon_r = 4$ close to the conductors and rubber with $\epsilon_r = 2.5$ as filler. In order to measure the field strength distribution, one can conveniently use an oversize model with the same geometric proportions. To represent the two dielectrics in direct contact, one selects two metals of the

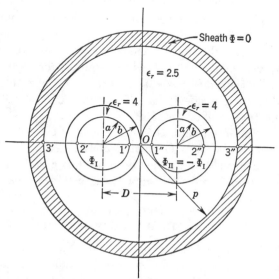

FIG. 18·1 Model of Two-conductor Cable with Two Dielectrics.

same ratio of conductivities, say copper and aluminum. According to Attwood,[A2] p. 118, one has as ratio of resistivities

$$\frac{\rho_{\text{Cu}}}{\rho_{\text{Al}}} = \frac{1.915}{3.14} = 0.61$$

as compared with $2.5/4 = 0.625$ for the dielectric constants. Using thin metal disks of copper and fitting these with good contact (preferably brazing) into an equally thin sheet of aluminum, one has the two-dimensional model of the dielectrics. Placing the composite sheet between copper blocks of about $\frac{1}{2}$-in. length, representing the conductors in proportional sizes, completes the overall model. If one now applies a potential difference with grounded center point between the cable conductors and connects the sheath to this center point, one can explore the potential lines in the current sheet by means of a needle contact and thus obtain practically the same result as in the original dielectric field.

One can then either trace by hand the flow lines, which are, of course, orthogonal to the equipotential lines, or use the same thin metal sheet composition to explore the field lines as the equipotential lines in the conjugate electrode arrangement. In order to do the latter, one has to place electrodes along properly selected field lines and restrict the current flow along the former electrode surfaces to satisfy the boundary conditions. In the example of Fig. 18·1 one would cut out the thin metal sheet along the two circles Φ_I and Φ_{II} constituting the cable conductors, and also cut along the radius p of the sheet; this will make these circular peripheries flow lines (previously equipotential surfaces), since the current cannot have a normal component there pointing out of the metal sheet. One would then clamp the sheet between thin vertical electrodes along the lines $3'-2'$, $1'-1''$, $2''-3''$, applying to the center one a positive potential Φ_I and to the outer two the negative potential Φ_{II}; or one could put a narrow slit in the metal sheet along the line $1'-1''$ and apply at the upper edge Φ_I and along the lower edge Φ_{II}. The conjugate electrode arrangement will generally give a better graph of the flow lines, particularly for the singular lines, than a free-hand plot can provide.

Measuring the total current permits evaluation of the resistance per unit thickness of the sheet, which can be converted into capacitance per unit length by using (8 11), namely, $C = \epsilon/\gamma R$, where ϵ and γ refer to the same set of equivalent materials, either gutta-percha and copper or rubber and aluminum. The proof is the same as that for (8·11).

This method, of course, is applicable only to models of two-dimensional fields but is rather convenient for single dielectrics. One difficulty in composite fields is finding metals of conductivities bearing the same ratio as the dielectric constants; it is also important to avoid contact potentials and be sure of solid contact at all points of any boundary. Space charge problems cannot be represented by this method.

Magnetic fields can be modelled in a similar manner, if one can define surfaces of constant magnetostatic potential. To represent, for example, the magnetic field produced by two parallel wires of arbitrary and large cross section is not possible, since the magnetostatic potential is not known in general along the surface, and within the conductor does not even exist. For thin conductors, however, it is possible to represent the magnetic field by utilizing the barrier surface as indicated in Fig. 6·1. Referring to Fig. 18·2, one takes a thin conductor sheet, punches the circular holes corresponding to the two parallel wires $+I_L$, $-I_L$, and makes a narrow slit connecting these holes. If then two metal plates are placed at the edges of this slit and the potential difference is applied between them, current can flow only in the sheet around the holes and the flow lines will be nearly identical with the magnetic field lines. From a plot of the equipotential lines one can readily construct the orthogonal flow lines and compute the

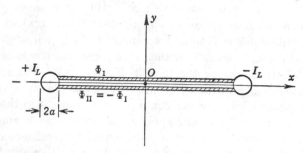

FIG. 18·2 Model for Magnetic Field of Two Parallel Long Wires.

local densities as indicated in section 16, or one can secure the flow lines by the conjugate electrode arrangement outlined above for the electrostatic field.

Measuring the total current I flowing between the electrodes permits the evaluation of the resistance R per unit thickness of the sheet. This can be converted into permeance $\mathcal{P}$ per unit length in the same manner as into capacitance C for the dielectric above, namely,

$$\mathcal{P} = \frac{\mu}{\gamma R} \tag{1}$$

where μ is the absolute permeability of the medium surrounding the conductors $\pm I_L$. This follows directly from table 9·1 for corresponding quantities; it can also be shown directly by establishing the flux-current relations.

Bringing a magnetic bar or core of very great length and of constant and high permeability near the parallel conductors presents the same problem as is treated above for two different dielectrics; one has to find two metals of about the same ratio of conductivities as that of the permeabilities. This usually means that one will use copper to represent the high permeability and a poor conductor to represent air. The only serious difficulty with models of magnetic fields is the proper interpretation of the magnetostatic potential values on surfaces where one must know this value in order to set up the problem.

The electric flow lines can also be made directly visible by using blotting paper soaked with a solution of copper sulphate and thin copper strips of proper shapes to represent the electrodes. As the water evaporates, the electrolytic action causes the copper to precipitate along the electric field lines and gives very striking reproductions of them.[1]

The Electrolytic Trough. A more general utilization of the analogy of electric fields in conductors to electrostatic fields, or any potential fields, is by means of electrolytic current distributions either at d-c voltages or at lower audiofrequencies where the magnetic induction effects are slight. The arrangement is usually referred to as an electrolytic trough and consists essentially of a large tank, preferably of glass or impregnated wood lined with copper or of lava slabs filled with distilled water and a slight amount of fresh spring water, in order to obtain a proper degree of conductivity. Frequently, one can use ordinary tap water; occasionally it may be preferable to use a very weak solution of copper sulphate. The electrodes, usually made of copper, are immersed in the electrolyte, and a probe, usually a short piece of nickel or platinum wire of about 0.02-cm diameter, is used to indicate the local potential. The probe must be insulated over its entire length, except for about 1 cm or less on its extreme end; it can be sealed in glass and should have a metal sheath on its outside for shielding purposes.

The electric circuit (see Fig. 18·3) is essentially a Wheatstone bridge, with two arms formed by the probe and the electrodes I and II; the other two arms are AD and BD on the calibrated potentiometer. The probe is moved until its potential is equal to the selected value on the tap D of the potentiometer as indicated by the detector. The position of the probe is transmitted to a stylus resting on a drafting table either by a carriage system fixed to the rim of the tank and permitting free motion in two perpendicular directions or by a pantograph as shown in Fig. 18·3. Usually, for a fixed position D on the potentiometer one traces

[1] K. Molin, *Fysisk Tidsskrift*, **18**, p. 3 (1919).

the complete equipotential line in a particular plane. Whenever balance is achieved, the stylus can be pressed into the recording paper, resulting in a series of points more or less closely spaced. Either the detection of balance is obtained by a sensitive telephone[2] or vacuum tube voltmeter,[3] or it is automatically recorded by means of an amplifier and solenoid which acts upon the indicating pencil whenever the scanning probe reaches a point with the selected potential value.[4]   A special circuit for increased

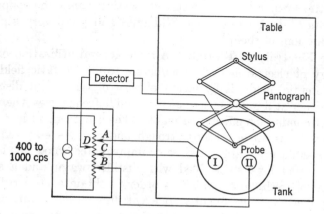

FIG. 18·3   Block Diagram of Electrolytic Trough.

sensitivity, using a tuned amplifier and compound rectifier and triode, is employed by Zworykin et al.,[B32] p. 393; it gives maximum reading at balance rather than zero indication.

Completely automatic plotting of all desired equipotential lines in a two-dimensional or axially symmetrical field can be achieved[5] by driving the probe at constant speed along one direction and adjusting its position in the orthogonal direction by means of a servomechanism which corrects to zero difference in probe potential with respect to the potential line to be mapped.   Here, the pantograph will trace a continuous line, with slight jitter where the probe motion needs considerable adjustment.   At the end of each travel on the border of the mapping region one can let the servomechanism select the position of the probe for the next equi-

[2] W. Estorff, *E.T.Z.*, **37**, pp. 60, 76 (1916).
[3] R. G. E. Hutter, *Jl. Appl. Physics*, **18**, p. 800 (1947).
[4] J. A. Simpson, jr., *Rev. Scient. Instr.*, **12**, p. 37 (1941).
[5] P. E. Green, jr., *Rev. Scient. Instr.*, **19**, p. 646 (1948).

potential line before the return travel is initiated; in this manner, complete regions can be mapped automatically at considerable saving in time even though the smoothed-out equipotential curves must be drawn by hand.

The electrolytic trough was first proposed by Fortescue,[6] who used d-c voltage. The disadvantage of polarization effects in the electrolyte led to the modification introduced by Estorff (*loc. cit.*), who used a-c potentials from low power frequencies up to about 500 cycles per second to study the potential distribution between two large spheres. Higher frequencies up to 1500 cps have been used; they usually have the disadvantage of increasing capacitive effects not permitting a zero balance, and thus reducing the sensitivity of the detector; according to Zschaage,[7] the zero reading can be restored by coupling the detector circuit inductively to the oscillator circuit; another proposal is to parallel the potentiometer branches by small capacitances.[8] It is, of course, important to keep the electrode surfaces very clean because slight oxidation can cause a rapid increase in the local surface resistance.

The advantage of the electrolytic trough method is the possibility of reproducing practically any three-dimensional field distribution in a uniform medium. For high accuracy it might be necessary to go to very large tanks in order to reduce the errors introduced by the walls, whether they be metal or insulating material. For two-dimensional fields, it is usually best to let the plane of the field coincide with the surface of the water and the electrode structures rest on the floor of the tank, which should be coated with insulating cement or paint. The current flow will then retain its two-dimensional character; studies of fields in multiconductor cables[9] and on transmission lines[10] were conducted in this way. A conductive side wall can be utilized as representation of perfect ground, whereas an insulated side wall can be used as plane of symmetry with simplification of the electrode structure. To obtain plane electron tube models, anode and cathode may be represented as heavy metal plates across the trough, and grids spaced such that the side wall coincides with a

---

[6] C. L. Fortescue and S. W. Farnsworth, *Trans. A.I.E.E.*, **32**, p. 893 (1913).

[7] W. Zschaage, *E.T.Z.*, **46**, p. 1215 (1925).

[8] J. F. H. Douglas, *Trans. A.I.E.E.*, **43**, p. 982 (1924).

[9] R. W. Atkinson, *Trans. A.I.E.E.*, **38**, p. 971 (1919) and **43**, p. 966 (1924); also Semenoff and Walther,[B18] p. 29.

[10] W. Zschaage. *loc. cit.*

plane of symmetry either between two grid wires or through one grid wire.[11]

The electrolytic trough can equally well be adapted to axially symmetrical geometries. The most obvious use is a semicylindrical trough with all electrodes as respective semicylinders; measure-

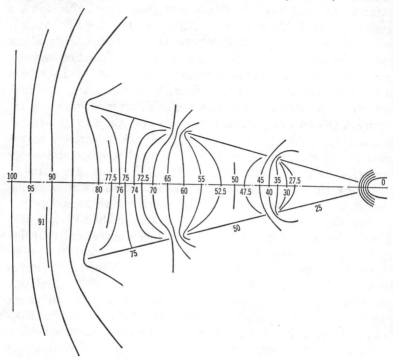

FIG. 18·4   Potential Map of Conical Electrode System.

ments can be made along the surface of the water. This can, of course, be reduced to a quarter cylinder, and, in fact, just to a wedge-shaped trough, either by tilting the floor of the tank or by tilting the whole tank.[12] It is usually satisfactory, then, to use plane electrodes and disregard the actual slight curvature of the electrodes. For exploration of fields close to the axis, as needed

[11] H. Barkhausen and J. Bruck, *E.T.Z.*, **54**, p. 175 (1933); Spangenberg,[B29] p. 75.

[12] Barkhausen and Bruck, *loc. cit.*, p. 176; M. Bowman-Manifold and F. H. Nicoll, *Nature*, **140**, p. 39 (1938); Zworykin *et al.*,[B32] p. 392; Myers,[B27] p. 95; Cosslett,[B22] p. 27; Hutter, *loc. cit.*, p. 801.

in electron optical systems, one should use very large-scale models in order to avoid the capillary rise of the electrolyte on the probe, which may cause considerable error in very shallow water. Figure 18·4 gives the potential distribution in a conical electrode system used in the study of emission from a small spherical area.

Since the electrolytic trough leads to a potential graph, it is necessary either to trace the field lines by hand as the orthogonal system of curves, or to use the conjugate electrode arrangement in which the equipotential lines become identical with the original field lines as outlined in the previous subsection. To restrict the current flow in the electrolyte, it is necessary only to provide insulating boundaries; replacing, therefore, all electrodes in the original set-up by insulating material of exactly the same shape will satisfy the flow boundary conditions. One can then place electrodes along field lines and apply appropriate potential values as outlined before.

Attempts have been made to reproduce the effect of two different dielectric materials in the field, as for the study of field distribution on porcelain insulators surrounded by air. Mixtures of graphite and binder[13] were selected to represent porcelain and the conductivity of the water was varied by salt additions, making it possible to obtain reasonably good field distributions. A simpler method consisted in varying the depth of water in the ratio of dielectric constants, essentially substituting increased volume for increased conductivity.[14] Neither method can be very accurate. It also has not been possible to adapt the electrolytic trough to the exploration of space charge fields, which would be of great value in many vacuum tube problems.

On the other hand, one can measure the individual resistances between any two desired electrodes or appropriately isolated electrode sections and thus obtain directly the mutual (or partial) capacitance coefficients in the same manner as described in the previous subsection and referred to in (3·9). As an illustrative application, take the model of a triode as shown in Fig. 18·5. Applying the desired potentials by means of the potentiometer as before, one can connect the ends of a slide wire potentiometer to two electrodes, say A and G, and connect a telephone as detector

[13] W. Estorff, *E.T.Z.*, **39**, pp. 53, 62, 76 (1918).
[14] R. H. George, K. A. Oplinger, and C. F. Harding, *Bull*. No. 29, Engg. Experiment Station, Purdue Univ., Lafayette, Indiana, p. 23.

between the third electrode C and the moving contact, thus reproducing again a Wheatstone bridge. For no sound in the telephone, the partial resistances are

$$R_{AC} = \frac{AC}{AG}\frac{V}{I_m}, \qquad R_{CG} = \frac{CG}{AG}\frac{V}{I_m}$$

whereby I_m is the current through the slide wire which must also be measured. The partial capacitances for the vacuum tube itself follow at once again from (8·11) by $C = \varepsilon/\gamma R$ with γ the conductivity of the electrolyte. In this particular example it is possible to obtain another characteristic number, the amplification factor μ, as

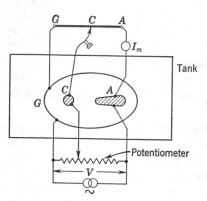

FIG. 18·5 Measurement of Partial Capacitances with Electrolytic Trough.

$$\mu = \frac{C_{GC}}{C_{AC}} = \frac{R_{AC}}{R_{GC}} = \frac{AC}{GC} \quad (2)$$

directly as the ratio of the slide wire lengths, not necessitating any other measurement.[15] Actually, for the determination of the amplification factor alone, one could use the main potentiometer itself, connecting the telephone between C and the variable tap, and adjusting the latter for zero tone.

Magnetostatic fields can be modelled in a similar manner to electrostatic fields if one can define surfaces of constant magnetostatic potential as outlined in the previous subsection. The field lines of a circular current loop, for example, can be measured by using the model of Fig. 18·2 in the wedge-type tank, letting the wetting line coincide with the axis of revolution, placing an insulating slab between the two potential electrodes, and representing the circular conductor I_L by an insulating rod in order to establish the proper flow boundary.

In applications to permanent magnets, as occur in instruments and in electron optical systems, one can frequently assume the

---

[15] Y. Kusonose, *Proc. I.R.E.*, **17**, p. 1726 (1929); also Barkhausen and Bruck, *loc. cit.*, p. 176.

magnetic material to be of infinite permeability[16] and to ascribe to it a magnetostatic potential difference which is given by the line integral of **H** across the air gap within the uniform section of the field distribution. Where the finite permeability must be taken into account, the electrolytic trough can generally not be used in any convenient manner.

The Rubber Membrane. A very effective means for the representation of two-dimensional potential fields is a rubber membrane stretched with practically uniform tension over a given

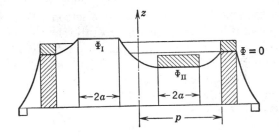

Fig. 18·6. Section of Rubber-membrane Model of Fig. 18·1 for a Single Dielectric; Radial Scale Compressed.

electrode arrangement in which height above a reference plane is proportional to the potential value. Figure 18·6 indicates the representation by a rubber membrane of a cross section along 3′–3″ of Fig. 18·1, with the electrode potentials Φ_I and Φ_{II} symmetrical about $\Phi = 0$, the sheath potential, and with a uniform dielectric.

Actually, the differential equation of the elastic membrane is[17]

$$\frac{\partial^2 z}{\partial x^2}\left[1 + \left(\frac{\partial z}{\partial y}\right)^2\right] + \frac{\partial^2 z}{\partial y^2}\left[1 + \left(\frac{\partial z}{\partial x}\right)^2\right] - \frac{\partial^2 z}{\partial x\,\partial y}\frac{\partial z}{\partial x}\frac{\partial z}{\partial y} = 0 \quad (3)$$

which reduces to the Laplacian differential equation if $(\partial z/\partial x)^2 \ll 1$, and $(\partial z/\partial y)^2 \ll 1$. These conditions can generally be satisfied if one keeps the tangent plane at any point to within 15° of the horizontal plane.[18] This requires rather large models of small

[16] Zworykin et al.,[B32] p. 477.

[17] P. H. J. A. Kleynen, *Philips Techn. Rev.*, **2**, p. 338 (1937); also Strutt,[B30] II, p. 4.

[18] Zworykin et al.,[B32] p. 419.

height differences.   One uses conveniently a surgical rubber sheet, about 0.1 cm thick, which is spread over the electrode surfaces and either pulled over a wooden frame and fastened to it or laced to a larger steel ring.   To assure uniform adherence to the lower electrode surfaces, counter weights are frequently provided as indicated in Fig. 18·6, in which the radial scale has been considerably compressed to make a better picture.   The electrode material is usually lead or sheet aluminum.

The rubber membrane has been used extensively for the design of plane electron optical systems, since it lends itself in an unusual manner to the solution of complicated electron trajectories as in the beam power tube[19] and in the electrostatic electron multiplier;[20] but it has also found excellent application to two-dimensional electric and magnetic problems in cables and machines.[21]

Hydraulic Analogies.   It has been pointed out in section 9 that the conditions (div **E** = 0) and (div **B** = 0) can be interpreted as characteristic for incompressible flow phenomena if **E** or **B** can be identified with the velocity vector.   This has led to a method which shows the magnetic field lines in the air gap of machines by means of finely distributed, colored glycerin forced into water flowing between glass plates; very clear photographs can be obtained in this manner.[22]   A recent adaptation of this fluid flow analogy uses a plaster slab and a parallel glass plate between which clear water flows; crystals of potassium permanganate are sprinkled on the slab model to visualize flow lines.   Excellent photographs have been made of source and sink flows confined by variously shaped barriers.[23]

Conversely, many studies of flow lines in hydrodynamics have direct applicability to electric and magnetic field problems; see particularly Prandtl and Tietjens[C24] and Eck[C20].

[19] O. H. Schade, *Proc. I.R.E.*, **26**, p. 137 (1938).

[20] V. K. Zworykin and J. A. Rajchman, *Proc. I.R.E.*, **27**, p. 558 (1939); E. G. Ramberg and G. A. Morton, *Jl. Appl. Phys.*, **10**, p. 465 (1939).

[21] M. Krondl, *Elektr. und Masch.*, **57**, p. 543 (1939).

[22] H. S. Hele-Shaw and A. Hay, *Phil. Trans.*, **A195**, p. 303 (1900); H. S. Hele-Shaw, A. Hay, and P. H. Powell, *Jl. I.E.E.*, **34**, p. 21 (1904); W. M. Thornton, *Electrician*, **56**, p. 959 (1906).

[23] A. D. Moore, *Jl. Appl. Phys.*, **20**, p. 790 (1949).

PROBLEMS

1. In Fig. 16·1 assume first only the two conductors Φ_I and Φ_{II} with the isolated small probe; show that the relative probe potential is $(\Phi_I - \Phi_p) = VC_{2p}/(C_{1p} + C_{2p})$. Connect next the electrostatic voltmeter as shown; assume that the capacitive effect of the new leads be negligible and that the voltmeter be sufficiently removed so as not to influence the field of the main conductors. If the voltmeter capacitance be C_v, show that the new probe potential is $(\Phi_I - \Phi_p') = VC_{2p}/(C_{1p} + C_{2p} + C_v)$, i.e., less than before. Demonstrate that connection to ground at A will restore the original probe potential. What will be the indication of the voltmeter?

2. Assume a point charge Q located at the origin O. Introduce an isolated sphere as probe electrode with center at P and radius R. Demonstrate that the potential on the surface of the spherical probe is identical in value with the potential value that existed at P before the probe was placed there, independently of the radius R. Show that this is still true if the field at P is produced by any number of point charges.

3. The straw probe in Fig. 16·5 is subject to the gravitational force. Find the error in indicating the direction of the electric field lines. Hint: assume a thin cylinder shell of uniform polarization and find the equivalent dipole.

4. Find the average flux linkage for the search coil in Fig. 17·1 if the magnetic field varies linearly across the coil area. Compute the effective coil area.

5. It is stated that (17·1) holds if the time constant of the circuit is *considerably* smaller than that of the galvanometer. What modification would have to be made if that were not the case? What error would one expect in using (17·1) nevertheless?

6. What is the influence of the magnetic field produced by the coil current itself upon the accuracy of relation (17·1)?

7. Design a two-dimensional current flow model for the magnetic field of a three-phase and (a) three-wire, (b) four-wire, transmission system.

8. Design a two-dimensional current flow model of the heat flow from the conductors of a three-phase three-conductor cable to the sheath, assuming a single uniform dielectric medium, circular cross section of the conductors and of the sheath, and a constant (steady-state) temperature of the sheath.

9. Design the two-dimensional current flow model of the electrostatic field of a triode which may also be assumed as two-dimensional. Show the determination of the capacitance coefficients between cathode, grid, and anode by means of current measurements.

10. Demonstrate that one can simulate the electrostatic field of the geometry in Fig. 18·1 by using copper sheaths of different thicknesses for the two different dielectrics. The error of current redistribution at the transitions can be made small by using a physically larger model.

11. Show the arrangement of electrodes in an electrolytic trough to represent the two-dimensional electrostatic field in a pentode. Demonstrate the current measurements necessary to determine all the mutual capacitance coefficients.

12. Evaluate the necessary size of the electrolytic trough in order to measure the field distribution between two spheres of unequal radii R_1 and R_2. Assume

that one uses hemispheres and measures the potential distribution along the water surface.

13. Design the electrode arrangement in an electrolytic trough in order to represent the magnetic field produced by two coaxial circular loops of radii a and b and small wire radii ρ_1 and ρ_2. Find the mutual inductance by simple current measurement.

14. Design the electrode arrangement in an electrolytic trough in order to measure the mutual capacitances of a three-wire transmission line above ground.

15. Design the electrode arrangement in an electrolytic trough to measure the mutual inductances of a three-wire aerial transmission line.

6· FIELD PLOTTING METHODS

As an alternative to experimental methods, a number of graphical and semigraphical methods (requiring simple computations) have been developed. It is certain that quick orientation with respect to a more complex field structure can be obtained best by a simple graphical construction; on the other hand, if higher accuracy is demanded, many trials of successively better approximation are needed so that experimental means then become more economical.

19· GRAPHICAL PLOTTING OF ELECTROSTATIC FIELDS

Although it is relatively simple to obtain qualitative information about field lines in a uniform dielectric by the powder patterns of freshly ground gypsum crystals (see section 16), there is no simpler method than the graphical one which furnishes quantitative information. Of course, a combination of a powder pattern with graphical quantitative interpretation, where such is possible, will give the speediest results.

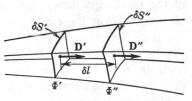

FIG. 19·1   Dielectric Flux Tube.

The foundation of most graphical methods is the concept of the dielectric flux tube formed by the vector **D** which has its base on a positive surface charge element $\delta Q = \sigma' \delta S'$ on some conductor, and which terminates on the equal and opposite surface charge element $-\delta Q = \sigma'' \delta S''$ on some other conductor. Everywhere between, the dielectric flux element $D \delta S$ remains constant and directed from positive to negative charge, even through dielectric

197

boundary surfaces as long as they are uncharged, which is the usual case (see sections 1 and 2). Selecting, then, two closely spaced equipotential lines as in Fig. 19·1, with

$$\Phi'' = \Phi' + \frac{\partial \Phi}{\partial l}\,\delta l = \Phi' - E\delta l \tag{1}$$

permits the definition of local capacitance as

$$\delta C = \frac{\delta Q}{\Phi' - \Phi''} = \frac{D\delta S}{E\delta l} \tag{2}$$

which is a unique value since for the entire volume element $\delta\tau$ the values $(D\delta S)$ and $(E\delta l)$ remain constant. One can, therefore, choose some arbitrary representative point within this element and, since at any point of a uniform homogeneous medium $D/E = \varepsilon$, obtain

$$\delta C = \varepsilon\,\frac{\delta S}{\delta l} \tag{3}.$$

in exact accordance with (14·3) giving the capacitance of a finite parallel plate condenser. If one, moreover, selects δl numerically equal to δS, the space becomes subdivided into cube-like units bounded by slightly curved surfaces exactly analogous to the true cubes in the parallel plate condenser, and, as there, one can now simply count the number of cubical units in series between two electrodes to establish the finite numerical value of the denominator of the total capacitance, and count the number of cubical units distributed over the surface of one of the electrodes to establish the respective numerical value of the numerator. This method can be applied to evaluate the partial capacitance coefficients in systems of conductors as well as the total capacitance of two conductors forming a condenser, and can be extended to any number of dielectrics in the field if proper account is taken of the refraction of the flux lines as defined by (2·9).

Field Plots for Line Charges. For a single line charge of great length, as shown in section 12, the field distribution is essentially two-dimensional and is axially symmetrical, with radial field lines and circular equipotential lines. In order to represent the field quantitatively, one chooses unit length in the direction perpendicular to the paper in Fig. 19·2 and thus has for (3) $\delta S = r\delta\phi$, $\delta l = \delta r$. Because of axial symmetry one might choose

$\delta\phi$ as $2\pi/n$, where n is the number of flux lines to be drawn. Assume $n = 16$, then $\delta\phi = 22.5° = 0.393$ radian; thus from (2), with δS and δl numerically equal, $\delta r/r = \delta(\ln r) = 2\pi/n$; the equipotential lines must be selected so that the ratio of successive radii is $r_2/r_1 = e^{2\pi/n}$ or $r_2 = 1.481 r_1$. The radius $r_m{}'$ which actually satisfies relation (3) is found by applying (3) to the subdivision of $ABCD$, namely, $\ln (r_2/r_m{}') = \ln (r_m{}'/r_1) = \pi/n$; this shows that $r_m{}' = (r_1 r_2)^{\frac{1}{2}}$ is the geometric mean of the radii r_1 and r_2.

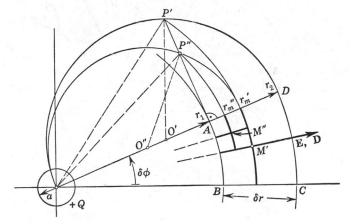

Fɪɢ. 19·2   Flux Plot for Single Line Charge.

The graphical construction for $r_m{}'$ is carried through in Fig. 19·2 as well as the further subdivision for $r_m{}''$. For the single line charge, the graph can be extended outward to infinity and inward to zero radius, finding in both directions no terminal; this difficulty was already pointed out in connection with (12·28). Ascribing a small but finite radius a to the wire removes the difficulty there and permits introduction of an absolute scale. The charge per unit length contained within a dielectric flux tube is $\delta q = D\delta S = (\lambda/2\pi)\delta\phi = \lambda/n$, if λ is the total charge on the conductor per unit length. The potential difference between successive potential lines must be, from (2), $\delta\Phi = \delta q/\delta C = \lambda/\varepsilon n$, since δS and δl in (3) have been chosen numerically equal. With a fixed potential value Φ_0 on the conductor surface, it is now possible to label the potential lines. The choice of the number n of representative flux lines immediately determines all the principal quantities.

For two or more parallel long line charges, a resultant field graph can be obtained by utilizing the principle of superposition. Take two line charges of values (-2λ) and $(+3\lambda)$ per unit length as shown in Fig. 19·3. Having chosen $n = 16$ for the charge (-2λ), one must choose $n = 24$ for $(+3\lambda)$ in order to have each flux tube carry the same dielectric flux; in turn, this means that the equipotential circles for the charge $(+3\lambda)$ are spaced in the

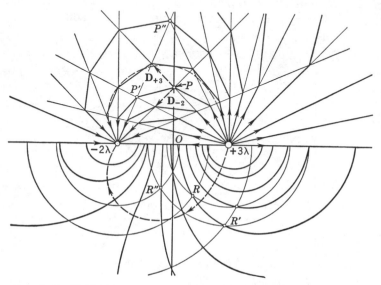

FIG. 19·3   Field Plot of Two Line Charges: upper half field lines, lower half potential lines.

ratio $e^{0.262} = 1.3$. The upper half of Fig. 19·3 shows the individual flux lines for each charge and their combination in broken straight lines as a first approximation to the resultant flux tubes. It is obvious that very close to the charged lines the individual flux distribution will remain practically unchanged; since any two successive flux lines delimit the same flux element, the diagonals of the quadrilaterals will approximately point in the direction of the resultant vector $\mathbf{D}$ as indicated in the figures by P–P'. This approximation will be closer the larger the value n is chosen; it was proposed by Maxwell,[A17] I, p. 183, for point charges, but applies equally well to line charges and line currents.[1] The necessary smoothing of the flux lines should be guided by the existence

[1] H. Ebert: *Magnetische Kraftfelder;* J. A. Barth, Leipzig, 1905.

of a center of gravity of the charges found by (10·46), which determines the character of the field at large distance; by the existence of singular points where $E = 0$, as at $x = -5d$ in the example if $2d$ is the distance between the charged lines; and by the potential graph.   The potential graph is shown on the lower half of Fig. 19·3 as the combination of the two individual families of equipotential circles.   Since all the circles are spaced at equal intervals $\delta\Phi$ in potential, in fact, equal decrease of positive or negative values as one recedes from $(+3\lambda)$ and (-2λ), respectively, one finds constant potential values by proceeding from one intersection of circles to that of succeeding circles of larger radius as indicated by $R-R'$.   For comparison, a selected field line is shown as the result of a first smoothing on the upper half, and as orthogonal line to the potential graph on the lower half, of Fig. 19·3.

If the line charges had been chosen of the same sign, $(+2\lambda)$ and $(+3\lambda)$, then the combination of the field lines would have to proceed in the direction of the other possible diagonal $P-P''$ indicated by reversing the vector $\mathbf{D}_{-2}$ at the point P in Fig. 19·3 in accordance with positive flux from $(+2\lambda)$.   The combination of the equipotential lines likewise would be changed, since now increasing radii mean for both charges decrease of positive potential.   Thus, from one intersection of two circles one has to proceed to that of the next larger circle belonging to $(+3\lambda)$, with the next smaller belonging to (-2λ), as from R to R''.

For more than two charged lines it is possible first to combine the field graphs of two and then combine this resultant with the third individual field graph, etc.; of course, considerable effort is usually spent before one arrives at a thoroughly satisfactory final graph which also satisfies (3).

Curvilinear Squares for Two-dimensional Field Plots. For general two-dimensional geometries, one cannot start, as with the line charge, from a known dielectric flux element.   The application of constant values δC as defined in (3) becomes a matter of trial and error with successive stages of systematic improvement after some experience.   Since for unit length normal to the graph paper the surface element becomes $\delta S = 1 \cdot \delta s$, the relation (3) reduces to

$$\delta c = \varepsilon \frac{\delta s}{\delta l} \qquad (4)$$

where δc is local capacitance element per unit length, δs the line element normal to the flux lines, and δl the orthogonal line element along the flux lines. If one now chooses $\delta s = \delta l$, one is led to curvilinear squares,[2] as indicated in Fig. 19·4, from which this method obtained its name. Many details and examples of plots are given in Attwood,[A2] pp. 178–185, so that only a brief summary need be given here. Obviously, this method applies to any potential field observing the analogies of table 9·1, where the capacitance of (3) or (4) is replaced by the appropriate conductance or permeance of the other types of fields.

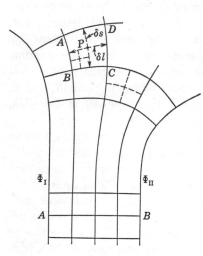

FIG. 19·4   Method of Curvilinear Squares.

In a practical electrostatic problem with a single dielectric, one will have given at least two conductor surfaces with known potentials, and either by symmetry or extrapolation into homogeneous fields one will know at least one field line and the approximate potential variation along it. With this as a basis, one can start in Fig. 19·4, for example, with field line AB and subdivide along it the potential difference $(\Phi_{\mathrm{I}} - \Phi_{\mathrm{II}})$ uniformly into a small number, say, m subdivisions. From this base line, one can now proceed to sketch the approximate equipotential lines and to select orthogonal field lines at such intervals that curvilinear squares result. Of course, this first sketch will show weak points of the plot, as in some places one or the other of the two major conditions—$\delta s = \delta l$, and orthogonality of field and equipotential lines—might not be satisfied. The plot must then be repeated until both conditions are satisfied everywhere, which may require considerable further subdivisions to gain in detail accuracy. Each subdivision should

[2] A. D. Moore: *Fundamentals of Electrical Design*, McGraw-Hill, New York, 1927; also A. D. Moore, *Elec. Jl.*, **23**, p. 355 (1926); Schwaiger,[B17] p. 181; H. Poritzky, *Trans. A.I.E.E.*, **57**, p. 727 (1938).

proceed along the check lines δs and δl, leading to smaller curvilinear squares which by themselves must satisfy $\delta s = \delta l$. With the final plot achieved, say, for two conductors in the field, one can get the total capacitance between these two conductors by counting the number of squares along a field line, say, m, and the number of squares along the conductor surface I, say, n, as $C = \varepsilon n/m$. With the given potential difference, this gives the charge on conductor I as $Q_I = C(\Phi_I - \Phi_{II})$. If there are several conductors in the electrostatic field, only partial capacitances can be evaluated (see section 3). In this case, $m_{\alpha\beta}$ would represent the number of squares along a field line between the two conductors α and β, and $n_{\alpha\beta}$ would be the number of squares along the surface of conductor α lying between the two field lines limiting the total mutual dielectric flux; one would have $C_{\alpha\beta} = \varepsilon n_{\alpha\beta}/m_{\alpha\beta}$. The partial charge on conductor α bound by conductor β is then $Q_{\alpha\beta} = C_{\alpha\beta}(\Phi_\alpha - \Phi_\beta)$.

If the subdivision by equipotential lines is reasonably close, one can evaluate the field strength E along any field line as the slope of the potential graph by the same method shown in Fig. 16·4. Plotting, as there, distance along a field line as abscissa and these field strength values at the respective points as ordinates, one can extrapolate the values at the surface of the conductors. The graph with distance along a conductor surface as abscissa and dielectric flux density or field strength values at the terminal points of the flux lines as ordinates should again lead to a smooth curve; it gives the charge distribution on the conductor and permits the evaluation of the total electrostatic force exerted upon the conductor (see section 3).

Once a satisfactory field plot has been developed for a given electrode arrangement, one can use it in many other ways. Thus, one can interchange field lines and equipotential surfaces and obtain the conjugate field distribution, which might be directly useful or might need some adjustments to make it physically realizable either as another electrostatic field or as any other type of potential field from table 9·1. One can also introduce a metallic surface along any equipotential line and thus obtain solutions to a different and useful electrode arrangement.

If there are two or more dielectric materials in the field, the procedure has to be suitably modified. Selecting for the medium

occupying the largest space curvilinear squares so that from
(4) $\delta c = \varepsilon_1$, one must then construct curvilinear rectangles in
medium 2, since there $\delta c = \varepsilon_1 \cdot \left(\dfrac{\varepsilon_2}{\varepsilon_1} \dfrac{\delta s}{\delta l} \right)$; one can either make
$(\varepsilon_2/\varepsilon_1)\delta s = \delta l$ or vice versa, depending on convenience. In addi-
tion, at each dielectric boundary the conditions of refraction given
in $(2 \cdot 9)$ must be satisfied. These problems count among the
most difficult ones; yet the graphical method is actually the only
feasible approach, since an-
alytically the difficulties are in-
superable, and experimentally
almost so.[3]

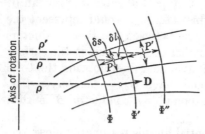

**Field Plots of Axially
Symmetric Systems.** The
general relation (3) applied to
axially symmetric systems gives

FIG. 19·5 Flux Plotting in Axially
        Symmetric Systems.

$$\delta C = 2\pi\varepsilon \frac{\rho\delta s}{\delta l} \qquad (5)$$

if ρ is the distance from the axis of rotation of the point P within
the volume element (see Fig. 19·5) and δs and δl the orthogonal
curvilinear line elements. To keep δC constant as in the two-
dimensional case means the selection of equal numerical values
for $\rho\delta s$ and δl. For a single homogeneous dielectric medium, this
condition requires for an assumed δs increasing length δl of the
curvilinear *rectangles* with increasing distance from the axis. The
field plot is in general more difficult to obtain than in the two-
dimensional case because ρ, the scale factor, changes with the shape
and location of the curvilinear rectangle.[4]

In a practical problem it is convenient to start from a section
where the field can be approximated either by the logarithmic
cylindrical potential distribution, as in Fig. 19·2, or by that of a
point charge or dipole, as in section 10. In general it is advisable
first to obtain a rough field sketch as if the problem were two-
dimensional and then to correct the sketch until the two major

[3] P. D. Crout: "The Determination of Fields Satisfying Laplace's, Poisson's,
and Associated Equations by Flux Plotting," *Radiation Laboratory Report* No.
1047. See also his extension to electric fields in magnetrons, *Jl. Appl. Phys.*,
18, p. 348 (1947).

[4] M. G. Leonard, *Elec. Jl.*, **32**, p. 31 (1935).

conditions are satisfied everywhere: orthogonality of flux lines and equipotential lines, and constancy of δC in (5). The evaluation of total capacitances, etc., follows the same outline as for the two-dimensional case.

The most exacting example is found in the original treatise on this method,[5] where the field distribution about a bushing of rather complex form is plotted; another example is the field graph of a charged grid consisting of parallel, equidistant coaxial circular rings.[6]

Field Plots for Point Charges. Though one could treat a single point charge or any number of collinear point charges by the method just described, since they form an axial symmetric system, it has become customary to follow the method of Maxwell,[A17] I, p. 183 (see also Attwood,[A2] p. 27), which refers to the spherical coordinate system. For the single point charge, the equipotential surfaces are spheres and the field lines point radially. The surface element of a sphere of radius r is $\delta S = 2\pi r^2 \sin \theta \delta \theta$ and $\delta l = \delta r$, so that from (3)

$$\delta C = 2\pi \varepsilon r^2 \sin \theta \frac{\delta \theta}{\delta r} \tag{6}$$

in which now r and θ are independent coordinates. To keep δC constant and equal to $2\pi\varepsilon$, one can therefore split the condition (6) into two selection rules, keeping $\sin \theta \delta \theta$ as well as $\delta r/r^2$ constant, or also

$$\delta(\cos \theta) = \delta \left(\frac{1}{r}\right) = \frac{1}{n}$$

The first relation determines the selection of the field lines; one can conveniently subdivide the radius of any circle along the assumed axis of rotation into, say, n equal parts; the radius vectors through the intersections of the ordinates at these points with the circle give then the field lines bounding annular cones of equal dielectric flux. The second relation determines the selection of the equipotential lines. It is best to plot the function $1/r$ and, starting from an arbitrary base radius, assume equal intervals of ordinates.

---

[5] K. Kuhlmann, *Arch. f. Elektrot.*, **3**, p. 203 (1914); see also Roth,[B16] pp. 39 and 200, and Schwaiger,[B17] p. 183.

[6] H. L. Poritzky, *Trans. A.I.E.E.*, **57**, 727 (1938).

The resultant field of two point charges can be readily obtained by superposition of the individual graphs of field lines and equipotential lines in exactly the same manner as was done for two line charges in Fig. 19·3. Examples of such combination plots are frequently found, in Maxwell,[A17] p. 183; in Harnwell,[A9] p. 35; and in others. Attwood[A2] gives many graphs for two or more collinear point charges with helpful guides for field sketching. Using the same principle, Maxwell,[A17] I, p. 180, also gives the combination plot of a point charge in a homogeneous electrostatic field.

**20· GRAPHICAL PLOTTING
OF MAGNETOSTATIC FIELDS**

For the representation of magnetostatic fields outside of conductors, two basically different methods are available, using either the scalar magnetostatic potential or the vector potential. Only the former belongs to table 9·1 of analogies because of its mathematical kinship to the electrostatic potential function; its use, however, needs caution. Selecting the vector **B** as representing the magnetic flux density, one can form magnetic flux tubes in analogy to the dielectric flux tubes in Fig. 19·1, enclosing $\delta\Phi_m = B\delta S$ flux lines anywhere in space. Their terminals must be created, however, as magnetic potential double sheets in all cases where the field is directly produced by currents (see Fig. 6·1 as example) in order to secure uniqueness of values. The total magnetic potential difference will then always be the value of the exciting current (or ampere-turns), $\mathcal{F}_\mathrm{I} - \mathcal{F}_\mathrm{II} = I$. For two closely spaced magnetic equipotential surfaces $\mathcal{F}'$ and $\mathcal{F}''$ one has the local permeance

$$\delta\mathcal{P} = \frac{\delta\Phi_m}{\mathcal{F}' - \mathcal{F}''} = \frac{B\delta S}{H\delta l} \tag{1}$$

as a unique value for the entire volume element as in Fig. 19·1 for the capacitance. Choosing some arbitrary representative point within the element and observing $B = \mu H$ for a uniform homogeneous medium, one obtains

$$\delta\mathcal{P} = \mu\frac{\delta S}{\delta l} \tag{2}$$

in exact analogy to (19·3) and therefore subject to the same interpretation for graphical field plotting methods.

If one considers the field outside of highly permeable magnetic materials for which one can assume $\mu = \infty$, and if no currents are in the space where the magnetic field is desired, one can ascribe to the surfaces of the magnetic materials constant magnetic potential values, establishing complete analogy to the electrostatic field. This will be true for the study of the magnetic field in the air gap of permanent magnets or electromagnets, of electrical machines, of relays, and in similar arrangements.

The use of the vector potential for graphical purposes is generally restricted to parallel line currents of great length, since it has a simple form only in such applications. It is not a directly observable physical quantity and therefore not of primary interest.

Field Plots for Line Currents. For a single line current of value $+I$ and of great length as shown in section 13, the field distribution is essentially two-dimensional and is axially symmetrical with circular field lines. To represent the field quantitatively, one chooses unit length in the axial direction and has thus for the surface element normal to the flux lines $\delta S = \delta r$, and also $\delta l = r\delta\phi$; both elements are interchanged as compared with the electrostatic flux plot in Fig. 19·2, so that the magnetic field is the exact conjugate of the electric field. One actually can proceed as there, make δS equal numerically to δl, and select $\delta\phi = 2\pi/n$, except that this means now subdividing the magnetic potential difference or current I by n and consequently selecting the circular field lines in the ratio of radii $e^{2\pi/n}$, leading to the same geometry as Fig. 19·2 shows. To have the vector **B** point in the direction of increasing $\delta\phi$ one must choose the magnetostatic potential values such as to identify $\phi = 0$ with I and $\phi = 2\pi$ with 0. The permeance in any volume element so chosen is $\delta\mathscr{P} = \mu$, and the magnetic flux within the tube becomes $\delta\Phi_m = \delta\mathscr{P} \cdot \delta\mathscr{F} = \mu(I/n)$, so that it is possible to count the number of flux elements between any two points along a radial line in order to obtain the total magnetic flux between these points. For the single line current, the graph can be extended outward to infinity and inward to zero radius, having no terminal in either direction; this difficulty was pointed out in connection with (13·1). Ascribing, as there, a small but finite radius a to the wire removes one of the difficulties; the internal magnetic field is then given by (13·3).

For two or more parallel long line currents, a resultant field graph can be obtained by utilizing the principle of superposition as shown by Maxwell,[A17] I, p. 287.[1] Assume two line currents of value $(-2I)$ and $(+3I)$ as analogous to the electrostatic example, Fig. 19·3. If one chooses $n = 16$ for the current $(-2I)$, then one must choose $n = 24$ for $(+3I)$ in order to mark equal potential differences between successive straight lines in the upper half of Fig. 19·3; this, in turn, means that for $(+3I)$ the field line circles are now spaced closer, namely, in the ratio $e^{2\pi/24} = 1.3$.

The absolute values of the magnetostatic potentials can be chosen in several ways, depending on where one places the discontinuity barrier. It is simplest to retain for $(+3I)$ the choice as for the single conductor, i.e., leave the discontinuity to the right

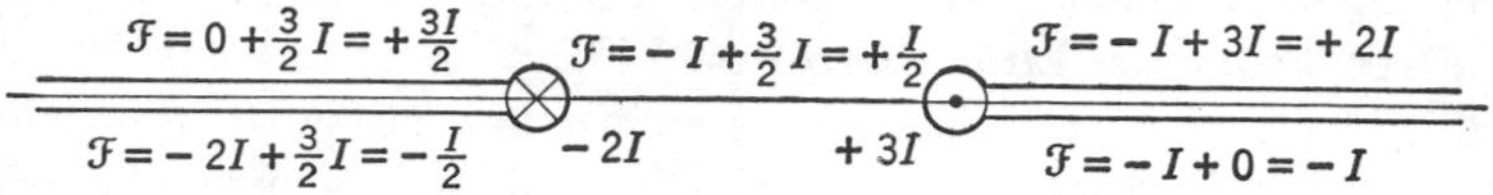

$$\mathfrak{F} = 0 + \tfrac{3}{2}I = +\tfrac{3I}{2} \qquad \mathfrak{F} = -I + \tfrac{3}{2}I = +\tfrac{I}{2} \qquad \mathfrak{F} = -I + 3I = +2I$$

$$\mathfrak{F} = -2I + \tfrac{3}{2}I = -\tfrac{I}{2} \qquad -2I \qquad\qquad +3I \qquad \mathfrak{F} = -I + 0 = -I$$

FIG. 20·1   Choice of Magnetostatic Potential Values for Two Line Currents.

of the current, and to choose for $(-2I)$ the discontinuity to the left of the current, leaving the space between the two currents continuous in potential values as shown in Fig. 20·1.

The combination of the equipotential lines in the upper half of Fig. 19·3 for constant resultant values is guided by the broken straight lines, whereas the combination of the circular field lines proceeds along the intersections of successive circles in the direction of the resultant field vector **B**. One can read from the graph at once the flux linkage that, for example, a rectangular linear loop would experience if its long sides were of length l and placed parallel to the line currents at R' and R'', respectively. Between R' and R'' are exactly two tubes of flux, each containing $\delta\Phi_m = \mu(2I/n)$, since $n = 16$ was referred to the current $(-2I)$; the total flux linkage is therefore $\Phi_m = 2\mu(2I/16)l = (\mu l/8)2I$, so that the mutual inductance becomes $M = \mu l/8$.

Had the line currents been chosen $(+2I)$ and $(+3I)$, then the same modification would have to be made as indicated in detail for the electrostatic analogue. This graphical combination of line current fields is very satisfactory; many excellent examples of more complicated field distributions in the presence of iron and involving theory of images (see section 23 for details) are given in Hague[B44].

---

[1] Extensive application was made by H. Ebert: *Magnetische Kraftfelder;* J. A. Barth, Leipzig, 1905; see also Hague,[B44] p. 351.

The inconvenience of using potential barriers for the field lines in connection with the magnetostatic potential suggests use of the vector potential **A**, which reduces for line currents to a single component

$$A_z = -\frac{\mu}{2\pi} I \ln \rho \tag{3}$$

as shown in section 13, where it was also demonstrated that in two-dimensional problems the lines of constant value A_z are identical with the field lines.   In addition, (6·23) gives the magnetic flux as the line integral of A_z, which reduces here for unit length and for the single conductor to $\delta\Phi_m = (\mu/2\pi)I \ \ln(r_2/r_1)$, if $\delta r = r_2 - r_1$, since only integration parallel to the axis gives a contribution.   To select, then, flux lines such as to give constant values $\delta\Phi_m$ simply means to keep $(I \ln r_2/r_1)$ constant, which is exactly the condition for selecting the field lines with the magnetostatic potential above.   The use of the vector potential is then fully equivalent as far as selection of flux lines is concerned, i.e., it will lead in the combination of the two line currents above to the lower half of Fig. 19·3; it will, however, not give the upper half, which is not too useful except as a check on the flux lines.

Curvilinear Squares for Two-dimensional Field Plots.   For general two-dimensional magnetic fields outside of conductors and with a known distribution of magnetostatic potential values along given surfaces, one can construct elements of constant value $\mathcal{P}$ as defined in (2) by trial and error with successive stages of improvement.   For unit length normal to the graph paper, the surface element $\delta S = 1 \cdot \delta s$, and (2) becomes

$$\delta p = \mu \frac{\delta s}{\delta l} \tag{4}$$

where δp is the local permeance per unit length, δs the line element normal to the flux lines, and δl the orthogonal line element along the flux lines.   Selecting further $\delta s = \delta l$, one arrives at curvilinear squares[2] as outlined for the electrostatic field; see also Fig. 19·4.

[2] This method was first introduced by Th. Lehmann, *E.T.Z.*, **30**, pp. 995 and 1015 (1909); see also Richter,[B49] Vol. I, 1924; A. D. Moore: *Fundamentals of Electrical Design;* McGraw-Hill, New York, 1927; A. R. Stevenson and R. H. Park, *Trans. A.I.E.E.*, **46**, p. 112 (1927); Hague,[B44] p. 268; and Bewley,[D1] p. 167.

Very much effort has been spent on the evaluation of the field distribution in the air gaps of electrical machines with salient poles in order to determine accurately useful flux linkages as well as leakage reactances.[3]   A first assumption makes the opposite magnetic materials, pole face on one side and smooth armature on the other, surfaces of constant magnetostatic potentials with $\mu = \infty$ and with a difference $\mathcal{F}_1 - \mathcal{F}_2 = H_0 g$, where H_0 is the value of magnetizing force in the uniform part of the field and g the respective air gap length.   Refinement is introduced by letting the magnetostatic potential vary along the smooth armature (keeping $\mu = \infty$) in accordance with the distributed armature winding; see for example Bewley,[D1] p. 176.   In all these cases there exists a region of uniform field in the pole center similar to the region below AB in Fig. 19·4, so that the actual flux plot can be carried forth as described for the electrostatic field, leading to a total permeance $\mathcal{P} = \mu n/m$ if m is the number of curvilinear squares along a field line across the gap, and n is the number of squares along the armature surface within one half pole pitch.   It is readily seen that, even with the simplifications made, an experimental investigation in the electrolytic trough would be utterly difficult because of the varying potential values on boundary surfaces. The graphical method has seemed to give most satisfactory results, leading to the composite field picture in the form of an orthogonal net.

Two-dimensional Field Plots Including Current-carrying Regions.   In many applications, the current regions cannot be excluded from consideration, since they directly affect the field distribution as the exciter windings on most electromagnets and on the poles of synchronous and d-c machines.   Inside current-carrying regions, certainly the magnetostatic potential does not exist, so that the method of curvilinear squares cannot be used. However, as demonstrated for two conductors of large circular cross section in (15·8), there exists a "kernel" into which the field lines shrink.   Since the boundary conditions on the surface of a conductor with finite current density require continuity of the magnetic field without any refraction (see section 6), one can con-

---

[3] See any advanced book on electrical machinery but particularly R. E. Doherty and C. A. Nickle, *Trans. A.I.E.E.*, **45**, p. 912 (1926); Stevenson and Park, *loc. cit.*; R. W. Wieseman, *Trans. A.I.E.E.*, **46**, p. 141 (1927); and Bewley,[D1] p. 167.

tinue the orthogonal lines as well, finding that they converge into this *kernel K* as in Fig. 20·2. Since they can now not be called potential lines of any sort,[4] but since they are orthogonal to the field lines, they are usually called[5] "lines of no work." Actually, the field lines suffer a change in radius of curvature, i.e., a second-order effect in passing across the boundary of a current-carrying region.

In order to continue graphical construction of the orthogonal net into current-carrying regions, the curvilinear elements have

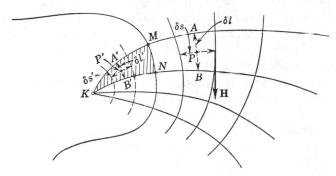

FIG. 20·2 Kernel and Field Lines within Current-carrying Regions.

to be modified. Applying the line integral of the magnetizing force in accordance with (6·3) to the closed path $(AKBA)$, and assuming uniform current density J, one obtains the result

$$H_P \delta l = SJ \tag{5}$$

where S is the area (MKN) within the conductor. Obviously, only δl makes a contribution to the line integral, since the other path elements are everywhere normal to $\mathbf{H}$. Applying the same line integral to the closed path $(A'KB'A')$ gives

$$H_P' \delta l' = S'J \tag{6}$$

where now S' is the area $(A'KB')$. With $\delta s'$ selected for constant flux element and with the same permeability μ inside and outside

[4] This method was developed by Th. Lehmann, *Revue gén. de l'élec.*, **14**, pp. 347 and 397 (1923); see also Stevenson and Park, *loc. cit.;* Hague,[B44] p. 270; and Bewley,[D1] p. 169.

[5] Stevenson and Park, *loc. cit.;* also in *Gen. Elec. Rev.*, **31**, pp. 99 and 153 (1928).

the conductor, one has $\delta\Phi_m = \mu H_P \delta s = \mu H_P{}'\delta s'$.   Combining this last relation with (5) and (6) leads to the condition

$$\frac{\delta s'}{\delta l'} = \frac{\delta s}{\delta l} \cdot \frac{S'}{S} \tag{7}$$

Inside a conductor, therefore, the curvilinear elements are rectangles of decreasing area as they approach the kernel.   In general configurations, the exact location of the kernel is, however, not a simple matter and frequently compromise methods are chosen.[6] Usually one plots first the field graph without regard for the current-carrying regions and guided only by the surfaces of known (or assumed) magnetostatic potential values as outlined above. One then introduces the modification caused by the conductor as a correction, estimating the location of the kernel and checking the adjustment of the curvilinear element with relation (7).   This might lead to slight changes of the assumed magnetostatic potential on iron surfaces close to the conductor.

As an alternative method one can use the superposition of two graphs[7] each of which is simpler to construct than the resultant. In two-dimensional fields, only the component of vector potential normal to the field exists, say, $A_z{}'$, and it satisfies (6·18)

$$\frac{\partial^2 A_z{}'}{\partial x^2} + \frac{\partial^2 A_z{}'}{\partial y^2} = -\mu J_z \tag{8}$$

a Poisson differential equation within the conductor.   The magnetic field is then

$$B_x{}' = -\frac{\partial A_z{}'}{\partial y}, \qquad B_y{}' = +\frac{\partial A_z{}'}{\partial x} \tag{9}$$

One can now look for a very simple solution of (8), preferably in one coordinate only, which vanishes on at least one conductor surface as far as the integration constants permit and plot the resulting field lines within the conductor.   One can then construct a normal Laplacian field plot by curvilinear squares for $B_x{}''$, $B_y{}''$ which satisfies the usual conditions of the magnetostatic potential values and *in addition* provides together with $B_x{}'$ and $B_y{}'$ the required continuity of the magnetic field vector across the

[6] Th. Lehmann, *Revue gén. de l'élec.*, **31**, p. 171 (1932) and **34**, p. 351 (1933).

[7] J. F. H. Douglas, *Electr. Engg.*, **54**, p. 959 (1935); H. Poritzky, *Trans. A.I.E.E.*, **57**, p. 727 (1938).

conductor boundaries. Obviously, this method requires very careful judgment and weighing of alternatives, but it can give excellent results particularly if the conductor is in direct contact with iron surfaces, which simplifies the satisfaction of boundary conditions.

Instead of separating the solution for the current-carrying region as above, one can use superposition of the complete field produced by the conductor alone, both inside and outside its boundaries, as taken from some analytical solution and plot it into the region in which the resultant field distribution is required, determine the correction needed at the boundaries of the field region to satisfy the boundary conditions there, and construct a curvilinear field plot for this correction. The combination will then be a complete solution of the problem. For the application of this method to a rectangular conductor within a rectangular armature slot see Poritzky (*loc. cit.*).

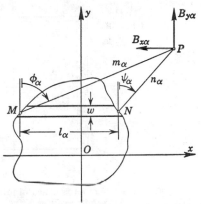

FIG. 20·3 Evaluation of Magnetic Field of Conductor of Large Section.

Two-dimensional Field Plot or Conductors of Arbitrary Section. If one desires the field distribution surrounding a long conductor of arbitrary large cross section but uniform current distribution, then it is frequently difficult to apply the method of curvilinear squares from the start. One can utilize the known field distribution of a very thin rectangular strip as given in (15·20), which is, referred to designations in Fig. 20·3,

$$B_x = -\frac{\mu}{2\pi}\frac{I_\alpha}{l_\alpha}(\phi_\alpha - \psi_\alpha), \qquad B_y = +\frac{\mu}{2\pi}\cdot\frac{I_\alpha}{l_\alpha}\ln\frac{m_\alpha}{n_\alpha} \qquad (10)$$

and apply it to the individual strips of equal width w into which the conductor may conveniently be divided.[8] The current in each strip is given as $I_\alpha = Il_\alpha/\sum_{(\alpha)} l_\alpha$, so that a constant factor $\left(\frac{\mu}{2\pi}I\right)$ can be deleted. At a point P, the contributions of the

[8] W. Kramer, *E.T.Z.*, **53**, p. 9 (1932).

strips can all be added and the resultant magnitude and the direction of **B** established. The orthogonal direction of the equipotential line can also be noted. The method is rather rapid, since the subdivision need not be made very fine, and will yet give good results except very close to the conductor surface. Having thus established several field lines and equipotential lines, one can continue with the method of curvilinear squares and proceed into the conductor as outlined above.

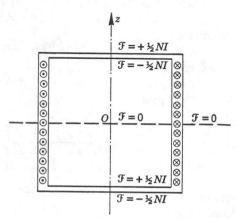

Fig. 20.4   Magnetostatic Potential Barriers for Cylindrical Coil.

Field Plots of Axially Symmetric Systems. The general relation (2) applied to axially symmetric systems gives as in (19·5)

$$\delta \mathcal{P} = 2\pi\mu \, \frac{\rho \delta s}{\delta l} \tag{11}$$

if ρ is the distance from the axis of rotation of the point P within the volume element as in Fig. 19·5. The utilization of (11) follows exactly the electrostatic case.

In practical problems, which usually involve cylindrical current coils, the field lines close to the axis are nearly parallel, so that δl along the lines is reasonably constant and $\delta s \approx \delta \rho$. The field lines should thus be selected in accordance with $(\rho \delta \rho) = \frac{1}{2}\delta(\rho^2) = \text{cons}$, so that their spacing is essentially as $(r_2/r_1)^{1/2}$ for $\delta r = r_2 - r_1$. At larger distances, the field of coils approximates that of a magnetic dipole given in (13·33). The values of the magnetostatic potentials have to be assumed in best agreement with the geometry and with the requirement of preventing completely closed field lines. For a cylindrical coil of N turns, a possible choice is the placement of $\pm \frac{1}{2}NI$ at the two end faces of the coil volume and a double cylindrical mantle along which the potential difference varies to zero value at the neutral zone $z = 0$ as shown in Fig. 20·4. A plot of the field lines for this type of coil with and without iron core is given in the reference to Poritzky (*loc. cit.*). The computation of inductance values from these graphs is in good agreement with analytical results.

21· METHOD OF ELECTRICAL IMAGES

The solution of the electrostatic field distribution caused by point charges and line charges in the presence of simple conductor or dielectric surfaces can frequently be obtained without analytical means by the method of *electrical images* introduced by W. Thomson.[1] It is based on the concept of *imaginary* point or line charges *not* located within the region of field evaluation but so chosen that together with the original point or line charges all boundary conditions in this region can be satisfied. Though these imaginary or *image charges* have no real existence, they can be used as if real in order to construct the final field by any one of the simple graphical methods, to compute the force actions on the original charges, and to construct models or analogies for other types of potential fields. Some very simple examples are included in sections 10 and 11, since they follow there rather naturally, and, indeed, have been the source of ideas for the generalization of the method. The material is here organized according to plane, cylindrical, and spherical boundaries, of conductors and dielectrics. No image theory exists for spherical dielectric boundaries.[2]

Images with Respect to Plane Conducting Boundaries. The solutions for fields of point and line charges near an infinite plane conducting surface have been given analytically in section 10 and extended to conductors of very small radii in section 11, so that charge distributions and capacitances could be evaluated. Frequently, one can interpret ground or walls of buildings for

[1] See W. Thomson: *Papers on Electrostatics and Magnetism*, p. 73; Macmillan, London, 1872; first published 1848; also Maxwell,[A17] I, p. 244; Jeans,[A10] p. 186; Mason and Weaver,[A16] p. 110; and Ramsay,[A21] p. 114.

[2] Smythe,[A22] p. 115; Stratton,[A23] p. 204.

electrostatic purposes as conducting planes, so that these solutions apply directly to many transmission line and related problems.

A point or line charge between parallel grounded metal planes as in Fig. 21·1 requires two infinite sequences of images,[3] which are summarized in table 21·1, giving signs as well as locations of the charges. For a point charge $+Q$ there is symmetry about the

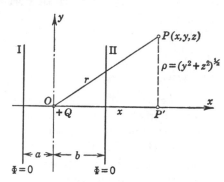

Fig. 21·1   Point or Line Charge between Two Parallel Conducting Planes.

x-axis, and the total potential at P will be the sum of all image contributions with $r_\alpha{}^2 = \rho^2 + (x - x_\alpha)^2$,

$$\Phi_P = \frac{1}{4\pi\varepsilon} \sum_{(\alpha)} \frac{Q_\alpha}{r_\alpha} \qquad (1)$$

whereby $Q_\alpha = \pm Q$ in accordance with table 21·1, from where also the x_α must be taken. The induced surface charge on either plane can be computed by (10·17) as the sum of contributions from the pairs of images with respect to each plane. Obviously, the series must converge to a finite value, since the total charge on planes I and II together must be $(-Q)$. It is therefore possible to take a partial sum as an approximation.

For the special case of $a = b = c$, the contributions of all the point charge images to the potential at the origin become, deleting the factor $4\pi\varepsilon$,

$$Q \sum_{\alpha=1}^{\infty} (-1)^\alpha \frac{2}{\alpha \cdot 2c} = -\frac{Q}{c} \ln 2$$

recognizing the series expansion for $\ln 2$. Admitting now a small

[3] Maxwell,[A17] I, p. 273.

but finite diameter d of the point charge, the total potential on its surface becomes in good approximation if $d \ll c$,

$$\Phi = \frac{Q}{4\pi\varepsilon}\left(\frac{2}{d} - \frac{1}{c}\ln 2\right) \tag{2}$$

where the first term is the potential of the original small sphere by itself, and where the second part is the influence of the two

TABLE 21·1

LOCATION OF IMAGE CHARGES FOR A POINT OR LINE CHARGE BETWEEN
TWO PARALLEL CONDUCTING PLANES

x_α Location of Images re I	Sign of Charge Original	x_α Location of Images re II	α Order of Image
	+		0
	$x = 0$		
$-2a$	$-$	$+2b$	1
$-(2a + 2b)$	$+$	$+(2a + 2b)$	2
$-(4a + 2b)$	$-$	$+(2a + 4b)$	3
$-(4a + 4b)$	$+$	$+(4a + 4b)$	4
	$\vdots$		
$-2n(a + b)$	$+$	$+2n(a + b)$	$2n$
$-[2n(a + b) + 2a]$	$-$	$+[2n(a + b) + 2b]$	$2n + 1$

grounded planes.   The capacitance is given by Q/Φ.   The maximum induced charge density at the center of either plane is, from (10·17), with $r = h = c$, $3c$, $5c$, etc., for the image pairs,

$$\sigma_{\max} = -\frac{Q}{2\pi}\frac{1}{c^2}\left[1 - \frac{1}{9} + \frac{1}{25} - + \cdots\right] \cong -\frac{Q}{2\pi}\frac{0.92}{c^2} \tag{3}$$

or about 92 per cent of the maximum density induced if only one plane is present, whereas one might have expected reduction to

50 per cent. The larger value indicates a compression of the induced charge distribution near the axis as the most pronounced
effect of the second plane.

This solution can also be interpreted in terms of current flow
from a small spherical source, or from a semispherical source
through one half the space between the planes. In the latter
case the resistance between the hemisphere and plane becomes

$$R = \frac{\Phi}{I} = \frac{1}{\pi\gamma d}\left(1 - \frac{d}{2c}\ln 2\right) \tag{4}$$

where γ is the conductivity of the medium, and the factor 2
entered because the total current I leaves through only one half
the spherical surface.[4]

For the line charge between the planes a two-dimensional field
results with no dependence on z. In this case,

$$\Phi_p = \frac{-1}{2\pi\varepsilon}\sum_{(\alpha)}\lambda_\alpha \ln r_\alpha \tag{5}$$

which can be interpreted as logarithm of the infinite product of
r_α values and identified with a closed expression.[5] Using the
alternation of the image signs, this can also be expressed as the
logarithm of the infinite product of ratios of two r_α values, thus
making the logarithmand a pure numeric. The closed form can
be obtained in simpler form by conformal mapping in section 27.

A line charge within a rectangular channel, obtained by adding
two conducting planes parallel to the x-z-plane in Fig. 21·1, leads
to infinite arrays along both x and y directions.[6] The complete
solution involving elliptic integrals is also found more readily by
conformal mapping, section 27.

Images with Respect to Plane Dielectric Boundaries. As-
sume any number of point and line charges in a dielectric medium ε_1
at distances h_α from a semi-infinite dielectric ε_2, as in Fig. 21·2.
Whatever the actual charge distribution in ε_1, its field must be so
arranged that across the boundary plane $x = 0$ continuity of
potential values and normal dielectric flux density are preserved.
If the actual charge distribution produces potentials $\Phi_\alpha(h_\alpha - x, y, z)$

[4] Ollendorff,[A18] p. 326.

[5] J. Kunz and P. L. Bagley, *Phys. Rev.*, Series II, **17**, p. 147 (1921); Smythe,[A22]
p. 84.

[6] C. M. Herbert, *Phys. Rev.*, Series II, **17**, p. 157 (1921).

and the effect of the dielectric ε_2 is to be represented by image charges, then they must be located at geometrical image points in order to permit satisfying the boundary conditions, i.e., they must produce potentials $\Phi_\alpha''(h_\alpha + x, y, z)$, which at $x = 0$ have the identical dependence on (y, z) as the Φ_α values.

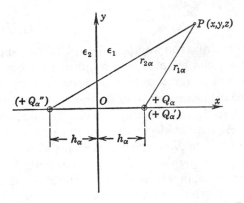

FIG. 21·2   Point or Line Charge and Plane Dielectric Boundary.

For any one point or line charge (see Fig. 21·2), the total potential in ε_1 is thus assumed to be

$$\Phi_{1\alpha} = Q_\alpha \phi(h_\alpha - x, y, z) + Q_\alpha'' \phi(h_\alpha + x, y, z) \qquad (6)$$

whereas the potential in medium ε_2 is assumed to be produced by a charge Q_α' at the location of the original charge, thus

$$\Phi_{2\alpha} = Q_\alpha' \phi(h_\alpha - x, y, z) \qquad (7)$$

To condense notation, Q_α has been chosen in this subsection for both point and line charge, though the latter has been designated λ elsewhere because it is a charge per unit length. The functions ϕ are identical with $1/4\pi\varepsilon_1 r_{1\alpha}$ and $1/4\pi\varepsilon_1 r_{2\alpha}$, respectively, for a point charge; and with $\dfrac{\ln r_0/r_{1u}}{2\pi\varepsilon_1}$ and $\dfrac{\ln r_0/r_{0u}}{2\pi\varepsilon_1}$, respectively, for a line charge, where r_0 is chosen arbitrarily as a scale reference value, which might be identical with h_α, since it represents an additive constant to the potential as in (12·28). Applying the boundary conditions and defining $\phi_{x=0} = \phi_0$, $\left(\dfrac{\partial \phi}{\partial x}\right)_{x=0} = \bar{\phi}_0$ give the two relations

$$Q_\alpha \phi_0 + Q_\alpha'' \phi_0 = Q_\alpha' \phi_0$$

$$\varepsilon_1(Q_\alpha \bar{\phi}_0 - Q_\alpha'' \bar{\phi}_0) = \varepsilon_2 Q_\alpha' \bar{\phi}_0 \tag{8}$$

from which the image charges can be evaluated

$$Q_\alpha' = \frac{2\varepsilon_1}{\varepsilon_1 + \varepsilon_2} Q_\alpha, \qquad Q_\alpha'' = \frac{\varepsilon_1 - \varepsilon_2}{\varepsilon_1 + \varepsilon_2} Q_\alpha \tag{9}$$

One can now construct the resultant field picture by superimposing the fields of the point or line charges appropriate for each region. Thus, in medium ε_1 for $x > 0$, one draws the resultant of Q_α and Q_α'', up to the plane $x = 0$; in medium ε_2 for $x < 0$, one draws the radial field picture of the single point or line charge Q_α'. In drawing the resultant field plot, a uniform dielectric material ε_1 must be assumed throughout space, since the difference in dielectric constants has been accounted for in the values of the image charges. Good field graphs or detail derivations are given in Attwood,[A2] p. 163, for the line charge; and for the point charge in Abraham and Becker,[A1] p. 77; in Jeans,[A10] p. 200; in Mason and Weaver,[A16] p. 148; in Harnwell,[A9] p. 66; and in Ramsay,[A21] p. 134; Smythe,[A22] p. 113, gives the generalized derivation. For $\varepsilon_1 < \varepsilon_2$, the image charge Q_α'' is negative and for $\varepsilon_2 \to \infty$ approaches $(-Q_\alpha)$, the image value for a conducting plane; in this latter case $Q_\alpha' \to 0$ as it should.

The force action upon a point charge Q_α is computed as the interaction with Q_α'', since their combined action defines the resultant field,

$$F = \frac{1}{4\pi\varepsilon_1} \frac{Q_\alpha Q_\alpha''}{(2h_\alpha)^2} = \frac{1}{4\pi\varepsilon_1} \cdot \frac{\varepsilon_1 - \varepsilon_2}{\varepsilon_1 + \varepsilon_2} \left(\frac{Q_\alpha}{2h_\alpha}\right)^2 \tag{10}$$

which means attraction to the dielectric for $\varepsilon_1 < \varepsilon_2$. Two equal charges placed symmetrically with respect to $x = 0$ in the two dielectrics will, therefore, not react with equal forces upon each other. Assuming charge Q_α to reside on a small sphere of radius a, then its potential can be found from (6) as

$$\Phi_\alpha = \frac{Q_\alpha}{4\pi\varepsilon_1 a} + \frac{Q_\alpha''}{4\pi\varepsilon_1 2h_\alpha} = \frac{Q_\alpha}{4\pi\varepsilon_1 a}\left[1 - \frac{\varepsilon_2 - \varepsilon_1}{\varepsilon_2 + \varepsilon_1}\frac{a}{2h_\alpha}\right] \tag{11}$$

The capacitance $C_\alpha = Q_\alpha/\Phi_\alpha$ is larger for $\varepsilon_2 > \varepsilon_1$ in the presence of the dielectric ε_2 than without it. The charge distribution can readily be found by applying (11·13) with the appropriate substitution of values.

The force action per unit length upon a line charge can be computed as $Q_\alpha E_\alpha''$, where Q_α is the charge per unit length and E_α'' is the value of the field strength at $x = h_\alpha$ produced by image charge Q_α''. This yields

$$f = \frac{1}{2\pi\varepsilon_1} \frac{\varepsilon_1 - \varepsilon_2}{\varepsilon_1 + \varepsilon_2} \frac{Q_\alpha{}^2}{2h_\alpha} \tag{12}$$

which means attraction to the dielectric for $\varepsilon_1 < \varepsilon_2$. With $r_0 = h_\alpha$ in the potential expression, $\Phi_{1\alpha} = 0$ at the origin. With Q_α

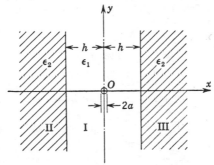

FIG. 21·3   Point or Line Charge Midway between Two Plane
Dielectric Boundaries.

assumed to reside on a cylinder of small radius a, then, with respect to the origin, the conductor has the potential value

$$\Phi_\alpha = \frac{Q_\alpha}{2\pi\varepsilon_1} \left[\ln \frac{h_\alpha}{a} - \frac{\varepsilon_2 - \varepsilon_1}{\varepsilon_2 + \varepsilon_1} \ln 2 \right] \tag{13}$$

The charge distribution can be found by appropriate application of (12·36).

A point or line charge between two parallel plane dielectric boundaries requires two infinite sets of images to satisfy the boundary conditions at both surfaces. Assume as in Fig. 21·3 a point or line charge in medium ε_1 midway between the two like dielectrics ε_2, then table 21·2 gives the necessary locations of the image charges for ε_1 now symmetrically distributed. The first-order images, $_1Q''$, satisfy the boundary conditions on the surfaces next to them but not on the farther surfaces, so that they must be taken as new original charges leading to second-order images, $_2Q''$, and so forth. If the factors in (9) are introduced as

$$\frac{2\varepsilon_1}{\varepsilon_1 + \varepsilon_2} = \eta', \qquad \frac{\varepsilon_1 - \varepsilon_2}{\varepsilon_1 + \varepsilon_2} = \eta'' \qquad (14)$$

then

$$_1Q'' = \eta''Q, \qquad _2Q'' = (\eta'')^2Q, \qquad _nQ'' = (\eta'')^nQ \qquad (15)$$

The fictitious charges $_1Q'$ serve to define the fields in II and III and by themselves need no further compensation, since their effects

TABLE 21·2

LOCATION OF IMAGE CHARGES FOR A POINT OR LINE CHARGE MIDWAY BETWEEN TWO PARALLEL PLANE DIELECTRIC BOUNDARIES

Charges Defining Field in II (ε_2)	Charges Defining Field in I (ε_1)		Charges Defining Field in III (ε_2)
	Original		
	Q at $x = 0$		
$_1Q'$ at $x = 0$	$_1Q''$ at $x = -2h$	$_1Q''$ at $x = +2h$	$_1Q'$ at $x = 0$
$_2Q'$ at $x = +2h$	$_2Q''$ at $x = -4h$	$_2Q''$ at $x = +4h$	$_2Q'$ at $x = -2h$
$_3Q'$ at $x = +4h$	$_3Q''$ at $x = -6h$	$_3Q''$ at $x = +6h$	$_3Q'$ at $x = -4h$
$_nQ'$ at $x = +(2n-2)h$	$_nQ''$ at $x = -2nh$	$_nQ''$ at $x = +2nh$	$_nQ'$ at $x = -(2n-2)h$

do not appear within I. Again, these charges are related to the $_nQ''$ values, and one has

$$_1Q' = \eta'Q, \qquad _2Q' = \eta'{}_1Q'' = \eta'\,\eta''Q, \qquad _nQ' = \eta'(\eta'')^{n-1}Q \qquad (16)$$

For each section, the resultant field can readily be determined by the infinite series which are certain to converge; one will assume a uniform medium ε_1 for this purpose, since the effects of the dielectrics are accounted for by the image charges.

For a quasi point charge Q at $x = 0$ of small radius a, one can determine the potential on its surface as the sum of contributions of the original charge and all the image charges defining the field in I. With $a \ll h$, one can take the distances directly from table 21·2 and obtain

$$\Phi = \frac{Q}{4\pi\varepsilon_1}\left[\frac{1}{a} + 2\sum_{n=1}^{\infty}\frac{(\eta'')^n}{2nh}\right] = \frac{Q}{4\pi\varepsilon_1}\left[\frac{1}{a} - \frac{1}{h}\ln(1 - \eta'')\right] \qquad (17)$$

since the absolute value of η'' is certainly less than unity.   For $\varepsilon_2 > \varepsilon_1$ this indicates an increase in capacitance Q/Φ caused by the presence of the two dielectrics, as compared with (11.2) for the single quasi point charge.   For $\varepsilon_2 \to \infty$ one obtains (2), the same result as for two conducting planes, as it should be.

Maxwell,[A17] I, p. 443, treats the more involved case of a point source within a medium of conductance γ_1 at a distance h from an infinite plane parallel slab of thickness $a > h$ and of conductance γ_2 followed by an infinite-extent medium of conductance γ_3. By analogy, this can be translated into the electrostatic problem[7] of a point charge in ε_1 in front of an infinite slab of ε_2, followed by an infinite-extent medium ε_3.   Two infinite series of images are necessary; their locations are found in the same manner as for conducting planes and their charge values by appropriate application of (9).

Images with Respect to Cylindrical Conductor Boundaries.   The solution for a line charge parallel to, and located at distance b from, the axis of a conducting cylinder surface of radius R was treated in section 12, locating the opposite and equal image line charge on the center line within the cylinder at a distance $d = R^2/b$ from the axis.   A point charge close to a conducting cylinder cannot be treated by simple image theory, since its potential function is incompatible with the logarithmic potential function of the two-dimensional cylinder (see section 32).   The method of images can be applied also to the potential solution for two parallel cylinders of finite cross section either excluding or including each other[8] (see section 12).

The application to a conducting cylinder with two symmetrically located opposite line charges as in Fig. 21·4 can readily be made.   The location of the image line charges is given by $d = R^2/b$; the field outside is the resultant of the four line charges, and the field inside is of course zero.   If now the two line charges recede to infinity, $b \to \infty$, the two images approach symmetrically the origin.   In the limit one has the case of a conducting cylinder in a uniform electric field produced by the two line charges, which can be taken from (12·33) at $x = y = 0$ and with c replaced by b as

$$E^0 = +\frac{1}{\pi\varepsilon}\left(\frac{\lambda}{b}\right) \tag{18}$$

[7] See also Smythe,[A22] p. 181, who uses direct analytical methods.

[8] Attwood,[A2] p. 149; A. Russell, *Jl. I.E.E.*, **64**, p. 238 (1925).

where both $\lambda \to \infty$ and $b \to \infty$ to produce a finite field. The field outside is now given as the superposition of E^0 and the dipole line formed by the image charges, which have a dipole moment per unit length

$$\mathbf{p} = +\lambda \left(2\frac{R^2}{b}\right) \mathbf{i} = 2\pi\varepsilon R^2 E^0 \mathbf{i} \qquad (19)$$

also directed along the positive x-axis. The field of the dipole

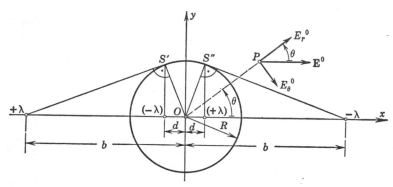

FIG. 21.4   Conducting Cylinder and Two Line Charges.   Limiting case for $b \to \infty$: conducting cylinder in uniform field $\mathbf{E}^0$.

lines is given directly by (12·53) in cylindrical coordinates, in which the uniform field has the components

$$E_r{}^0 = E^0 \cos \theta, \qquad E_\theta{}^0 = -E^0 \sin \theta$$

The direct addition of the fields and use of (19) give the resultant field

$$E_r = E^0 \left(1 + \frac{R^2}{r^2}\right) \cos \theta, \qquad E_\theta = -E^0 \left(1 - \frac{R^2}{r^2}\right) \sin \theta \quad (20)$$

which is the solution usually obtained by expansion into circular harmonics; see Smythe,[A22] p. 65.   The field graph can very readily be drawn as graphical combination of the circles and parallel lines of the individual fields, leading to local convergence upon the conducting cylinder with proper orthogonality there.   As seen from (20), the electrical field strength doubles at the surface of the conductor for $r = R$, $\theta = 0$.   The same solution occurs, of course, in hydraulics, with interchange of field lines and potential lines, as for example Bewley,[D1] p. 32, and references in Appendix 4, C, c.

The two-conductor cable shown in Fig. 21·5 can be treated in the same way by the method of images if the conductor radii are small compared with the radius of the sheath, $a \ll R$. The images of the given line charges with respect to the sheath are located at distance $b = R^2/d$ from the origin, if $2d$ is the center

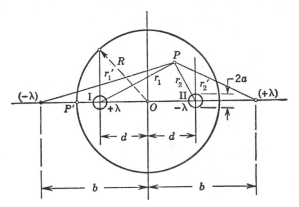

FIG. 21·5   Two-conductor Cable.

distance of the two conductors. Combined with the original charges they produce the potential at P

$$\Phi_P = \frac{\lambda}{2\pi\varepsilon} \ln \frac{r_1' r_2}{r_1 r_2'} \tag{21}$$

which gives zero value on the sheath, as is easily demonstrated for point P'. To establish the capacitance of the conductor pair in the presence of the sheath, one can form the potential difference $\Phi_I - \Phi_{II}$ by introducing into (21) the distances to the centers of the conductors, except that $r_1 = a$ for Φ_I and $r_2 = a$ for Φ_{II}. This leads to

$$\Phi_I - \Phi_{II} = \frac{\lambda}{2\pi\varepsilon} \ln \left(\frac{b-d}{b+d} \cdot \frac{2d}{a} \right)^2$$

or, if one uses $b = R^2/d$

$$\Phi_I - \Phi_{II} = \frac{\lambda}{\pi\varepsilon} \ln \left(\frac{R^2 - d^2}{R^2 + d^2} \cdot \frac{2d}{a} \right) \tag{22}$$

from which the capacitance per unit length can be obtained[9]

[9] Attwood,[A2] p. 144.

as $\lambda/(\Phi_{\mathrm{I}} - \Phi_{\mathrm{II}})$. If one plots the resultant field and equipotential lines by graphical superposition of the line charge fields, one can find a better approximation, particularly for larger radii a, by shifting the conductor centers slightly away from the line charge location towards the sheath.[10] One can also obtain closer approximations by taking more images with respect to the conductor cylinders and imaging these in turn on the sheath. With this method, two- and four-conductor cables have been treated.[11]

If the two conductors are transmission wires suspended within the cylindrical sheath, then they can be spaced so that they experience no force. On lead I the resultant force would be

$$\frac{\lambda}{2\pi\varepsilon} \left[\frac{(-\lambda)}{(b-d)} - \frac{(-\lambda)}{2d} - \frac{(+\lambda)}{(b+d)} \right]$$

where the signs account for force directions and signs of charges. For vanishing force one computes at once $2d = R\sqrt{\sqrt{5} - 2}$.

Images with Respect to Dielectric Cylindrical Boundaries. The problem of line charges parallel to a dielectric cylinder is very similar to that of a plane dielectric boundary, considering the latter as a cylinder of infinite radius. One expects, therefore, that a line charge $(+\lambda)$ in Fig. 21·6, located in medium ε_1 outside the dielectric cylinder ε_2 of radius R requires an image charge $\lambda'' = \eta''\lambda$ from (14) at the geometric image point $d = R^2/b$ with respect to the cylinder surface in order to describe the field external to the cylinder. However, that puts effectively a line charge within a medium that must remain uncharged, so that another line charge $(-\lambda'')$ is necessary at the axis; this neutralizes the first image charge and, being spaced from it a distance d, produces the effect of a dipole line. The total external potential is, therefore, the combination of three line charges

$$\Phi_p = -\frac{\lambda}{2\pi\varepsilon}\left(\ln\frac{r_1}{R} - \eta'' \ln\frac{r_1^{\,0}}{r_1''} \right) + \Phi_0 \tag{23}$$

where Φ_0 and $\ln R$ are constants. The field within the dielectric cylinder is determined, as in the plane case, by a line charge $\lambda' = \eta'\lambda$ from (14) located at the place of the original charge. If the radius $R \to \infty$, the solution for the plane dielectric boundary

---

[10] Breisig,[A4] p. 68, also gives good field graph.
[11] H. Meinke, *E.N.T.*, **17**, p. 42 (1940); F. Sommer, *E.N.T.*, **17**, p. 281 (1940).

results.   A general verification of the image arrangement is given by means of circular harmonic functions in Smythe,[A22] p. 67.

The extension to two symmetrically located line charges $(-\lambda)$ and $(+\lambda)$ as in Fig. 21·6 is rather obvious; the compensating charges at the axis are not necessary, since the images $\pm\lambda''$ already neutralize the dielectric cylinder.   If the two external line charges recede to infinity, $b \to \infty$, the images $(\pm\lambda'')$ approach

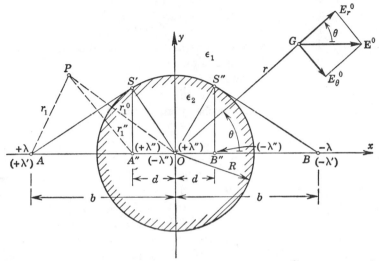

FIG. 21·6 Dielectric Cylinder and Two Line Charges. Limiting case for $b \to \infty$: dielectric cylinder in uniform field $\mathbf{E}^0$.

symmetrically the origin.   The case is entirely analogous to that of the conducting cylinder with the only adjustment in value of line charges!   In analogy, in the limit $b \to \infty$, the problem is the one of the dielectric cylinder in a uniform field and the resultant external field in cylindrical coordinates is given by (20) with the extra factor η'', for the dipole line contribution, and the adjustment in sign

$$E_{r\text{ex}} = E^0 \left(1 - \eta'' \frac{R^2}{r^2}\right) \cos \theta,$$

$$E_{r\text{in}} = -E^0 \left(1 + \eta'' \frac{R^2}{r^2}\right) \sin \theta \quad (24)$$

If one lets $\varepsilon_2 \to \infty$, then $\eta'' \to (-1)$ and (20) results again.   The internal field is defined by the two symmetrical line charges

$(\pm\lambda')$ located at the same place as the original charged lines, which, however, have receded to infinity. Thus, inside the dielectric cylinder, a uniform field remains, weakened by the factor η', or

$$E_{in} = \eta' E^0 \tag{25}$$

This solution (24) and (25) is the same as obtained by means of circular harmonics by Smythe,[A22] p. 67. If $\varepsilon_1 > \varepsilon_2$, the field strength inside the cylinder becomes larger than E^0 and in the limit can reach twice that value. Since frequently the dielectric of lower dielectric constant has also lower breakdown strength, such a physical combination is rather unfortunate.

If a line charge is placed within the dielectric cylinder ε_2, say, λ at A'' in Fig. 21·6, then it requires an image line charge λ'' at A to describe the field inside the cylinder, but no further neutralizing charge; here, of course, $\lambda'' = (\varepsilon_2 - \varepsilon_1/\varepsilon_2 + \varepsilon_1)\lambda$ because of the interchange of relative positions. The field outside the dielectric cylinder is again given by $\lambda' = (2\varepsilon_1/\varepsilon_1 + \varepsilon_2)\lambda$ located at A'' and a balancing line charge λ'' at the origin, so that the effective charge within the cylinder remains $\lambda' + \lambda'' = \lambda$, as it should. It is easily demonstrated that the boundary conditions requiring continuity of D_r and E_θ in the cylindrical coordinates are satisfied if one selects a point on the periphery of the cylinder and equates with proper algebraic signs the sum of the local components on either side of $r = R$. Again, if $R \rightarrow \infty$, the origin 0 moves also to infinity and the solution of the plane dielectric boundary results. For the composition of the resultant outside field graph from the individual line charges one must assume uniform space of ε_1; conversely, for the composition of the inside field one must assume uniform space of ε_2. This method has been applied to the computation of cable capacitances to take into account the influence of the dielectric constants.[12]

Images with Respect to Spherical Conductor Boundaries. The effect of a single point charge upon a sphere of radius R has been extensively treated in section 10 and for a given point charge of small finite radius in section 11. If the actual point charge is located a distance b from the center of the sphere, then the image point charge of value $\left(-\dfrac{R}{b}Q\right) = -Q'$ lies within the sphere

[12] H. H. Meinke, *E.N.T.*, **17**, p. 108 (1940).

along the center line at a distance $d = R^2/b$ from the center.

The application to a conducting sphere with two symmetrically located opposite point charges, as in Fig. 21·7, can readily be made; their images are symmetrically located at $d = R^2/b$ from the origin and their values are $\mp QR/b$, respectively. The field outside the sphere is axially symmetric and is the resultant of the four point charges; the field inside is, of course, zero. Because of symmetry, the sphere will have zero potential and zero resultant

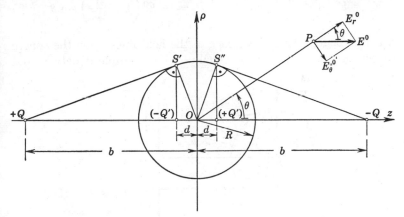

Fig. 21·7 Conducting Sphere and Two Point Charges. Limiting case for $b \to \infty$: conducting sphere in uniform field $\mathbf{E}^0$.

charge. One can add any arbitrary point charge at the origin O without disturbing the symmetry or the boundary conditions.

If now, for the uncharged sphere, the two point charges in Fig. 21·7 recede to infinity, $b \to \infty$, and the two image charges approach symmetrically the origin. In the limit one has the case of an uncharged conducting sphere in a uniform electric field produced by the two point charges, which can be taken from (10·12) at the origin ($z' = 0$) as

$$E^0 = + \frac{1}{2\pi\varepsilon} \frac{Q}{b^2} \tag{26}$$

where both $Q \to \infty$ and $b \to \infty$ to produce a finite uniform field. The two image charges form a dipole of dipole moment

$$\mathbf{p} = \frac{R}{b} \cdot Q \cdot \frac{2R^2}{b} \mathbf{k} = 4\pi\varepsilon R^3 E^0 \mathbf{k} \tag{27}$$

also directed along the positive z-axis. The field of the dipole is directly given by (10·35) in spherical coordinates, in which the uniform field E^0 has the components

$$E_r{}^0 = E^0 \cos \theta, \qquad E_\theta{}^0 = -E^0 \sin \theta$$

The direct superposition of the two field expressions and use of (27) give for the resultant field

$$E_r = E^0 \left(1 + \frac{2R^3}{r^3}\right) \cos \theta, \qquad E_\theta = -E^0 \left(1 - \frac{R^3}{r^3}\right) \sin \theta \quad (28)$$

which indicates the convergence of the field lines upon the sphere to terminate thereon orthogonally. The complete details and

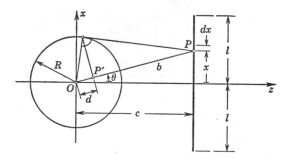

FIG. 21·8   Grounded Sphere and Uniformly Charged Wire.

graph of the field lines are found in Jeans,[A10] p. 192; and in Ramsay,[A21] p. 132. As seen from (28), the field strength has the largest value at $r = R$, $\theta = 0$, at the positive "pole" of the sphere, where it reaches $3E^0$. Again, the analogous problem occurs in hydraulics with a spherical obstacle in the uniform flow of an incompressible fluid, known as the *Dirichlet problem;* see references in Appendix 4, C, c.

Extension of the image theory to the effect of a uniformly charged line of finite length upon a grounded sphere is possible by dividing the line into point charge elements $(Q/2l)dx$ as in Fig. 21·8. Each element has associated an image element dQ', whereby

$$b = (c^2 + x^2)^{1/2}, \qquad d = \frac{R^2}{b}, \qquad dQ' = -\left(\frac{Q}{2l} dx\right)\frac{R}{b} \quad (29)$$

The total image charge within the sphere is also the charge Q'

induced on the sphere and is obtained by direct integration; see Ramsay,[A21] p. 123:

$$Q' = -\frac{Q}{2l}R \int_{x=-l}^{x=+l} \frac{dx}{b} = -\frac{Q}{l}R \sinh^{-1}\frac{l}{c} \tag{30}$$

which reduces to the expression for a single point charge if l/c is very small so that $\sinh^{-1} l/c \approx l/c$.

The electrostatic field of *two finite conducting spheres* can be described only by an infinite sequence of images. If the two spheres have radii R_1 and R_2, potentials Φ_1 and Φ_2, and a center distance $2c$, one uses the principles of linear superposition to evaluate the respective charges Q_1 and Q_2 which will accumulate on these spheres. One first assumes Φ_1 on sphere 1 with a fictitious point charge $Q_1 = 4\pi\varepsilon R_1\Phi_1$ at its center, which would produce this potential were this sphere alone. The presence of the second sphere can be accounted for only if it has potential zero by placing an image point charge $-(R_2/2c)Q_1$ at a distance from its center $R_2^2/2c$ towards sphere 1. However, this requires a new image charge within sphere 1 whose charge and location follow from the elementary image theory; this process goes on *ad infinitum* but with quick convergence of the charge values so that a few terms are generally sufficient. Complete details for the general case are given in Maxwell,[A17] I, p. 270, who also computes the force action and in Kirchhoff,[A13] p. 64, based on an earlier paper;[13] a very complete account is found in Russell,[B11] I, p. 236, who also gives many numerical values for the image series and computes maximum field strength and forces based on earlier papers,[14] to which Jeans,[A10] p. 196, also refers. A treatment can also be given in terms of a difference equation leading to solutions in terms of hyperbolic functions, as in Smythe,[A22] p. 117, and in Ollendorff,[A18] p. 266.

For two spheres of equal radii, or plane and sphere, the relations are somewhat simpler; see in addition to above references Attwood,[A2] p. 147; Schwaiger,[B17] p. 87, gives a rather comprehensive treatment in connection with the practical application as calibrated sphere gap for high-voltage measurements. It is important to note that the actual charges on the spheres and therefore the

---

[13] B. Kirchhoff, *Crelle's Jl.*, **59**, p. 89 (1861).
[14] A. Russell, *Phil. Mag.*, VI, **6**, p. 237 (1906); *Proc. Phys. Soc.*, **87**, p. 485 (1912), **24**, p. 22 (1913), and **97**, p. 120 (1920).

field strength on their surface and in the space between them depend on the values of the potentials assigned to the spheres, so that the distributions $\Phi_1 = +V/2$, $\Phi_2 = -V/2$, or $\Phi_1 = V$, $\Phi_2 = 0$ will give different results. The successive images define the induction coefficients $k_{\alpha\beta}$ in accordance with table 21·3; only

TABLE 21·3

POTENTIALS AND CHARGES ON TWO FINITE CONDUCTING SPHERES

	Sphere 1	Sphere 2
Case 1		
Potential	$\Phi_1 > 0$	0
Charge	$Q_{11} = k_{11}\Phi_1 > 0$	$Q_{12} = k_{12}\Phi_1 < 0$
Case 2		
Potential	0	$\Phi_2 < 0$
Charge	$Q_{21} = k_{21}\Phi_2 > 0$	$Q_{22} = k_{22}\Phi_2 < 0$
Case 3		
Potential	$\Phi_1 = +\dfrac{V}{2}$	$\Phi_2 = -\dfrac{V}{2}$
Charge	$Q_1 = (k_{11} - k_{21})\dfrac{V}{2}$	$Q_2 = -(k_{22} - k_{12})\dfrac{V}{2}$
Capacitance	$C_1 = k_{21} - k_{21}$	$C_2 = k_{22} - k_{12}$
Case 4		
Potential	Φ_1	Φ_2
Charge	$Q_1 = k_{11}\Phi_1 + k_{21}\Phi_2$	$Q_2 = k_{22}\Phi_2 + k_{12}\Phi_1$

the symmetrical potential distribution permits the general concept of capacitance for each conductor, and only if the two spheres are alike, so that $Q_1 = -Q_2$, does a capacitance of the system exist,

$$C = \frac{Q_1}{V} = 2(k_{11} - k_{12}) \tag{31}$$

in which case

$$k_{11} = k_{22} = R \sinh \beta \sum_{n=1}^{\infty} [\sinh (2n - 1)\beta]^{-1}$$

$$\tag{32}$$

$$k_{12} = -R \sinh \beta \sum_{n=1}^{\infty} [\sinh 2n\, \beta]^{-1}$$

where β is defined by $\cosh \beta = R/c$, with R the radius of the spheres and $2c$ their center distance.

22· METHOD OF MAGNETIC IMAGES

The solution of the magnetic field distribution caused by line currents in the presence of magnetic materials has not been as generally common as the corresponding electrostatic case. Though the principles can be formulated in rather similar manner, the actual application frequently does not lend itself to simple transfer of a known electrostatic solution because of the restrictions which one must impose upon the scalar magnetostatic potential (see section 6). It must be borne in mind, too, that the mirror image of the electrostatic field of a positive charge is again that of a positive charge because of its essential source nature; the mirror image of the magnetic field of a positive current is, however, that of a negative current, since the circulation of the field lines reverses in the mirror, so that for geometrical imaging one must substitute negative current values. Finally, since there is no magnetic conductor analogous to electrical conductors, a boundary of a magnetic material, even if of infinite permeability, need not be an equipotential surface; if it should be one, it must be specified explicitly in order to state the boundary conditions in an unambiguous way.

Images with Respect to Ideal Plane Equipotential Boundaries. The solution for the magnetic field of any line currents in air (confined to mathematical lines but of arbitrary geometry) near a plane equipotential boundary of magnetic material of infinite permeability is found by substituting the geometric image of the line conductors, with the currents flowing in the *same* direction as in the original in place of the magnetic material, and finding the combined magnetic field in air. This is analogous to the procedure on a plane conductor surface in electrostatics with the appropriate change in sign of the source image, and, indeed, the magnetic field lines will be identical with the equipotential lines of the positive line charges of the same geometry, placing the positive image behind the boundary plane[1] which, of course, cannot be then a conductor. The magnetic field will not extend into the magnetic

---

[1] Hague,[B44] p. 93; also S. P. Thompson and Miles Walker, *Phil. Mag.*, V, **39**, p. 213 (1895), and H. Ebert: *Magnetische Kraftfelder;* J. A. Barth, Leipzig, 1905.

material because of $\mu = \infty$, as the law of refraction (6·11) indicates.

If one long straight line current flows in close proximity of such an ideal magnetic boundary, as in Fig. 22·1, the field in air is the combination of two like and equal line currents which can readily be obtained by the simple graphical methods of section 20; see also Attwood,[A2] p. 395, and Russell,[B11] p. 448. The placement of the potential barrier is subject to choice; it would, however,

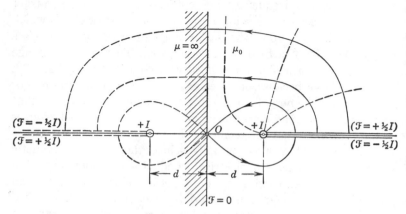

FIG. 22·1	Long Line Current Parallel to Ideal Plane Magnetic Boundary.

cause difficulty in the boundary plane if one chose the image barrier to the right of the image current.

For a parallel pair of long transmission line wires, Fig. 22·2 shows the arrangement of the pair of image currents; a good field graph can be found in Attwood,[A2] p. 398. The proximity of the magnetic material increases the self-inductance of the line; this increase can be computed from the flux produced by the image conductors and linked with the original loop. Thus, from (13·20) it follows at once per unit length

$$\Delta L_1 = + \frac{\mu_0}{2\pi} \ln\left[1 + \left(\frac{c}{d}\right)^2\right] \tag{1}$$

where the appropriate values from Fig. 22·2 were substituted. Obviously, as d decreases, ΔL_1 increases to the maximum external inductance of the original loop when it touches the surface; one usually assumes doubling of the entire self-inductance since the

internal inductance is a very small amount.   The same procedure
can be used for any linear current loop, so that the forms of section
13 become directly applicable.   For uniform current densities,
this method can be extended to conductors of finite cross sections,
subdividing them into current elements $J\,dS$ and applying the
imaging method to each in turn.

Intersecting plane boundaries of magnetic materials can be

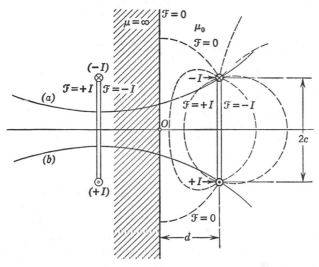

FIG. 22·2   Two Long Transmission-line Wires Parallel to
Ideal Magnetic Boundary.

treated similarly.   Assume a long straight line current in air
between planes $\mathcal{F} = 0$ which intersect at any angle π/n, where n
is an integer.   The geometrical location of the $(2n - 1)$ images is
the same as for point charges discussed in section 10, but all the
image currents have the *same* direction as the original.   The
resultant field distribution can readily be composed as the superposition of the total $2n$ line currents.   The image location is given
in Hague,[B44] p. 100, and a resultant field graph for right-angle
intersection in Attwood,[A2] p. 397, and in Hague,[B44] p. 102; other
resultant graphs equally applicable to $2n$-conductor cables with
symmetrical arrangement in Russel,[B11] p. 462.

A long straight line current in air between two parallel ideal
magnetic equipotential surfaces similar to Fig. 21·1 requires an

infinite series of images which are located exactly as shown in table 21·1 for the corresponding electric arrangement, except that again all the image currents are positive here; see Hague,[B44] pp. 172 and 169, and also Bewley,[D1] pp. 158 and 137.　It is advantageous to use the vector potential for the original and image line currents, since the magnetostatic potential becomes somewhat unwieldy.　According to (13·23), the resultant vector potential is

$$A_z = - \frac{\mu}{2\pi} I \sum_{(\alpha)} \ln r_\alpha \tag{2}$$

quite similar to the electrostatic potential (21·5) for the analogous problem; with μ for $1/\varepsilon$ and I for the alternating charges, one can get (2) from (21·5).　Now $r_\alpha = [(x - x_\alpha)^2 + y^2]^{1/2}$, with x_α from table 21·1, and the two infinite products can be identified in closed form; this can be obtained more simply by conformal mapping (see section 27).　Graphs are given in Hague,[B44] p. 169, and in Bewley,[D1] p. 137; Attwood,[A2] p. 400, shows related ones of several currents between two ideal iron boundary surfaces.　Should one feel uneasy about the logarithms of distances in (2), then one could introduce some fixed distance R as reference and write $\ln r_\alpha/R$; however, all these $\ln R$ terms would collect into an additive constant in (2) whose value would remain unknowable since the vector potential itself is not observable.　Because the field vectors, as the derivatives of the vector potential, would in no case contain these arbitrary constant terms, the vector potential will generally be written in the form (2).

A long straight line current within a rectangular channel in iron of infinite permeability and bounded by equipotential surfaces leads to infinite arrays of positive image currents;[2] the solution can be obtained more simply by conformal mapping.

Images with Respect to Plane Magnetic Boundaries. Assume any number of parallel straight line currents I_α in medium μ_1 at distances h_α from the plane boundary of the semi-infinite medium μ_2 similar to Fig. 21·2.　Whatever the line current distribution in μ_1, the total field must satisfy the boundary conditions (6·7) and (6·10), excluding the presence of a current sheet in the boundary plane $x = 0$.　If the individual line currents produce two-dimensional vector potentials with only z-components, $A_{z\alpha}(h_\alpha - x, y)$, and the effect of the medium μ_2 is to be represented by

[2] B. Hague, *World Power*, **5**, pp. 124 and 205 (1926).

image line currents, then they must be located at geometrical image points in order to permit satisfying the boundary conditions, i.e., they must produce vector potentials $A_{z\alpha}''(h_\alpha + x, y)$ which have at $x = 0$ the identical dependence on y that the $A_{z\alpha}$ values have.

For any one line current the total vector potential in μ_1 is then assumed to be

$$A_{z\alpha}^{(1)} = \mu_1 I_\alpha \cdot \Psi(h_\alpha - x, y) + \mu_1 I_\alpha'' \cdot \Psi(h_\alpha + x, y) \qquad (3)$$

whereas the vector potential in μ_2 is assumed to be produced by a line current I_α' at the location of the original line current,

$$A_{z\alpha}^{(2)} = \mu_2 I_\alpha' \cdot \Psi(h_\alpha - x, y) \qquad (4)$$

The functions Ψ are identical, respectively, with $(1/2\pi) \ln(1/r_{1\alpha})$, and $(1/2\pi) \ln(1/r_{2\alpha})$, where $r_{1\alpha}$ and $r_{2\alpha}$ are designated in Fig. 21·2; the more general functional form is chosen to indicate the possible extension to the more general arrangements. In the chosen coordinate system, the boundary conditions require continuity of $B_x = +(\partial A_z/\partial y)$ and $H_y = -(1/\mu)(\partial A_z/\partial x)$. Defining $(\partial \Psi/\partial y)_{x=0} = \Psi_{\mathrm{I}}$, and $(\partial \Psi/\partial x)_{x=0} = \Psi_{\mathrm{II}}$, the boundary conditions give with (3) and (4)

$$\mu_1 I_\alpha \Psi_{\mathrm{I}} + \mu_1 I_\alpha'' \Psi_{\mathrm{I}} = \mu_2 I_\alpha' \Psi_{\mathrm{I}}$$
$$I_\alpha \Psi_{\mathrm{II}} - I_\alpha'' \Psi_{\mathrm{II}} = I_\alpha' \Psi_{\mathrm{II}} \qquad (5)$$

from which the image currents can be evaluated

$$I_\alpha' = \frac{2\mu_1}{\mu_1 + \mu_2} I_\alpha, \qquad I_\alpha'' = \frac{\mu_2 - \mu_1}{\mu_2 + \mu_1} I_\alpha \qquad (6)$$

The field picture in medium μ_1 for $x > 0$ is obtained by (3) as the resultant of the given line current I_α and the image current I_α'', which, as comparison with (21·9) shows, has again the opposite sign of the image charge Q_α'' in the electrostatic case. In medium μ_2 with vector potential by (4) the field lines are drawn as coming from a line current I_α' located at the same place as the given original.[3] In a more general geometry of line currents, all three components of the vector potential must be used as in Smythe,[A22] p. 282; the final result is, however, exactly the same as (6) since both tangential components H_y and H_z give identical equations.

It is now seen that, for $\mu_2 > \mu_1$, the image I_α'' will be positive;

[3] G. F. C. Searle, *Electrician*, **40**, p. 453 (1898).

for $\mu_2 < \mu_1$, i.e., if the line current were imbedded in iron, the image I_α'' would be negative. As $\mu_2 \to \infty$, $I_\alpha'' \to I_\alpha$ and $I_\alpha' \to 0$, as used in the preceding subsection; conversely, when $\mu_1 \to \infty$, $I_\alpha'' \to (-I_\alpha)$ and $I_\alpha' \to 2I_\alpha$, a case which will be taken up later in more detail. Excellent graphs for a single line current are given in Attwood,[A2] pp. 403, 405; in Hague,[B44] pp. 105, 107; and in Moullin,[B48] p. 224.

The force action on the single line current I_α can be computed by Ampère's law $(5 \cdot 1)$. Since the resultant field in medium μ_1 is the combined action of I_α and I_α'', one can assume the actual force to be that between these two currents, so that per unit length

$$f_m = \frac{\mu_1}{2\pi} \frac{I_\alpha I_\alpha''}{2h_\alpha} = \frac{\mu_1}{2\pi} \frac{\mu_2 - \mu_1}{\mu_2 + \mu_1} \frac{I_\alpha^2}{2h_\alpha} \tag{7}$$

exactly analogous to $(21 \cdot 12)$, giving the force action between two parallel line charges. The same result can be obtained by using the force expression in terms of the magnetic field B_α'' produced by I_α''. There will be attraction to the iron for $\mu_2 > \mu_1$, since the force is positive.

For a pair of long transmission line wires in air parallel to a plane iron surface of μ, as shown in Fig. $22 \cdot 2$, the resultant field in air is determined by the original current and the image I_α'' from (6). The proximity of the iron increases the self-inductance of the line, and this increase can be found as in the previous subsection, except that the factor from (6) enters,

$$\Delta L_1 = \frac{\mu_0}{2\pi} \frac{\mu - \mu_0}{\mu + \mu_0} \ln \left[1 + \left(\frac{c}{d} \right)^2 \right] \tag{8}$$

For decreasing distance d, the total external inductance increases to a maximum value on the surface when image and original become geometrically identical

$$L_{\text{max}1} = \left(1 + \frac{\mu - \mu_0}{\mu + \mu_0} \right) L_{\text{ex}1} = \frac{2\mu}{\mu + \mu_0} L_{\text{ex}1} \tag{9}$$

where $L_{\text{ex}1}$ is to be taken from $(13 \cdot 17)$. This form (9) holds for any wire loop placed on the surface of a semi-infinite iron block.

A single very long straight line current in air between two infinite-extent blocks of iron a distance $2h$ apart, analogous to Fig. $21 \cdot 3$, requires two infinite series of images to satisfy the boundary conditions. For symmetrical arrangement the geometrical location of all the images can be taken from table 21·2, and the image current values can be found quite analogously to the electrostatic problem. It is important to combine the vector potentials of the individual images with the proper permeability in each medium as indicated by (2) and (3); this is different from the electrostatic case. Thus, in air one has

$$A_z = -\frac{\mu_0}{2\pi} I\left[\ln r + \sum_{n=1}^{\infty} (\tau'')^n \ln(r_{\mathrm{II}_n} r_{\mathrm{III}_n})\right] \qquad (10)$$

where in analogy to (21·14) but with the pertinent modifications

$$\frac{2\mu_0}{\mu + \mu_0} = \tau', \qquad \frac{\mu - \mu_0}{\mu + \mu_0} = \tau'' \qquad (11)$$

and where

$$r_{\mathrm{II}_n}{}^2 = (x + 2nh)^2 + y^2, \qquad r_{\mathrm{III}_n}{}^2 = (x - 2nh)^2 + y^2$$

For two parallel very long wires arranged as in Fig. 22·2 but midway between two blocks of iron a distance $2h$ apart, one has from (10)

$$A_z = \frac{\mu_0}{2\pi} I\left[\ln\left(\frac{r^-}{r^+}\right) + \sum_{n=1}^{\infty} (\tau'')^n \ln\frac{(r_{\mathrm{II}_n}{}^-)\,(r_{\mathrm{III}_n}{}^-)}{(r_{\mathrm{II}_n}{}^+)\,(r_{\mathrm{III}_n}{}^+)}\right] \qquad (12)$$

with the radii to positive and negative currents as indicated. The first term is the vector potential of the original current pair exactly as in (13·13); the summation term is the effect of the image pairs. The total inductance of the loop can be found exactly as in (13·16), taking the difference of the vector potential values at the two wires. Again the first term gives the normal external inductance in air (13·17) if the loop is by itself, so that the increase in inductance becomes

$$\Delta L_1 = \frac{\mu_0}{\pi} \sum_{n=1}^{\infty} (\tau'')^n \ln\left[1 + \left(\frac{c}{nh}\right)^2\right] \qquad (13)$$

since on conductor $+I$

$$r_{\mathrm{II}_n}{}^+ = r_{\mathrm{III}_n}{}^+ = 2nh, \qquad r_{\mathrm{II}_n}{}^- = r_{\mathrm{III}_n}{}^- = [(2nh)^2 + (2c)^2]^{1/2}$$

and vice versa on conductor $-I$. Comparing (13) with (8), one recognizes the additive effect of all the image pairs of currents. Obviously, this principle can be extended at once to any plane linear current loop between two blocks of iron.

The same result can also be used for two parallel wires imbedded in the center plane of an infinite slab of iron of thickness $2h$. Interchanging μ and μ_0, one obtains

$$\Delta L_1 = \frac{\mu}{\pi} \sum_{n=1}^{\infty} (-\tau'')^n \ln\left[1 + \left(\frac{c}{nh}\right)^2\right] \qquad (14)$$

and recognizes that there is a decrease in inductance on account of the finite thickness of iron, since (14) is an alternating series and the first and largest term is negative. Again, this can be extended to any plane linear current loop.

Images with Respect to Cylindrical Magnetic Boundaries. The problem of long straight line currents parallel to a cylinder of magnetic material is similar to that of a plane magnetic boundary and completely analogous to the electrostatic case in section 21. For a single long line current $+I$ as in Fig. 22·3, located at A in air with μ_0, at a distance b from the center of the magnetic cylinder with μ, the field in air will be described by placing an image line current $(+I'')$ into the geometric image line $d = R^2/b$ from the axis; additionally, one must place another line current $(-I'')$ along the axis in order to neutralize the first image line. The total external vector potential at a point P will therefore be with (11)

$$A_{z\text{ex}} = -\frac{\mu_0}{2\pi} I\left(\ln r' + \tau'' \ln \frac{r''}{r}\right) \qquad (15)$$

The field within the magnetic cylinder will be that of a single line current $(+I)'$ located at the place of the original current; the field lines will therefore be circular arcs and the vector potential

$$A_{z\text{in}} = -\frac{\mu}{2\pi} I\tau' \ln r' \qquad (16)$$

By interchange of μ and μ_0, one obtains the solution for a straight cylindrical tunnel in iron with the line current placed in the iron. Excellent field graphs for both alternatives are given in Hague,[B44] p. 115.

The extension to two symmetrically located line currents $\pm I$ as in Fig. 22·3 is rather obvious; the compensating line currents $\mp I''$ at the origin are now not needed. If the two line currents $\pm I$ recede to infinity as $b \to \infty$, the images $(\pm I'')$ approach the origin as $d = (R^2/b) \to 0$, so that they form a dipole line current. In the limit one has the case of a magnetic cylinder in a uniform magnetic field produced by the two line currents, which can be taken from $(13 \cdot 16)$ at $x = y = 0$ as

$$B_x{}^0 = + \frac{\mu_0}{\pi} \left(\frac{I}{b} \right) \tag{17}$$

where both $I \to \infty$ and $b \to \infty$ to produce a finite field, quite similar to $(21 \cdot 18)$.   The field outside is given as the superposition of

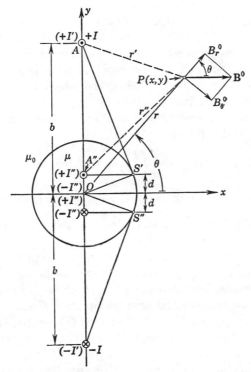

FIG. $22 \cdot 3$ Magnetic Cylinder and Two Line Currents.   Limiting case for $b \to \infty$: magnetic cylinder in uniform field $\mathbf{B}^0$.

this uniform field and the current dipole line formed by the image currents, which have a dipole moment per unit length from $(13 \cdot 19)$

$$\mathbf{m} = I \left(2 \frac{R^2}{b} \right) \mathbf{i} = \frac{2\pi}{\mu_0} R^2 B_x{}^0 \mathbf{i} \tag{18}$$

directed along the positive x-axis.   The field of the dipole line is given in section 13 in the cylindrical coordinates r, θ, x, in which the uniform field $B_x{}^0$ has the components

$$B_r{}^0 = B_x{}^0 \cos \theta, \qquad B_\theta{}^0 = -B_x{}^0 \sin \theta$$

The direct addition of the fields and use of (18) give the resultant field

$$B_r = B_x{}^0 \left(1 + \tau'' \frac{R^2}{r^2}\right) \cos \theta, \qquad B_\theta = -B_x{}^0 \left(1 - \tau'' \frac{R^2}{r^2}\right) \sin \theta \quad (19)$$

which checks with the solution obtained with circular harmonics; see also Moullin,[B48] p. 198. If one lets $\mu \to \infty$, then $\tau'' \to 1$ and the forms become analogous to (21·20), which describe a conducting cylinder in a uniform electric field; the field lines will therefore be normal to the cylinder surface. The internal field is given by the two symmetrical line currents ($\pm I'$) which receded like the originals to infinity and therefore produce a uniform field given by (17), but with μ for μ_0,

$$B_{x\text{in}} = \frac{\mu}{\pi} \left(\frac{I'}{b}\right) = \frac{\mu}{\mu_0} \tau' B_x{}^0 \tag{20}$$

which is much stronger than the original one by the factor $\dfrac{2\mu}{\mu + \mu_0}$. As $\mu \to \infty$, the field inside will approach twice the original uniform field.

If a line current $+I$ is placed within the magnetic cylinder μ, say, at A'' in Fig. 22.3, then it requires, as in the electrostatic analogue, an image line current $(+I'')$ at A, the geometrical image point of A'' to describe the field within the cylinder, where now $I'' = (\mu_0 - \mu)/(\mu_0 + \mu)I = -\tau''I$ from (11) because of the interchange in relative position; the field outside the magnetic cylinder is given by a current $I' = 2\mu_0/(\mu + \mu_0)I = \tau'I$ at A'', the location of the original, but now it requires another line current of value I'' at the axis in order to have the external field determined by the effective current $I = I' + I''$ within the cylinder. The demonstration that these images satisfy all the boundary conditions, i.e., continuity of B_r and H_θ in cylindrical coordinates, is simply given by selecting a point at the periphery and equating with proper algebraic signs the componental contributions on either side. Hague,[B44] p. 111, gives considerable details and also shows excellent graphs for the above case as well as the reverse, a line current in a cylindrical air tunnel in a block of iron. In the latter application, μ and μ_0 must be interchanged and the mechanical force per unit length upon the current is simply the interaction of it and the image determining the field in the air tunnel, namely,

$$f = \frac{\mu_0}{2\pi} \frac{II''}{b-d} = \frac{\mu_0}{2\pi} \frac{\mu - \mu_0}{\mu + \mu_0} \frac{d}{R^2 - d^2} I^2 \qquad (21)$$

if d is distance of the current from the axis (A'' in Fig. $22 \cdot 3$). The force is attraction to the iron, as the positive sign indicates.

Currents within Ideal Magnetic Materials.   If a line current is imbedded in a magnetic material of infinite permeability $\mu = \infty$, then the image relations (6) and (11) place the *negative* image current into the ambient medium at the geometric image point in order to describe the field within the magnetic material.   In this case, then, the electrostatic image solutions apply directly with interchange of electric equipotential lines to magnetic field lines and vice versa.

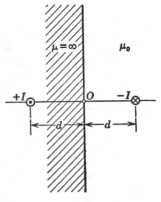

In this manner, a long straight line current within $\mu = \infty$ and parallel to a plane boundary surface, as in Fig. $22 \cdot 4$, has a magnetic field given by

Fig. $22 \cdot 4$ Long Line Current within Ideal Magnetic Material Parallel to Plane Boundary.

the equipotential lines of a long straight charged line parallel to a plane conducting surface; they will be the family of circles described in ($13 \cdot 15$).   Thus, the equipotential boundary surface of the electrostatic analogue becomes a field line surface in the magnetic material, even though it is boundary to a medium $\mu = \infty$.   The field in air is supposedly given by a line current $I' = 2I$ at the place of the original; this would represent circles in air quite inconsistent with the fact that the boundary surface itself coincides with field lines.   One usually disregards the external field completely and suppresses the image I!

For a long straight line current within a magnetic cylinder of infinite permeability, the field lines will again be wholly contained within the cylinder and will be identical with the equipotential lines of two eccentric cylindrical conductors enclosing each other; see ($12 \cdot 43$).

23. METHOD OF INVERSION

The method of electrical images has been expanded into a more general tool by using the geometrical process of imaging for the transformation of certain given geometries into simpler ones. This is of particular value in three-dimensional problems involving spherical surfaces; it is of less importance in two dimensions where one has available the very powerful method of conformal representation.

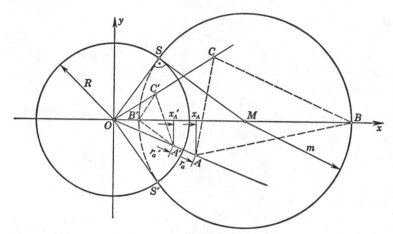

Fig. 23·1   Inversion in a Sphere.

The Kelvin Transformation. Geometrically, the inverse point to A with respect to the sphere of radius R, center O in Fig. 23·1, is point A' with radial distance $r_A' = \dfrac{R^2}{r_A}$ and the coordinates

$$x_A' = \frac{R^2}{r_A{}^2}x_A, \qquad y_A' = \frac{R^2}{r_A{}^2}y_A, \qquad z_A' = \frac{R^2}{r_A{}^2}z_A \qquad (1)$$

since $x_A'/x_A = r_A'/r_A$, etc.; similarly for other points B and C. If the three points lie on any closed surface wholly outside the sphere R, then the inverse in the sphere will again be a closed surface in which the successive points are arranged as the mirror images of the points of the original. In particular, one can show that spheres remain spheres or degenerate into planes as special cases of spheres. Thus, a sphere S_2 of radius m and center M in Fig. 23·2 tangent to the sphere of inversion at T becomes again a sphere S_2' tangent at T but of radius $m' = R - d = R(1 - R/b)$. As $m \to \infty$, the sphere S_2 becomes the plane S_1 and its inverse becomes the sphere S_1' of radius $R/2$ passing through the origin 0; this point 0 becomes obviously the inverse of the point P as it moves into infinity. To preserve one-to-one relationship, it is conventional to consider infinity as a single point, as the inverse of the origin. This then

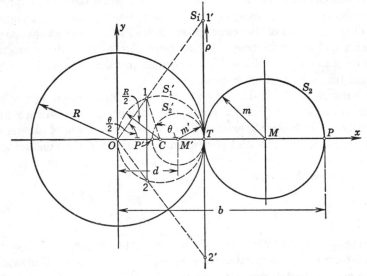

Fig. 23·2 Inversion of Spheres in a Sphere.

also means that any sphere through the origin 0 and of radius $p < R$ has as inverse a plane at a distance $b = R^2/2p$ from the origin and normal to the center line.

Spheres which intersect the sphere of inversion orthogonally are transformed into themselves. Take the sphere through point B in Fig. 23·1 with radius m and center M. Its equation is

$$(x - x_M)^2 + y^2 + z^2 = r^2 - 2x_M x + x_M{}^2 = m^2 \qquad (2)$$

Introducing $r = R^2/r'$ and $x = x'r^2/R^2$ gives, upon reordering into the same form as (2),

$$(r')^2 - \frac{2x_M R^2}{x_M{}^2 - m^2} x' + \frac{R^4}{x_M{}^2 - m^2} = 0 \qquad (3)$$

but $x_M{}^2 - m^2 = R^2$ form the right triangle MSO, so that (3) can at once be written in identical form as (2) with $(r')^2$ and x' instead of r^2 and x. Therefore, the segment $SB'S'$ of the spherical surface within the sphere of inversion will be point by point the inverse of the spherical surface SBS' outside. One can use this property to show in simple manner that this transformation by inversion on a sphere is *conformal;* the angle between any two line elements is the same as that between their images. One need only consider the line elements ds_1 and ds_2 as elements of great circles of spheres intersecting orthogonally the sphere of inversion; then their images will be elements of the same great circles intersecting at the same point and at its inverse. It has been shown[1] that there are no more general possibilities of conformal transformations in space than the Kelvin transformation.

Suppose that it is desired to find a potential function $\Phi(x, y, z)$ for some given conductor configuration with known surface potentials. Introducing arbitrarily a convenient sphere of inversion of radius R, one can find the inverse geometry of the conductors. The potential function solving the problem in the inverse coordinates is then given by

$$\Phi'(x', y', z') = \frac{R}{r'} \Phi\left(\frac{R^2}{r'^2} x', \quad \frac{R^2}{r'^2} y', \quad \frac{R^2}{r'^2} z'\right) \tag{4}$$

To show this, one might transform the Laplacian differential equation for Φ from coordinates (x, y, z) to those (x', y', z'). Following the general transformation equation $(31 \cdot 27)$, one has for example for the x-coordinate because of the symmetry of the Cartesian coordinate system

$$\frac{\partial^2 \Phi}{\partial x^2} = h^{-3} \frac{\partial}{\partial x'}\left(h \frac{\partial \Phi}{\partial x'}\right) = \left(\frac{r'}{R}\right)^6 \frac{\partial}{\partial x'}\left(\frac{R^2}{r'^2} \frac{\partial \Phi}{\partial x'}\right) \tag{5}$$

where $dx = (R^2/r'^2)\, dx'$ from (1) defines the uniform scale factor $h = R^2/r'^2$ But one can write

$$\frac{\partial^2}{\partial x'^2}\left(\frac{1}{r'} \Phi\right) = \frac{1}{r'} \frac{\partial^2 \Phi}{\partial x'^2} + 2 \frac{\partial \Phi}{\partial x'} \frac{\partial}{\partial x'}\left(\frac{1}{r'}\right) + \Phi \frac{\partial^2}{\partial x'^2}\left(\frac{1}{r'}\right) \tag{6}$$

The last term in (6), when taken with the corresponding terms in y' and x', gives the Laplacian of $(1/r')$ which must be zero since

[1] Kellogg,[C10] p. 235, who refers to Blaschke: *Vorlesungen über Differentialgeometrie*, Vol. I; J. Springer, Berlin, 1924.

$(1/r')$ defines the potential of a single point charge; see $(10 \cdot 2)$. The first two terms in (6), however, are also

$$r' \left[\frac{1}{r'^2} \frac{\partial^2 \Phi}{\partial x'^2} + \frac{2}{r'} \frac{\partial \Phi}{\partial x'} \frac{\partial}{\partial x'} \left(\frac{1}{r'} \right) \right] = r' \frac{\partial}{\partial x'} \left(\frac{1}{r'^2} \frac{\partial \Phi}{\partial x'} \right)$$

This leads with (5), adding the corresponding expressions in the other coordinates, to

$$\nabla^2 \Phi(x, y, z) = \left(\frac{r'}{R} \right)^5 (\nabla')^2 \left[\frac{R}{r'} \Phi(x, y, z) \right] = 0 \qquad (7)$$

where ∇' means differentiation with respect to the inverse coordinates and where of course the original coordinates must be expressed in terms of the inverse ones as in (4). Omitting the extra factor $(r'/R)^5$, one sees that (4) will be the potential solution for the inverse function, satisfying the boundary conditions in the inverse geometry[2] if there the charge values are multiplied by (R/r'). The entire potential problem is therefore transformed, not actually solved, by this Kelvin inversion in a sphere. It will be helpful in all cases where inversion reduces the problem to one already solved at least in part, or readily solvable by means of images.

The transformation ratio of a line charge density λ can be found by noting that line elements transform as in (1), and charges transform in the ratio $R/r' = r/R$, so that

$$\frac{\lambda}{\lambda'} = \frac{r}{R} \div \left(\frac{r}{R} \right)^2 = \left(\frac{R}{r} \right) = \left(\frac{r'}{R} \right) \qquad (8)$$

In general it will become a variable charge density unless r is a constant. Surface charge densities transform in the ratio

$$\frac{\sigma}{\sigma'} = \frac{r}{R} \div \left(\frac{r}{R} \right)^4 = \left(\frac{R}{r} \right)^3 = \left(\frac{r'}{R} \right)^3 \qquad (9)$$

Intersecting Spheres. Assume two spheres of radii R_1 and R_2 intersecting orthogonally as in Fig. $23 \cdot 3$, carrying a total charge Q. By inversion on a sphere selected with center at O in the intersection of the given spheres and of radius $2R_2$, the two spheres become planes intersecting normally at U' the inverse point to U. Now, if the original conductor had a charge Q, all the field lines

---

[2] W. Thomson: *Papers on Electrostatics and Magnetism;* Macmillan, London, 1872; first published in *Jl. de math.*, **12**, p. 256 (1847). See also Kirchhoff,[A13] p. 53; Maxwell,[A17] I, p. 253; Ollendorff,[A18] p. 335; Kellogg,[C10] p. 232; and Murnaghan,[C13] p. 141.

from it go to infinity, which in the sense of inversion is a point and must be the location of a point charge $(-Q)$. This point charge has been transferred to the point O with respect to the two planes, but its value must be changed, though it cannot be determined in the usual manner. Assume that its value be $(-Q')$.

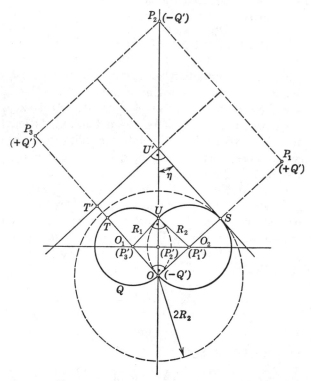

FIG. 23·3 Two Orthogonally Intersecting Spheres.

In the inverse geometry the problem is now to find the solution of a point charge $(-Q')$ in the space between two conducting planes intersecting at right angles, a problem treated in section 10, Fig. 10·3. Placing image charges at P_1, P_2, P_3 as shown in Fig. 23·3, one can at once find the potential anywhere in the space between the two planes, which by (4) can be transformed into the potential solution outside the two intersecting spheres. One can also solve directly in the original geometry if one now inverts all the image charges on the sphere of inversion, as shown in table 23·1.

TABLE 23·1

INVERSION OF CHARGES ON SPHERE FOR FIG. 23·3

Charges for Intersecting Planes $-Q'$ at origin 0 (original)	Inverse Charges for Intersecting Spheres $-Q$ at infinity	
Images	*Inverse images*	
$Q_1 = +Q'$ at P_1	$Q_1' = +Q' \dfrac{2R_2}{OP_1} = \dfrac{1}{2}Q'$	at $d_1 = \dfrac{(2R_2)^2}{OP_1} = R_2$ (i.e, at O_2)
$Q_2 = -Q'$ at P_2	$Q_2' = -Q' \dfrac{2R_2}{OP_2} = -\dfrac{Q'}{2\sqrt{1+\tau^2}}$	at $d_2 = \dfrac{(2R_2)^2}{OP_2} = \dfrac{R_2}{\sqrt{1+\tau^2}}$ (i.e., at P_2')
$Q_3 = +Q'$ at P_3	$Q_3' = +Q' \dfrac{2R_2}{OP_3} = \dfrac{1}{2\tau}Q'$	at $d_3 = \dfrac{(2R_2)^2}{OP_3} = R_1$ (i.e., at O_1)

$$(\tau = R_2/R_1)$$

The total charge on the intersecting spheres is the sum of the three inverse images

$$Q = Q_1' + Q_2' + Q_3' = Q' \frac{(1 + \tau)\sqrt{1 + \tau^2} - \tau}{2\tau\sqrt{1 + \tau^2}} \quad (10)$$

where $\tau = R_2/R_1$, and the potential of the spheres can be determined as the superposition of the three point charge potentials for any one point of the surface, say, U, where

$$\Phi(U) = \frac{1}{4\pi\varepsilon}\left(\frac{Q_1'}{R_2} + \frac{Q_2'}{d_2} + \frac{Q_3'}{R_1}\right) = \frac{1}{4\pi\varepsilon}\frac{Q'}{2R_2} \quad (11)$$

if one uses the values of table 23·1. The capacitance is then, with (10),

$$C = \frac{\Phi(U)}{Q} = 4\pi\varepsilon R_2\left(\frac{1 + \tau}{\tau} - \frac{1}{\sqrt{1 + \tau^2}}\right) \quad (12)$$

When $\tau \to \infty$, the capacitance approaches that of the larger sphere R_2, and if $\tau \to 0$, it approaches that of sphere R_1. The surface charge density can be evaluated by inversion of the charge distribution on the planes, using relation (9). The field vector and the field graph can best be found as the superposition of the three point charges. A field graph and the complete solution originally given by W. Thomson (*loc. cit.*) are given in Maxwell,[A17] I, p. 261, and in Fig. IV there; a brief treatment is in Ramsay,[A21] p. 128; see also Smythe,[A22] p. 123, and Murnaghan,[C13] p. 152.

Two spheres intersecting at any angle π/n, where n is integer, can be treated by the same method, the inversion leading to planes intersecting at angles π/n; see Maxwell,[A17] I, p. 261. From Fig. 23·3 it is also seen that a spherical lens as formed by the overlapping dotted spherical segments between O and U is inverted into the space between the dotted continuations of the planes containing the point P_2. The field distribution desired is now the one *outside* the dotted right-angle plane corner with the point charge $(-Q')$ at O, which cannot be obtained by the image method but requires the construction of Green's function[3] (see section 34).

If the intersecting spheres are to be considered isolated and under the influence of an external point charge Q_0, then in addition

[3] Bateman,[C1] p. 472.

to the solution above, one has to solve the plane geometry for the effect of the inverse charge Q_0', i.e., add another set of three images $\pm Q_0'$, and transfer these back into the intersecting spheres. The sum total of all charges within these spheres must be zero, which determines the value of the charge Q' from above. The potential is that obtained by the superposition of all point charges within finite distance of the origin O.

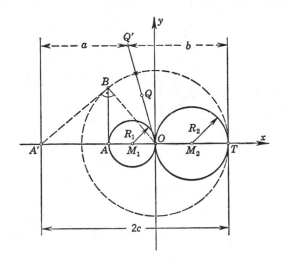

Fɪɢ. 23·4   Two Spheres in Contact and Point Charge Q.

As a special case one might consider two spheres of radii R_1 and R_2 contacting each other as in Fig. 23·4 under the influence of a point charge Q. Assume the spheres to be grounded and at zero potential; then inversion on a sphere with center at the point of contact and radius $2R_2$ produces two parallel planes with the inverse Q' of the point charge between them. The solution of this problem leads to an infinite number of image charges and has been indicated in section 21 (see also Maxwell,[A17] I, p. 274). For equal spheres $R_1 = R_2 = R$ and the point charge in the center plane, the solution is symmetrical and $2c = 4R$.

Maxwell,[A17] I, p. 263, considers also three spheres intersecting orthogonally and gives the charge distribution.

Segments of a Sphere. If the segment of a spherical surface or a spherical bowl is given like $1–T–2$ in Fig. 23·2 of sphere

$S_1{}'$, then one can choose a sphere of inversion (as shown) which will transform $S_1{}'$ into the plane S_1 and the spherical bowl into the circular disk $1'$-$2'$. Assume the charge on the bowl as $+Q$; then its field lines go out into infinity defined as a point for purposes of inversion, and terminate there on a point charge $(-Q)$. The inversion brings this charge into the point O but of value $(-Q')$ as in the previous subsection. Thus in the inverse geometry one has to find the solution of a circular disk exposed to the influence

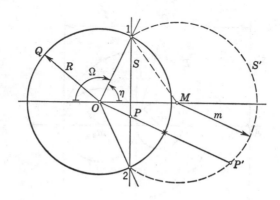

FIG. 23·5   Spherical Bowl.

of a single point charge $(-Q')$ located at O; this cannot be solved by usual image methods. It is seen, however, that the side of the circular disk facing the point charge will have the larger charge density induced; by inversion this becomes the convex side of the spherical bowl which will therefore carry the larger charge.

The field of a charged spherical bowl can be found also by superposition of partial solutions satisfying the boundary conditions on the surface of the bowl and that of the sphere S' in Fig. 23·5 obtained by inversion of the circular area S on the sphere of which the bowl is part. With Φ_0 as the potential of the spherical bowl, R its radius, and Ω its segmental angle, one finds the total charge on its inner and outer surface, respectively, as

$$Q_{i,e} = 2\varepsilon R\Phi_0\left[\sin\Omega + \Omega \mp \frac{\pi}{2}(1-\cos\Omega)\right] \tag{13}$$

For $\Omega \to \pi$, $Q_i \to 0$ and $Q_e \to 4\pi\varepsilon R\Phi_0$, as they should. The total charge defines then the capacitance

$$C = \frac{Q_i + Q_e}{\Phi_0} = 4\varepsilon R(\sin \Omega + \Omega) \tag{14}$$

Extensive details are found in the original treatise by W. Thomson, *loc. cit.*, p. 178, who gives specific applications for several values of Ω; also in Maxwell,[A17] I, p. 276; in Jeans,[A10] p. 250; and in Kirchhoff,[A13] p. 58. Ollendorff,[A18] p. 366, gives a very thorough treatment and applies the results to the computation of the capacitance of suspension insulators; he also uses the inversion of this problem to solve a circular disk and a plate with a circular hole under the influence of a point charge.

Stereographic Projection. As discussed in connection with Fig. 23·2, the plane S_1 and the spherical surface S_1' are related as mutual images by inversion on the sphere R, center O. A different interpretation is possible, stating that any point 1 on sphere S_1' is projected from the center O onto the plane S_1 in a one-to-one relationship such that angles are preserved. In fact, if a potential distribution on the spherical surface S_1' satisfies the two-dimensional Laplace equation [see Appendix 3, (40)]

$$\sin \theta \frac{\partial}{\partial \theta}\left(\sin \theta \frac{\partial \Phi}{\partial \theta}\right) + \frac{\partial^2 \Phi}{\partial \phi^2} = 0 \tag{15}$$

where θ measures the colatitude and ϕ the longitude; then the transformed relation in terms of the polar coordinates ρ and ϕ in the plane is again the pertinent form of Laplace's differential equation.[4] Designating the radius $R/2 = a$, then

$$\rho = 2a \tan \frac{\theta}{2}, \qquad \rho \frac{\partial}{\partial \rho} = \left(\rho \frac{d\theta}{d\rho}\right)\frac{\partial}{\partial \theta} = \sin \theta \frac{\partial}{\partial \theta}$$

so that (15) becomes

$$\rho \frac{\partial}{\partial \rho}\left(\rho \frac{\partial \Phi}{\partial \rho}\right) + \frac{\partial^2 \Phi}{\partial \phi^2} = 0 \tag{16}$$

Any solution of Laplace's differential equation in the plane can therefore, if expressed in polar coordinates, be projected directly

[4] Maxwell,[A17] I, p. 286; Kirchhoff,[A13] p. 139; Smythe,[A22] p. 239.

upon the spherical surface and constitute a solution of Laplace's equation on the sphere.   This interpretation is called *stereographic projection* and is particularly useful for the solution of current flow problems in thin spherical shells and bowls.

Assume two point electrodes on the sphere with a potential difference V and in locations θ_1, ϕ_1 and θ_2, ϕ_2, constituting current entry and exit points which, of course, can readily be made very small circular areas to keep densities finite.   In the projection on the plane, the locations become

$$\rho_1 = 2a \tan \frac{\theta_1}{2}, \quad \phi_1, \qquad \rho_2 = 2a \tan \frac{\theta_2}{2}, \quad \phi_2 \qquad (17)$$

and the problem is identical with the two-dimensional one of finding the electric field distribution between two parallel long straight lines solved in (12·29).   Introducing there by analogy the current I for λ, the conductivity γ for ε, one has

$$\Phi(\theta, \phi) = \frac{I}{2\pi\gamma} \ln \left(\frac{r_2}{r_1} \right)$$

$$= \frac{I}{2\pi\gamma} \ln \frac{\tan^2 \frac{\theta}{2} + \tan^2 \frac{\theta_1}{2} - 2 \tan \frac{\theta}{2} \tan \frac{\theta_1}{2} \cos (\phi - \phi_1)}{\tan^2 \frac{\theta}{2} + \tan^2 \frac{\theta_2}{2} - 2 \tan \frac{\theta}{2} \tan \frac{\theta_2}{2} \cos (\phi - \phi_2)} \qquad (18)$$

where r_1 and r_2, the radius vectors from the source points to the point of observation in the plane $P(\rho, \phi)$, have been expressed in terms of the spherical coordinates.   Special choices of the values (17) permit simplifications.   For example,[5] $\theta_1 = \theta_2 = \alpha$, $\phi_1 = -\phi_2 = \pi/2$, representing two electrodes on one great circle of the sphere, leads to

$$\Phi(\theta, \phi) = \frac{I}{2\pi\gamma} \coth^{-1} \frac{\tan^2 \frac{\theta}{2} \tan^2 \frac{\alpha}{2}}{2 \tan \frac{\theta}{2} \tan \frac{\alpha}{2} \sin \phi}$$

$$= \frac{I}{2\pi\gamma} \coth^{-1} \frac{1 - \cos \alpha \cos \phi}{\sin \alpha \sin \theta \sin \phi} \qquad (19)$$

[5] Smythe,[A22] p. 240.

Assume two small diameters d_1 and d_2 for the actual electrodes; the total resistance can be found by analogy from (12·46), if one uses (8·11) and admits a small finite thickness t

$$R = \frac{\varepsilon}{\gamma C_1 t} = \frac{1}{\pi \gamma t} \ln \frac{2D}{\sqrt{d_1' d_2'}} \tag{20}$$

where the distance D between the electrode centers in the plane is

$$D = 2a \left[\tan^2 \frac{\theta_1}{2} + \tan^2 \frac{\theta_2}{2} - 2 \tan \frac{\theta_1}{2} \tan \frac{\theta_2}{2} \cos (\phi_1 - \phi_2) \right]^{1/2}$$

$$\rightarrow 4a \tan \frac{\alpha}{2} \tag{21}$$

The first form is the general expression, and the second form holds for the special arrangement above. The diameters d_1' and d_2' in the plane are approximately given in the special case $\alpha < \pi/2$ as

$$d_1' = d_1 \left(1 - \tan^2 \frac{\alpha}{2} \right), \qquad d_2' = d_2 \left(1 - \tan^2 \frac{\alpha}{2} \right) \tag{22}$$

if one projects the ends of the diameters upon the plane and uses in first approximation $d \approx a \delta \alpha$, and $\tan (\alpha + \delta \alpha / 2) \approx \tan (\alpha/2) + (\delta \alpha / 2)(1 - \tan^2 \alpha/2)$. Combining (21) and (22) with (20), one finally has

$$R = \frac{1}{\pi \gamma t} \ln \left(\frac{4a}{\sqrt{d_1 d_2}} \tan \frac{\alpha}{2} \right) \tag{23}$$

The same method can be applied to a segment of a spherical surface, such as the spherical bowl $1-T-2$ Fig. 23·2. The projection on the plane S_1 is now a circular area of diameter $1'-2'$ and the flow problem has to be solved within the circle, usually with boundary condition preventing flow out of the circle. However, one could assume a heavy ring as border of the bowl and a single electrode contacting the surface at some point. All these problems in the plane can be solved best by means of suitable conformal transformations of the circular area as shown in sections 26 and 28.

Two-dimensional Inversion. Quite analogously to the three-dimensional inversion with respect to a sphere, one can formulate inversion of two-dimensional fields with respect to a cylinder which is different from the method of conformal representation.[6] Geomet-

---

[6] For example Smythe,[A22] p. 87.

rically, the inverse point to A in Fig. $23 \cdot 1$ (all figures can readily be interpreted geometrically as applying to spheres or cylinders) with respect to the cylinder of radius R, axis O, is point A' with axial distance $r_A' = R^2/r_A$ and the coordinates

$$x_A' = \frac{R^2}{r_A{}^2} x_A, \qquad y_A' = \frac{R^2}{r_A{}^2} y_A \tag{24}$$

As with spheres, so with cylinders; upon inversion, cylinders remain cylinders or degenerate into planes and vice versa. Thus, a cylinder S_2 of radius m, axis M in Fig. $23 \cdot 2$ tangent to the cylinder of inversion at T, becomes again a cylinder S_2' tangent at T but of radius $m' = R(1 - R/b)$. As $m \to \infty$, cylinder S_2 becomes the plane S_1, and its inverse becomes the cylinder of radius $R/2$ passing through the axis O, which is obviously the inverse of the infinitely distant cylinder. To preserve one-to-one relationship, it is conventional to consider two-dimensional infinity as a line, as the inverse of the axis at O. This then means that any cylinder through the axis O and of radius $p < R$ has as inverse a plane at a distance $b = R^2/2p$ from the axis O and normal to the center line.

Cylinders which intersect the cylinder of inversion orthogonally are transformed into themselves; the proof is exactly the same as in (2), (3), with the omission of the coordinate z. Thus, in Fig. 23.1, the segment $SB'S'$ of the cylindrical surface within the cylinder of inversion will be point by point the inverse of the cylindrical surface SBS' outside. The transformation is *conformal*. Angles between line elements in the x-y-plane are the same as between the inverted line elements, which could readily be demonstrated by considering these line elements as belonging to cylinders intersecting the cylinder of inversion orthogonally.

In two dimensions, the transfer of the Laplacian differential equation to the inverse geometry can be done in the same manner as in the Kelvin transformation, only that now $h_1 = h_2 = h$ as before, and $h_3 = 1$, since no change takes place in the z-direction. As consequence,

$$\Phi'(x', y') = \Phi\left(\frac{R^2}{r'^2} x', \ \frac{R^2}{r'^2} y'\right) \tag{25}$$

that means that the same function solves the potential problem in the two inversely related geometries; no adjustment of charge values becomes necessary. However, surface charge densities will transform in the ratio of the surface elements; since the depth is uniform, surface elements will transform in the same manner as line elements in (24), and, therefore,

$$\frac{\sigma}{\sigma'} = \left(\frac{r}{R}\right)^2 \tag{26}$$

As an example, take a single conductor formed of two orthogonally intersecting cylinders as in Fig. 23·3, carrying a charge λ per unit length. By inversion on a cylinder selected with axis at O in the intersection of the two cylinders and of radius $2R_2$, the cylinders become the orthogonally intersecting planes. If the original conductor carries the charge λ, its field lines go into infinity and terminate there on a line charge $(-\lambda)$ which by inversion is distributed on the axis. The problem in the inverse geometry is, therefore, that of a line charge $(-\lambda)$ in the corner formed by the orthogonally intersecting conducting planes, as in section 12. The solution requires three image charges $(+\lambda)$, $(-\lambda)$, $(+\lambda)$ at P_2, P_3, P_4, respectively; and transferring these back into the original geometry, their locations are given in table 23·1, where d_1, d_2, d_3 are, respectively, their distances from the axis O. The sum of these three image charges is $(+\lambda)$, which is also the charge on the intersecting cylinders, and the potential in the outside space is simply the superposition of the three line charges. The actual field graph can also be obtained by corresponding graphical superposition. The potential of the intersecting cylinders themselves presents the same difficulty as that of a single wire (12·28), so that it is not possible to define a unique value of capacitance. However, the distribution of the surface charge can be obtained by inverting the surface charge densities on the two planes by means of (26) onto the cylinders.

With the addition of a line charge $(-\lambda)$ parallel to O and located at P_1 in Fig. 23·3 as the return wire, the field lines from the intersecting cylinders will all terminate on this charge $(-\lambda)$. The inversion leads now to the two planes as before with the inverse of $(-\lambda)$ located at P_1', which is also O_2. The solution of the problem with the planes now requires locations of the three images as shown in table 23·2. The total charge on the intersecting cylinders is again $(+\lambda)$; their potential is the superposition of the four line charge potentials given in the right-hand column.

TABLE 23·2

Inversion of Charges on Cylinder for Fig. 23·3

Charges for Intersecting Planes

Inverse of original

$\longrightarrow \quad (-\lambda)$ at P_1^{I}; $OP_1^{\mathrm{I}} = R_2$

Images of inverse

$(+\lambda)$ at P_1^{II}; $OP_1^{\mathrm{II}} = 3R_2$

$(-\lambda)$ at P_1^{III}; $OP_1^{\mathrm{III}} = \left[(3R_2)^2 + \left(\dfrac{4R_2{}^2}{R_1} \right)^2 \right]^{\frac{1}{2}}$

$(+\lambda)$ at P_1^{IV}; $OP_1^{\mathrm{IV}} = \left[R_2{}^2 + \left(\dfrac{4R_2{}^2}{R_1} \right)^2 \right]^{\frac{1}{2}}$

Inverse Charges for Intersecting Cylinders

$\longrightarrow$ *Original* $(-\lambda)$ at P_1; $OP_1 = 4R_2$

Inverse of images

$(+\lambda)$ at $\dfrac{(2R_2)^2}{OP_1^{\mathrm{II}}} = \dfrac{4}{3} R_2$

$(-\lambda)$ at $\dfrac{(2R_2)^2}{OP_1^{\mathrm{III}}} = \dfrac{4R_2}{\sqrt{9 + 16\tau^2}}$

$(+\lambda)$ at $\dfrac{(2R_2)^2}{OP_1^{\mathrm{IV}}} = \dfrac{4R_2}{\sqrt{1 + 16\tau^2}}$

$(\tau = R_2/R_1)$

For example, for point O for which the distances are those given in the table, one has

$$\Phi(0) = \frac{\lambda}{2\pi\varepsilon} \ln \frac{4R_2\sqrt{1 + 16\tau^2}}{\tfrac{4}{3}R_2\sqrt{9 + 16\tau^2}} = \frac{\lambda}{4\pi\varepsilon} \ln \frac{9(1 + 16\tau^2)}{9 + 16\tau^2} \quad (27)$$

and the capacitance per unit length is then simply

$$C_1 = \frac{\lambda}{\Phi(0)} = \frac{4\pi\varepsilon}{\ln \dfrac{9(1 + 16\tau^2)}{9 + 16\tau^2}}$$

Two cylinders intersecting at any angle π/n, where n is an integer, can be treated in a similar manner. The orthogonal intersection of three cylinders leads to a rectangular metallic slot in the inversion.

24· NUMERICAL METHODS

For very complicated two-dimensional or axially symmetrical boundaries of electrostatic or magnetic fields, numerical iterative processes have been developed to solve in successive approximations the system of difference equations which can be substituted[1] for the partial differential equation of the potential. The systematic process of satisfying the difference equations only at distinct points in the desired field region by reducing step by step the local error to an inappreciable value is now called the *relaxation method*[2] because of the early application to problems of stress calculations in frame works where the errors can be construed as residual unwanted forces which are gradually relaxed[3] or "liquidated." These *relaxation* methods lead to a net of potential values through which equipotential lines can be drawn; because of the numerical computation of the potential values, the solutions can be obtained more accurately than by the purely graphical method of curvilinear squares.

---

[1] L. F. Richardson, *Phil. Trans.*, **A210**, p. 307 (1910); see also Bateman,[C1] p. 144.

[2] R. V. Southwell: *Relaxation Methods in Theoretical Physics*; Oxford University Press, England, 1946.

[3] R. V. Southwell, *Proc. Roy. Soc.*, **A151**, p. 56 (1935) and **A153**, p. 41 (1935); see also R. V. Southwell: *Relaxation Methods in Engineering Science*; Oxford University Press, England, 1940.

Relaxation Method for Two-dimensional Potential Fields.
The Laplace differential equation for the electrostatic and magnetostatic potentials, $(2 \cdot 2)$ and $(6 \cdot 6)$, respectively, can be solved
for a circular boundary with known values on it by means of the
Poisson integral $(28 \cdot 1)$ expressing the potential value anywhere
within the circle in terms of the boundary values. In particular,
at the center of the circle taken as the origin of the cylindrical
coordinates one has

$$\Phi(0) = \frac{1}{2\pi} \int_{\phi=0}^{2\pi} \Phi_R(\phi) \, d\phi = \lim_{N \to \infty} \left[\frac{1}{N} \sum_{n=1}^{N} \Phi_n \right] \tag{1}$$

where $\Phi_R(\phi)$ are the boundary values as a continuous function of
angle ϕ and where the summation is extended over discrete values
along the circular periphery. Relation (1) defines the value of
the potential in a Laplacian field as the *average* of all the equidistant values. It is this property that can be used for a numerical
trial and error procedure by choosing upon first inspection a set
of potential values at equidistant points throughout the field
region and then applying the criterion (1) and noting the differences
between the assumed values and those expected according to (1).
A revision of the first set must then be made, guided by the discrepancies in the first choice, with a second check by relation
(1). A final solution is obtained if everywhere in the field region
equation (1) is satisfied.

In a practical problem, one will first draw at rather large scale
the given arrangement of known potential boundaries, as for
example Fig. $24 \cdot 1$. Selecting, to begin with, a rather wide square
net[4] with intersection points as indicated by 0, 1, 2, 3, 4, one fills
the entire area and indicates at each point a guessed-at potential
value, preferably guided by a crude field plot. Obviously, one
will start in regions, like Ⓐ and Ⓑ, where the potential distribution
is practically linear between boundaries. With a square net, (1)
reduces to

$$-4\Phi(0) + \Phi_1 + \Phi_2 + \Phi_3 + \Phi_4 = R(0) \tag{2}$$

where for the exact solution $R(0) = 0$, but where for the assumed
distribution a finite residual $R(0)$ is obtained which is indicative

---

[4] Instead of a square net of points, one can choose either hexagonal or
triangular nets of points, of which only the latter have attained some practical
significance; see Southwell, footnote 2.

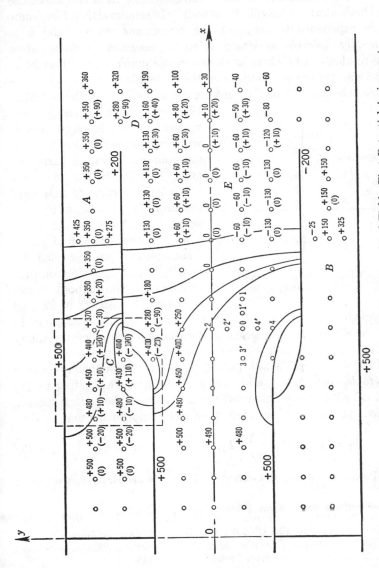

Fig. 24·1 Relaxation Method Applied to Two-dimensional Field; First Potential Assignment.

of the degree of approximation obtained. Certainly $R(0)$ must go to zero eventually, but any correction at 0 itself will affect the residuals at all its neighbors as well. It requires, therefore, some little experience to estimate the corrections needed, and it is generally desirable to note next to the assumed potential values the residuals in brackets as shown in the upper part of Fig. 24·1. One will use the distribution of the residuals for the second estimate, which might best be entered on a duplicate of the potential boundary sketch. It is to be expected that the largest residuals will occur in the region of greatest non-uniform potential variation, as at Ⓒ and Ⓓ in Fig. 24·1, but it is also important to note that the procedure is a definitely convergent one,[5] even if one starts from a rather crude first guess. Good results are recorded by Strutt,[B30] p. 38, for electron tube problems.[6] The method[7] is illustrated in Cosslett,[B22] p. 22, and Zworykin et al.,[B32] p. 386, for electron optical problems, and in Southwell[8] for the magnetic flux distribution in a generator; many applications have been made to elastic and heat problems.[9]

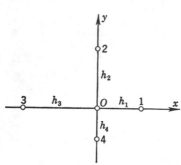

FIG. 24·2 General Spacing of Potential Points.

Instead of equidistant points, one can choose points in any desirable combination and derive relations corresponding to (1) and (2) with appropriate coefficients. Assume the general spacing of four points as in Fig. 24·2; then in first approximation

$$\Phi_1 = \Phi(0) + \left(\frac{\partial \Phi}{\partial x}\right)_{01} h_1, \qquad \Phi_3 = \Phi(0) - \left(\frac{\partial \Phi}{\partial x}\right)_{30} h_2 \qquad (3)$$

[5] Bateman,[C1] p. 147; R. Courant, K. Friedrichs, and H. Lewy, *Math. Ann.*, **100**, p. 32 (1928).

[6] See also M. J. O. Strutt, *Ann. d. Physik*, **87**, p. 153 (1928).

[7] See particularly G. Shortley and R. Weller, *Jl. Appl. Phys.*, **9**, p. 334, (1938) and *Bull*. No. 107, Ohio State Univ. Engg. Exper. Station, 1942.

[8] R. V. Southwell: *Relaxation Methods in Theoretical Physics*, p. 92 and Figs. 37, 38; Oxford University Press, England, 1946.

[9] D. G. Christopherson and R. V. Southwell, *Proc. Royal Soc.*, **A168**, p. 317 (1938); R. Weller, G. Shortley, and B. Fried, *Jl. Appl. Phys.*, **11**, p. 283 (1940); M. M. Frocht and M. M. Leven, *Jl. Appl. Phys.*, **12**, p. 596 (1941); and H. W. Emmons, *Trans. A. S.M.E.*, **65**, p. 607 (1943).

where the derivatives can be chosen, for better approximation, as the average values between the end points indicated by the subscripts.   Thus,

$$\left(\frac{\partial \Phi}{\partial x}\right)_{01} = \left(\frac{\partial \Phi}{\partial x}\right)_0 + \frac{1}{2}\left(\frac{\partial^2 \Phi}{\partial x^2}\right) h_1$$

$$\left(\frac{\partial \Phi}{\partial x}\right)_{30} = \left(\frac{\partial \Phi}{\partial x}\right)_0 - \frac{1}{2}\left(\frac{\partial^2 \Phi}{\partial x^2}\right) h_3$$

(4)

Introducing (4) into (3) and adding the two forms (3) after dividing, respectively, by $h_1{}^2$ and $h_3{}^2$, one has

$$\left(\frac{\partial^2 \Phi}{\partial x^2}\right) = \frac{\Phi_1 - \Phi_0}{h_1{}^2} + \frac{\Phi_3 - \Phi_0}{h_3{}^2} + \left(\frac{\partial \Phi}{\partial x}\right)_0 \left(\frac{1}{h_1} - \frac{1}{h_3}\right) \quad (5)$$

An identical relation obtains for $(\partial^2 \Phi / \partial y^2)$ if one expresses Φ_2 and Φ_4 in a manner analogous to Φ_1 and Φ_3 above.   The sum of the second derivatives must vanish, being the Laplacian of the potential $\Phi(0)$.   On the other hand, one can take the sum of $1/h_1$ of the first line in (4) and $1/h_3$ of the second line, and with (3) express the first derivative in terms of the distinct potential values, namely,

$$\left(\frac{\partial \Phi}{\partial x}\right)_0 = \frac{1}{h_1 + h_3}\left(\frac{h_3}{h_1}\Phi_1 - \frac{h_1}{h_3}\Phi_3\right) + \frac{h_1 - h_3}{h_1 h_3}\Phi_0 \quad (6)$$

and exactly analogous for $(\partial \Phi / \partial y)_0$ by changing subscripts 1 and 3 to 2 and 4, respectively.   Using these values for the derivatives in the Laplacian, one has the single exact relation

$$\left(\frac{1}{h_1 h_3} + \frac{1}{h_2 h_4}\right)\Phi(0) = \frac{\Phi_1}{h_1(h_1 + h_3)} + \frac{\Phi_3}{h_3(h_1 + h_3)}$$
$$+ \frac{\Phi_2}{h_2(h_2 + h_4)} + \frac{\Phi_4}{h_4(h_2 + h_4)} \quad (7)$$

which can be applied in rectangular spacing with $h_1 = h_3$ and $h_2 = h_4$, or in any local change in spacing, or in case of points close to irregular boundary surfaces.   If $h_1 = h_2 = h_3 = h_4 = h$, (7) immediately goes over into (2) with $R(0) = 0$; conversely, one can write (7) in the form of (2) with the residual $R(0)$ not necessarily zero but approaching it.

With some experience, one usually finds reasonably satisfactory residuals after about six to eight complete traverses of the field region, or after that many approximations for a particular point

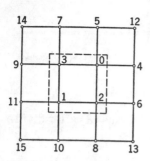

FIG. 24·3 Four-block Improvement Relation.

spacing. However, this might not permit a good field graph to be drawn, so that closer spacing at least in the regions of rapid potential variation might become necessary. Since halving of the spacing means fourfold slower convergence, it is advisable to start in any case with the wider spacing. One can expedite convergence by a factor n with the use of improvement formulas[10] which give better potential values for blocks of n^2 points in terms of the bordering potential values, thus smoothing out the effect of any one change upon the neighboring residuals. For a four-block as (0, 1, 2, 3) in Fig. 24·3 one can obtain an improved value at 0 by

$$\Phi(0) = \tfrac{1}{24}[7(\Phi_4 + \Phi_5) + 2(\Phi_6 + \Phi_7 \\ + \Phi_8 + \Phi_9) + \Phi_{10} + \Phi_{11}] \quad (8)$$

and with this one can now successively improve

$$\left. \begin{array}{l} \Phi_1 = \tfrac{1}{4}(\Phi_0 + \Phi_8 + \Phi_9 + \Phi_{15}) \\ \Phi_2 = \tfrac{1}{4}(\Phi_0 + \Phi_1 + \Phi_6 + \Phi_8) \\ \Phi_3 = \tfrac{1}{4}(\Phi_0 + \Phi_1 + \Phi_7 + \Phi_9) \end{array} \right\} \quad (9)$$

where Φ_0 and Φ_1 are the improved values from (8) and (9), respectively. Instead of applying such improvement formulas to the potential values themselves, one can apply them with advantage to the differences in successive approximations, as $\delta^r \Phi(0) = \Phi^{r+1}(0) - \Phi^r(0)$, if the superscript indicates the order number of the approximation.

As illustration consider the 4^2 region of values in the dotted box C of Fig. 24·1, which has rather irregular potential values. The first set of values as shown in the figure was chosen after drawing the few representative field lines free hand and with no attempt to be accurate. Apparently, the choice of potential values left much to be desired, because the residuals in the center

[10] Shortley and Weller, footnote 7.

of the C-block are rather large; for convenient reference the values
are reproduced here:

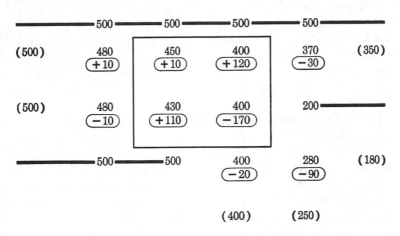

The heavy lines indicate the fixed potential values of the electrodes;
the numbers in parentheses are the potential values just outside
of C, which are needed to compute the residuals $R(\alpha)$.   The latter
are the encircled numbers with the proper sign in accordance with
(2).   Applying the system of numbering given in Fig. 21·3 to
the sixteen points above, and computing the improved potential
values by (8) and (9) for the four center points, lead to this new
set of potential values and residuals:

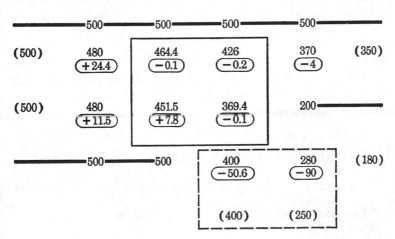

Though the changes in potential values in the center block are not large, they are so much in the right sense that the residuals have become very small. One can now proceed to the adjoining 4^2 block to improve the four values shown in the dotted line right above. After having reduced the residuals everywhere to rather uniformly small values, it becomes necessary to go to a finer mesh as indicated in Fig. 24·1 by the primed points $1'2'3'4'$; again, the four-block improvement formulas (8) and (9) will be very helpful.

Since it is well established that the method gives a convergent iteration for the potential function $\Phi(x, y)$, one can either attempt to establish directly the limiting value[11] or attempt to minimize the error in the sense of the least-squares method.[12] The former becomes necessarily very complicated for any practical boundary geometry. The latter is of value after several steps of approximation have been carried through; one can then select for example the best correction of the potential at 0 by adding

$$\delta\Phi(0) = - \tfrac{1}{20}[R_1 + R_2 + R_3 + R_4 - 4R(0)] \qquad (10)$$

where R_α are the residuals at the indicated points in accordance with (2). This introduces a smoothed-over correction similar to the improvement formulas (8) and (9) but directly in terms of the residuals. Thus, for example, one can correct the value to the left of Ⓔ in Fig. 24·1 by $\delta\Phi = -1$, that to the right of Ⓔ by $\delta\Phi = -2$; these small changes tend to reduce the local residual appreciably but to affect the neighboring residuals only little.

The extension of the relaxation method to the Poisson equation of the form (2·4)

$$\frac{\partial^2\Phi}{\partial x^2} + \frac{\partial^2\Phi}{\partial y^2} = - \frac{\rho}{\varepsilon}$$

is easily made. Restricting attention to uniform spacing, one has with (5) and the corresponding form for $(\partial^2\Phi/\partial y^2)$

$$\frac{\partial^2\Phi}{\partial x^2} + \frac{\partial^2\Phi}{\partial y^2} = \frac{1}{h^2}[\Phi_1 + \Phi_2 + \Phi_3 + \Phi_4 - 4\Phi(0)] \qquad (11)$$

which is to be equal to $(-\rho/\varepsilon)$. Thus,

$$-4\Phi(0) + \Phi_1 + \Phi_2 + \Phi_3 + \Phi_4 + h^2\frac{\rho}{\varepsilon} = R(0) \qquad (12)$$

[11] D. Moskowitz, *Quart. Appl. Math.*, **2**, p. 148 (1944).
[12] O. L. Bowie, *Jl. Appl. Phys.*, **18**, p. 830 (1947).

constitutes the modified form taking the place of (2). Knowing the value of density $\rho(x, y)$ as a function of the local coordinates, one can readily carry through the same procedure as above.

The relaxation method can also be extended to two-dimensional non-homogeneous and even non-isotropic electric current fields by replacing the field region by a network of resistors with nodes at arbitrarily selected points.[13]

Plotting of Field Graph. A satisfactory numerical plot of the potential function as obtained by the relaxation method gives a more or less dense set of discrete point values. It is possible to draw the equipotential lines by inspection and then construct the field lines as the orthogonal curves; in such case, however, the accuracy needs to be checked by the graphical method of curvilinear squares to give reliable results.

It is better also to compute the field vector and the direction of the field lines at each point of the final numerical plot and thus determine more accurately the direction of the equipotential lines themselves. The field vector is essentially known by relation (6) and its corresponding expression for the y-derivative

$$E_x(0) = -\left(\frac{\partial \Phi}{\partial x}\right)_0 = \frac{1}{h_1 + h_3}\left(\frac{h_1}{h_3}\Phi_3 - \frac{h_3}{h_1}\Phi_1\right) + \frac{h_3 - h_1}{h_3 h_1}\Phi_0$$

$$E_y(0) = -\left(\frac{\partial \Phi}{\partial y}\right)_0 = \frac{1}{h_2 + h_4}\left(\frac{h_2}{h_4}\Phi_4 - \frac{h_4}{h_2}\Phi_2\right) + \frac{h_4 - h_2}{h_4 h_2}\Phi_0 \tag{13}$$

where all the potential values are the final numerical solutions at a selected point 0 and its neighbors as in Fig. 24·1. The angle of the field line with the x-axis is given by $\tan \phi = E_y/E_x$.

In the regions of uniform point raster, one has all $h_\alpha = h$, and thus much simpler

$$E_x(0) = \frac{(\Phi_3 - \Phi_1)}{2h}, \qquad E_y(0) = \frac{(\Phi_4 - \Phi_2)}{2h} \tag{14}$$

so that the value of the field vector becomes[14]

$$E(0) = \frac{1}{2h}\left[(\Phi_3 - \Phi_1)^2 + (\Phi_4 - \Phi_2)^2\right]^{1/2} \tag{15}$$

[13] L. Tasny-Tschiassny, *Jl. Appl. Phys.*, **20**, p. 419 (1949).
[14] B. Van der Pol, *Jl. I.E.E.*, **81**, p. 381 (1937).

and the direction of the field lines is defined by

$$\tan \phi = \frac{E_y}{E_x} = \frac{\Phi_4 - \Phi_2}{\Phi_3 - \Phi_1}$$

where ϕ is the angle with x-axis. Thus, the equipotential lines have directions defined by

$$\tan \phi' = -\frac{E_x}{E_y} = \frac{\Phi_1 - \Phi_3}{\Phi_4 - \Phi_2}$$

The application of the method to magnetic fields with boundaries of known magnetostatic potential $\mathcal{F}$, or in fact to any Laplacian potential field, follows by direct analogy. Though in the Cartesian coordinate system the vector potential outside of electric currents reduces in two-dimensional problems to a single component satisfying the Laplacian differential equation, application of the relaxation method needs considerable modification because the vector potential does not define a gradient field.

Relaxation Method for Axisymmetrical Potential Fields. For axially symmetric fields, the potential equation has the form

$$\frac{\partial^2 \Phi}{\partial \rho^2} + \frac{1}{\rho} \frac{\partial \Phi}{\partial \rho} + \frac{\partial^2 \Phi}{\partial z^2} = \left(\frac{\partial^2 \Phi}{\partial \rho^2} + \frac{\partial^2 \Phi}{\partial z^2} \right) + \frac{1}{\rho} \frac{\partial \Phi}{\partial \rho} = 0 \quad (16)$$

where ρ is the distance from the axis. For any selected point 0 as in Fig. 24·2, with 1–0–3 parallel to the axis, one can again evaluate the second derivatives exactly as in the (3) to (6), except that now the extra term with the first derivative appears in (14) with the absolute scale factor $1/\rho$, which adjusts the scale of potential values in accordance with the distance from the axis. Calling this ρ_0 for the selected point 0, which is, of course, the same also for the points 1 and 3, one can use the analogous form (6) applied to points 2 and 4 and obtains upon collection and ordering of all terms,

$$\left(\frac{2\rho_0}{h_1 h_3} + \frac{2\rho_0 + h_4 - h_2}{h_2 h_4} \right) \Phi(0) = \frac{2\rho_0}{h_1(h_1 + h_3)} \Phi_1$$

$$+ \frac{2\rho_0}{h_3(h_1 + h_3)} \Phi_3 + \frac{2\rho_0 + h_4}{h_2(h_2 + h_4)} \Phi_2 + \frac{2\rho_0 - h_2}{h_4(h_2 + h_4)} \Phi_4 \quad (17)$$

which corresponds to (7) for any general spacing of the points neighboring on 0.

For uniform spacing of the points with all $h_\alpha = h$, and designating the axial distance $\rho_0 = mh$, relation (17) reduces to

$$-8m\Phi(0) + 2m\Phi_1 + (2m+1)\Phi_2 + 2m\Phi_3$$
$$+ (2m-1)\Phi_4 = R(0) \quad (18)$$

where $R(0) = 0$ for the exact solution. For a particular problem, one assumes again, as in the two-dimensional problem, a set of potential values throughout the field region and computes the residuals in accordance with (18), noting these next to the originally assumed potentials. A revision of the first set must then be made, guided by these residuals, with a second check by (18). A final solution is obtained if equation (18) is satisfied everywhere. One can expedite the convergence of the method by certain improvement formulas[15] for which coefficients have been computed and tabulated. Again, it is simpler to work with the difference values of potentials $\delta^r\Phi(0) = \Phi^{r+1}(0) - \Phi^r(0)$, where the superscripts indicate the order of the approximation.

The final result is a net of potential values through which equipotential lines can be drawn. It is advisable, however, to compute the field vector also, which for electrostatic problems is given by

$$E_\rho(0) = -\left(\frac{\partial\Phi}{\partial\rho}\right)_0, \qquad E_z(0) = -\left(\frac{\partial\Phi}{\partial z}\right)_0 \quad (19)$$

if ρ and z are the coordinates taking, respectively, the places of x and y of the two-dimensional field. The expressions for the field components are, therefore, identical with (13) and (14), and the directions of the field lines as well as the equipotential lines are defined in the same manner as there.

The extension of the method to the solution of Poisson's differential equation is made in exactly the same way as for the two-dimensional problem.

Automatic Computing Aids. With the increasing perfection of mathematical machines,[16] numerical methods for the solution of partial differential equations have become very economical in

---

[15] G. Shortley, R. Weller, P. Darby, and E. H. Gamble, *Jl. Appl. Phys.*, **18**, p. 116 (1947).

[16] F. J. Murray: *The Theory of Mathematical Machines;* Columbia University Press, New York, 1947; D. R. Hartree: *Calculating Instruments and Machines;* University of Illinois Press, 1948.

time, assuming that a machine is available at the time of need. For two-dimensional potential problems, for example, one proceeds by first laying out the set of points and ascribing some reasonable potentials to them. Then, one uses (2) or (18) directly for the improved second set, by computing the new $\Phi(0)$, setting $R(0) = 0$. This process, which is normally slowly convergent, becomes efficient if one employs automatic high-speed computing machines, such as punched card machines,[17] or electronic digital computers.[18]

A different approach is by means of analogue computers. Network analogues for partial differential equations have been developed[19] and models built[20] which allow the automatic solution of potential problems of the Laplace and Poisson type, as well as of the various types of wave equations.

PROBLEMS

1. Construct the resultant electrostatic field lines and equipotential lines for two parallel line charges as in Fig. 19·3 but with line charge densities $(+2\lambda)$ and $(+3\lambda)$. What will be the field picture at great distance from the charged lines?

2. Assume three symmetrically located line charges of linear densities $(+\lambda)$, (-3λ), $(+2\lambda)$ in free space. Construct the resultant equipotential lines and field lines. What will be the field picture at great distance from the charged lines?

3. A long cylindrical conductor of large radius R extends parallel to two planes which intersect orthogonally. Construct the field plot if the cylinder has center distances $2R$ and $3R$, respectively, from the two planes. (a) Find the mutual capacitance per unit length. (b) Find the charge density induced in the planes, using a relative scale. (c) Find the breakdown voltage for $R = 10$ cm.

4. Using the same cross-sectional geometry as in the preceding problem, assume an axis of rotation parallel to the line with center distance $3R$ from the circle and a distance $2R$ from this line. Construct the field plot of the resulting geometry, i.e., a toroid outside and coaxial with a cylinder of radius

---

[17] W. J. Eckert: *Punched Card Methods in Scientific Computation;* the Thomas J. Watson Astronomical Computing Bureau, Columbia University, 1940. See also M. Kormes, *Rev. Scient. Instr.*, **14**, p. 248 (1943).

[18] "Proceedings of Symposium on Large Scale Digital Calculating Machinery," *Annals of Computation Lab., Harvard Univ.*, **16** (1948); C. F. West and J. E. DeTurk, *Proc. I.R.E.*, **36**, p. 1452 (1948).

[19] G. Kron, *Electr. Engg.*, **67**, p. 672 (1948); S. A. Schelkunoff, *Bell System Techn. Jl.*, **27**, p. 489 (1948).

[20] K. Spangenberg and G. Walters, "An Electrical Network for the Study of Electromagnetic Fields," *Techn. Report*, No. 1, ONR, Contract N6-ORI-106, Stanford Univ., 1947.

$2R$ located above a plane orthogonal to the cylinder. (a) Find the mutual capacitance. (b) Find the breakdown voltage for $R = 10$ cm.

5. A long cylindrical conductor of large radius R extends in air parallel to the boundary plane of a solid dielectric of absolute dielectric constant ε. Construct the field plots for a distance $2R$ of the axis of the cylinder from the dielectric. Find the charge density distribution on the cylinder, using a relative scale. Find the force action upon the cylinder.

6. Using the same cross-sectional geometry as in problem 5, assume an axis of rotation within the dielectric at a distance $2R$ from the boundary line and parallel to it. Construct the field plot for the resulting geometry, i.e., a toroid outside and coaxial with a dielectric cylinder. (a) Find the capacitance of the toroid. (b) Find the critical voltage for appearance of corona if $R = 10$ cm.

7. Construct the field plot in free space of two very small spheres of radii R_1 and $R_2 = 2R_1$, with a distance of the two centers $d = 10R_2$, and with charges $Q_2 = 3Q_1$. Find the singular point. What is the field picture at large distance from the spheres? Define the field maps in terms of capacitance coefficients and give their relative values.

8. A long rectangular bus bar of dimensions $2a$ and $2b < 2a$ extends parallel with its broader side to an infinite conducting plane at a distance $4b$ from its plane of symmetry. Construct the field plot if $a/b = 5$, and (a) find the capacitance with respect to the plane, (b) find the breakdown voltage if $b = 2$ cm, (c) find the capacitance and breakdown voltage between two like bus bars with $b = 2$ cm for which the infinite plane is the plane of symmetry.

9. Three parallel long rectangular bus bars form a three-phase transmission system. Construct the field plot for three identical bars with $a/b = 5$ and with mutual distances $c = 2a$ if the voltages to the very distant ground are, respectively, V_1, $V_2 = -V_1 \cot 15°$, $V_3 = V_1 \cdot \dfrac{\sin 45°}{\sin 15°}$. (a) Find the mutual capacitance coefficients per unit length; (b) find the charges per unit length on all three conductors; (c) find the forces acting on the conductors.

10. Assume the same cross-sectional geometry as in problem 8 and take the line parallel to the rectangle as axis of rotation. Construct the field plot if $a = b$ and find the capacitance of the annular ring.

11. Construct the resultant magnetic field lines in air for two parallel line currents of values I_1 and $I_2 = -3I_1$, by using (a) the vector potential, (b) the magnetostatic potential function. Find the field at large distance from the wires.

12. Construct the resultant magnetic field lines for a three-wire, three-phase transmission system of symmetrical geometry carrying the currents (a) I_1, $I_2 = -2I_1$, $I_3 = I_1$; (b) I_1, $I_2 = -4I_1$, $I_3 = +3I_1$. Find the field at large distance from the wires.

13. Assume four parallel wires in air so arranged that in a cross-sectional plane they are located at the vertices of a square. Find the resulting magnetic field plot if the currents in the upper two wires are $\pm I_1$, in the lower two wires $\mp 2I_1$, so that the magnetic fluxes oppose. Obtain the mutually linked flux per unit length from the resulting field plot and compare with the analytically predicted value. (See also section 7.)

14. Construct the magnetic field plot in the space between two ideal magnetic boundary surfaces of constant magnetostatic potentials if one surface is an infinite plane and the opposite surface has a perpendicular distance varying as $g_0/\cos \dfrac{2\pi x}{\tau}$, where g_0 is the minimum distance of the two boundaries, x the linear distance along the plane surface, and τ the spatial period of the field distribution. Find the magnetic reluctance per unit length.

15. The symmetrical poles of a magnet have pole faces of width $2a$ from which the steel tapers linearly over a height $h = 5a$ to the larger cross section of the pole core of width $2b = 5a$. Taking it as a two-dimensional field problem (of great length normal to the cross section) between ideal magnetic surfaces of constant magnetostatic potentials, construct the field plot for an air gap $2g = a/2$. Find the magnetic reluctance per unit length. Find the variation of the magnetic flux density in the plane of symmetry halving the air gap.

16. Assume a single long conductor of square cross section carrying uniformly distributed current. Construct the field plot both inside and outside the conductor by using (20·10). Verify for several points along a field line, that $A_z = $ cons in accordance with (15·21). Verify the validity of (20·7) inside the conductor.

17. The vector potential of a long thin rectangular bar is given by (15·19), and the lines $A_z = $ cons represent the magnetic field lines. Apply this to a single conductor of square cross section carrying uniformly distributed current in order to obtain its magnetic field lines. Choose a subdivision into six strips and check several points by the exact solution (15·21).

18. Apply the method of the preceding problem to two long parallel and identical conductors of square cross sections with sides $2a$ and center spacing $6a$. Find the resulting magnetic field lines for equal and opposite currents. Find the location of the kernels and check the validity of (20·7) inside the conductors.

19. Apply the method of problem 17 to two long parallel conductors with equal and opposite currents, of circular cross sections and of radii R_1, $R_2 = 2R_1$, and with center spacing $2R_2$. Find the magnetic field lines and the location of the kernels and check with the exact solution in section 15.

20. The inductance of a loop formed by two long parallel conductors of finite cross sections with equal and opposite currents is defined by (7·1) and (7·2) and reiterated in (15·11). Assume the two conductors of identical square cross sections with sides $2a$ and center spacing $6a$ as in problem 18. Knowing the magnetic vector potential values, one can evaluate the integrals (15·11) graphically; find the inductance per unit length of the current loop.

21. A single long conductor of square cross section with sides $2a$ carrying uniformly distributed current extends parallel to an ideal magnetic boundary surface of constant magnetostatic potential. Find the magnetic field lines and the location of the kernel for a distance $4a$ of the plane from the center of the conductor; compare the location of the kernel with that in problem 16.

22. In problem 21 assume the cross section of the conductor oriented with its diagonal normal to the magnetic boundary plane, keeping the same center distance. Find the magnetic field lines and the location of the kernel.

23. A cylindrical coil of mean diameter $2R$ carries a total current-turns value NI uniformly distributed over a rectangular cross section of small radial width δa and of height $2b = 2R$. Construct the magnetic field plot, utilizing the superposition of solutions for a circular loop of current given in section 13. Demonstrate the validity of the superposition. Find the inductance of the cylindrical coil.

24. A circular cylinder of magnetic steel with relative permeability $\mu_r = 200$, radius R, and height $h = 2R$, carries a circular loop of wire on its surface in the orthogonal plane of symmetry. Construct the field plot. Find the inductance if the wire loop has a small radius a.

25. A flat pancake coil has a mean radius R, a small height δb, a width $2a = R$, and carries a total current-turns value NI uniformly distributed over its cross section. Construct the magnetic field plot, utilizing the superposition of solutions for a circular loop of current given in section 13. Demonstrate the validity of the superposition. Find the inductance of the coil.

26. Two identical flat pancake coils as defined in problem 25 are arranged coaxially with a center distance $2c = R_1$. Find the mutual inductance, utilizing the field plot of problem 25.

27. Two thin flat pancake coils of mean radii R_1 and $R_2 = \frac{3}{2}R_1$, small heights $\delta b_1 = \delta b_2$, and widths $2a_1 = \frac{2}{3}R_1$, $2a_2 = R_1$, are arranged coaxially with a center distance $2c = R_1$. Find the mutual inductance if the numbers of turns are N_1 and N_2, respectively. Utilize the result of problem 25.

28. A circular cylinder of magnetic steel of relative permeability $\mu_r = 100$, radius R_1, and height $h = 2R$ carries on its surface a thin cylindrical coil of the same height h and with a total current-turns value NI. Construct the magnetic field plot. Find the inductance of the coil if the layer of wires is thin but finite.

29. Two small spheres of equal radii ρ are located at large distance $2c$ from each other in the plane $x = 0$ of Fig. 21·1. Assume one of the spheres to be the source of current I and the other to be the sink within the infinite stratum of conductivity γ and thickness $(a + b)$. Find the resistance R if the space outside the stratum is non-conductive.

30. Consider the same geometry as in problem 29 but assume the spheres to carry charges $\pm Q$, respectively, and to be in air bounded by two conducting planes. Find the capacitance between the spheres as influenced by the proximity of the conducting planes. Find the induced charge densities on the planes.

31. Find in first approximation the charge distribution on the small sphere of Fig. 21·1 with $a \neq b$; assume then $a = b$.

32. Find the force action between the two spheres of problem 30; demonstrate that the force follows Coulomb's law if one defines appropriately an equivalent center distance r'.

33. A long thin wire is located midway between one conducting plane and one plane dielectric boundary, as for example in Fig. 21·3, if the medium II is replaced by a perfect conductor. Find the capacitance per unit length between the wire of radius a and the conducting plane. Find the charge density induced in the conducting plane.

34. Two parallel very long wires of small radii a and with mutual center distance $2c$ are located with their axis in the boundary plane between two media of conductivities γ_1 and γ_2 and dielectric constants ε_1 and ε_2. Find the capacitance per unit length between the wires; find the current per unit length between the wires if their potential difference is V.

35. Two homogeneous thin cylinders of radii a and temperatures T_1 and T_2 extend parallel to the plane boundary of two media of thermal conductivities k_1 and k_2; the cylinder at T_1 is located in medium 1 with its axis a distance $10a$ from the boundary plane, the cylinder at T_2 is located in medium 2 with its axis a distance $20a$ from the boundary plane. Find the heat flow (exchange) between the two cylinders per unit length.

36. A small dipole of large moment **p** in arbitrary direction is located between the two plates of an infinite plane condenser similar to Fig. 21·1, if one assumes a potential difference V between the plates. Find force and torque action upon the dipole.

37. Find the induced charge density in the cylinder of radius R in Fig. 21·4 if it is grounded and exposed to the two parallel symmetrically located line charges $\pm\lambda$. Demonstrate the identity of the solution with (21·20) for $r = R$ if the line charges recede to $\pm\infty$.

38. In a three-phase, three-conductor cable, the three cylindrical conductors are located within the grounded sheath symmetrically with respect to each other at distance d from the central axis. Find the approximate potential distribution if the radii of the conductors are a and their potentials with respect to the sheath V_1, $-\frac{1}{2}V_1$, $-\frac{1}{2}V_1$. Find all the capacitance coefficients. Check the degree of approximation by computing the resultant potential values over the surfaces of the conductors.

39. Show that in problem 38 one can get a better approximation if the equivalent line charges of the conductors are not located in their axis but shifted slightly radially towards the central axis.

40. A thin long wire of radius a and linear charge density $+\lambda$ extends parallel to a dielectric cylinder with distance b between axes as in Fig. 21·6. Find in first approximation the charge distribution over the surface of the wire and demonstrate the influence of the proximity of the dielectric cylinder. Plot the maximum charge density as a function of the dielectric constant ε_2 of the cylinder.

41. For the same geometry as in problem 40, compute the maximum charge density on the wire as a function of the radius R of the dielectric cylinder, keeping constant the distance from the axis of the wire to the nearest surface point of the dielectric cylinder. Show that for $R \to \infty$ one obtains the same value as for a wire parallel to an infinite plane dielectric boundary.

42. Two metal pins are molded into a plastic cylinder giving the same geometry as in Fig. 21·6 with the pin centers at A'' and B'', the plastic cylinder of dielectric constant ε_2 surrounded by air. Find the potential distribution between the pins if they have a potential difference V applied between them. Find the capacitance per unit length and compare it with the value in air alone.

43. A thin circular ring of charge is coaxial with a grounded sphere of radius R, i.e., the axis of the ring passes through the center of the sphere.

Find the capacitance of the ring with respect to the sphere if the plane of the ring is at distance c from the center of the sphere, and if its wire radius a is small compared with all other dimensions.

44. Find the increase in external inductance for a thin circular loop of current lying parallel to (a) an ideal equipotential magnetic boundary plane, (b) a boundary plane of magnetic material of permeability μ. Find the force upon the loop in both cases.

45. Assume the plane of the two-wire transmission line in Fig. 22·2 to make an angle β with the magnetic boundary plane. Find the total external inductance if the magnetic material has permeability μ. Plot the variation of this inductance as a function of the angle β, keeping the distance d constant and equal to c, one half the spacing of the wires.

46. A single thin wire carrying current I lies in a slot formed by two parallel solid blocks of iron a distance $2h$ apart and closed by an orthogonal block. Find the magnetic field in the slot if the axis of the wire has distances a and $b = 2h - a$ from the parallel boundaries, and distance c from the base block. Find the force upon the wire.

47. A long thin wire carrying current $+I$ extends parallel to a magnetic cylinder of relative permeability $\mu_r = 200$ as shown in Fig. 22·3. Construct the magnetic field plot if the distance $b = 2R$. Find the force upon the wire.

48. A cylindrical shell of magnetic material of permeability μ has outer radius R_1 and inner radius R_2 and is brought into a uniform magnetic field B_0. Find the resultant magnetic field if the axis of the shell is orthogonal to the magnetic field.

49. A thin long wire carrying current I is located halfway in the space between a solid magnetic cylinder of radius R_1 and a coaxial shell of inner radius R_2 and outer radius R_3. Construct the magnetic field plot if the magnetic materials have the same relative permeability $\mu_r = 100$ and if $R_3 = 2R_2 = 3R_1$.

50. The end connections of windings in electrical machines might be considered as rectangular loops extending normal to the iron core. Assume, then, a thin wire carrying current I and forming a rectangular loop of sides a normal to, and $2b = 5a$ parallel to, an infinite plane magnetic boundary. Find the inductance of the loop section in air if the permeability of the iron is μ and the radius of the round wire is ς.

51. Two isolated and conducting spheres are intersecting orthogonally as in Fig. 23·3. Find the electric field distribution if a point charge $+Q$ is located at the intersection of the line $\overline{UO}$ with the sphere of inversion on the opposite side of U. Find the force upon the point charge. Find the capacitance of a small sphere of radius a carrying the charge $+Q$ and having its center at the location of the point charge.

52. Two spheres contacting each other as in Fig. 23·4 are grounded and under the influence of a point charge $+Q$ located at the intersection of the x-axis with the sphere of inversion. Find the electric field distribution. Find the induced charge density on the spheres.

53. Use the same cross-sectional geometry as in problem 52, but solve it as a two-dimensional problem with a line charge $+\lambda$ replacing the point charge and cylinders replacing the spheres.

54. Two parallel cylinders intersecting at $\pi/3$ form a single conductor carrying a charge $+\lambda$ per unit length. Find the potential distribution. Find the charge distribution over the cylinder surfaces.

55. A very thin hemispherical shell of radius R has two point electrodes applied to its surface at diametrically opposite points of the parallel circle of radius $R/2$. Find the resistance of the shell if the electrodes can be assumed as small equipotential circles of radii a and if the shell has thickness t and conductivity γ. Find the current distribution in the shell.

56. Assume that the hemispherical shell of problem 55 is reduced to a zone by cutting off the section below the parallel circle of radius $R/2$ so that the electrodes are applied with their centers on the rim of the zone. Find the resistance.

57. A long cylinder of radius R is coaxial with a rectangular sheath of small sides $2a = 4R$ and large sides $2b = 10R$. Find the capacitance between the two conductors. Hint: solve for the potential distribution first by the relaxation method, assuming the potential difference $V = 100$ volts; then construct curvilinear squares to obtain the capacitance.

58. Demonstrate the validity of the improvement formulas $(24 \cdot 8)$ and $(24 \cdot 9)$.

59. Two identical long bus bars of rectangular cross sections are arranged parallel with their larger sides $2b$ at a center distance $2c = 6a$, where $2a$ is the smaller side. Find the potential distribution between them by the relaxation method if a potential difference V is applied. Find the capacitance.

60. Find the potential distribution between the two deflecting plates of an oscilloscope inclined symmetrically at an angle of $20°$ with respect to the center plane. Assume the plates as very thin of width $2b$, with a minimum distance $0.2b$, and infinitely long normal to the cross-sectional plane. Find the value of the transverse electric field vector along the axis if the potential difference is V. Find the capacitance per unit length.

61. Find the magnetic field distribution for the two-dimensional geometry shown in Fig. $27 \cdot 13c$ if the finite distances are defined as follows: $6'-6'' = g$, $4-5 = 10g$, $3-4 = 20g$, $2'-2'' = 40g$. Establish the boundary line for homogeneous field distribution. Find the reluctance per unit length for the inhomogeneous part of the field.

7. TWO-DIMENSIONAL ANALYTIC SOLUTIONS

For many purposes it is desirable to secure analytic solutions of field problems, since they permit deduction of broad design principles as long as they remain manageable. Two-dimensional potential theory has had the great benefit of the branch of mathematics known as "Theory of Functions of a Complex Variable" (see Appendix 4, D), which has led to many rigorous solutions in singularly simple form particularly well adapted to the interpretation of the field geometry.

25 · CONJUGATE FUNCTIONS

To fix any point in a plane, two real coordinates have to be given. With an orthogonal coordinate system, any number pair, as for example (x, y) for the plane Cartesian, or (r, ϕ) for the plane polar system, signifies a point P. Such a number pair or a point can also be denoted in complex form[1] by $z = (x + jy)$ with $j = \sqrt{-1}$, and $j^2 = -1$.

As one lets x and y take on all possible real values between $(-\infty)$ and $(+\infty)$, z covers the entire plane, usually then referred to as the complex z-plane. From Fig. 25·1 one also takes for point P

$$z = r + jy = r \cos \phi + jr \sin \phi = re^{j\phi} \tag{1}$$

where $r = |z| = (x^2 + y^2)^{1/2}$ is the *absolute value* of the complex number z, sometimes also called *modulus*, and where ϕ is the

---

[1] Mathematical texts normally designate complex numbers by $z = x + iy$ with $i = \sqrt{-1}$; in electrical engineering, it has become customary to use j for the imaginary unit in order to avoid confusion with the symbol for electric current which traditionally is chosen as i.

argument of z; $e^{j\phi}$ can be interpreted as a *direction factor*, having the absolute value unity, similar to a unit vector in vector analysis. However, there are basic differences between plane vector analysis and complex function theory which make the latter vastly more powerful as a mathematical method of analysis.

Obviously, the absolute value of a complex number can also be obtained by writing

$$|z|^2 = (x + jy)(x - jy) \equiv z\bar{z} = x^2 + y^2 \qquad (2)$$

if again $j^2 = -1$ is observed. The combination $x - jy = \bar{z}$, which in the z-plane leads to the image point $(x, -y)$ of the point

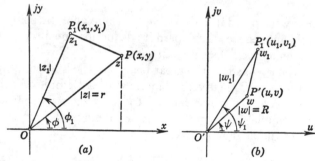

FIG. 25·1   Representation of Functions of a Complex Variable: (*a*) complex z-plane, (*b*) complex $w(z)$-plane.

(x, y) with respect to the x-axis, is called the *conjugate complex number* of z.

The product of two complex numbers is again a complex number

$$z_1 z_2 = (x_1 + jy_1)(x_2 + jy_2) = (x_1 x_2 - y_1 y_2) + j(x_1 y_2 + x_2 y_1)$$

as is also the square of a complex number

$$z^2 = (x + jy)^2 = (x^2 - y^2) + j2xy \qquad (3)$$

and, indeed, any conceivable functional operation will always again result in a complex number (of which real or imaginary numbers are then only special cases). Complex numbers thus form a *closed number system*. It is, therefore, possible to interpret any function $f(z) = w$ again as covering a plane with $w = u + jv$, as in Fig. 25·1, in which any point w is then the *image* of the generating point z of the z-plane. The possible relationships between w and z planes are the primary object of function theory; see particularly the references in Appendix 4, D, b, and Kellogg, [C10] chapter XII.

Analytic Functions of a Complex Variable.   For applications to linear field problems, functions must be *regular* within the regions considered and they may have prescribed discontinuities on the boundaries corresponding to physical sources like charges, currents, etc.   It is therefore natural to restrict study of complex functions to *regular* or *analytic* functions in the same sense as with real functions, i.e., require single valuedness, continuity, and differentiability within the regions of interest. *Single valuedness* can usually be met by proper restriction of the variables and introduction of barriers as already done in the case of the magnetostatic potential, section 6; for complex functions one must require that, to every point z_α chosen in the neighborhood of z in Fig. 25·1a, there corresponds one and only one point $w_\alpha = f(z_\alpha) = u_\alpha + jv_\alpha$ in the neighborhood of w in Fig. 25·1b.   *Continuity* requires that the point w_α can be made to move arbitrarily close to w by selecting z_α properly close to z and that, in the limit, w_α goes into w as z_α goes into z, no matter in what direction the latter is done.

With respect to *differentiability* one has to consider that

$$w = f(z) = u(x, y) + jv(x, y) \tag{4}$$

is the complex combination of two functions each of which depends on the two real variables x and y.   Differentiability means, therefore, the existence of the continuous first partial derivatives of u and v with respect to x and y as well as that $\lim_{\Delta z \to 0} \Delta w/\Delta z \to dw/dz$ exists, i.e., has the same value at a point z, no matter how $\Delta z \to 0$. Whereas with a real variable only two opposite directions are possible in approaching a point x, with a complex variable z there are infinitely many directions in which to approach this point z. Choosing for convenience once the x- and once the y direction, the partial derivatives follow with the use of (4) as

$$\frac{\partial w}{\partial x} = \frac{\partial u}{\partial x} + j\,\frac{\partial v}{\partial x}, \qquad \frac{\partial w}{\partial jy} = \frac{\partial u}{\partial jy} + j\,\frac{\partial v}{\partial jy} \tag{5}$$

Assuming the existence of the continuous partial derivatives, both results must have the same value, so that upon equating and separating the expressions in u and v into real and imaginary parts one finds

$$\frac{\partial u}{\partial x} = \frac{\partial v}{\partial y}, \qquad \frac{\partial u}{\partial y} = -\frac{\partial v}{\partial x} \qquad (6)$$

the fundamental *Cauchy-Riemann differential equations*, which bring to light the inherent regularity of the analytic functions and constitute the necessary and sufficient conditions for any complex function to be analytic at a point $P(x, y)$. The sufficiency follows from the fact that, if one now formulates the general expression for the derivative

$$\lim_{\Delta z \to 0} \frac{\Delta w}{\Delta z} = \frac{\left(\dfrac{\partial u}{\partial x} + j\dfrac{\partial v}{\partial x}\right)\Delta x + \left(\dfrac{\partial u}{\partial y} + j\dfrac{\partial v}{\partial y}\right)\Delta y}{\Delta x + j\Delta y}\Bigg|_{\substack{\Delta x \to 0 \\ \Delta y \to 0}}$$

and uses relations (6), one reproduces the expressions (5).

It is also desirable to assure *integrability* of the analytic function $f(z)$ in the complex plane. With (4) one has

$$\int f(z)\,dz = \int (u + jv)(dx + j\,dy)$$

$$= \int (u\,dx - v\,dy) + j\int (u\,dy + v\,dx) \qquad (7)$$

For a closed regular path (which has no cross overs or discontinuities) in the real x-y-plane, each of the line integrals can be transformed[2] into a surface integral of the partial derivatives of u and v which already have been assumed to exist and to be continuous, namely,

$$\int (u\,dx - v\,dy) = -\iint \left(\frac{\partial u}{\partial y} + \frac{\partial v}{\partial x}\right) dx\,dy$$

$$\int (u\,dy + v\,dx) = +\iint \left(\frac{\partial u}{\partial x} - \frac{\partial v}{\partial y}\right) dx\,dy \qquad (8)$$

However, for the analytic function, the Cauchy-Riemann equations (6) make the integrands on the right-hand side vanish at every

[2] This is essentially the divergence theorem (Gauss's theorem) in two dimensions; for the specific form see any book on advanced calculus, like Doherty and Keller,[D3] p. 247; Sokolnikoff and Sokolnikoff,[D9] p. 173; as well as all references on functions of a complex variable.

regular point, so that for any *closed* regular path entirely within a regular region one has

$$\oint f(z)\,dz = 0 \tag{9}$$

Therefore the integral over any *open* path in a regular region cannot depend on the path itself but only on the end points (Cauchy's integral theorem) and will itself be an analytic function of either one of the limits, since its derivative is $f(z)$ which was assumed to be analytic in the first place. It further follows that for analytic functions derivatives of any order exist and that, in turn, they are all analytic functions.

Conjugate Functions and Potential Fields. From the above it is assured that the higher partial derivatives of $u(x, y)$ and $v(x, y)$ exist. Differentiating, therefore, the first of equations (6) with respect to x and the second with respect to y and adding both, or, conversely, differentiating the first with respect to y and the second with respect to x and subtracting both, one obtains

$$\frac{\partial^2 u}{\partial x^2} + \frac{\partial^2 u}{\partial y^2} = 0\,, \qquad \frac{\partial^2 v}{\partial x^2} + \frac{\partial^2 v}{\partial y^2} = 0 \tag{10}$$

Both the real and imaginary part of $w = f(z)$, considered as functions of the ordinary real coordinates x and y, satisfy the Laplacian differential equation and thus are harmonic functions and solutions of potential problems (see section 2).

As real functions of the two variables x and y, $u = $ cons, as well as $v = $ cons, defines families of curves in the real x-y-plane as in Fig. 25·2; the slopes of these two families are related, as division of the Cauchy-Riemann differential equations (6) reveals

$$\frac{\partial u/\partial x}{\partial u/\partial y} = -\frac{\partial v/\partial y}{\partial v/\partial x} \tag{11}$$

i.e., the two families of plane curves are *mutually orthogonal*. It is customary to identify the real part of the complex harmonic function w as the potential function; then in the form $w = u + jv$, v is called the *conjugate*[3] function or the harmonic conjugate to u; in the form $(-jw) = v - ju$, $(-u)$ is called the conjugate function, or harmonic conjugate to v. Since u and v can be conjugate to

---

[3] This should not be confused with the definition of *conjugate complex* numbers given in connection with (2).

each other, one frequently designates them as "conjugate functions." Because of the mutual orthogonality, the conjugate function defines the gradient lines or field lines of the potential field, so that the complex harmonic function gives at once the *entire orthogonal field geometry* without necessitating further computations. On the other hand, if only $u(x, y)$ is given as a real harmonic function (satisfying the Laplacian differential equation),

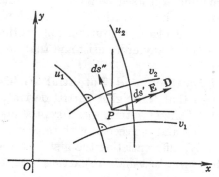

Fig. 25·2   Use of Conjugate Functions in Electrostatic Field.

then one can construct an analytic function $(u + jv)$, whereby v is found for example from (6) by integration of the derivatives of $u(x, y)$

$$v = \int \left(\frac{\partial v}{\partial x}\, dx + \frac{\partial v}{\partial y}\, dy \right) = \int \left(-\frac{\partial u}{\partial y}\, dx + \frac{\partial u}{\partial x}\, dy \right) \quad (12)$$

It is self-evident that the sum of two complex harmonic functions $(w_1 + w_2)$ is again a harmonic function and therefore sums of conjugate functions are again conjugate functions. It is also readily shown that, if $t = r + js$ is an analytic function of $w = u + jv$, and this in turn an analytic function of $z = x + jy$, then t is also an analytic function of $(x + jy)$ and r and s are conjugate functions of x and y. Since

$$\frac{\partial r}{\partial x} = \frac{\partial r}{\partial u}\, \frac{\partial u}{\partial x} + \frac{\partial r}{\partial v}\, \frac{\partial v}{\partial x}$$

and the Cauchy-Riemann equation are valid, one has

$$\frac{\partial r}{\partial x} = \frac{\partial s}{\partial v}\, \frac{\partial v}{\partial y} + \frac{\partial s}{\partial u}\, \frac{\partial u}{\partial y} = \frac{\partial s}{\partial y}$$

showing the validity of the Cauchy-Riemann equations for r and s in terms of x and y and therefore their conjugate relationship.

The use of conjugate functions will be discussed as they apply to the mapping of electrostatic potential fields, but transfer to any other field problem can readily be made by means of table $9 \cdot 1$. Assume, then, in the complex harmonic function $w = u + jv$, the real part $u(x, y) = \Phi$ as the potential function; the field strength vector **E** follows as gradient in the real x-y-plane

$$E_x = -\frac{\partial u}{\partial x}, \qquad E_y = -\frac{\partial u}{\partial y} \tag{13}$$

and the complex combination, taking into account the second relation (6), gives[4]

$$E_x + jE_y = E = -\frac{\partial u}{\partial x} + j\frac{\partial v}{\partial x} \tag{14}$$

Comparison with the first relation in (5) shows that this can also be expressed as

$$E = -\overline{\left(\frac{dw}{dz}\right)}, \qquad |E| = \left|\frac{dw}{dz}\right| \tag{15}$$

so that the absolute value of the complex derivative is a direct measure of the field strength and the conjugate complex derivative is the equivalent of the two-dimensional gradient of vector analysis.

The dielectric flux per unit length in a two-dimensional Cartesian system between any two points in the field is given by

$$\psi_1 = \int_1^2 \mathbf{D} \cdot \mathbf{dS} = \int_1^2 (D_x \, dy - D_y \, dx)$$

Using (13) but substituting the derivatives of v from (6), one has

$$\psi_1 = -\varepsilon \int_1^2 \left(\frac{\partial v}{\partial y} \, dy + \frac{\partial v}{\partial x} \, dx\right) = \varepsilon(v_1 - v_2) \tag{16}$$

or the dielectric flux between 1 and 2 is measured by the difference of the values of the conjugate function at the two points.   There-

---

[4] In what follows, any vector field quantity appearing as a complex number will be designated without indices or other distinctive marks; the absolute value will be designated by two vertical bars and any component by a suitable subscript.

fore, one frequently calls the conjugate function also the *flux function* (or stream function in hydrodynamic problems).

One can also establish the relationship to the method of curvilinear squares (section 19). Selecting two equipotential lines u_1 and u_2 in Fig. 25·2 with a potential difference

$$\Delta\Phi = u_1 - u_2 = |E|\Delta s' = E_x\Delta x' + E_y\Delta y' \tag{17}$$

and two flux lines v_1 and v_2 to give the same numerical difference

$$v_1 - v_2 = |E|\Delta s'' = E_x\Delta y'' - E_y\Delta x'' \tag{18}$$

then one must have

$$\Delta y'' = \Delta x', \qquad \Delta x'' = -\Delta y'$$

the two elements $\Delta s'$ and $\Delta s''$ must be of *equal* length and, of course, orthogonal to each other. Or also, with the potential difference between electrodes divided into equal increments and flux lines selected by choosing values of v with the same increments, one obtains at once the analytic equivalent of the curvilinear squares. The capacitance of the individual curvilinear square is then again ε as in section 19.

Given two electrode surfaces of potentials $\Phi_I \equiv u_I$ and $\Phi_{II} \equiv u_{II}$, with values of flux function v_I and v_{II} measuring the total flux of the vector **E** between these electrodes (or those parts of interest), the capacitance per unit length (total or partial) is then

$$C_1 = \varepsilon\frac{v_I - v_{II}}{u_I - u_{II}} \tag{19}$$

This can at once be translated into all other potential fields by means of table 9·1.

Finally, one can take from (14) with (5)

$$-E_x + jE_y = \frac{\partial u}{\partial x} + j\frac{\partial v}{\partial x} = \frac{\partial w}{\partial x} = \frac{dw}{dz}$$

or, taking the logarithm of both sides,

$$\frac{1}{2}\ln(E_x{}^2 + E_y{}^2) + j\left(\pi - \tan^{-1}\frac{E_y}{E_x}\right) = \ln\left(\frac{dw}{dz}\right) = P + jQ \tag{20}$$

The lines of constant field strength are thus defined[5] by $P =$

[5] Re(w) means the real part of the complex function, Im(w) the imaginary part.

$\mathrm{Re}\left(\ln\dfrac{dw}{dz}\right)$, and the lines of constant direction of field lines by

$Q = \mathrm{Im}\left(\ln\dfrac{dw}{dz}\right)$. This is of particular interest in flow problems, but has significance in all design problems.

An investigation of all analytic functions will, therefore, lead to a corresponding array of potential solutions, whereby again simple types of fields can be superimposed to give solutions for more complex cases.

Line Charges and Line Currents (Source and Vortex Lines). One of the most widely used functions is $w = F \ln z$, where F is a constant to adjust for physical scale quantities. Assuming F to be real, then,

$$w = F \ln z = F \ln r + jF\phi = u + jv \qquad (21)$$

representing concentric circular equipotential lines and radial field lines as the charged line (12·28). To stay within physical interpretability, i.e., make $\ln z$ single valued, the angle ϕ must be restricted to $0 \leqslant \phi < 2\pi$, laying a barrier plane at $\phi = 2\pi$, for example. As an analytic function, $\ln z$ is regular in the entire z-plane except at the origin $z = 0$, where the derivative $1/z$ becomes infinite, corresponding to the location of the line charge. To avoid this singularity one can admit a very small but finite radius of the charged line, making it a quasi line charge, as indicated in section 12. The total dielectric flux per unit length from the line according to (16) is the difference between the extreme values of the flux function along an equipotential line, i.e.,

$$\Psi = \varepsilon(v_{\phi=0} - v_{\phi=2\pi}) = -\varepsilon F 2\pi \equiv \lambda \qquad (22)$$

so that $F = -\lambda/2\pi\varepsilon$ as noted in table 25·1. The field vector is according to (15)

$$E = +\frac{\lambda}{2\pi\varepsilon}\overline{\left(\frac{1}{z}\right)} = \frac{\lambda}{2\pi\varepsilon r}\varepsilon^{j\phi} \qquad (23)$$

and is directed radially outward.

Interchanging potential and flux lines (with V real)

$$w = -jV \ln z = V\phi - jV \ln r = u + jv \qquad (24)$$

one has the magnetic field of a line current (vortex line) as in (13·3b), for which the magnetostatic potential $\mathcal{F} \equiv u$. The

TABLE 25·1
POTENTIAL SOLUTIONS BY SIMPLE ANALYTIC FUNCTIONS

Analytic Function* (Conjugate Functions)	Field Geometry	References†
$w = -S \ln z$ $u = -S \ln r$ $v = -S\phi$	Single line charge (+) (Source line) Concentric circles Radial lines	Rothe et al.,[D8] p. 85; p. 105 (hydr.) Walker,[D10] p. 35 Bewley,[D1] p. 29
$w = -jV \ln z$ $u = +V\phi$ $v = -V \ln r$	Single line current (−) (Vortex line) Radial lines Concentric circles	Rothe et al.,[D8] p. 105 (hydr.) Bateman,[C1] p. 79 (hydr.) Lamb,[C22] p. 203
$w = -S \ln (z - z_1/z - z_2)$ $u = -S \ln r_1/r_2$ $v = -S(\phi_1 - \phi_2)$	Two line charges (+ −) Circles, centers on center line Circles through z_1 and z_2	Rothe et al.,[D8] p. 88; p. 105 (hydr.) Harnwell,[A9] p. 38 Smythe,[A22] p. 74 Walker,[D10] p. 38; p. 41 (curr.) Bewley,[D1] p. 43
$w = -jV \ln (z - z_1/z - z_2)$ $u = +V(\phi_1 - \phi_2)$ $v = -V \ln r_1/r_2$	Two parallel line currents (− +) Circles through z_1 and z_2 Circles, centers on center line	Lamb,[C91] p. 204 (hydr.)
$w = -E^0z$ $u = -E^0x$ $v = -E^0y$	Uniform field in pos. (→) x-direction	
$w = -2aS (1/z)$ (a very small) $u = -2aS \, x/r^2$ $v = +2aS \, y/r^2$	Dipole line charge (+ −) Circles through origin, centers on x-axis Circles through origin, centers on y-axis	Jeans,[A10] p. 267 Rothe et al.,[D8] p. 109 (hydr.) Bewley,[D1] p. 9; p. 30 (hydr.)

TABLE 25·1   (Continued)

Field Geometry	Analytic Function* (Conjugate Functions)	References†
Line current in uniform field (→)	$w = -H^0 z - jV \ln z$ $u = -H^0 x + V\phi$ $v = -H^0 y - V \ln r$	Hague,[B44] p. 152 Maxwell,[A17] II, p. 153 Bewley,[D1] p. 36 (hydr.)
Circular cylinder in uniform field (→) Cylinder radius	$w = -E^0 z + 2aS(1/z)$ (a very small) $u = -E^0 x + 2aS\,x/r^2$ $v = -E^0 y - 2aS\,y/r^2$ $R^2 = 2aS/E^0$	Walker,[D10] p. 101 Lamb,[C22] p. 74 (hydr.) Rothe et al.,[D8] p. 110 (hydr.) Bewley,[D1] p. 32 (hydr.)
Current flow around circular hole	$w_1 = -jw$ $u_1 = v, \quad v_1 = -u$	
Quadripole line (Fig. 25-3b)	$w = -2a^2 S(1/z^2)$ (a very small) $u = -2a^2 S \cos 2\phi/r^2$ $v = +2a^2 S \sin 2\phi/r^2$	
Right-angle corner and infinitely far line charge	$w = -kz^2$ $u = -k(x^2 - y^2)$ $v = +k2xy$	Walker,[D10] p. 16 Jeans,[A10] p. 266 Bewley,[D1] p. 8 (hydr.)

*$S = \lambda/2\pi\varepsilon$ (electrostatics) or $I/2\pi\gamma$ (for current flow in thin sheets)
$V = -I/2\pi$ (current in negative direction in right-handed system) or $\Gamma/2\pi$ (for hydrodynamic circulation).
† hydr. = hydrodynamic example; curr. = current flow example.

potential values must now be made unique by introducing the same barrier plane as before, restricting $0 \leqslant \phi < 2\pi$; as seen, the potential increases with angle ϕ, so that the field lines are directed clockwise. The constant V must now be determined from the fact that the line integral of the field vector which equals the potential difference across the barrier is also the value of the current causing the field; thus, integrating in the mathematically positive sense,

$$\oint \mathbf{H} \cdot \mathbf{ds} = \mathcal{F}_{\phi=0} - \mathcal{F}_{\phi=2\pi} = V(0 - 2\pi) = I \qquad (25)$$

so that $V = -I/2\pi$. To avoid this negative sign, which just expresses the fact that clockwise field lines belong to a current in the negative third axis direction of a right-handed coordinate system, one could, of course, choose a positive sign in (24), but then either the potential values would be negative or one would have to introduce $u = V(2\pi - \phi)$ as potential function; all these possibilities have been used. In hydrodynamics, where the concept of vortex line originated, this difficulty does not arise because the velocity vector is usually defined as positive gradient of the potential function (table $25 \cdot 1$).

The single vortex line can also be used to represent the field between two coplanar potential surfaces with an infinitesimal gap between them as shown in Fig. $25 \cdot 4a$. In this case, the constant V is to be chosen as $(\Phi_1 - \Phi_2)/\pi$ and one adds the constant Φ_2 which is always possible, obtaining

$$w = -j \cdot \frac{\Phi_1 - \Phi_2}{\pi} \ln z + \Phi_2$$

$$= \left[(\Phi_1 - \Phi_2) \frac{\phi}{\pi} + \Phi_2 \right] - j \frac{\Phi_1 - \Phi_2}{\pi} \ln r \qquad (26)$$

as the complete solution for the upper half z-plane.

Superposition of two equal line charges with opposite sign, i.e., of a source and a sink line, leads to the same results as in section 12, permitting the same general use for finite cylinders. Table $25 \cdot 1$ gives the function as well as several references using it and showing graphs; the notation is illustrated in Fig. $25 \cdot 3$ for a convenient choice of coordinates. If the two charged lines recede symmetrically to infinity, one has

$$w = -\frac{\lambda}{2\pi\varepsilon} \lim_{M \to \infty} \left(\ln \frac{z + M}{z - M} \right) \to -\left(\frac{1}{\pi\varepsilon} \cdot \frac{\lambda}{M} \right) z = -E^0 z \qquad (27)$$

a uniform field of gradient E^0 in the x-direction (a non-essential constant has been dropped). If the two line charges approach symmetrically very closely the axis 0, one has

$$w = -\frac{\lambda}{2\pi\varepsilon} \lim_{a \to 0}\left(\ln \frac{z+a}{z-a}\right) \to -\frac{\lambda}{2\pi\varepsilon}\frac{2a}{z} = -\frac{p}{2\pi\varepsilon}\cdot\frac{1}{z} \quad (28)$$

a dipole line charge as in $(12\cdot52)$ with the dipole moment $p = \lambda\cdot 2a$ in the negative x-direction.

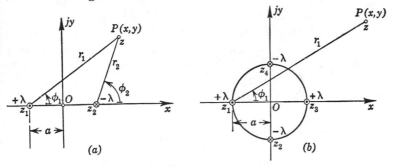

FIG. $25\cdot3$ Several Line Charges (Source Lines): (a) source and sink, (b) source pair and sink pair.

The combinations of the homogeneous field (27) with line current (24) and with dipole line (28) are listed in table $25\cdot1$; further combinations are found particularly in hydrodynamic flow studies.

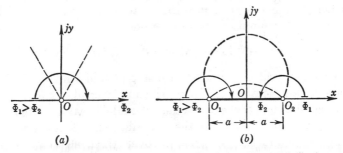

FIG. $25\cdot4$ Vortex Flow as Solution of Coplanar Potential Surfaces: (a) single vortex, (b) vortex pair.

Superposition of two parallel, equal line currents of opposite direction leads to the same results as in $(13\cdot16)$; see table $25\cdot1$. This superposition can also be used to represent the field between three coplanar potential surfaces as indicated in Fig. $25\cdot4b$. To obtain the correct constants for the potential function $u = V(\phi_1 - \phi_2)$, one should add the value Φ_1, since at $\phi_1 = \phi_2 = 0$, u would otherwise vanish. Then, for $\phi_1 = \pi$, $\phi_2 = 0$, one should have $u = \Phi_2$ which requires $V = (\Phi_2 - \Phi_1)/\pi$; for $\phi_1 = \phi_2 = \pi$ one finds then Φ_1 again. Thus,

$$
\begin{aligned}
w &= +j\,\frac{\Phi_1 - \Phi_2}{\pi}\,\ln\frac{z+a}{z-a} + \Phi_1 \\
&= \left[-\frac{\Phi_1 - \Phi_2}{\pi}\,(\phi_1 - \phi_2) + \Phi_1 \right] + j\,\frac{\Phi_1 - \Phi_2}{\pi}\,\ln\frac{r_1}{r_2} \quad (29)
\end{aligned}
$$

is the complete solution for the upper half z-plane.

For more than two source or vortex lines, the same process of superposition can be followed. Solutions have been given for N coplanar charged lines[6] and for N equally charged lines equally spaced on a cylindrical surface of radius R_2 and parallel to its axis. In the latter case, one can write the sum

$$
-\frac{\lambda_g}{2\pi\varepsilon}\sum_{\alpha=1}^{N}\ln\,(z - z_\alpha) = -\frac{\lambda_g}{2\pi\varepsilon}\ln\,(z^N - z_\alpha{}^N) \quad (30)
$$

since $z_\alpha = R_g \exp\,(j2\pi\alpha/N)$ are simply the n unit roots multiplied by the constant radius R_g. Close to the individual wires, the potential lines are practically radial; at a distance a little more than the mutual spacing, the potential lines merge into practically concentric circles; see Bewley,[D1] p. 53, for $N = 6$.

Superimposing onto the cylindrical array (30) a concentric field by placing a line charge q_c into the center of the cylinder, one has the model of a cylindrical vacuum triode, with

$$
2\pi\varepsilon_v w = -\lambda_c \ln z - \lambda_g \ln\,(z^N - z_\alpha{}^N) - 2\pi\varepsilon_v\Phi_0 \quad (31)
$$

where Φ_0 is a real constant to adjust potential values. Making the assumption that the grid wire spacing is small compared with the radial distances of the centers of the grid wires from both anode and cathode, one can take the contributions of the grid wire potentials as practically constant over these electrodes. The conditions are, therefore (see also Fig. 25·5),

$$
\left.
\begin{aligned}
u &\equiv \Phi = 0 && \text{on cathode} && \text{where } z = R_c e^{j\phi} \\
u &\equiv \Phi = V_g && \text{on grid wires} && \text{where } z = z_\alpha + \rho_g e^{j\psi} \\
u &\equiv \Phi = V_a && \text{on anode} && \text{where } z = R_a e^{j\phi}
\end{aligned}
\right\} \quad (32)
$$

[6] W. H. Barkas, *Phys. Rev.*, **49**, p. 627 (1936).

With $R_a{}^N \gg R_g{}^N \gg R_c{}^N$ one can simplify the rationalization of $\ln (z^N - z_\alpha{}^N)$, so that corresponding to (32) one has

$$\left.\begin{aligned}
0 &= -\lambda_c \ln R_c - \lambda_g \ln R_g{}^N - 2\pi\varepsilon_v \Phi_0 \\
2\pi\varepsilon_v V_g &= -\lambda_c \ln R_g - \lambda_g \ln (R_g{}^{N-1} N \rho_g) - 2\pi\varepsilon_v \Phi_0 \\
2\pi\varepsilon_v V_a &= -\lambda_c \ln R_a - \lambda_g \ln R_a{}^N - 2\pi\varepsilon_v \Phi_0
\end{aligned}\right\} \quad (33)$$

from which one can readily evaluate the line charge values.   The amplification factor, defined as the ratio of the partial capacitance

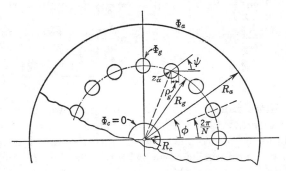

Fig. 25·5   Schematic of a Triode with Cylindrical Structure.

between grid and cathode to that between anode and cathode, follows then as[7]

$$\mu = \frac{\partial\lambda_c/\partial V_g}{\partial\lambda_c/\partial V_a} = \frac{N \ln R_a/R_g}{\ln R_g/N\rho_g} \quad (34)$$

Using a double grid of line charges, N positive on an inner and N negative on an outer cylinder at the same equal angular spacing, one obtains close to each doublet potential lines which closely approximate cable conductors.[8]   For $N = 3$ and $N = 4$ complete solutions for electrical and thermal characteristics are given in the references.

Infinite Arrays of Line Charges or Currents.   The periodic functions of the meromorphic type, i.e., functions which behave like rational functions anywhere in the finite z-plane (excluding

[7] W. Schottky, *Arch. f. Elektrot.*, **8**, p. 1 (1919) and M. v. Laue, *Ann. d. Physik*, **59**, p. 465 (1919); see also Rothe *et al.*,[D8] p. 89; Ollendorff,[A18] p. 156; Chaffee,[B21] p. 173; Dow,[B23] p. 39; and Spangenberg,[B29] p. 138.

[8] G. Mie, *E.T.Z.*, **26**, p. 1 (1905); Ollendorff,[A18] p. 134.

the point at infinity), generally represent infinite plane arrays of line charges or line currents. Thus, with proper restriction to single values of the logarithm itself,

$$w = -\frac{\lambda}{2\pi\varepsilon} \ln\left[\exp\left(2\pi \frac{z}{a}\right) - 1\right] \tag{35}$$

is non-analytic at $z_n = \pm nja$, at periodic intervals along the imaginary axis. It behaves near these singularities like $\ln z$, i.e., represents positive line charges, since one can write there $(2\pi/a)z = 2\pi jn + (2\pi/a)\zeta$, with $\zeta = \eta + j\sigma$ small, so that

$$w_{\text{near } z_n} = -\frac{\lambda}{2\pi\varepsilon} \ln\left[\cosh\frac{2\pi}{a}\zeta + \sinh\frac{2\pi}{a}\zeta - 1\right]$$

$$\approx -\frac{\lambda}{2\pi\varepsilon} \ln\left(\frac{2\pi}{a}\zeta\right) \tag{36}$$

The field lines from the positive grid go towards $+\infty$, where $w = -(\lambda/\varepsilon)(z/a)$; there is no field at $z \to -\infty$. Thus, (35) represents an infinite plane array of positive line charges with a superimposed uniform electric field parallel to the positive x-direction and large enough to cancel the grid field as $z \to -\infty$. An excellent graph is shown in Maxwell,[A17] I, Fig. XIII.

For numerical application, one needs the real potential function, which is obtained by expanding

$$\exp\left(2\pi \frac{z}{a}\right) = \exp\left(\frac{2\pi x}{a}\right)\left[\cos\frac{2\pi y}{a} + j\sin\frac{2\pi y}{a}\right]$$

and, expressing the logarithm in polar form,

$$\Phi \equiv u(x, y) =$$

$$-\frac{\lambda}{4\pi\varepsilon} \ln\left[\exp\left(4\pi \frac{x}{a}\right) + 1 - 2\exp\left(\frac{2\pi x}{a}\right)\cos\frac{2\pi y}{a}\right] \tag{37}$$

For distances from the grid array along the positive x-direction of the order of a, the grid wire spacing, one can disregard all but the first term, since $e^{2\pi} \approx 500$, and one has left a uniform field directed in the positive x-direction with

$$\Phi_{x \geqslant a} \approx -\frac{\lambda}{4\pi\varepsilon} \frac{4\pi x}{a} = -\frac{\lambda}{\varepsilon a} x \tag{38}$$

with field gradient $E^0 = \lambda/\varepsilon a$.   Closer to the wires one can write

$$\Phi\left(\frac{a}{2} < x < a\right) \approx -\frac{\lambda}{4\pi\varepsilon}\left\{\frac{2\pi x}{a}\right.$$
$$\left. + \ln\left[\exp\left(\frac{2\pi x}{a}\right) - 2\cos\left(\frac{2\pi y}{a}\right)\right]\right\}$$

indicating a slight variation in the y-direction, producing a wavy potential line.   For values of $|z| \leqslant 0.2(a/2\pi)$, one can use the approximation (36), which means that one could use the same field picture for finite wire radii of the order of $(0.2a/2\pi)$ or less. Assume now a conducting plane of ground potential placed at distance $h \geqslant a$ parallel to the plane of the grating as in Fig. 25·6a and add to the potential function (37) an arbitrary constant Φ_0. Then, with (38) and (36), one has, respectively,

$$\Phi_{x=h} = 0 = -\frac{\lambda}{\varepsilon a}h + \Phi_0, \qquad \Phi_{|\zeta|=\rho} = -\frac{\lambda}{2\pi\varepsilon}\ln\frac{2\pi\rho}{a} + \Phi_0 \quad (39)$$

where $\Phi(|\zeta| = \rho)$ is the grid wire potential.   Eliminating Φ_0, one has

$$\Phi_{|\zeta|=\rho} = \frac{\lambda}{2\pi\varepsilon}\left(\frac{2\pi h}{a} + \ln\frac{a}{\pi d}\right) \qquad (40)$$

which defines the capacitance of the "Maxwell" grating with respect to ground per unit length and for one section as

$$C_1 = \frac{\lambda}{\Phi} = \frac{2\pi\varepsilon}{\left(\dfrac{2\pi h}{a} + \ln\dfrac{a}{\pi d}\right)} \qquad (41)$$

This field distribution can be used for the capacitance of parallel antenna wires,[9] for the grid-cathode capacitance if the grid is very close to the cathode, and for the approximation of the wire effect in high-voltage windings.[10]   With the superposition of a uniform field it approximates also an infinite grid between two distant planes and has been used to compute the effect of grid wires in triodes on electron paths.[11]

[9] P. O. Pedersen, *Zeits. f. Hochfrequenztechnik*, **7**, p. 434 (1913).

[10] W. Grösser, *Arch. f. Elektrot.*, **25**, p. 193 (1931).

[11] K. Spangenberg, *Proc. I.R.E.*, **28**, p. 226 (1940).

Similarly, the function

$$w = -\frac{\lambda}{2\pi\varepsilon} \ln \sin \frac{\pi z}{a} \qquad (42)$$

with restriction to the principal part of the logarithm to assure single valuedness, is non-analytic at $z_n = \pm na$. Setting in the neighborhood of these singular points $z = na + \zeta$, one has

$$w_{\text{near } z_n} \approx -\frac{\lambda}{2\pi\varepsilon} \ln \left(\pm \frac{\pi}{a} \zeta \right)$$

again equal positive line charges spaced at intervals a along the x-axis. The potential function is upon rationalization

$$\Phi \equiv u(x, y) = -\frac{\lambda}{4\pi\varepsilon} \ln \left[\cosh \frac{2\pi y}{a} - \cos \frac{2\pi x}{a} \right] + \frac{\lambda}{4\pi\varepsilon} \ln 2 \qquad (43)$$

which for values $|y| \geqslant (a/2)$ is practically a constant potential, so that one can introduce symmetrically located plane equipotential surfaces and thus have an infinite grid midway between two parallel conducting planes. Proceeding as in the previous application, one finds

$$\Phi_{|\zeta| = \rho} = \frac{\lambda}{2\pi\varepsilon} \left[\frac{\pi h}{a} + \ln \frac{a}{\pi d} \right] \qquad (44)$$

from which again the capacitance can be computed,[12] or the resistance by use of (8·11). Interchanging potential and field lines by using $w_1 = -jw$ in (42), one has the solution for the magnetic field of a line current between two parallel magnetic equipotential surfaces of infinite permeability and a distance a apart shown in dotted lines in the left part of Fig. 25·6b; see Hague,[B44] p. 167, and Walker,[D10] p. 69. For an infinite array of vortex lines see Lamb,[C22] p. 207. Adding a second grid of negative wires as in Fig. 25·6c, one has

$$w = -\frac{\lambda}{2\pi\varepsilon} \left[\ln \sin \frac{\pi}{a} (z - jb) - \ln \sin \frac{\pi}{a} (z + jb) \right] \qquad (45)$$

which gives at the plane $y = 0$ the potential $\Phi = 0$ and represents an infinite grid very close to a grounded conductor plane so that the image grid has to be used,[13] or the current flow in a thin metal

---

[12] In different form, but same result see Ollendorff,[A18] p. 158.

[13] J. H. Fremlin, *Phil. Mag.*, **27**, p. 709 (1939); also Spangenberg,[B29] p. 162.

sheet of width a between two cylindrical electrodes[14] of small radius ρ as in the shaded area in Fig. 25·6c. The capacitance between two of the opposite grid wires within one of the periodic

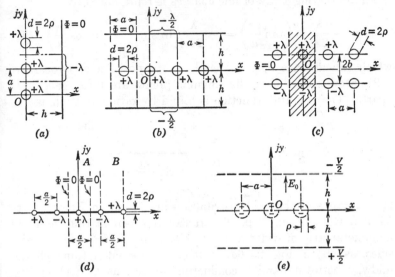

(a) (b) (c)

(d) (e)

FIG. 25·6 Infinite Plane Arrays of Line Charges: (a) Maxwell grating, (b) grating midway between parallel conducting planes, (c) parallel positive and negative gratings, (d) alternating grating, (e) dipole grating.

strips can be obtained from (44) if one substitutes $2b$ for h. The resistance between the two electrodes if the metal foil has thickness t is then given by

$$R = \frac{1}{2\pi\gamma t}\left[\frac{2\pi b}{a} + \ln\frac{a}{\pi d}\right] \qquad (46)$$

Interchanging the potential and field lines in (45) leads to the magnetic field of two opposite line currents midway in an air gap of length a between two infinitely permeable magnetic pole faces; see Hague,[B44] p. 177, and Bewley,[D1] pp. 158 and 137. Hague also uses two coplanar infinite plane grid arrays of like sign to simulate the effect of magnetic imaging if a single line current is in arbitrary position between ideal pole faces. All computations follow the same pattern as given above. It does not matter

[14] F. Ollendorff, *Arch. f. Elektrot.*, **19**, p. 123 (1927); also Ollendorff,[A18] p. 159, and Rothe *et al.*,[D8] p. 96.

whether one uses trigonometric or hyperbolic functions, whether sin z or cos z; as complex functions they differ only by constants or irrelevant shifts of the origin.

An alternating array of line charges is represented by

$$w = -\frac{\lambda}{2\pi\varepsilon} \ln\left(\tan\frac{\pi z}{a}\right) = -\frac{\lambda}{2\pi\varepsilon}\left(\ln\sin\frac{\pi z}{a} - \ln\cos\frac{\pi z}{a}\right) \quad (47)$$

which can at once be considered a superposition of two arrays (42) interlaced so that the singular points are now spaced $a/2$ apart. The potential function is found by rationalization as

$$\Phi \equiv u(x, y) = -\frac{\lambda}{4\pi\varepsilon} \ln \frac{\cosh\dfrac{2\pi y}{a} - \cos\dfrac{2\pi x}{a}}{\cosh\dfrac{2\pi y}{a} + \cos\dfrac{2\pi x}{a}} \quad (48)$$

Good graphs of the field distribution are found in Bewley,[D1] p. 55, and Rothe et al.,[D8] p. 96. It can represent a thin infinitely long metal strip of width $a/2$ with two thin electrodes at opposite sides, as (B) in Fig. 25·6d, or it can represent a thin cylinder midway between parallel conducting planes, as at (A) in Fig. 25·6d and also treated in section 21. In the latter case, the potential vanishes at $x = \pm(a/4)$; on the cylinder of radius ρ it becomes

$$\Phi_{|z|=\rho} \approx -\frac{\lambda}{2\pi\varepsilon}\ln\frac{\pi\rho}{a} = +\frac{\lambda}{2\pi\varepsilon}\ln\frac{a}{\pi\rho}$$

because $\tan(\pi z/a) \approx (\pi z/a)$ near the origin. The capacitance per unit length is then

$$C_1 = \frac{2\pi\varepsilon}{\ln(a/\pi\rho)} \quad (49)$$

One can as well select any one of the equipotential surfaces which are of oval shape for example to simulate the cross-sectional shape of poles in a large generator and find the leakage flux between adjacent poles.[15]

An infinite plane array of dipole lines is described by the function

$$w = +j\frac{\lambda}{2\pi\varepsilon}\cot\left(\frac{\pi z}{a}\right) \quad (50)$$

[15] B. Hague, *Jl. I.E.E.*, **61**, p. 1072 (1923).

for which the potential function becomes

$$\Phi = u(x, y) = + \frac{\lambda}{2\pi\varepsilon} \frac{\sinh \dfrac{2\pi y}{a}}{\cosh \dfrac{2\pi y}{a} - \cos \dfrac{2\pi x}{a}} \tag{51}$$

The analytic function has singularities at $z_n = \pm na$; in their neighborhood, one has $z = na + \zeta$, so that

$$w_{\text{near } z_n} \approx + j \frac{\lambda}{2\pi\varepsilon} \frac{a}{\pi\zeta}$$

which represents a dipole line of dipole moment $\lambda a/\pi$ per unit length directed in the positive y-direction as indicated in Fig. 25·6e. Superimposing a uniform field E^0 in the positive y-direction with a potential $\Phi^0 = -E^0 y$ produces resultant field lines convergent in the neighborhood upon the dipole lines and remaining uniform at larger distance from the grid, as in the case of the single dipole line (21·20); this is readily seen by letting y become large in (51).   There will exist an almost circular equipotential line surrounding each dipole, which can be used to define a comparatively large cylinder and simulate the problem of a grating with radii ρ not negligible compared with mutual distance a.   This radius can be determined by finding the point along the x-axis where $E_y = 0$, where the imposed uniform field E^0 equals the opposing field of the individual dipole.   The field vector of the dipole grating can be found from (50), using (15),

$$E = - \overline{\left(\frac{dw}{dz}\right)} = -j \frac{\lambda}{2\pi\varepsilon} \frac{\pi}{a} \overline{\left[\sin^2 \left(\frac{\pi z}{a} \right) \right]}^{-1}$$

Along the x-axis, $y = 0$, so that ρ can be determined from

$$E^0 = \frac{\lambda}{2\pi\varepsilon} \frac{\pi}{a} \left[\sin^2 \left(\frac{\pi\rho}{a} \right) \right]^{-1} \tag{52}$$

or one can select the dipole moment for a given radius ρ.   Assuming the resultant potential $(\Phi^0 + \Phi)$ to be defined as shown in Fig. 25·6e, namely, $\Phi_r = +(V/2)$ at $y = -h$ and $\Phi_r = -(V/2)$ at $y = +h$, one has with $h > a$ the conditions

$$y = \mp h: \qquad \pm \frac{V}{2} = \pm E^0 h \mp \frac{\lambda}{2\pi\varepsilon} \tanh \frac{2\pi h}{a}$$

With (52) these relations permit now the evaluation of the capacitance. The charge per unit area on the conductor $+(V/2)$ is (εE^0), since a uniform field gradient exists on it; the capacitance of the parallel plate condenser per unit depth and for a length $Na \gg 2h$ with the grating becomes with (52)

$$C_1 = \frac{Na\varepsilon E^0}{V} = \frac{Na\varepsilon}{2h - 2\dfrac{a}{\pi}\sin^2\left(\dfrac{\pi\rho}{a}\right)\tanh\left(\dfrac{2\pi h}{a}\right)} \tag{53}$$

is therefore increased considerably as ρ increases. Lamb,[C22] p. 68, has treated the flow of an incompressible fluid through such a grating of finite diameters. Ollendorff,[A18] p. 165, has used the interchange of potential and field lines to simulate the effect of round holes in transformer laminations upon the magnetic flux, assuming the uniform magnetic field lines parallel to the x-axis.

Elliptic Geometries. The inverse trigonometric or hyperbolic functions lead to confocal conics. Because these are many valued, it is necessary to define the principal values carefully.[16] The function

$$\left.\begin{array}{l} w = \sin^{-1} z \\ z = \sin w = \sin u \cosh v + j \cos u \sinh v \end{array}\right\} \tag{54}$$

gives upon separation of real and imaginary parts

$$x = \sin u \cosh v, \qquad y = \cos u \sinh v$$

from which, by elimination of u, and respectively v, one finds

$$\left.\begin{array}{l} \left(\dfrac{x}{\sin u}\right)^2 - \left(\dfrac{y}{\cos u}\right)^2 = 1 \\[4mm] \left(\dfrac{x}{\cosh v}\right)^2 + \left(\dfrac{y}{\sinh v}\right)^2 = 1 \end{array}\right\} \tag{55}$$

These relations define the lines $u = \text{cons}$ as confocal hyperbolas and those $v = \text{cons}$ as confocal ellipses. One can interpret the field as that produced by two coplanar equipotential planes with a gap of width 2 between their edges, as shown in Fig. 25·7. Interchange of the confocal families by using

$$w_1(z) = -jw = -j\sin^{-1} z = -\sinh^{-1}(jz) \tag{56}$$

[16] H. B. Dwight, *Trans. A.I.E.E.*, **61**, p. 851 (1942).

leads to elliptic cylinders as equipotential surfaces; see Maxwell,[A17] I, p. 290, and also Fig. X; in the limit these become a plane strip, the reverse of Fig. 25·7, which has been used to evaluate the capacitance of bus bars.[17]   Flow of an incompressible fluid through

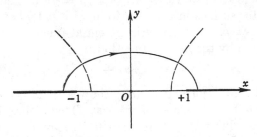

FIG. 25·7   Geometry of $\sin^{-1} z$.

a slit as in Fig. 25·7 or around a plane strip is treated in Lamb,[C22] p. 69.

As a special case one might consider

$$w = z^{\frac{1}{2}}, \qquad z = w^2 \tag{57}$$

which leads upon rationalization to

$$u^2 = +\tfrac{1}{2}[x \pm \sqrt{x^2 + y^2}]$$
$$v^2 = -\tfrac{1}{2}[x \mp \sqrt{x^2 + y^2}] \tag{58}$$

constituting confocal parabolas and giving the flow of an incompressible fluid around a single plate, as the left-hand one in Fig. 25·7; see Prandtl-Tietjens,[C24] p. 157.

Construction of Conjugate Functions.   It would, of course, be desirable to construct for a given equipotential surface $f(x, y) = 0$ directly that analytic function which is the complex potential solution with $f(x, y) = 0$ as boundary. This, however, can be done only for *unicursal* curves which are uniquely defined by a single parameter.

To find the complex potential $w(z)$, describe the conductor surface $f(x, y) = 0$ in complex form as

$$z^* = x^*(p) + jy^*(p) \tag{59}$$

---

[17] D. Gabor, *Arch. f. Elektrot.*, **14**, p. 247 (1924).

where p is the real parameter.   On the other hand, the inversion of $w(z)$ would lead to

$$z = x + jy = x(u, v) + jy(u, v)$$

If one lets here $u = 0$ and selects $x \equiv x^*, y \equiv y^*$, he again describes the conductor surface in complex form with potential $u = 0$ and parameter $v \equiv p$.   The analytic potential function $w(z)$ is then actually found by the inverse function

$$z(w) = x^*(-jw) + jy^*(-jw) \tag{60}$$

or essentially by replacing in (59) the real parameter $p \equiv v$ by the conjugate functions $v - ju \equiv -jw$, which assures analyticity of $z(w)$ and reduces to (59) for $u = 0$.   Expressing from (60) w as a function of z gives the final explicit solution;[18] this, however, is frequently not possible.

Assume an elliptical cylinder as conductor, with major axis $2a$ and minor axis $2b$.   The expression for the ellipse in normal and parametric forms is

$$\left(\frac{x}{a}\right)^2 + \left(\frac{y}{b}\right)^2 = 1, \qquad x = a \cos p, \qquad y = b \sin p$$

where the parameter p is actually the generating angle of the ellipse from the two bounding circles of radii a and b.   In complex form this gives

$$z^* = a \cos p + jb \sin p$$

and, replacing p by $-jw$, one has

$$z = a \cos (-jw) + jb \sin (-jw) \tag{61}$$

This can be transformed into

$$w = \cosh^{-1} (z[a^2 - b^2]^{-\frac{1}{2}}) - \tanh^{-1} \frac{b}{a} \tag{62}$$

an inverse hyperbolic function, as one would expect from the preceding subsection; Jeans,[A10] p. 270.   The equipotential lines can be found more directly from (61) as

$$\left(\frac{x \cosh \alpha}{a \cosh (u + \alpha)}\right)^2 + \left(\frac{y \sinh \alpha}{b \sinh (u + \alpha)}\right)^2 = 1, \qquad \alpha = \tanh^{-1} \left(\frac{b}{a}\right) \tag{63}$$

[18] Jeans,[A10] p. 269; S. Higuchi, *Technology Reports of Tohoku Univ., Sendai, Japan,* **10**, No. 4, p. 38 (1932); Smythe,[A22] p. 78.

From this, one can find the potential u_1 of another elliptic cylinder of major axis $a_1 = a \cosh (u_1 + \alpha)/\cosh \alpha$; with the flux function from (62) one can then evaluate the capacitance by (19). For other unicursal curves such as the cycloid, epicycloid, catenary, and some spirals see Higuchi, *loc. cit.*

26· CONFORMAL MAPPING

The discussion of properties of functions of a complex variable $w = f(z)$ has already introduced in Fig. 25·1 the concept of a one-to-one relationship of points in the $w = u + jv$ plane to those in the $z = x + jy$ plane and vice versa. One considers the w-plane

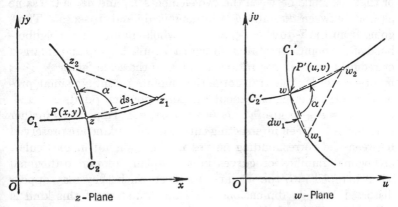

FIG. 26·1   Conformal Mapping by Analytic Functions.

a *map* or *representation* or *transformation* of the z-plane. The existence of a non-vanishing derivative of $f(z)$ at and in the neighborhood of z, which assures that the function is analytic there, has unique geometric consequences. Consider Fig. 26·1; let w_1 and w_2 be in this order the images of z_1 and z_2, and assume their respective distances from w and z to be the infinitesimal and corresponding elements dw_1, dw_2, and dz_1, dz_2. Obviously, dw_1 must be the map of dz_1 and dw_2 that of dz_2 and, in polar form.

$$dw_1 = dS_1 e^{jA_1}, \qquad dz_1 = ds_1 e^{j\alpha_1} \left.\begin{array}{c}\\\\\end{array}\right\}$$
$$dw_2 = dS_2 e^{jA_2}, \qquad dz_2 = ds_2 e^{j\alpha_2} \qquad (1)$$

Now, because of the existence of a non-vanishing derivative, the ratios of the two pairs of elements must have the same value, so that

$$\frac{dw_1}{dz_1} = \frac{dS_1}{ds_1} e^{j(A_1-\alpha_1)} = \frac{dw_2}{dz_2} = \frac{dS_2}{ds_2} e^{j(A_2-\alpha_2)} = Me^{j\mu} \qquad (2)$$

Both $M = \left|\dfrac{dw}{dz}\right|$ and μ can depend only on the location of the point $P(x, y)$ or on the value of z. Comparison of the arguments shows also

$$A_1 - A_2 = \alpha_1 - \alpha_2 = \alpha$$

or that the angle between the two elements dz_1 and dz_2 is the same as that between dw_1 and dw_2 in magnitude and in sense. Thus, going from the z- to the w-plane, the whole infinitesimal neighborhood of the point z is rotated through a definite angle μ and enlarged or reduced in a definite ratio according to the scale factor $M \gtrless 1$; in other words, the transformation maintains infinitesimal proportionality: the regions about the corresponding points $z = x + jy$ and $w = u + jv$ are *infinitesimally similar*. This means further that angles between intersecting curves in the z-plane are preserved between the corresponding curves in the w-plane; in particular, orthogonal families of curves in the z-plane remain orthogonal when mapped into the w-plane, however much they may appear distorted in finite dimensions. A transformation of this kind is called *conformal transformation* or *conformal representation* or *conformal mapping*.

Any analytic function provides conformal mapping at all its regular points where its derivative does not vanish. It can be shown also that the converse is true, that functions $u(x, y)$ and $v(x, y)$ which provide conformal mapping can always be combined into an analytic function $u + jv = f(z)$.

Transformation of Potential Problems. Potential fields satisfying the Laplacian differential equation in the x-y-plane are described by harmonic functions (see section 2), or analytic functions in the complex domain. To find a solution in the x-y-plane one can either use conjugate functions as described in section 25 or one can conformally map the geometry of the x-y-plane onto a u-v-plane by means of an analytic function $w = f(z)$ and then solve the potential problem in the transformed geometry. In the first case one identifies the potential function $\Phi(x, y)$ with the real part $u(x, y)$ of the complex function $w(z)$; in the latter case, now to be discussed, one has to find the potential solution Φ as a function of the new coordinates u, v. One can obviously find or construct a complex potential solution

$$P(w) = \Phi(u, v) + j\Xi(u, v) \tag{3}$$

where Ξ is the conjugate to $\Phi(u, v)$ and is the electric flux function, so that the dielectric flux between any two points becomes

$$\Psi = \varepsilon(\Xi_1 - \Xi_2) \tag{4}$$

as in (25·16); the curves $\Phi(u, v) = \text{cons}$ and $\Xi(u, v) = \text{cons}$ will again form curvilinear squares in the u-v-plane if one selects equal increments.

The transformation of the Laplacian differential equation for Φ from the x-y-coordinates to the u-v-coordinates (which are assumed to be harmonic functions of x, y because of the analyticity of the mapping function) can be performed directly, since

$$\frac{\partial \Phi}{\partial x} = \frac{\partial \Phi}{\partial u}\frac{\partial u}{\partial x} + \frac{\partial \Phi}{\partial v}\frac{\partial v}{\partial x}$$

$$\frac{\partial^2 \Phi}{\partial w^2} = \frac{\partial \Phi}{\partial u}\frac{\partial^2 u}{\partial w^2} + \frac{\partial^2 \Phi}{\partial u^2}\left(\frac{\partial u}{\partial x}\right)^2 + \frac{\partial \Phi}{\partial u}\frac{\partial^2 v}{\partial x^2} + \frac{\partial^2 \Phi}{\partial n^2}\left(\frac{\partial v}{\partial x}\right)^2$$

and similarly for the y-derivatives. In the sum representing the Laplacian in x, y, the first derivatives $\partial \Phi/\partial u$ and $\partial \Phi/\partial v$ appear multiplied by the Laplacians of u and v, respectively; both of these vanish because of (25·10). Using for the remaining terms the Cauchy-Riemann equations (25·6), one finds

$$\frac{\partial^2 \Phi}{\partial x^2} + \frac{\partial^2 \Phi}{\partial y^2} = \left(\frac{\partial^2 \Phi}{\partial u^2} + \frac{\partial^2 \Phi}{\partial v^2}\right)\left[\left(\frac{\partial u}{\partial x}\right)^2 + \left(\frac{\partial v}{\partial x}\right)^2\right] = 0 \tag{5}$$

The factor to the Laplacian in u, v is the absolute value $\left|\frac{\partial w}{\partial w}\right|^2 = \left|\frac{dw}{dz}\right|^2$ because of (25·5) and on the basis of the existence of the derivative of $w(z)$; but it must be further required that $dw/dz \neq 0$ in order to obtain for $\Phi(u, v)$ again the Laplacian potential equation. The Laplacian potential equation is therefore *invariant to conformal mappings* of the geometry at all regular points of the analytic mapping function where the derivative does not vanish.

The field vector in the u-v-plane is given as in (25·15) by

$$E_u + jE_v = -\frac{\partial \Phi}{\partial u} - j\frac{\partial \Phi}{\partial v} = -\overline{\left(\frac{dP}{dw}\right)} \tag{6}$$

It can readily be transformed into the original geometry in the x-y-plane by

$$E_x + jE_y = -\frac{\partial \Phi}{\partial x} - j\frac{\partial \Phi}{\partial y} = -\overline{\left(\frac{dP}{dz}\right)} = -\overline{\left(\frac{dP}{dw}\cdot\frac{dw}{dz}\right)} \tag{7}$$

since P as analytic function in the w-plane is also analytic in the z-plane (section 25). Indeed, one can evaluate it in the z-plane directly from the mapping function without first finding it in the w-plane, as long as one has evaluated the complex potential solution P. The absolute value of the field vector is from (7)

$$|E|_{(z)} = |E|_{(w)} \left|\frac{dw}{dz}\right| \tag{8}$$

and transforms in the direct geometric transformation ratio at each point, so that integrations of charge densities over corresponding conductor surfaces in the two planes give the same result. Therefore, capacitances, inductances, resistances evaluated in the w-plane geometry and expressed in terms of z-plane dimensions have the same values as if evaluated directly in the z-plane from the potential distribution there.

This can also be seen if one considers the field energy. The energy density as given in (3·20) can be expressed by using (8) and observing that on account of (2) for two orthogonal elements $du\ dv = \left|\frac{dw}{dz}\right|^2 dx\ dy$; thus

$$\frac{1}{2}\varepsilon\,|E|_{(z)}^2\,dx\,dy = \frac{1}{2}\varepsilon\,|E|_{(w)}^2 \left|\frac{dw}{dz}\right|^2 \frac{du\,dv}{\left|\frac{dw}{dz}\right|^2} \tag{9}$$

demonstrating that it is invariant to conformal transformations. The total field energy in corresponding field spaces will therefore be the same.

One might inquire into the transformation possibilities of space charge problems. Since field energy density can be expressed in the alternate form $(3\cdot 18)$ and the potential is invariant, one has

$$(\rho)_{(z)}\, dx\, dy = (\rho)_{(z)} \frac{du\, dv}{\left|\dfrac{dw}{dz}\right|^2} \equiv (\rho)_{(w)}\, du\, dv \tag{10}$$

or one must transform space charge densities in the ratio $\left|\dfrac{dw}{dz}\right|^{-2}$ from the x-y-plane into the u-v-plane in order to preserve invariance of the Poisson equation, which now becomes with the Laplacian from (5)

$$\frac{\partial^2 \Phi}{\partial u^2} + \frac{\partial^2 \Phi}{\partial v^2} = -\frac{(\rho)_{(w)}}{\varepsilon} \tag{11}$$

The same is, of course, true for the two-dimensional magnetic field problems involving current distributions and being described by one component of the vector potential.[1]

Points of Non-conformality of Mapping.   The fact that conformality is maintained only at regular points of the mapping function at which its derivative does not vanish requires a brief and reassuring examination of the properties of analytic functions and their derivatives. All discussions refer to one-valued functions or to the properly restricted domains of many-valued functions.

Assume $f(z)$ to be analytic at every point in a region R of the x-y-plane around a point z_0. Then $f(z)/z - z_0$ will also be analytic there and even very close to $z = z_0$, except directly at $z = z_0$, where the derivative does not exist; one might exclude this point z_0 by a small circle C' as in Fig. $26\cdot 2$. The integral of $f(z')$ over any closed curve Γ around z_0 and with points z' wholly within R vanishes because of Cauchy's integral theorem $(25\cdot 9)$. Now the integral of $f(z')/(z' - z_0)$ over the same closed curve Γ will not so vanish; but because of $(25\cdot 9)$ it can be contracted into the small circle C' along which one can express

$$(z' - z_0) = \rho e^{j\psi}, \qquad dz' = j\rho e^{j\psi}\, d\psi, \qquad z' = z_0 + \rho e^{j\psi} \tag{12}$$

This then gives

$$\int_{C'} \frac{f(z')\, dz'}{z' - z_0} = j \int_{\psi=0}^{2\pi} f(z_0 + \rho e^{j\psi})\, d\psi \approx 2\pi j f(z_0) \tag{13}$$

---

[1] For an interesting application to inductance calculations of eccentric circular annular bars see T. J. Higgins, *Jl. Math. and Phys.*, **21**, p. 159 (1942).

where ρ can be made so very small that $f(z') \rightarrow f(z_0)$.   Relation (13) leads to *Cauchy's integral*,

$$f(z_0) = \frac{1}{2\pi j} \oint \frac{f(z')\,dz'}{z' - z_0} \tag{14}$$

which states that the value of an analytic function at any point z_0 in a regular region R can always be expressed in terms of the known values along a regular closed curve within R surrounding that

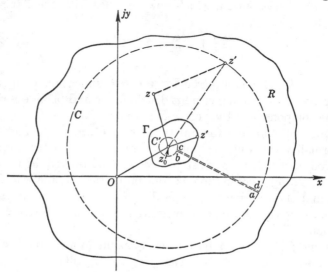

FIG. 26·2   Series Expansion of Analytic Functions.

point.   Not only the function itself, but also its derivatives at z_0, can be expressed by integrals because of the assumed regularity of $f(z')$,

$$\frac{df(z_0)}{dz_0} = f'(z_0) = \frac{1}{2\pi j} \oint \frac{f(z')\,dz'}{(z' - z_0)^2}$$

$$f^{(n)}(z_0) = \frac{n!}{2\pi j} \oint \frac{f(z')\,dz'}{(z' - z_0)^{n+1}} \tag{15}$$

Designating the distance $|z' - z_0| = r'$, then one can see at once that the derivatives have as upper bound

$$|f^{(n)}(z_0)| \leqslant n! \frac{|f(z')|}{r^{n+1}} \tag{16}$$

The value of the function $f(z)$ at a point z in the region R (Fig. $26 \cdot 2$) can now be expressed in a power series with the point z_0 as center and with a range of validity, say, to circle C. Since

$$\frac{1}{z' - z} = \frac{1}{(z' - z_0) - (z - z_0)}$$

$$= \frac{1}{z' - z_0} \left[1 + \frac{z - z_0}{z' - z_0} + \left(\frac{z - z_0}{z' - z_0} \right)^2 + \cdots \right]$$

is absolutely convergent because $|z - z_0| < |z' - z_0|$, one can multiply each term by $f(z') \, dz'$ and integrate over the circle C, which gives with (14) and (15) at once

$$f(z) = f(z_0) + f'(z_0)(z - z_0) + \frac{1}{2!} f''(z_0)(z - z_0)^2 + \cdots$$

$$= \sum_{\alpha=0}^{\infty} a_\alpha (z - z_0)^\alpha \quad (17)$$

This is a Taylor series expansion; breaking off at a finite value α, one can estimate the remainder by (16). The series (17) is definitely convergent within any circle C within which the function $f(z)$ is analytic at every point; this form illustrates that the derivatives are also given by convergent Taylor series expansions. For rational functions, the Taylor series reduces to a polynomial with no derivatives of higher order than the polynomial.

If in the Taylor series (17) the first coefficient vanishes, or $a_0 \equiv f(z_0) = 0$, then z_0 is a *root of the first order;* in this case, $f(z)$ has a vanishing derivative of the first order and can be written

$$f(z) = (z - z_0)[a_1 + a_2(z - z_0) + \cdots] = (z - z_0)g(z) \quad (18)$$

where now $g(z)$ is without root at $z = z_0$. If the first m coefficients are zero, then z_0 is a root of mth order, a factor $(z - z_0)^m$ can be isolated, and the first m derivatives vanish. It is important to note, however, that a root occurs only at an *isolated point,* since (18), for example, gives non-vanishing values for any z except exactly $z = z_0$. Indeed, one can show (for example Kellogg,[C10] p. 352) that, if $f(z)$ should vanish in infinitely many points within R, then it must vanish all through R. This means for conformal mapping that within any finite regular region of a mapping function there can be only a *finite number of zeros* or roots of the function where the derivative vanishes, that all these roots occur *at isolated points* and can be excluded by extremely small circles around each of them, and that in the immediate neighborhood of the root values conditions of conformality exist.

Should $f(z)$ be regular everywhere within R in Fig. 26·2 except at the point where $f'(z_0) \to \infty$ or, better, where the derivative $f'(z_0)$ does not exist, then the Taylor series expansion cannot be used, since its very basis (14) does not apply. It is possible, however, to give a power series expansion for the region bounded by C on the outside and by the small circle C' on the inside, if one extends the integral (14) over C and C' and connects these two circles by the closely spaced parallel lines ab and cd in Fig. 26·2 to provide essentially one single continuous and completely analytic path without encircling z_0 itself.[2] Because the contributions of ab and of cd are equal and opposite, one can really disregard them and consider only C and C'. On C one proceeds as for the Taylor series; for z' on C' one develops, because of opposite direction of integration,

$$-\frac{1}{z' - z} = \frac{1}{(z - z_0) - (z' - z_0)}$$
$$= \frac{1}{z - z_0}\left[1 + \frac{z' - z_0}{z - z_0} + \left(\frac{z' - z_0}{z - z_0}\right)^2 + \cdots \right]$$

This again is absolutely convergent because now $|z' - z_0| < |z - z_0|$ along C'. Multiplying this expansion term by term by $f(z') \, dz'$ and integrating over C' give its contribution to the closed integral. Combining this latter with the Taylor series for C gives the total result

$$f(z) = T(z - z_0) + \frac{b_1}{z - z_0} + \frac{b_2}{(z - z_0)^2} + \cdots \qquad (19)$$

where $T(z - z_0)$ is the right-hand side of (17), portraying the regular behavior of the function far from z_0, whereas the extra terms portray the singularity existing at z_0. The values of the coefficients b_α are from the above

$$b_1 = \frac{1}{2\pi j} \oint_{C'} f(z') \, dz'; \qquad b_\alpha = \frac{1}{2\pi j} \oint_C (z' - z_0)^{\alpha-1} f(z') \, dz' \qquad (20)$$

---

[2] The direction of integration along the boundary of any region shall always be such that the region lies to the left of the path of integration.

If only b_1 is different from zero, the function $f(z)$ is said to have a *pole of the first order* at $z = z_0$; it is obvious from (19) that the derivative does not exist at $z = z_0$, in fact, that it must have a pole of second order there; indeed, all higher derivatives must have poles of one order higher than their order. The function $(z - z_0)$ $f(z) = g(z)$ is, of course, regular in the entire region R and can again be represented by a positive power series like (17). If the highest order non-vanishing coefficient is b_m, then z_0 is a pole of the mth order and one can segregate a factor $(z - z_0)^{-m}$. It is again important to note, however, that a pole occurs only at an isolated point, since (19), for example, gives non-infinite values for any z except $z = z_0$. This means for conformal mapping that within any finite regular region of a mapping function there can be only a *finite number of poles* of the function, that all these poles occur *at isolated points* and can be excluded by extremely small circles around each of them, and that in the immediate neighborhood of the poles conditions of conformality exist.

If the number of coefficients b_α is unending at a point z_0, then it is called an essentially singular point, and it can be shown that in its neighborhood there exists an infinite sequence of points (a distinct point set) at which $f(z)$ either takes on the same value or has a pole of first order. The neighborhood of essentially singular points is therefore unsuited for conformal mappings and must be carefully avoided.

Whether or not a transformation can be considered conformal at $z = \infty$ is a matter of convention. Mathematically, it has become customary to attach to $z = \infty$ the characteristics of a point because by a transformation

$$t = \frac{1}{z}$$

the region $z = \infty$ of the z-plane is transformed into a definite point, $t = 0$ (origin), of the t-plane. In fact, one defines the characteristic of a function at the point $z = \infty$ as identical with the character of the same function of argument $t = 1/z$ at $t = 0$. Thus $w = z^2$ has a pole of second order at $z = \infty$, because $w^* = 1/t^2$ has a pole of second order at $t = 0$. In fact, all positive power polynomials are regular in the entire z-plane and have a pole at $z = \infty$ of the same order as the highest power of z indicates. If, therefore, an analytic function is regular everywhere, including $z = \infty$, it can only be a constant (theorem of Sturm-Liouville).

Simple Linear Mapping Functions. The only class of functions that assures one-to-one relationship between the entire z- and the entire w-plane without restriction except for a zero or a pole is the class of linear functions. It illustrates rather well a great variety of possibilities in simple form. To identify corresponding points and regions, it is advisable to use numbered or lettered coordinate lines of either uniform square mesh or of polar type.

The function

$$w = z + z_0, \qquad u = x + x_0, \qquad v = y + y_0 \tag{21}$$

is a simple *translation* or shift of the origin. The function

$$w = mz = |m|e^{j\mu}re^{j\phi} = |m|re^{j(\phi+\mu)} \tag{22}$$

is for $|m| = 1$ a pure rotation of the z-plane by an angle μ; for $\mu = 0$ a pure scale change by a factor $|m|$, uniform in all directions, a contraction for $|m| < 1$ and a dilation for $|m| > 1$; and for the general case a combined rotation and scale change which could be done in two steps

$$z_1 = |m|z, \qquad w = e^{j\mu}z_1$$

The combination of (21) and (22) superimposes also a shift of the origin, or a translation. These transformations have not introduced any finite distortion, circles remain circles, and straight lines remain straight lines.

The transformation by

$$w = \frac{1}{z} = \frac{1}{r}e^{-j\phi} \tag{23}$$

is of the type of inversion; however, because of the change in sign of the argument, angles are mirrored. In addition to inversion at the *unit circle* there is also inversion at the real axis. Figure 26·3 indicates the relationship between z- and w- planes. Any potential problem in the border-shaded infinite region outside the quarter circle 1–4 in the w-plane has its counterpart within the small region 0–1–4–0 in the z-plane. The function $1/z$ is analytic everywhere in the plane except at the origin $z = 0$, where it has a pole of the first order; thus, the origin is to be excluded from the mapping region by a very small circle, corresponding in the w-plane to a very large circle, excluding $w = \infty$ as a "point." Any potential solution can, therefore, not be considered to remain regular in the point $z = 0$ itself. This can be seen at once if one considers current flow in a thin metal sheet shaped as the quarter circle 0140 in the z-plane and thin rod electrodes applied, a positive one at 1 and a negative one at 4. If the point 0 is admitted, the current density would have two directions, one from 1 towards 0 and the other from 0 towards 4; this condition does not exist ever so close to 0, it holds only for the mathematical point $z = 0$; the exclusion of 0, which resolves this difficulty, can be interpreted

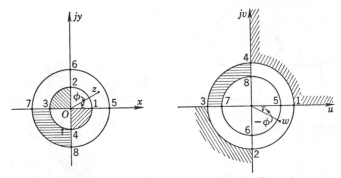

FIG. 26·3   Mapping by $w = 1/z$, Complex Inversion.

as admission that no physical metal sheet could ever actually possess the mathematically sharp corner. The same argument will apply in all cases of poles and roots of a mapping function.

A different interpretation of the same mapping function is obtained by writing it

$$w = u + jv = \frac{1}{z} = \frac{x}{x^2 + y^2} - j\,\frac{y}{x^2 + y^2} \qquad (24)$$

As Fig. 26·4 illustrates, the square net of lines parallel to u- and v-axes in the w-plane corresponds to circles passing through the origin in the z-plane. Several corresponding areas are indicated; if they are cut out in the shapes shown to be the maps of the shaded squares of the w-plane, they will all present exactly the same resistance between electrodes placed at opposite corners, such as 24-1, 2-13, 6-19, 23-I; in the last case, I itself is actually excluded but one can go ever so close.

This mapping function can be used to solve any problem involving orthogonally intersecting cylinders. The two cylinders drawn in dotted lines in the z-plane and marked $u = +1$, $v = -2$ become the two corresponding planes in the w-plane, the exterior of the cylinders corresponding to the area in the right angle. It is as if the cylinder surfaces had been separated at I and straightened out into planes and stretched to infinity at the same time, preserving the original right angle at A. Placing a line charge $+\lambda$ anywhere outside the cylinders and parallel to them one can find their capacitance by solving the problem of a line charge $+\lambda$ between orthogonally intersecting planes in the w-plane. Specifically, take

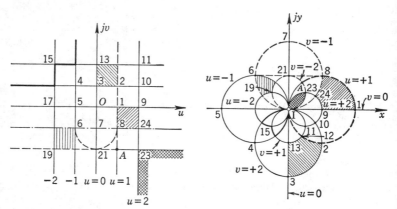

Fig. 26·4   Mapping by $w = 1/z$.

the diameter of the larger cylinder as d; then that of the smaller is $d/2$; locate the line charge $(+\lambda)$ at point 7 with $x = 0$, $y = d$. The introduction of diameter d for unity in the z-plane means that the unit circle is replaced by a circle of radius d, and thus $w_1 = d^2/z$, the mapping function instead of (24); this is readily evident from (23). The geometric image of the line charge 1 in the w-plane has then distance d from both planes; its electrical images are therefore at the corners of the square of side $2d$, center A. Ascribing zero potential to the cylinders and a small radius ρ to the line charge $(+\lambda)$ in the z-plane gives zero potential to the planes and radius ρ' to the geometric image, namely,

$$\rho' = \left| \frac{dw_1}{dz} \right|_{z=jd} \cdot \rho = \left| \frac{-d^2}{z^2} \right|_{z=jd} \cdot \rho = \rho \qquad (25)$$

using the basic relation (2) for small distances and realizing that circles remain circles and that on the circle of inversion no scale change takes place. The potential on the surface of ρ' in the w-plane will be the resultant of the four line charges and will be identical with that of the original wire in the z-plane

$$\Phi_{\rho'} = \Phi_\rho = \frac{\lambda}{2\pi\varepsilon}\left(-\ln\rho + 2\ln 2d - \ln 2\sqrt{2}d\right)$$

$$= \frac{\lambda}{2\pi\varepsilon}\ln\left(\frac{d}{\rho}\sqrt{2}\right) \tag{26}$$

so that the mutual capacitance between wire and cylinders per unit length is

$$C_1 = \frac{\lambda}{\Phi_\rho} = \frac{2\pi\varepsilon}{\ln\left(\dfrac{d}{\rho}\sqrt{2}\right)} \tag{27}$$

The treatment is somewhat similar to, but very much more straightforward than, inversion on the cylinder in section 23. The same method can be used if the two cylinders are of dielectric material ε with the line charge at 7; in this case one would have to use the image theory, section 21, to solve the line charge between two orthogonally intersecting dielectric plane boundaries. Many other similar problems can be simplified in field geometry by this elementary mapping function.

As a further example take the cylindrical surface of diameter d (so that again $w_1 = d^2/z$ is used) in the z-plane passing through 7 and I and marked as $v = -1$ in Fig. 26·4 as a conductor, split it along 7 and I with a very small gap and apply potential Φ_1 to the right half containing point 8, and $\Phi_2 < \Phi_1$ to the left half containing point 6; find the capacitance and field distribution. The map in the w-plane will be the line $v_2 = -d$ with point 7 on the v-axis and point I at infinity. These are now two coplanar equipotential surfaces of the same arrangement as in Fig. 25·4 for which the complex potential solution is known. To provide identity, one has to use a shift of origin and a rotation through π, so that by (21) and (22)

$$w_2 = (w_1 + jd)e^{j\pi} = \left(\frac{d^2}{z} + jd\right)e^{j\pi}$$

gives the exact z-plane arrangement of Fig. 25·4. For this, the solution in form of the complex potential function (3) is from (25·26)

$$P = \Phi + j\Xi = -j\,\frac{\Phi_1 - \Phi_2}{\pi}\,\ln w_2 + \Phi_2 \qquad (28)$$

Upon simple rationalization one finds the complete solution

$$\Phi(x, y) = \Phi_1 - \frac{\Phi_1 - \Phi_2}{\pi}\,\tan^{-1}\left[\frac{yd - (x^2 + y^2)}{xd}\right] \qquad (29)$$

$$\Xi(x, y) = -\frac{\Phi_1 - \Phi_2}{2\pi}\,\ln\frac{d^2}{(x^2 + y^2)^2}\,[(xd)^2 + (yd - x^2 - y^2)^2]$$

Along the two conducting semicircles one has $yd = (x^2 + y^2)$, so that $\tan^{-1}[\ ]$ in the potential will be zero for $x > 0$ and π for $x < 0$ thus describing the electrode potentials. The capacitance per unit length can be found by dividing the dielectric flux $\varepsilon(\Xi_1 - \Xi_2)$ by the potential difference. Choosing on the right hand semicylinder point 1 as $x = +g,\ y = d$ and point 2 as $x = +g,\ y = 0$ (avoiding the pole), one has immediately

$$C_1 = \frac{2\varepsilon}{\pi}\,\ln\frac{d}{g} \qquad (30)$$

with d the diameter of the cylinder and $2g \ll d$ the gap between the cylinder halves. A solution for the potential function alone by means of circular harmonics is given in Zworykin *et al.*,[B32] p. 371. The electric field can readily be computed by (7). Actually the field lines are identical with the magnetic field lines of two equal and opposite line currents placed at 7 and I.

The Bilinear Transformation. The general linear function

$$w = \frac{Az + B}{Cz + D}, \qquad z = \frac{-Dw + B}{Cw - A} \qquad (31)$$

with $AD - BC \neq 0$ is the most general transformation mapping the whole of the z-plane in one-to-one relationship upon the whole of the w-plane, preserving conformity at all points except $z = -(B/A)$, which is a root, and $z = -(D/C)$, which is a pole of first order of the mapping function. Circles and straight lines are again mapped into circles and straight lines, and any series of linear transformations will maintain the same type; the linear transformations form a *group*. The transformation (31) has as special cases all the previous simpler linear functions and, in fact, can be made up in three distinct steps,

$$w_1 = z + \frac{D}{C}, \qquad w_2 = \frac{1}{w_1}, \qquad w = \frac{A}{C} + \frac{AD - BC}{C^2} w_2$$

This represents first a shift of the origin or translation, then an inversion, and finally a combination of translation, rotation, and scale change. Obviously, if $AD - BC = 0$, the last step would contract the whole w_2-plane into a single point A/C and is therefore excluded as singular.

Three arbitrary constants are available which can generally be chosen to transform three specified points in the z-plane (for example a circle) into three specified points in the w-plane. This is also apparent from the first and last steps above. The constants are best evaluated by using the form of (31)

$$B + Az - Dw - Czw = 0 \tag{32}$$

where B appears as a superfluous additive constant, which can be divided out in (31). Instead of three points, one can select one point and an assigned direction through this point in both planes. One can also map the upper half plane upon itself in an infinite number of ways; in this case the constants must be all real. If $w = u + jv$, $z = x + jy$, rationalization of (31) and elimination of u give the condition

$$v[(Cx + D)^2 + (Cy)^2] = (AD - BC)y \tag{33}$$

which means that positive y-values will become positive v-values only if one has $AD - BC > 0$. Other interesting characteristics are discussed in Bateman,[C1] pp. 270 and 274.

A particularly important application is the transformation of the unit circle upon the upper half w-plane. Take the function

$$w = j\frac{1 - z}{1 + z}, \qquad z = \frac{j - w}{j + w} \tag{34}$$

On the unit circle $z = 1e^{j\phi}$, and introducing this into (34) simplifies it to

$$w = \frac{\sin \phi}{1 + \cos \phi} \tag{35}$$

showing that w is real and the points correspond as shown in Fig. 26·5; the origin $z = 0$ becomes $w = j$. Concentric circles in the z-plane become excentric circles about $0'$ which are exactly like the potential surfaces between two charged lines, one located at $0'$ and one symmetrically located in the lower half plane. Correspondingly, radial lines become the orthogonal family of circles through $0'$. The function (34) has one root value at $z = +1$, where no conformity exists; it corresponds to the origin in the w-plane which cannot be part of the analytic field solution. There is also a pole at $z = -1$, corresponding to the point infinity in the w-plane; the mapping will, therefore, not be conformal there;

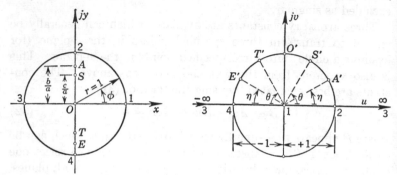

FIG. 26·5 Mapping of Unit Circle upon Upper Half Plane.

however, as has been stressed, one can go arbitrarily close. If one chooses in (34) $r \neq 1$ but keeps the correspondence of w-points and z-points, then the mapping function has to be modified to

$$w = j\frac{r - z}{r + z}, \qquad z = r\frac{j - w}{j + w} \qquad (36)$$

This permits the solution of any field distribution within the cylinder $|z| < r$ by solving the corresponding problem in the upper half plane. In particular, the case above of the split cylinder can be transformed upon the upper half plane with the split along 1–0–3 to utilize the singularities which have to be excluded in any case.

The unit circle can be mapped upon itself in the most general way[3] by the function

$$w = e^{j\beta}\frac{z - a}{1 - \bar{a}z} \qquad (37)$$

[3] Bateman,[C1] p. 280.

where β is a real angle, a any complex number, and $\bar{a}$ its conjugate complex value. This linear function maps the interior of unit circle in the z-plane upon the interior of unit circle in the w-plane; the point $z = a$ becomes the origin in the w-plane, and the angle β means a general rotation.

A pertinent example of the transformation (34) is a circular thin metal disk of radius a with two current-carrying electrodes and two separate potential-measuring electrodes to minimize contact effects. With the radius a as scale factor, the distances are as indicated in Fig. 26·5. The electrodes are shown placed along the diameter 2–4 which in the w-plane becomes unit circle as seen from (34). If one sets $z = jy$, one finds, indeed,

$$w = j\frac{1 - jy}{1 + jy} = \frac{2y + j(1 - y^2)}{1 + y^2},$$

$$|w| = 1, \quad \arg w = \tan^{-1}\frac{1 - y^2}{2y}$$

This gives the transformed location of the electrodes in the w-plane

$$\eta = \tan^{-1}\frac{a^2 - b^2}{2ab}, \qquad \theta = \tan^{-1}\frac{a^2 - c^2}{2ac} \qquad (38)$$

The current flow must be restricted to the unit circle in the original, or to the upper half w-plane. This is accomplished by placing image electrodes below the u-axis of the same sign as those above the axis. Taking A' as the positive, and E' as the negative electrodes, the total complex potential is the superposition of that of the two source lines A' and its mirror image with respect to the u-axis, and that of the two sink lines E' and its similar mirror image. Using appropriately table 25·1, one has

$$P = \Phi + j\Xi = \frac{I}{2\pi\gamma}\ln\left(\frac{w - e^{j(\pi-\eta)}}{w - e^{j\eta}}\cdot\frac{w - e^{-j(\pi-\eta)}}{w - e^{-j\eta}}\right) \qquad (39)$$

Rationalization gives $\Phi(u, v)$ or, with (34), $\Phi(x, y)$. The potential at point T' is the negative of that at S' because of symmetry; the potential difference between these points, which is to be measured, is obtained in complex form with $w = e^{j\theta}$ from (39). With obvious simplifications, the real part becomes

$$V_{S'T'} = \frac{I}{\pi\gamma} \ln \frac{\cos\eta + \cos\theta}{\cos\eta - \cos\theta} = \frac{I}{\pi\gamma} \ln \frac{b(a^2 + c^2) + c(a^2 + b^2)}{b(a^2 + c^2) - c(a^2 + b^2)} \quad (40)$$

The resistance for a thickness t of the plate is[4] V/It.

Rational Mapping Functions.   Rational functions of z are essentially fractions of two polynomials with as many zeros as the numerator polynomial and with as many poles as there are zeros of the denominator polynomial.   The simplest function

$$w = z^n = r^n e^{jn\phi}, \qquad z = w^{1/n} \quad (41)$$

for integer values of n multiplies angles in the z-plane by n and stretches the radial scale.   One obviously has to restrict regions in the z-plane in such manner that the mapping on the w-plane does not cover the w-plane more than once, i.e., one has to limit the regions in the z-plane so that they are contained within $2\pi/n$. The function (41) has a zero of nth order at $z = 0$, and a pole of the nth order at $z = \infty$ (by convention).   A simple example is a line charge in the space defined by two orthogonally intersecting dielectric boundaries.   The function $w = z^2$ will stretch these boundaries into a single plane boundary for which the solution is known by the method of images; see section 21.

The electrostatic field in a cylindrical triode as in Fig. 25·5 can be treated by selecting a sector $2\pi/N$ in the z-plane, preferably with the grid wire centrally located, and applying to it the transformation $w = z^N$, which will spread it out into the entire w-plane where now the concentric cylinders of anode and cathode have radii $R_a{}^N$ and $R_c{}^N$, respectively, and where the single grid wire also has enlarged but has lost its circular section.   Only for rather small grid wires such that $N\rho_g/R_g\pi < \frac{1}{5}$ will the approximation by a circle be feasible.   The further treatment can consider the cathode, which has shrunk appreciably, and the grid wire as two line charges within the large anode cylinder.   The final solution is found either by means of images with respect to the anode cylinder, or by transforming the anode by (36) onto the upper half plane.   Many treatments of this important problem have been

[4] J. H. Awberry, *Phil. Mag.*, **13**, p. 674 (1932); the mapping used there is different and considerably more complicated.

given; in first approximation the results are the same as (34).[5]
The same mapping procedure has been used to evaluate the
magnetic field of a long line current parallel to two intersecting
planes.[6]

The function

$$w = z + \frac{a^2}{z}, \qquad z = \frac{w}{2} \pm \sqrt{\left(\frac{w}{2}\right)^2 - a^2} \qquad (42)$$

with a real is also listed in table $25 \cdot 1$ as the solution by conjugate

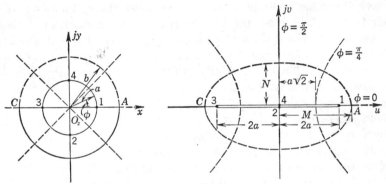

FIG. $26 \cdot 6$ Mapping of Ellipses into Circles.

functions for a conducting cylinder in a uniform electrostatic field.
As mapping function, with $z = re^{j\phi}$,

$$u = \left(r + \frac{a^2}{r}\right) \cos \phi, \qquad v = \left(r - \frac{a^2}{r}\right) \sin \phi \qquad (43)$$

it transforms the concentric circles and radial lines in the z-plane
into confocal ellipses and hyperbolas in the w-plane, as indicated
in Fig. $26 \cdot 6$. From (43) one has by elimination of either r or ϕ

$$\left(\frac{u}{r + a^2/r}\right)^2 + \left(\frac{v}{r - a^2/r}\right)^2 = 1,$$

$$\left(\frac{u}{2a \cos \phi}\right)^2 - \left(\frac{v}{2a \sin \phi}\right)^2 = 1 \qquad (44)$$

[5] M. Abraham, *Arch. f. Elektrot.*, **8**, p. 42 (1919); R. W. King, *Phys. Rev.*,
15, p. 256 (1920); F. B. Vodges and F. R. Elder, *Phys. Rev.*, **24**, p. 683 (1924);
B. Salzberg, Thesis M.E.E., Polytechnic Institute of Brooklyn, 1932; also
Proc. I.R.E., **30**, p. 134 (1942); Dow,[B23] p. 45; and Spangenberg,[B29] p. 135.
[6] J. Kucera, *Revue gén. de l'élec.*, **42**, p. 355 (1938).

the normal forms of the conics. The circle $r = a$ transforms into the plane strip of width $4a$ in the w-plane with the areas outside corresponding to each other. Obviously, the function (42) is two-valued, since it is necessary to restrict the mapping to $|z| \geqslant a$ in the z-plane for one complete coverage of the w-plane. If one wanted to map the interior of circle $r = a$, then $|z| \leqslant a$, and one would obtain a second coverage again by (43), in which positive values of v correspond to negative values of ϕ; the numbering on the plane strip would be reversed, but otherwise one would have the same conic geometry. One must think, therefore, of circle $r = a$ in the z-plane as a *barrier*. The singularities of the mapping function (42) are a pole of first order at $z = 0$ which, however, does not occur in the region of z values $|z| \geqslant a$; and a pole of second order at infinity, which can conveniently be excluded, since it occurs in the w-plane also at infinity. There are also two root values $z = \pm ja$ at which the conformality does not hold; these occur on the surface of the cylinder and can be avoided by very small circles around them.

Having established the proper regions for one-to-one relationship, one can use the z-plane to solve problems involving conic boundaries. The capacity of two confocal elliptical cylinders, the larger with major axis M and minor axis N, the smaller with M' and N', can be found from the concentric cylinder geometry. The axes define $(2a)^2 = M^2 + N^2$, the necessary width of the limit strip and the base radius in the z-plane; further, from (43) for point A

$$u = \left(b + \frac{a^2}{b} \right), \qquad v = 0, \qquad b = \frac{1}{2} (M + \sqrt{M^2 - 4a^2})$$

the radius of the image circle; only the positive sign can be used for the square root since $b > a$. Similarly, one gets b' for M'. For the coaxial cylinders the capacitance is taken from (14·11), and with b and b' one has per unit length for the elliptic cylinders[7]

$$C_1 = \frac{2\pi\varepsilon}{\ln b/b'} = 2\pi\varepsilon \left[\ln \frac{M + N}{M' + N'} \right]^{-1} \tag{45}$$

If the inner elliptic cylinder degenerates into the plane strip, its capacitance is

$$C_1 = 2\pi\varepsilon \left[\ln \frac{1}{2a} \cdot (M + \sqrt{M^2 - 4a^2}) \right]^{-1} \tag{46}$$

[7] Küpfmüller,[A14] p. 101.

which might also be used for a plane strip in a circular cylinder of large radius M for which

$$C_1 \cong \frac{2\pi\varepsilon}{\ln (M/a)} \tag{47}$$

In a similar manner, one can transfer solutions for a dielectric cylindrical shell of radii b and a into the solution of a dielectric elliptical cylinder, as Smythe,[A22] p. 93. One can also start in the z-plane with the solution of a conducting cylinder of radius b in a vertical uniform field and transfer the upper half of the field, which is a circular cylindrical mound on a conducting plane[8] or ground, into the w-plane where it becomes a flat elliptical mound[9] on ground; or one can rotate the field by $\pi/2$ and have a steep elliptical mound.

The same function has been used extensively as mapping function in hydrodynamics,[10] particularly in the form

$$\frac{w - 2a}{w + 2a} = \left(\frac{z - a}{z + a}\right)^2 \tag{48}$$

This can be obtained from (42) by using the second form $(2z - w)^2 = (w^2 - 4a^2)$, dividing by $(w + 2a)^2$, and substituting on the left-hand side w from the first form (42). Of particular interest is the mapping of excentric circles from the z-plane, which yield circular arcs in the w-plane and by further treatment the famous wing profiles of Kutta-Joukowski and others; see references in Appendix 4, C, c, and Bateman,[C1] p. 311.

Transcendental Functions. The mapping function

$$w = \ln z = \ln r + j\phi \tag{49}$$

transforms the entire z-plane in one single strip of width $0 \leqslant v \leqslant 2\pi$, whereby the interior of the unit circle becomes the negative half of the strip and the exterior its positive half, as in Fig. 26·7. To have a one-to-one correspondence, one must limit $0 \leqslant \phi \leqslant 2\pi$ and place a barrier on the positive x-axis; its upper side becomes the line $v = 0$, its lower side the line $v = 2\pi$, forming the fundamental region of the mapping function. Any curve drawn in the

---

[8] Bateman,[C1] p. 261.
[9] Ollendorff,[A18] p. 185.
[10] Prandtl and Tietjens,[C24] p. 173; Rothe et al.,[D8] p. 115; and Bateman,[C1] p. 311; Bewley,[D1] p. 108, gives extensive discussions and many graphs.

z-plane across the barrier would obviously be entirely discontinuous in the w-plane. Should it be inconvenient to have the barrier along the positive x-axis, it can be rotated at will, since its only function is to prevent ambiguity in mapping. One can imagine that the mapping proceeds by cutting along the positive real axis (or any corresponding barrier) so as to separate the two sides of it which are indicated in Fig. 26·7, rotating the lower side and simultaneously rushing 0 towards negative infinity, about getting there when the lower side of the x-axis reaches the position parallel to the upper side and 2π above it. This can indeed be used to solve the problem of a double potential plane along the positive

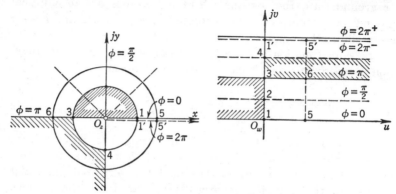

FIG. 26·7   Mapping of z-plane into Strip of w-plane.

real axis with potentials $+(V/2)$ on its upper and $-(V/2)$ on its lower side, forming an extremely thin condenser for which the external or stray field is desired. In the w-plane this becomes a uniform electric field between two infinite parallel planes.

Since the derivative is $dw/dz = 1/z$, there is only one singularity at $z = 0$, and this is a branch point, the point around which the z-plane could be rotated infinitely often were it not for the barrier. The neighborhood of $z = 0$ must be excluded from the mapping region; this can be done usually without sacrifice in the region of real interest. Considering only the upper half z-plane, $0 \leqslant \phi \leqslant \pi$, it becomes the infinite parallel strip $0 \leqslant v \leqslant \pi$ in the w-plane. The rectangle 1–5–6–3–1 in the w-plane corresponds to the annular ring with like numbers. Having an infinite plane parallel strip in the w-plane parallel to the v-axis such as the continuation of 1–5–5'–1', then one can consider the mapping function (49) to wind this strip onto the z-plane around $z = 0$ into the corresponding annular ring an infinite number of times. If the strip in the w-plane has a periodic pattern adjusted to period 2π, then each layer in the z-plane is identical and one can go back to the fundamental region to solve the physical problem. A planar triode with equally spaced grid wires can be treated this way,[11] reducing the problem in the z-plane to the same as the mapping function z^n in the cylindrical triode above. Similarly, one can treat a grid of thin parallel strips, individually inclined at any angle against the plane through their centers.[12] With a superimposed uniform electric field one can compute the amplification factor in first approximation as

$$\mu \approx \frac{2\pi h/d}{\ln\,(d/\pi c)} \tag{50}$$

where h is the distance between anode and grid planes, d the spacing between the grid strip centers, and $2c$ their individual lengths.

Since the inverse function $z = e^w$ is closely related to the complex trigonometric and hyperbolic functions, one expects in all cases infinite periodicity, which requires the definition of fundamental regions for useful applications. Thus,

$$w = \cosh z = \cosh x \sin y + j \sinh x \cos y \tag{51}$$

gives upon elimination of either x or y

$$\left(\frac{u}{\cosh x}\right)^2 + \left(\frac{v}{\sinh x}\right)^2 = 1, \qquad \left(\frac{u}{\cos y}\right)^2 - \left(\frac{v}{\sin y}\right)^2 = 1 \tag{52}$$

These are again confocal ellipses and hyperbolas as in (44) above, but it is a single infinite strip $0 \leqslant y \leqslant 2\pi$ which maps upon the entire w-plane; see Sokolnikoff and Sokolnikoff,[D9] p. 445, who applies this function to examine seepage under a dam.

The function

$$w = jc \cot \frac{z}{2} \quad \text{or} \quad \frac{w + c}{w - c} = e^{-jz} \tag{53}$$

transforms the square net of the z-plane into the biaxial circles identical with the equipotential circles and field lines around two

---

[11] Dow,[B23] p. 24, gives much detail and many graphs.
[12] S. D. Daymond and L. Rosenhead, *Quart. Jl. Math.*, Oxford Series, **9**, p. 89 (1938).

parallel equal and opposite line charges, a distance $2c$ apart. One has, then,[13] as in Fig. 12·5,

$$y = \ln \left| \frac{w+c}{w-c} \right| = \ln \frac{r_2}{r_1}, \qquad x = \phi_2 - \phi_1$$

Graphical Superposition of Maps. In many instances, it may not readily be possible to handle more complex mapping functions analytically, so that graphical methods of superposition become desirable. Since the sum of two analytic functions is again analytic, and all analytic functions provide conformal mappings, one can make use of

$$w = w_1 + w_2 = (u_1 + u_2) + j(v_1 + v_2) \tag{54}$$

by combining plots of simple functions. Taking for example $w_1 = \ln z$ from (49) and $w_2 = \ln (z-2)/(z+2)$ as inversion of (53), numbering the u and v values in each individual graph as pertaining to the same value of z, one can then construct points with coordinates which are the sums of the individual coordinates, again noting the specific values of $z = re^{j\phi}$. In the example,

$$\left.\begin{aligned}
u_1 &= \ln r, & u_2 &= \frac{1}{2} \ln \frac{r^2 + 1 - 2r \cos \phi}{r^2 + 4 - 4r \cos \phi} = \frac{1}{2} \ln \frac{r_2}{r_1} \\
v_1 &= \phi, & v_2 &= \tan^{-1} \frac{r \sin \phi}{-1 + r \cos \phi} + \tan^{-1} \frac{r \sin \phi}{2 + r \cos \phi} = \phi_1 - \phi_2
\end{aligned}\right\} \tag{55}$$

The analytical addition of the two functions is obviously rather difficult; but the graphical combination[14] can be made simple if the individual graphs have been prepared carefully for repeated use.

If $w(z)$ is a function which can be separated into two functional relations, as for example the bilinear function (31), then another type of graphical combination is possible. Having a plot of $w_2 = 1/(z+d)$, which is a dipole line shifted with its origin to $z = -d$, and another graph of $w = a + bw_2$, which is a simple linear operation, one selects the w_2-plane to plot in it $w = u + jv$ with curves $u = $ cons; one also plots in the same plane $z = (1/w_2) - d = x + jy$ with curves $x = $ cons and $y = $ cons.

[13] Bateman,[C1] p. 260.
[14] Y. Ikeda, *Jl. Faculty of Science, Hokkaido Univ.*, Series II (Physics), **2**, p. 1 (1938); see particularly Fig. 48.

Intersections of the families of $x(w_2)$ and $y(w_2)$ with the family $u(w_2)$ give for each particular w_2 the values $u(x, y)$ which can be transposed into a new graph presenting $w(z)$ directly. Application of this method to $w = 1/(e^z + 1)$ by splitting it into $w_2 = e^z$, and $w = 1/(w_2 + 1)$ is shown by Y. Ikeda (*loc. cit.*), who also constructs $w = \sqrt[4]{z^3(1 - z)}$, giving the flow of water over a plane with a short inclined wall representing a weir; other examples can be found there.

27 · CONFORMAL MAPPING
OF STRAIGHT-LINE POLYGONS

A systematic method of mapping polygonal regions bounded by straight lines upon the upper half plane has been developed

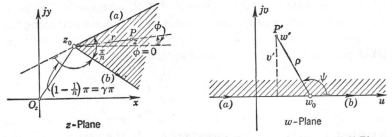

FIG. 27·1   Mapping of Polygon with Single Vertex upon Upper Half Plane.

independently by Schwarz and Christoffel,[1] It is probably the most powerful method for the solution of Laplacian potential problems in two dimensions.

Single Vertex. As shown in section 26, the mapping function

$$w - w_0 = A(z - z_0)^n = |A|\, r^n e^{j(\alpha + n\phi)} \tag{1}$$

requires the restriction $0 \leqslant \phi \leqslant 2\pi/n$ in order to lead to a one-to-one relationship between z- and w-planes. The inverse function, with n real but of any value,

$$z - z_0 = k(w - w_0)^{1/n} \tag{2}$$

where $k = A^{-1/n}$ maps the *upper half w-plane* into the sector π/n of the z-plane, as shown in Fig. 27·1. One has $r = (\rho/|A|)^{1/n}$ and $\phi = (\psi - \alpha)/n$, which uniquely determine one point P of the z-plane as the corresponding one to a point P' in the w-plane, and

---

[1] H. A. Schwarz, *Crelle's Jl.*, **70**, p. 105 (1869); E. B. Christoffel, *Ann. di mat.*, (2), **1** (1867); also *Göttinger Nachrichten*, 1870.

conversely, for values $\frac{1}{2} \leqslant n \leqslant \infty$. The function $z(w)$ is analytic in the entire plane except at $w = w_0$ for $n > 1$ and at $w = \infty$ for $n < 1$ as the derivative

$$\frac{dz}{dw} = \frac{k}{n} (w - w_0)^{(1/n-1)} \tag{3}$$

indicates; for $n = 1$, the transformation is of the linear type and need not be discussed here.

As a point in Fig. 27·1 in the w-plane travels along the boundary (a) where $u < u_0$ and $v = 0$, the corresponding point in the z-plane travels along the straight line (a) towards z_0. When the point in the w-plane changes to the section (b), where $u > u_0$ and $v = 0$, the corresponding point in the z-plane changes its direction of travel by the angle $(-1)^{-(1/n-1)} = e^{j\pi(1-1/n)}$, as shown in Fig. 27·1. This is also seen from (3), since dw and $(w - w_0)$ are real along the u-axis and the factor $(w - w_0)$ only changes sign as the travelling point passes w_0. One may introduce the angle

$$\gamma\pi = \left(1 - \frac{1}{n}\right)\pi \tag{4}$$

as defining the *change in the direction of progression* along the boundary of the corresponding regions. At the vertex itself, the mapping will never be conformal except for $n = 1$, since the derivative either vanishes (for $n < 1$) or does not exist (for $n > 1$). A very small circle excluding the point $w = w_0$ suffices to relieve this difficulty as emphasized in section 26. Similarly, one needs to exclude the point $w = \infty$, as the conventional investigation for the inverse variable demonstrates, except that the derivative vanishes for $n > 1$ and does not exist for $n < 1$.

Assume the boundaries (a) and (b) in the z-plane to be conductive planes and to have the same electrostatic potential Φ_0 and place a line charge $(+\lambda)$ at point P; then the problem in the w-plane is simply that of an infinite conductive plane with a line charge $(+\lambda)$ at P'. The complex potential solution in the w-plane is in accordance with table 25·1, line 3,

$$P = -\frac{\lambda}{2\pi\varepsilon} \ln \frac{w - w'}{w - \overline{w}'} + \Phi_0 \tag{5}$$

where w' is the location of the point P' and $\overline{w}'$ that of its electrostatic image below $v = 0$. The value of w' can be found from the location (r, ϕ) of the line charge in the z-plane, and w can be expressed in terms of z by (1), so that the complete solution is obtained at once for *any* value of the angle (π/n). In section 12, the method of images was convenient only if n was an integer; no such restriction exists here as long as $n \geqslant \frac{1}{2}$. With (5) one can determine the potential distribution as well as the capacitance of the line charge if one admits a small but finite diameter d for it. On the surface of this wire one can take $w - w' \approx \dfrac{d}{2} \left| \dfrac{dw}{dz} \right|_{\text{at } P'}$, similar to (26·25), and $w - \overline{w}' = 2v'$, so that

$$\Phi_s = + \frac{\lambda}{2\pi\varepsilon} \ln \frac{4v'}{d \left| \dfrac{dw}{dz} \right|_{\text{at } P'}} + \Phi_0$$

and the capacitance with respect to the conducting planes becomes

$$C = \frac{\lambda}{\Phi_s - \Phi_0} = 2\pi\varepsilon \left[\ln \frac{4v'}{d \left| \dfrac{dw}{dz} \right|_{\text{at } P'}} \right]^{-1} \tag{6}$$

For the special case that $z_0 = 0$ and therefore $w_0 = 0$, the mapping function (1) reduces to $w = Az^n$, where $|A|$ is arbitrary and α so selected that (a) and (b) become the negative and positive portions of the u-axis, respectively. If, further, the line charge is located in the plane of symmetry in the z-geometry at a distance $a \gg d$ from the corner, the image of the line charge in the w-plane is located on the v-axis at $v' = |A| a^n$. With $\left| \dfrac{dw}{dz} \right| = n |A| |z|^{n-1}$, the capacitance is now

$$C = \frac{2\pi\varepsilon}{\ln (4a^n/dna^{n-1})} = \frac{2\pi\varepsilon}{\ln (4a/nd)} \tag{7}$$

for any value $n \geqslant \frac{1}{2}$.

For several special values, Fig. 27·2 shows the regions of the z-plane corresponding to the upper half w-plane. For $n = \frac{1}{2}$ one has an infinitesimally thin plate, whose upper and lower sides become sections (a) and (b) of the u-axis, respectively; or one can interpret it as an infinitesimally thin slit in the infinite z-plane. For the example with the parallel quasi line charge of diameter d one can also find the charge density induced on the two sides of the plate by the use of (26·7). The case $n = \frac{2}{3}$ with a parallel line charge was one which could not be treated by image theory (see section 21); the solution can readily be found with this mapping method. The case $n = 2$ is, of course, the same as treated in section 12.

A particularly important case is obtained by letting $n \to \infty$; this gives from (3) with $k/n = k'$,

$$\frac{dz}{dw} = \frac{k'}{w - w_0} \tag{8}$$

If $k' = 1$, the actual mapping function is of the same type as (26·49) and represents, as shown in Fig. 26·7, the mapping of an

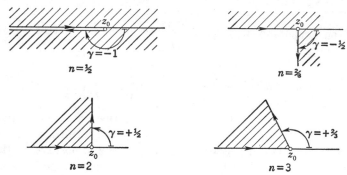

FIG. 27·2 Special Cases of Single Vertex Polygons.

infinite strip of width π in the z-plane upon the upper half w-plane. For $k' = b/\pi$, with b real, the function maps the strip of width b(real) upon the upper half w-plane. Obviously, this cannot be obtained from the integral functions (1) or (2), demonstrating the more powerful treatment by means of (3). Placing a line charge between the planes of the z-geometry, one has the same problem as presented in (21·5); it is readily solved here by (5) in conjunction with the mapping function. This method has been used by Smythe,[A22] p. 83, for a single line charge,[2] and by Frankel[3] for one-, two-, and three-line-charge arrangements in order to find the characteristic impedance of transmission lines.

[2] See also E. Kehren, Dissertation, Tech. Hochschule Aachen; J. A. Barth, Leipzig, 1932.

[3] S. Frankel, *Proc. I.R.E.*, **30**, p. 182 (1942).

It is interesting to note that (3) also gives

$$\frac{d}{dw}\left(\ln\frac{dz}{dw}\right) = \frac{\frac{1}{n}-1}{w-w_0} = \frac{-\gamma}{w-w_0} \tag{9}$$

a form completely independent of the scale and rotation factor k and containing only the outside angle γ and the vertex location w_0.

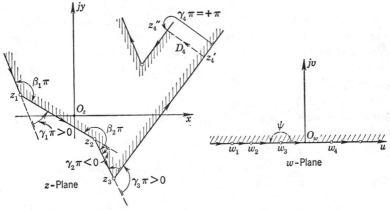

FIG. 27·3   Mapping of Inside of Polygon upon Upper Half Plane.

Mapping of Inside of Closed Polygons. In analogy to (3) one can now construct the expression[4]

$$\frac{dz}{dw} = C(w-w_1)^{-\gamma_1}(w-w_2)^{-\gamma_2}\cdots(w-w_\nu)^{-\gamma_\nu}\cdots$$

$$= C\prod_{(\alpha)}(w-w_\alpha)^{-\gamma_\alpha} \tag{10}$$

which, as indicated in Fig. 27·3, maps the real axis of the w-plane into the broken line of the polygon in the z-plane. At each vertex only the pertinent factor $(w-w_\alpha)$ changes sign, causing dz to change angle by exactly $\gamma_\alpha\pi$ in the direction indicated by the algebraic sign of γ_α. The constant C acts as scale and rotation factor and must be determined by the correlation of one of the polygon sides $(z_\alpha - z_{\alpha+1})$ with the image $(w_\alpha - w_{\alpha+1})$ which, of

---

[4] Π is the conventional product notation defining a product of similar terms with order numbers α.

course, requires the integration

$$z = C \int \prod_{(\alpha)} (w - w_\alpha)^{-\gamma_\alpha} dw + C_1 \qquad (11)$$

The further integration constant C_1 essentially locates the origin. Application of (9) gives the sum

$$\frac{d}{dw} \left(\ln \frac{dz}{dw} \right) = \sum_{(\alpha)} \frac{-\gamma_\alpha}{w - w_\alpha} \qquad (12)$$

which has been taken as the starting point for the general proof of the uniqueness of (11) as mapping function of the inside regions of polygons.   Actually, (11) is analytic everywhere except possibly at vertices (those for which $\gamma_\alpha > 0$) and therefore conformal everywhere except at all vertices as seen from (10).   For proofs one can consult the original articles (*loc. cit.*) and most of the advanced books in Appendix 4, D, as well as Kellogg,[C10] p. 370, and Bateman,[C1] p. 296.

Very close to a finite vertex image w_ν, one can approximate $w - w_\alpha \approx w_\nu - w_\alpha$ for all $\alpha \neq \nu$, and elect polar coordinates referred to w_ν such that

$$w - w_\nu = \rho_\nu e^{j\psi}, \qquad dw = e^{j\psi} d\rho_\nu + j\rho_\nu e^{j\psi} d\psi \qquad (13)$$

The integral (11) gives then along a small circle in the w-plane with center at w_ν

$$z = C \prod_{\alpha \neq \nu} (w_\nu - w_\alpha)^{-\gamma_\alpha} \int (\rho_\nu e^{j\psi})^{-\gamma_\nu} j\rho_\nu e^{j\psi} d\psi + C_1 \qquad (14)$$

where the integration constant C_1 can be selected as z_ν in accordance with (2) for the single vertex.   This gives

$$z - z_\nu = \left[\frac{C}{1 - \gamma_\nu} \rho_\nu^{1-\gamma_\nu} \cdot \prod_{\alpha \neq \nu} (w_\nu - w_\alpha)^{-\gamma_\alpha} \right] e^{j\psi(1-\gamma_\nu)} \qquad (15)$$

which for any value $(-1) \leqslant \gamma_\nu < (+1)$ represents a small circle with z_ν as center, vanishing as $\rho_\nu \to 0$.   For a total variation of ψ in the w-plane between 0 and π, the argument of (15) changes over the range zero to $(1 - \gamma_\nu)\pi = \beta_\nu\pi$, or the internal polygon angle, as it should be.   For $\gamma_\nu = +1$, the integral (14) becomes

$$z = [C \prod_{\alpha \neq \nu} (w_\nu - w_\alpha)^{-\gamma_\alpha}] j\psi + C_1 \qquad (16)$$

which is a straight line at right angles to the directions of progression before and after the vertex z_ν. As shown in Fig. 27·3, the angle $\gamma_\nu = +1$ represents a vertex at $z = \infty$, or the intersection of two parallel lines as at z_4, and their distance is defined by $\psi = 0$ for z_4'' and $\psi = \pi$ for z_4'; thus from (16)

$$D_\nu = z_\nu'' - z_\nu' = -j\pi \left[C \prod_{\alpha \neq \nu} (w_\nu - w_\alpha)^{-\gamma_\alpha} \right] \qquad (17)$$

That a vertex of this singular type can be admitted is readily appreciated from the fact that in the complex plane $z = \infty$ is defined as a point and can be transformed into finite distance by inversion (see section 25).

For any closed polygon of N vertices, the sum total of the internal angles is $(N - 2)\pi$; this also means

$$\sum_{\alpha=1}^{N} \gamma_\alpha = \sum_{\alpha=1}^{N} (1 - \beta_\alpha) = N - (N - 2) = 2 \qquad (18)$$

which is valuable as a check.

If one of the vertex images w_ν is located at $w = \infty$, or also $w_\nu' = +\infty, w_\nu'' = -\infty$ as the opposite ends of the real $u =$ axis, (10) will not contain the factor $(w - w_\nu)$ because of the more basic form (12) in which the corresponding additive term $-\gamma_\nu/(w - w_\nu)$ vanishes. Near w_ν one can then approximate in (10) $w_\nu - w_\alpha \approx w_\nu = \rho e^{j\psi}$ with $\rho \to \infty$. The integral (11) becomes, therefore, with (18)

$$z = C \int (\rho e^{j\psi})^{-(2-\gamma_\nu)} \rho j e^{j\psi} d\psi + C_1 \qquad (19)$$

since in (10) only γ_ν is missing. Performing the integration gives, with proper choice of the constant C_1,

$$z - z_\nu = \left[\frac{C}{-(1 - \gamma_\nu)} \rho^{-(1-\gamma_\nu)} \right] e^{-j\psi(1-\gamma_\nu)} \qquad (20)$$

which for any value $(-1) \leqslant \gamma_\nu < (+1)$ represents a small circle with z_ν as center, vanishing as $\rho \to \infty$. For a total variation of ψ in the w-plane between π and 0, the argument of (20) changes over the range $-(1 - \gamma_\nu)\pi = -\beta_\nu\pi$ to zero, as it should be. For $\gamma_\nu = +1$, the integral (19) reduces to

$$z = Cj\psi + C_1 \qquad (21)$$

which is a straight line at right angles to the directions of progression before and after z_ν as above in (16). The distance of the two parallel lines is defined now by $\psi = 0$ for z_ν' and $\psi = \pi$ for z_ν'', so that from (21)

$$D_\nu = z_\nu'' - z_\nu' = j\pi C \qquad (22)$$

leading to the direct evaluation of the integration constant C.

For practical applications it is desirable to make use of all simplifications in the mapping function that are possible. With reference to Fig. 27·3, the following points should be observed for best economy:

a. The order of the vertex points in the z-plane and of their images in the w-plane must be the same and such that, in the sense of progression, the region to be transformed is at the left.

b. All angles are counted positive in the counterclockwise sense.

c. For any conformal representation upon the upper half plane, three of the vertex images w_α can be chosen freely (see section 26); the choice should be so as to make the integral (11) of simplest type and of standard form.

d. If a vertex image is located at $w_\alpha = \infty$, the corresponding factor $(w - w_\alpha)$ does not appear in the mapping integral (11); one should choose that vertex at $w_\alpha = \infty$ which leads to greatest simplification.

e. The sum of all vertex exponents γ_α is equal to two; this should be used as a check when tabulating the individual factors.

f. If the neighborhood of w_α is the map of the region between two parallel lines in the z-plane, then their distance is given by (17); if the neighborhood of $w = \infty$ is the map of the region between two parallel lines in the z-plane, then their distance is given by (22).

g. The mapping of the upper half w-plane upon the polygon in the z-plane is conformal at all points except at the vertices themselves. These vertices are, however, isolated points of non-conformality and can be approached arbitrarily closely.

h. Since three values w_α can be chosen arbitrarily, and since the total number of constants in the mapping integral is $(N + 2)$, namely, the N vertex images w_α and the two integration constants C and C_1, there must be established $(N - 1)$ independent relations of the type (17) or (22) or similar integrals in order to solve the mapping problem completely.

i. It is advisable to tabulate the relations between corresponding vertices in the z-plane and images in the w-plane in a systematic manner such as:

Vertex location in z-plane	z_1	z_2	z_α	
Change in direction of progression at vertex	$\gamma_1\pi$	$\gamma_2\pi$	$\gamma_\alpha\pi$	
Exponent in mapping function	γ_1	γ_2	γ_α	$(\Sigma\gamma_\alpha = 2)$
Location of vertex image	$w_1 <$	$w_2 <$	$w_\alpha <$	$\cdots$

In the last line, three values can be assumed arbitrarily, the remaining $(N-3)$ values enter as unknown constants into the mapping function (11).

It might also be emphasized here that the integral (11) is actually a *real integral*, since it is taken along the real axis of the w-plane. However, depending upon the relative value w in a particular section of the real axis, several of the factors might assume complex values. To be sure of the correct values of the generally multivalued terms, one should bring the integrand into such form that all factors with $|w - w_\alpha| < 0$ are written $(w - w_\alpha)^{-\gamma_\alpha} (-1)^{-\gamma_\alpha}$; the methods of integration of real functions will then suffice for the proper evaluation. As w takes on complex values in the interior of the upper half plane, continuity in $z(w)$ can be checked by letting $v \to 0$ and checking the correctness of $\wp(u)$.

Parallel Plate Condenser. As an illustrative example of a complete solution take the classical problem of evaluating the fringing flux for the *parallel plate condenser*. Assuming two very thin plates as in Fig. $27 \cdot 4a$ of infinite extension and utilizing the symmetry of the field and potential distribution, one has Fig. $27 \cdot 4b$ as the z-plane geometry to be mapped upon the w-plane $(27 \cdot 4c)$. The mapping table is, if one observes (a) above,

z-plane	1	2	3	
Vertex location	$1'\begin{cases} +\infty + j0 \\ -\infty + ia \end{cases}$	$0 + ja$	$3'\begin{cases} -\infty + ja \\ -\infty + j0 \end{cases}$	
$\gamma_\alpha\pi$	2π	$-\pi$	$+\pi$	
γ_α	$+2$	-1	$+1$	$(\Sigma\gamma_\alpha = 2)$
w_α	$\pm\infty$	-1	0	

where all three points w_α can be selected freely. Because vertex 1 has the highest coefficient γ_1, it is best chosen at $w_1 = \infty$; vertex 3 separates the two potential values, so it is best chosen at $w_3 = 0$ in order to lead to a standard problem in the w-plane;

vertex 2 must be on the negative u-axis, and one can normalize the geometry in the w-plane by selecting $w_2 = -1$.   The mapping function is thus defined by (10) and in accordance with (d) above as

$$\frac{dz}{dw} = C(w + 1)w^{-1} \tag{23}$$

or, integrated,

$$z = C(w + \ln w) + C_1 \tag{24}$$

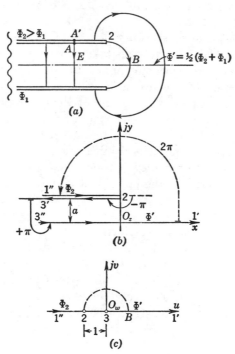

Fig. 27·4   Parallel Plate Condenser: (a) actual geometry, (b) z-plane, (c) w-plane.

Selecting $w = |w|e^{j\psi}$, with $0 \leqslant \psi \leqslant \pi$, and restricting $\ln w$ to the fundamental region, so that $\ln w = \ln|w| + j\psi$, make the relation (24) one-valued and suitable for determination of the constants. Thus, (17) gives for vertex $\nu = 3$ and $w_3 = 0$

$$-ja = -j\pi C, \qquad C = \frac{a}{\pi}$$

and the location of vertex 2 defines C_1 from (24) as

$$0 + ja = \frac{a}{\pi}(-1 + j\pi) + C_1, \qquad C_1 = \frac{a}{\pi}$$

so that in the final form

$$z = \frac{a}{\pi}(1 + w + \ln w) \tag{25}$$

It is desirable to check the exact correspondence of boundaries by letting z travel along the distinct sections in the z-geometry and verifying that w travels along the u-axis within the corresponding limits or vice versa. For example, as $(-1) < w < 0$ with $v = 0$, so that $u = -|u|$, one has

$$z = \frac{a}{\pi}(1 - |u| + \ln|u| + j\pi) = ja + \frac{a}{\pi}(1 + \ln|u| - |u|)$$

or $x < 0$, $y = a$; this describes in the z-plane the boundary from 2 to $3'$ as required.

The potential solution in the upper half w-plane is now very simply given by (25·26) with the appropriate change in notation as in (26·28)

$$P = \Phi + j\Xi = -\frac{j}{\pi}(\Phi_2 - \Phi')\ln w + \Phi' \tag{26}$$

where equipotential lines are concentric circles and the field lines are the radial lines from the origin. It would, of course, be desirable to introduce into (26) w as an explicit function of z and thus find the field geometry directly in the z-plane; but this is usually not possible. The field vector E can be obtained from (26·7) as

$$E = -\overline{\left(\frac{dP}{dw}\cdot\frac{dw}{dz}\right)} = -j\frac{\Phi_2 - \Phi'}{a}\overline{(w+1)^{-1}} = -j\frac{E_0}{w+1} \tag{27}$$

Along the boundary, $w \equiv u$ is real and the field vector is always parallel to the imaginary axis, or normal to the boundary; it is positive for $u < (-1)$, negative for $u > (-1)$, and becomes infinitely large as $u \to (-1)$ as in the case of any convex corner of the polygon.

Since E_0 is the uniform value of field strength between the parallel plates, one can easily determine a point A to define the practical limit of the uniform field by finding the value u from (27) for which $|E| = \eta E_0$ and by choosing for example $\eta = 1 + \delta/100$ for δ per cent tolerance. One obtains $u_A = -\delta/100$, and thus from (25)

$$z_A = \frac{a}{\pi} \left(1 - \frac{\delta}{100} + \ln \frac{\delta}{100} + j\pi \right)$$

$$= ja - \frac{a}{\pi} \left[\ln 100 + \frac{\delta}{100} - (1 + \ln \delta) \right] \tag{28}$$

For $\delta = 1$ per cent, this gives $x_A = -1.144a$, the location of point A in Fig. $27 \cdot 4a$; generally, the end effects penetrate into homogeneous field regions to a distance of the same order as the length of the uniform field line. Since the field lines in the w-plane are circles, one can find point B of Fig. $27 \cdot 4a$ and c by using (25) with $w_B \equiv u = 1$, namely, $z_B = 2a/\pi$. The total dielectric flux from A to the corner 2 is given by $(26 \cdot 4)$

$$\Psi_{A,2} = \varepsilon(\Xi_A - \Xi_2) = -\frac{\varepsilon}{\pi} (\Phi_2 - \Phi') \ln \frac{u_A}{u_2}$$

$$= \frac{\varepsilon}{\pi} (\Phi_2 - \Phi') \ln \frac{100}{\delta} \tag{29}$$

For the idealized condenser with uniform field up to the corner 2, the corresponding dielectric flux would be $\Psi_{A,2}{}^0 = E_0 |x_A|$ with x_A from (28). Comparison of this latter with (29) shows that fringing results in an actual increase of dielectric flux over the idealized condition of amount

$$\delta\Psi_f = \frac{\varepsilon}{\pi} (\Phi_2 - \Phi') \left(1 - \frac{\delta}{100} \right)$$

$$= \Psi_{A,2}{}^0 \frac{1 - \delta/100}{\ln 100 + \delta/100 - (1 + \ln \delta)} \tag{30}$$

Figure $27 \cdot 5$ gives the value $|x_A|/a$ from (28) as a function of the tolerance value δ and also $f(\delta)$, the correction factor in (30) to the idealized dielectric flux $\Psi_{A,2}{}^0$ in order to account for the fringing from the underside of the upper condenser plate. From Fig. 27·5 one can also take that, for $|x_A|/a = 1$, the actual field strength is $1.016E_0$, and that fringing increases the flux contribution computed on the basis of E_0 by 31.1 per cent.

The first treatment of this problem by conformal mapping is due to Kirchhoff,[A13] p. 104,[5] who also applied it to compute the edge correction of circular condenser plates;[6] subdividing the total space into three regions, Kirchhoff assumed homogeneous field between the plates up to A, fringing field as computed above

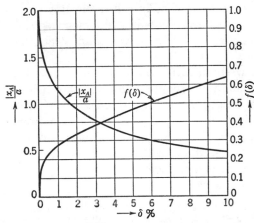

Fig. 27·5 Fringing Correction for Parallel Plate Condenser.

extending to A', and then a space field as produced by two uniformly and oppositely charged circular disks of infinitesimal spacing. An excellent graph of the fringing field distribution is given in Maxwell,[A17] I, Fig. XII, who used, however, Helmholtz's approach by conjugate functions. Good treatments are also found in Jeans,[A10] p. 272; in Ollendorff,[A18] p. 212; in Rothe et al.,[D8] p. 138; in Reddick and Miller,[D7] p. 377; and in Bewley,[D1] p. 121. Hydrodynamic applications are given in Prandtl and Tietjens,[C24] p. 179, and in Lamb,[C22] p. 70.

Writing in Fig. 27·4c $w = |w|e^{j\psi}$, then one obtains the field lines for constant $|w|$, and the equipotential lines for constant ψ.

---

[5] See also *Monats. d. Akad. d. Wissenschaften*, Berlin, p. 144, March 1877.

[6] For extensive study of edge corrections see A. H. Scott and H. L. Curtis, *Jl. Research Natl. Bur. of Stand.*, **22**, p. 747 (1939).

Translation into the z-plane is simplest by (25)

$$\left. \begin{array}{l} x = \dfrac{a}{\pi} \left[1 + |w| \cos \psi + \ln |w| \right] \\[2mm] y = \dfrac{a}{\pi} \left[\psi + |w| \sin \psi \right] \end{array} \right\} \tag{31}$$

One can then investigate the field strength distribution along any particular equipotential line and find $\psi = \pi/2$ as the largest value of ψ for which the field is nowhere larger than E_0. The corresponding conductor shape is usually called the Rogowski electrode; it assures that breakdown occurs in the homogeneous field E_0, which permits the definition of the breakdown strength of gases and liquids.[7]

Polygons with Parallel Boundaries. More general cases of boundaries made up of parallel lines are shown in Figs. $27 \cdot 6a$ to $27 \cdot 6c$. The arrangement Fig. $27 \cdot 6a$ can be used for fringing problems as in Bateman,[C1] p. 300, who also computes the charge distribution, or in Grösser[8] for the evaluation of electric fields in high-voltage transformer shell windings of unequal height. The mapping function is defined by the table

z-plane	1	2	3	4
Vertex location $\begin{array}{l}1'\\1''\end{array}$	$\begin{cases} -\infty + j0 \\ -\infty + ja \end{cases}$	$0 + ja$	$\begin{array}{l}3'\\3''\end{array}\begin{cases} -\infty + ja \\ -\infty + j0 \end{cases}$	b
$\gamma_\alpha \pi$	$+3\pi$	$-\pi$	$+\pi$	$-\pi$
γ_α	$+3$	-1	$+1$	-1 $\quad (\Sigma \gamma_\alpha = 2)$
w_α	$\pm \infty$	-1	0	$+\tau$

where the change of the angle of progression at point 1 must be chosen as 3π in order to rotate direction 4–1$'$ into that of 1$''$–2, since a rotation by 2π only produces a parallel line of same sense of direction (see below under c). From the table one has

$$\frac{dz}{dw} = \frac{C}{w} \, (w+1)(w-\tau) \tag{32}$$

so that

$$z = C \left[\frac{w^2}{2} + (1-\tau)w - \tau \ln w \right] + C_1 \tag{33}$$

[7] W. Rogowski, *Arch. f. Elektrot.*, **12**, p. 1 (1923); also H. Rengier and W. Rogowski, *Arch. f. Elektrot.*, **16**, p. 73 (1926) and Rengier, *ibid.*, p. 76.
[8] W. Grösser, *Arch. f. Elektrot.*, **25**, p. 193 (1931).

The unknowns are C, C_1, and τ for which three relations can be established, one for the distance $3'$-$3''$ in accordance with (17),

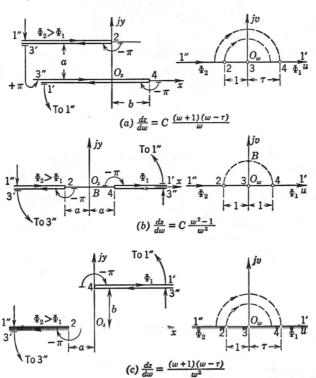

(a) $\dfrac{dz}{dw} = C\,\dfrac{(w+1)(w-\tau)}{w}$

(b) $\dfrac{dz}{dw} = C\,\dfrac{w^2-1}{w^2}$

(c) $\dfrac{dz}{dw} = \dfrac{(w+1)(w-\tau)}{w^2}$

FIG. 27·6   Several Arrangements of Two Parallel Conducting Planes.

and two for the correspondence of the points z_2 and z_4 and their images w_2 and w_4, respectively. Thus, by (17),

$$z_3'' - z_3' = -ja = -j\pi C\,[(w+1)(w-\tau)]_{w=0} = +j\pi\tau C \quad (34)$$

giving $C = -a/\pi\tau$. Further,

$$\left. \begin{aligned} z_2 &= 0 + ja = C\left[\tfrac{1}{2} - (1-\tau) - \tau j\pi\right] + C_1 \\ z_4 &= b = C\left[\frac{\tau^2}{2} + (1-\tau)\tau - \tau \ln \tau\right] + C_1 \end{aligned} \right\} \quad (35)$$

This illustrates a frequent difficulty even for comparatively simple mapping functions, namely, the definition of τ in terms of a transcendental equation obtained by subtraction of the two equations (35)

$$\frac{b}{a}\pi = \ln \tau + \frac{1}{2}\left(\tau - \frac{1}{\tau}\right) \tag{36}$$

A simple graphical solution can readily be given. The total potential solution in the w-plane is again (26) with Φ_1 replacing Φ' there. The electric field is thus by (26·7)

$$E = +j\frac{\Phi_2 - \Phi_1}{a}\tau\overline{[(w+1)(w-\tau)]^{-1}} \tag{37}$$

indicating infinite values at both sharp corners 2 and 4.

Two oppositely charged coplanar planes as in Fig. 27·6b lead to the mapping function $z = \frac{a}{2}\left(w + \frac{1}{w}\right).$ As conjugate function pair, this gave in section 25 the solution for a conducting cylinder in a uniform electrostatic field. Here, in the upper half w-plane, however, the solution is given by (26) with Φ_1 replacing Φ' there; see also Smythe,[A22] p. 90, and Ollendorff,[A18] p. 203. Inserting the mapping function into (26) requires the inversion $w = \frac{z}{a} \pm \sqrt{\left(\frac{z}{a}\right)^2 - 1}$, where the upper sign must be chosen to have point B, i.e., $z = 0$ located at $w = +j$. One then obtains with $\ln(t + \sqrt{t^2 - 1}) = \cosh^{-1} t,$

$$P = \Phi + j\Xi = -\frac{j}{\pi}(\Phi_2 - \Phi_1)\cosh^{-1}\frac{z}{a} + \Phi_1 \tag{38}$$

as the direct solution for the complex potential in the z-plane. In the upper half z-plane one has thus a typical potential solution for two coplanar planes with a gap of width $2a$ between their parallel edges. This solution will frequently be needed; it leads to the same geometry as Fig. 25·7. By interchanging field and equipotential lines, one obtains the field of a single infinitely thin strip of width $2a$; thus, multiplying (38) by j and replacing $(\Phi_2 - \Phi_1)$ by $\lambda/2\pi\varepsilon$ for a single conductor,

$$P = \frac{\lambda}{2\pi\varepsilon}\cosh^{-1}\left(\frac{z}{a}\right) \tag{38a}$$

This gives the total dielectric flux λ for the slab, since for z real and $z < a$, $\cosh^{-1}\left(\dfrac{z}{a}\right) = \ln\left[\dfrac{z}{a} + j\sqrt{1 - \left(\dfrac{z}{a}\right)^2}\right]$

so that

$$P_{z<a} = j\frac{\lambda}{2\pi\varepsilon}\tan^{-1}\left(\frac{\sqrt{1 - (z/a)^2}}{(z/a)}\right)$$

At $z = +a$, $\tan^{-1}(+0) = \pi$; at $z = -a$, $\tan^{-1}(-0) = -\pi$; therefore $(\Xi_{+a} - \Xi_{-a}) = \lambda/\varepsilon$.

For two parallel planes as in Fig. 27·6c, the mapping function[9] becomes

$$z = C\left[w + \frac{\tau}{w} + (1 - \tau)\ln w\right] + C_1 \tag{39}$$

with the upper half plane identical with case a; the reference also gives the field strength near corner 2 and along the equipotential line $w = |w|e^{\frac{j\pi}{8}}$.

For three parallel planes in symmetrical arrangement as in Fig. 27·7a, the mapping function contains two unknown parameters p and q. Application of (22) to point 5 gives at once $jb = j\pi C$, or $C = b/\pi$; application of the corresponding relation (17) to point 1 gives

$$-jb = -j\pi C\left[\frac{(w - p)(w - q)}{(w - 1)^2}\right]_{w=0} = -j\pi Cpq$$

from which $pq = 1$. Integration and use of the correspondence of points z_2, z_4 and w_2, w_4, respectively, give finally

$$z = \frac{b}{\pi}\left[\frac{1}{2}\left(\frac{1}{p} - 1\right)(1 - p)\frac{w + 1}{w - 1} + \ln w - j\pi\right] \tag{40}$$

where p must be determined graphically from

$$\frac{a}{h}\pi = \frac{1 - p^2}{2p} + \ln\left(\frac{1}{p}\right)$$

with $p < 1$; values are shown in Fig. 27·8. The field strength is, by (26·7),

$$E = -j\frac{\Phi_2 - \Phi_1}{b}\left[\frac{(w - 1)^2}{\left(w - p\right)\left(w - \dfrac{1}{p}\right)}\right] \tag{41}$$

[9] E. Kehren, footnote 2, p. 378.

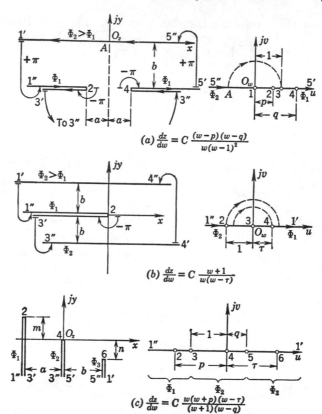

$$(a) \frac{dz}{dw} = C \frac{(w-p)(w-q)}{w(w-1)^2}$$

$$(b) \frac{dz}{dw} = C \frac{w+1}{w(w-\tau)}$$

$$(c) \frac{dz}{dw} = C \frac{w(w+p)(w-\tau)}{(w+1)(w-q)}$$

FIG. 27·7 Several Arrangements for Three Parallel Conducting Planes.

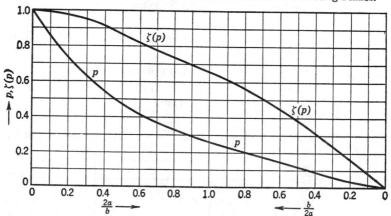

FIG. 27·8 Parameters for the Geometry Shown in Fig. 27·7a.

and its value along the center line $x = 0$, which is the unit circle in the w-plane, can be found with $w = e^{j\psi}$. Specifically, for the point A one has $w = -1$, so that

$$E_A = -jE_0 \frac{4}{(1+p)\left(1+\dfrac{1}{p}\right)} = -jE_0 \frac{4p}{(p+1)^2} = -jE_0\zeta(p)$$

where $E_0 = (\Phi_2 - \Phi_1)/b$ and $\zeta(p)$ is shown in Fig. 27·8 as a function of $2a/b$; as is evident, the presence of the gap $2a$ lowers the field value at A but has little influence for ratios $2a/b < 0.3$. An approximation to this solution is given by Smythe,[A22] p. 90, by superimposing a uniform field in Fig. 27·6b.

In a similar manner, the fringing from the center plate in Fig. 27·7b[10] can be evaluated, as well as the electrostatic field distribution for three parallel plates arranged as in Fig. 27·7c.[11] The extension to more than two different potential values requires a more general solution for the potential in the upper half w-plane as shown in section 28, particularly (28·8).

Polygons with Two Right Angles and One Scale Parameter. The simple right corner opposite a plane, as in Fig. 27·9a, is mapped on the upper half w-plane according to the table

z-plane	1	2	3
Vertex location	$1'\begin{cases}0-j\infty \\ a-j\infty\end{cases}$	$a+j0$	$3'\begin{cases}\infty+j0 \\ 0+j\infty\end{cases}$
$\gamma_\alpha\pi$	$+\pi$	$-\dfrac{\pi}{2}$	$+\dfrac{3\pi}{2}$
γ_α	$+1$	$-\dfrac{1}{2}$	$+\dfrac{3}{2}$
w_α	0	$+1$	$\pm\infty$

so that the mapping function becomes

$$\frac{dz}{dw} = \frac{C}{w}\sqrt{w-1} \qquad (42a)$$

$$z = 2C[\sqrt{w-1} - \tan^{-1}\sqrt{w-1}] + C_1 \qquad (42b)$$

The constant $C = a/\pi$ is determined by applying (17) to point $\nu = 1$, and $C_1 = a$ by the use of the correspondence between

[10] *Handbuch der Experimental Physik*, Vol. 19, p. 29; J. Springer, Berlin, 1935.

[11] W. Grösser, *Arch. f. Elektrot.*, **25**, p. 193 (1931).

points z_2 and w_2. The correspondence of the boundaries can be checked readily; for example between points 1 and 2, where $0 < w < 1$, one can write better

$$z = 2j \frac{a}{\pi} \left[\sqrt{1-w} - \frac{1}{2} \ln \frac{1 + \sqrt{1-w}}{1 - \sqrt{1-w}} \right] + a$$

with the terms in brackets real and negative. As $w \to 0$, the logarithmic term approaches

$$\ln_{w \to 0} \frac{2 - (w/2)}{w/2} = \ln 2 - \ln_{w \to 0} (w/2) = + \infty$$

It is important to consider the logarithm of a fraction as the difference of two logarithms in order to preserve the correct sign.

In the arrangement of Fig. 27·9a the conductor Φ_2 might represent the grounded core of a high-voltage transformer, and Φ_1 the negative end of the high-voltage winding, so that (26) is applicable to the upper half w-plane. One can then find the end point A of the most dangerous field line by setting $w = -1$ in (42). Computing the electric field vector along various equipotential lines, one can estimate the effect of rounding off the sharp corner as in Rothe et al.,[D8] p. 130. One thus finds that along the equipotential line of value $[\Phi_1 + 0.05(\Phi_2 - \Phi_1)]$ the smallest radius of curvature is $\rho_{max} = 0.052a$ and the maximum field strength $E_{max} = 2.75E_0$, if $E_0 = (\Phi_2 - \Phi_1)/a$; and on $[\Phi_1 + 0.1(\Phi_2 - \Phi_1)]$ one has $\rho_{max} = 0.108a$ and $E_{max} = 2.0E_0$. Actually, this geometry was first used by Carter[12] to evaluate the fringing flux from a magnetic pole with air gap a in an electrical machine, as also treated in Bewley,[D1] p. 130, where good graphs are shown. Since the height 2–3' is unlimited, the fringing flux can be defined only within arbitrary limits, as in the case of the plate condenser, Fig. 27·4.

The slot of infinite depth in Fig. 27·9b leads to the mapping function

$$z = a + 2j \frac{a}{\pi} \{ \sqrt{1-w^2} + \ln w - \ln [1 + \sqrt{1-w^2}] \} \qquad (43)$$

with (26) as solution for the upper half w-plane. Point A is defined by $w = +j$ or $z = j(b/\pi)[\sqrt{2} - \ln(1 + \sqrt{2})] = j0.34b$

[12] F. W. Carter, Jl. I.E.E., **29**, part 146, p. 925 (1900).

and frequently serves to separate tooth tip flux from the actual slot flux.   Brief treatments[13] are given in Frank and Mises,[C6] II, p. 664, and in Bateman,[C1] p. 300.   One could, of course, restrict the mapping region to one of the symmetrical halves; the upper

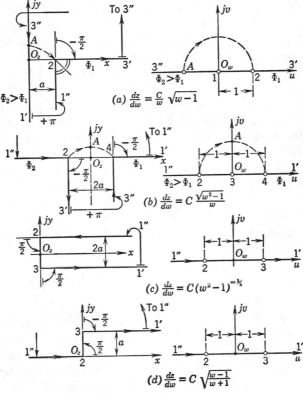

FIG. 27·9   Polygons with Two Right Angles and One Scale Parameter.

half w-plane would then present the problem of Fig. 27·2 for $n = \frac{1}{2}$.

The semi-infinite strip, Fig. 27·9c, has the mapping function

$$z = \frac{2a}{\pi} \cosh^{-1} w - ja \qquad (44)$$

[13] See also R. Gans in Vol. V, part 2, of *Encyclopädie der Mathematischen Wissenschaften;* B. G. Teubner, Leipzig, 1906; J. Kucera, *Elektrot. und Masch.*, **58**, p. 329 (1940).

which is quite similar to (38); if $1''$–2 carries potential Φ_2 and 3–$1'$ potential Φ_1, then the z-plane represents a semi-infinite ideal parallel plane condenser with 2–3 as field line; see Smythe,[A22] p. 88, and Rothe et al.,[D8] p. 143. Assuming the strip of very thin conducting material and placing a source line at the origin 0 of the z-plane, then one has in the w-plane the radial flow lines of a single source line at origin 0 of the w-plane; see Walker,[D10] p. 66, for graph. Interchanging in this latter geometry flow lines and equipotential lines, one obtains the magnetic field of a line current midway in the air gap between two infinitely permeable iron blocks, as in Walker,[D10] p. 71, and in Bewley,[D1] p. 136. Finally, assuming in the w-plane a uniform field parallel to the u-axis, one obtains in the z-plane the flow between a source line at $1''$ and a sink line at $1'$ as in Walker,[D10] p. 46, and in Reddick and Miller,[D7] p. 376. An infinite grating of like charged strips of width $2b < 2a$ located along the y-axis with center spacing $2b$ is treated by Smythe,[A22] p. 89, by mapping one sample as in Fig. $27 \cdot 9c$. In the w-plane one has a single strip on the u-axis and the potential solution is (38a) with w/b for z/a.

A rectangular step in the boundary as in Fig. $27 \cdot 9d$ has the mapping function

$$z = \frac{a}{\pi} [\sqrt{w^2 - 1} - \cosh^{-1} w] + ja \qquad (45)$$

It has been used by Ollendorff,[A18] p. 199,[14] to compute the effect of a vertical rise in ground (walls or trees) upon the capacitance of parallel communication lines in a manner as shown in (6). Considering a thin conducting sheet of this shape and applying potential Φ_2 along $1''$–2, and potential Φ_1 along 3–$1,''$ give a flow pattern for which (38) is the solution in the w-plane.[15]

Polygons with Two Right Angles and Two Scale Parameters. A very thin plate in a right-angle corner as in Fig. $27 \cdot 10a$ requires a mapping function

$$z = \frac{a}{\pi} \left[\frac{2}{m} \sqrt{w + 1} + \ln \frac{\sqrt{w + 1} + 1}{\sqrt{w + 1} - 1} \right] + ja \qquad (46)$$

[14] Also F. Ollendorff, *E.N.T.*, **4**, p. 405 (1927).
[15] Y. Ikeda, *Jl. Faculty of Sciences, Hokkaido Univ.*, Series II (Physics), **2**, p. 1 (1938); see particularly Fig. 33.

where m must be determined (graphically) from

$$\frac{b}{a}\pi = \frac{2}{m}\sqrt{m+1} + \ln \frac{\sqrt{m+1}+1}{\sqrt{m+1}-1}$$

which results from the correspondence of the points z_4 and w_4.
The other constants have been determined in accordance with the

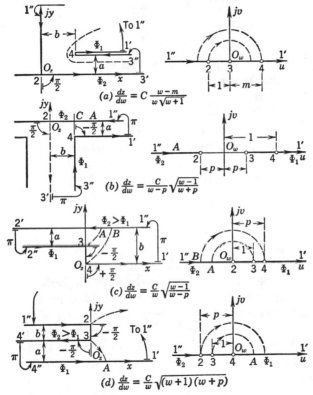

$$(a) \frac{dz}{dw} = C\,\frac{w-m}{w\sqrt{w+1}}$$

$$(b) \frac{dz}{dw} = \frac{C}{w-p}\sqrt{\frac{w-1}{w+p}}$$

$$(c) \frac{dz}{dw} = \frac{C}{w}\sqrt{\frac{w-1}{w-p}}$$

$$(d) \frac{dz}{dw} = \frac{C}{w}\sqrt{(w+1)(w+p)}$$

FIG. 27·10 Polygons with Two Right Angles and Two Scale Parameters.

previous illustrations. Detail computations of the field distribution were made by Walker,[D10] p. 88 who applied this geometry to leakage problems between pole and armature of electrical machines; he also introduced one of the equipotential surfaces as a feasible pole shoe geometry, shown dotted in Fig. 27·10a.

A very widely used geometry is that of the slot, Fig. 27·10b.

Restricting the mapping region to the right half slot, one includes as part 2–3' of the boundary a field line so that the w-plane requires as solution the complex potential function (38) with w/p replacing z/a. The mapping upon the w-plane is according to the table

z-plane	1	2	3	4
Vertex location	$1'\begin{cases}\infty - ja\\\infty + j0\end{cases}$ $1''$	0	$3'\begin{cases}0 - j\infty\\b - j\infty\end{cases}$ $3''$	$b - ja$
$\gamma_\alpha \pi$	$+\pi$	$+\dfrac{\pi}{2}$	$+\pi$	$-\dfrac{\pi}{2}$
γ_α	$+1$	$+\dfrac{1}{2}$	$+1$	$-\dfrac{1}{2}$
w_α	$\pm\infty$	$-p$	$+p$	$+1$

defined by the expression

$$\frac{dz}{dw} = \frac{C}{w - p}\sqrt{\frac{w - 1}{w + p}}$$

Application of (22) to point 1 gives at once $C = a/\pi$; and (17) applied to point 3 gives $p = a^2/(a^2 + 2b^2)$, so that the major constants are all determined. Integration gives then

$$z = \frac{a}{\pi}\left[\ln\frac{1 + R}{1 - R} + 2\sqrt{q}\tan^{-1}\left(\sqrt{q}R\right)\right] \tag{47}$$

where $R = [(w + p)/(w - 1)]^{\frac{1}{2}}$, $q = (1 - p)/2p = (b/a)^2$, and where $C_1 = 0$, as the correspondence of points z_2 and w_2 demonstrates. The form (47) is obviously more difficult to deal with than previous forms, which is to be expected as the geometry becomes more involved.

In applying this geometry to armature tooth-slot combinations of electrical machines, the potential values Φ should be replaced by the magnetostatic potential $\mathcal{F}$ and the solution in the w-plane is from (38)

$$P = \mathcal{F} + j\Xi = -\frac{j}{\pi}(\mathcal{F}_2 - \mathcal{F}_1)\cosh^{-1}\frac{w}{p} + \mathcal{F}_1 \tag{48}$$

where Ξ is the mathematical flux function. Since the potential $\mathcal{F}$ actually defines H, the magnetic field vector B is then from (25·7)

$$B = -\mu\overline{\left(\frac{dP}{dw}\Big/\frac{dz}{dw}\right)} = -jB_0\overline{\left(\frac{w - p}{w - 1}\right)^{\frac{1}{2}}} \tag{49}$$

where $B_0 = (\mu/a)(\mathcal{F}_2 - \mathcal{F}_1)$ is the uniform magnetic field in the air gap far from the slot. Along $1''$–2 one has $w = -|u|$, $|u| > p$, so that

$$B = -jB_0 \sqrt{\frac{|u| + p}{|u| + 1}} \qquad (50)$$

is directed normal to the pole surface $1''$–2 and has a minimum value at point 2 given by $|u| = p$, namely,

$$B_{\min} = -jB_0 \sqrt{\frac{2p}{p+1}} = -jB_0 \frac{a}{\sqrt{a^2 + b^2}} \approx -jB_0 \frac{a}{b} \qquad (51)$$

if the slot width $2b \gg a$, as usually is the case. To evaluate the effect of fringing one can define a point A at which $|B| = 0.98 B_0$ and form the ratio of the actual magnetic flux leaving between points 2 and A to the idealized magnetic flux between C and A with uniform field value B_0. Thus, from (50), $|u_A| = 0.96/0.04 = 24$, and therefore

$$R_A = \sqrt{(-u_A + p)/(-u_A - 1)} \approx \sqrt{u_A/(u_A + 1)} = 0.98,$$

so that from (47)

$$\frac{z_A}{b} = \frac{1}{\pi} \frac{a}{b} \ln \frac{1.98}{0.02} + \frac{2}{\pi} \tan^{-1} \left(0.98 \frac{b}{a} \right)$$

which is plotted as function of a/b in Fig. 27·11. Obviously, in order to be applicable to finite tooth widths, the slot pitch must certainly be larger than $2z_A$. The actual magnetic flux between points 2 and A is, from (48) with $w_2 = -|u_2| = -p$, $w_A = -|u_A|$, and observing $\cosh^{-1}\left(\dfrac{-|u|}{p}\right) = j\pi + \ln\left[|u| - \sqrt{u^2 - p^2}\right]$,

$$\Phi_m = \mu(\Xi_2 - \Xi_A) = -\frac{\mu}{\pi}(\mathcal{F}_2 - \mathcal{F}_1) \ln \left\{ 48 \left[1 + 2\left(\frac{b}{a}\right) \right]^2 \right\}$$

where $\sqrt{1 - (p/u)^2} \approx 1 - \frac{1}{2}(p/u)^2$ has been used for simplification. The idealized magnetic flux is $\Phi_0 = -B_0(z_A - b)$; the negative sign derives from the negative direction of the magnetic field, having assumed $\mathcal{F}_2 > \mathcal{F}_1$. The fringing factor is thus

$$\zeta_f = \frac{1}{\pi} \frac{a}{b} \frac{\ln 48 + \ln[1 + 2(b/a)^2]}{(z_A/b) - 1} \qquad (52)$$

which is also shown as a function of a/b in Fig. 27·11. This factor agrees in value with others computed on the basis of comparable assumptions; it has the advantage that it applies with uniform accuracy in all cases where the slot pitch $\tau > 2z_A$. The ratio of

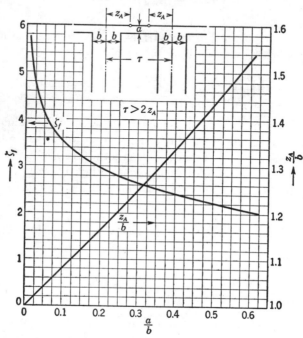

FIG. 27·11   Fringing Factor for Armature Slot in Electrical Machines.

actual magnetic flux for one full slot pitch to the idealized magnetic flux for one tooth can be computed with the designations of Fig. 27·11 as

$$\left(\frac{\Phi_m}{\Phi_0}\right)_{\text{total}} = \frac{2\Phi_m + (\tau - 2z_A)B_0}{(\tau - 2b)B_0} = 1 + \frac{z_A - b}{(\tau/2) - b}(\zeta_f - 1) \quad (53)$$

where ζ_f is the value from (52). Evaluations of a similar type were first made by Carter[16] in terms of an equivalent air gap; rather complete treatments of the slot are given in Walker,[D10]

---

[16] F. W. Carter, *Jl. I.E.E.*, **29**, part 146, p. 925 (1900) for pole leakage, and F. W. Carter, *Electr. World and Engr.*, **38**, p. 884 (1901) for slot fringing; see also the extensive recent treatment in J. Kucera, *Elektrot. und Masch.*, **58**, p. 329 (1940).

p. 81; in Smythe,[A22] p. 294; in Ollendorff,[A18] p. 216; and Bewley,[D1] p. 139.   The same geometry has been used to evaluate the temperature field and heat flow between conductor and slot in electrical machines.[17]

The same mapping function (47) is applied to the problem of the right-angle bend obtained by letting 0–3′ in the z-plane of Fig. 27·10b also take the potential Φ_2.   In the w-plane one has then only two potentials and the complex potential solution is given by (26) with an appropriate shift of the origin.   Jeans,[A10] p. 277, has used this for the evaluation of the electric field in the Leyden jar; also Bewley,[D1] p. 126, who gives a good field graph. It has also been applied to pole leakage by Walker,[D10] p. 73, to the elastic torsion problem of an idealized L steel bar,[18] and by interchange of field and equipotential lines in the w-plane to the magnetic flux in a transformer core.[19]

The arrangement in Fig. 27·10c leads to the mapping function

$$z = \frac{b}{\pi}\left[\cosh^{-1}\frac{2w-(p+1)}{p-1} - \frac{a}{b}\cosh^{-1}\frac{(p+1)w-2p}{(p-1)w}\right] - (b-a)$$

$$(54)$$

where $p = (b/a)^2$.   It has been used to represent the field distribution in large cable end sections;[20] by interchange of equipotential and field lines, one obtains either flow in a channel of two different widths, as Walker,[D10] p. 53, who gives much detail and a good graph, or the current flow in a very thin sheet, as Smythe,[A22] p. 230, and Bewley,[D1] p. 125.

The finite plate thickness of a parallel plate condenser (see Fig. 27·4) can be taken into account as shown in Fig. 27·10d. The mapping function with the assumed location of corresponding points becomes

$$z = \frac{a}{\pi}\left[\frac{p+1}{\sqrt{p}}\tanh^{-1}R + \frac{p-1}{\sqrt{p}}\frac{R}{1-R^2} + \ln\frac{R\sqrt{p}-1}{R\sqrt{p}+1}\right] \quad (55)$$

where $R = [(w+1)/(w+p)]^{1/2}$, $p = -1 + 2k^2 + 2k\sqrt{k^2-1}$, and $k = 1 + b/a$; the sign of the square root in p is so chosen that

[17] W. W. Peters, *Wiss. Veröff. a. d. Siemens-Konzern*, **4**, p. 197 (1925).

[18] E. Trefftz, *Math. Annalen*, **82**, p. 97 (1921); C. Dassen, *Zeits. angew. Math. und Mech.*, **3**, p. 258 (1923).

[19] G. M. Stein, *Trans. A.I.E.E.*, part I, **67**, p. 95 (1948).

[20] P. Andronescu, *Arch. f. Elektrot.*, **14**, p. 379 (1925).

$p > 1$. The field lines from the lower side 3–4' do not spread as much as in the case of the infinitely thin plate; for example, if $b/a = \frac{1}{4}$, then point A in Fig. 27·10d has a distance $0.403a$ compared with distance $(2/\pi)a = 0.636a$ for point B in Fig. 27·4. The fringing field becomes particularly important if the condenser represents the deflection plates of a cathode-ray tube, since it can influence the electron path configuration markedly; an analogous effect of the magnetic fringing field upon the path of ions exists in mass spectrometers.[21]

Polygons with Two Right Angles and Three Scale Parameters. In Fig. 27·12a potential Φ_2 designates a high-voltage winding, Φ_1 the low-voltage winding, as well as the core 5″–1' of a transformer.[22] Because of the three pairs of parallel lines it is possible to determine all parameters explicitly without performing the integration of the mapping derivative; one has

$$C = -\frac{c}{\pi}, \qquad q = m + \sqrt{m^2 + \left(\frac{c}{b}\right)^2}, \qquad p = \left(\frac{b}{c}\right)^2 q$$

where $m = \frac{1}{2}[(a/b)^2 + 1 - (c/b)^2]$. The solution in the w-plane is given by (26), so that the electric field distribution can readily be computed.

The same geometry in the z-plane can represent two other applications if one considers the symmetry of Fig. 27·12b. As a simple electric lens system,[23] one can take Φ_1 as an aperture (usually very thin but then more difficult to map) and Φ_2 as the first anode; the center line is then a field line, and the solution in the upper half w-plane is again (38) with w replacing z/a there. As above, the parameters can be evaluated without integration, giving

$$C = j\frac{b}{\pi}, \quad p = \frac{1}{2}[-m + \sqrt{m^2 + 4n}], \quad q = \frac{1}{2}[+m + \sqrt{m^2 + 4n}]$$

where $m = (2/b^2)(a^2 - c^2)$, $n = 1 + (2/b^2)(a^2 + c^2)$. The electric field is by (25·7)

$$E = -\overline{\left(\frac{dP}{dw}\bigg/\frac{dz}{dw}\right)} = -E_0 \overline{\left[\frac{w^2 - 1}{(w + p)(w - q)}\right]}^{\frac{1}{2}} \tag{56}$$

[21] N. D. Coggeshall, *Jl. Appl. Phys.*, **18**, p. 855 (1947).
[22] L. Dreyfus, *Arch. f. Elektrot.*, **13**, p. 125 (1924).
[23] R. Herzog, *Arch. f. Elektrot.*, **29**, p. 790 (1935).

where $E_0 = (1/b)(\Phi_2 - \Phi_1)$. In electron optics one is mostly interested in the field along the axis, for which in the w-plane $w \equiv u$, and $(-1) < u < +1$. Therefore,

$$E_{\text{axis}} = -E_0 \left[\frac{1 - u^2}{(p + u)(q - u)} \right]^{1/2} \quad |u| < 1 \quad (57)$$

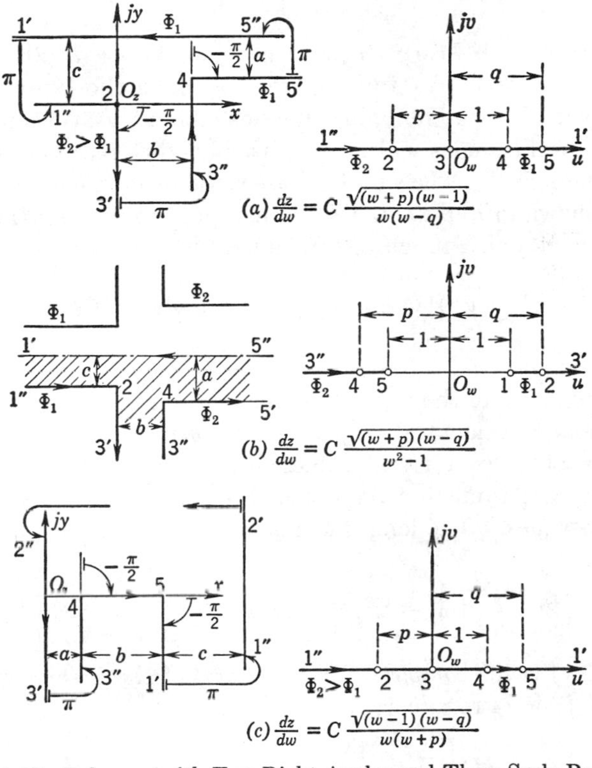

FIG. 27·12   Polygons with Two Right Angles and Three Scale Parameters.

This field has a maximum at $u = -(a - c)/(a + c)$. The exact correspondence of points in the two planes can, however, only be established after integration, which is straightforward but becomes rather unwieldy.

The other application of Fig. 27·12b is to opposing stator and rotor slots of electrical machines, assuming $\Phi_1 \equiv \mathcal{F}_1$ as the magnetostatic potential of the rotor and $\Phi_2 \equiv \mathcal{F}_2$ as that of the stator;[24] the line of symmetry is then a magnetic field line through

[24] J. Kucera, *Elektrot. und Masch.*, **58**, p. 328 (1940).

the centers of the opposing slots at the moment where these coincide. The reference gives extensive treatment of the various parts of slot reactance.

Another transformer problem[25] is illustrated in Fig. $27 \cdot 12c$, where the three pairs of parallel lines again permit direct evaluation of the unknown parameters in very much the same manner as above.

Polygons with More than Two Right Angles.   Since every right angle contributes a square root factor in the expression for the derivative of the mapping function, the integrations for more than two right angles will lead invariably to elliptic and hyperelliptic functions.[26]   The simplest case is the rectangle with uniform field as shown in Fig. $27 \cdot 13a$. Because of the symmetry in the w-plane, the mapping function can be written

$$z = kC \int_0^w [(1 - w^2)(1 - k^2 w^2)]^{-\frac{1}{2}} \, dw + C_1 = kCF(k, w) + C_1$$

(58)

where the limits of the integral are chosen so as to identify it with the standard (Legendre) *elliptic integral of the first kind* $F(k, w)$, which is tabulated for real values of w; k is the *modulus* which must be determined from point-by-point correspondence in z- and w-planes.   The length a from z_2 to z_3 corresponds by symmetry to

$$a = 2kC \int_0^1 [(1 - w^2)(1 - k^2 w^2)]^{-\frac{1}{2}} \, dw = 2kCK(k)$$

where $K(k)$ is the *complete elliptic integral* of the first kind.   The length jh from z_3 to z_4 corresponds to

$$jh = kC \left[F\left(k, \frac{1}{k}\right) - F(k, 1) \right] = jkCK(k')$$

since $F\left(k, \dfrac{1}{k}\right) = K(k) + jK(k')$, where $k' = \sqrt{1 - k^2}$.   From

[25] L. Dreyfus, *loc. cit.*

[26] For good treatment see Pierpont,[D16]   for numerical values Jahnke and Emde: *Tables of Functions;* reprinted by Dover Publications, New York, 1943.   More extensive treatises are H. Hancock: *Elliptic Integrals;* John Wiley, New York, 1917; A. G. Greenhill: *Applications of Elliptic Functions;* Macmillan, London, 1892; and A. Hurwitz and R. Courant: *Vorlesungen über allgemeine Funktionentheorie und elliptische Funktionen;* J. Springer, Berlin, 1929.

these two relations one has

$$C = \frac{a}{2kK(k)} \, , \qquad \frac{a}{2h} = \frac{K(k)}{K(k')} \qquad (59)$$

so that for a given $1/k$ in the w-plane one can determine the ratio a/h, or vice versa.   The value of C_1 is best obtained by identifying $w = 0$ with $z = a/2$ by symmetry, which gives from (58) immediately $C_1 = a/2$.   Thus, (58) becomes

$$z = \frac{a}{2K(k)} F(k, w) + \frac{a}{2} \qquad (60)$$

Bateman,[C1] p. 302, gives this solution, and Ikeda[27] gives a good field graph in the w-plane.

The complex potential solution in the z-plane is by inspection

$$P = \Phi_2 - E_0 z, \qquad E_0 = \frac{\Phi_2 - \Phi_1}{a} \qquad (61)$$

Introducing (60) into this form yields actually the complex potential solution for the w-plane directly, which will be used as one of the standard solutions, namely,

$$P = -\frac{1}{2} (\Phi_2 - \Phi_1) \frac{F(k, w)}{K(k)} + \frac{1}{2} (\Phi_2 + \Phi_1) \qquad (62)$$

This is, of course, also the complete solution of two coplanar parallel strips;[28] by interchange of field lines and equipotential lines it becomes the solution of three coplanar strips, the center one of finite width 2, the symmetrically located outer ones extending to infinity.[29]

To find the solution for other potential distributions in the rectangle, one first maps the rectangle geometrically by (60) upon

[27] Y. Ikeda, *Jl. Faculty of Sciences, Hokkaido Univ.*, Series II (Physics), **2**, p. 1 (1938).

[28] For graphs of the field distribution for the cases $k = \sin 10°$, $\sin 45°$, $\sin 80°$ see Y. Ikeda and M. Kuwaori, *Scient. Papers Inst. of Phys. and Chem. Research*, **26**, p. 208 (1935); see also F. Cap, *Oesterr. Ing.-Archiv*, **2**, p. 207 (1948) for the case $k = 0.1$.

[29] H. Petersohn, *Zeits. f. Physik*, **38**, p. 727 (1926), who also studies mappings by several types of elliptic functions; also J. J. Thomson: *Recent Researches in Electricity and Magnetism;* Oxford University Press, 1893.

the upper half w-plane and then transforms this upper half plane upon itself so as to identify the potential problem with one of the three standard forms (26), (38), or (62). If the rectangle is a thin conducting sheet with potentials Φ_1 and Φ_2 applied over small sections of the periphery, the solution[30] requires two mappings of

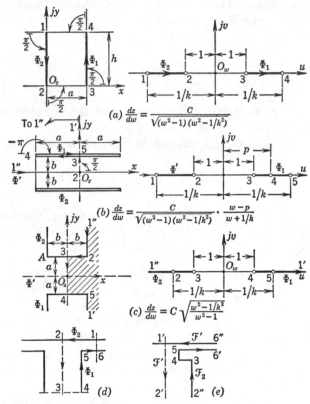

FIG. 27·13   Polygons with More than Two Right Angles.

the type (60). Wires in rectangular ducts of either conducting[31] or dielectric material can be treated in this same manner, the mapping function (60) leading to a wire above conducting, or dielectric, half space in the w-plane.

Two parallel finite strips constituting a parallel plate condenser as in Fig. 27·13b have potential $\Phi' = \frac{1}{2}(\Phi_2 + \Phi_1)$ at the plane of

---

[30] H. F. Moulton, *Proc. London Math. Soc.*, **3**, p. 104; also Jeans,[A10] p. 354.
[31] C. M. Herbert, *Phys. Rev.*, II, **17**, p. 157 (1921); also Strutt,[B30] p. 36.

symmetry. Mapping of one quadrant in accordance with the table

z-plane		1	2	3	4	5
Vertex location	$1'$ { $1''$ {	$0 + j\infty$ $-\infty + j0$	0	jb	$-a + jb$	jb
$\gamma_\alpha \pi$		$\dfrac{3\pi}{2}$	$\dfrac{\pi}{2}$	$\dfrac{\pi}{2}$	$-\pi$	$\dfrac{\pi}{2}$
γ_α		$+\dfrac{3}{2}$	$+\dfrac{1}{2}$	$+\dfrac{1}{2}$	-1	$+\dfrac{1}{2}$ $(\Sigma\gamma_\alpha = 2)$
w_α		$-\dfrac{1}{k}$	-1	$+1$	$+p$	$+\dfrac{1}{k}$

leads to the integral

$$z = kC \int_0^w \frac{w - p}{w + 1/k} \left[(1 - w^2)(1 - k^2 w^2)\right]^{-\frac{1}{2}} dw + C_1 \quad (63)$$

This form can be resolved into a sum of standard elliptic integrals[32] which are also involved in the evaluation of the parameters k and p, as well as of the constants C and C_1. The complex potential solution in the w-plane is given by (62). The fact that $1/k$ in the location of the vertex points in the w-plane is left undetermined makes the choice of symmetry equivalent to the definite choice of one more vertex. One could, of course, have chosen $w_1 = \pm \infty$ so as to reduce the order of the integral; in that case the mapping function would lead to the Weierstrass type of elliptic integrals which would then also appear in the solution in the upper half w-plane as in Frank and Mises,[C6] p. 668;[33] Kármán and Burgers,[C21] p. 83, apply this and similar mappings to aerodynamic flow problems. The above solution is obviously identical with that for a single strip above an infinite conducting plane of potential Φ'; Kehren (*loc. cit.*) has extended this to the case of the single strip in a right-angle corner as in a Leyden jar, and Y. Ikeda and M. Kuwaori (*loc. cit.*) have extended it to one and two parallel strips midway between parallel infinite planes and normal to these, as well as other arrangements. If the two parallel strips have the same potential, then the line of symmetry between the strips is a field line and the same mapping function leads to a single

---

[32] See Pierpont,[D16] p. 384.

[33] As also in E. Kehren, Dissertation; J. A. Barth, Leipzig, 1932, and H. B. Palmer, *Electr. Engg.*, **56**, p. 363 (1937).

charged strip 3–5 in the upper half w-plane, as shown in Fig. 27·13b, for which the complex potential solution is (38a); see Frank and Mises,[C6] p. 668, Case II.

Two semi-infinite rectangular electrodes as in Fig. 27·13c, with the plane of symmetry of potential $\Phi' = \frac{1}{2}(\Phi_2 + \Phi_1)$, can be mapped by considering the right half of the H-shaped region. The mapping function is then symmetrical and becomes

$$z = \frac{C}{k} \int_0^w (1 - k^2 w^2)^{\frac{1}{2}} (1 - w^2)^{-\frac{1}{2}} \, dw + C_1 = \frac{C}{k} E(k, w) + C_1$$

(64)

with the standard form of the (Legendre) *elliptic integral of the second kind.* In the w-plane, the complex potential solution is (38) with (z/a) replaced by w. One could also have chosen one quadrant bounded by $1''$–2–3–0 and the positive x-axis; in this case integrals of the Weierstrass type would again be encountered, though the geometry of the upper w-plane remains the same. Treatments are found in Frank and Mises[C6] II, p. 664, and in Bateman,[C1] p. 304; for extensive details of numerical computations and of electric resistance or magnetic reluctance see Davy.[34] The current distribution in a thin conducting sheet in the shape of an H is found by the same mapping function; for potential Φ_2 applied along A–2 and Φ_1 along the opposite side of the bridge, the upper half w-plane has the same geometry as in Fig. 27·13a, so that (62) can be used. A graph of the field lines (or flow lines in the corresponding hydrodynamic application) is again given in Ikeda and Kuwaori (*loc. cit.*).

The armature slots in electrical machines have actually the form of Fig. 27·13d; with the simplification of infinite depth, the mapping function involves standard elliptic integrals.[35] Without simplifying assumptions, the mapping function becomes a hyperelliptic integral involving six right angles, which can only be approximated by elliptic integrals; the same applies to one quadrant of a rectangular transformer core.[36] Salient pole machines have

[34] N. Davy, *Phil. Mag.*, (7), **35**, p. 819 (1944); for graphs see also Y. Ikeda and M. Kuwaori, *loc. cit.*

[35] R. Gans, *Arch. f. Elektrot.*, **9**, p. 231 (1920); R. Frey, Vol. IV of *Arbeiten aus dem Elektrotechnischen Institut Karlsruhe;* J. Springer, Berlin, 1925.

[36] S. Bergmann, *Math. Zeits.*, **19**, p. 8 (1923); *Zeits. angew. Math. und Mech.*, **5**, p. 319 (1925).

pole shoes which can be represented as shown[37] in Fig. 27·13e. Assume the center line 1'–2' between neighboring poles of the same magnetic potential $\mathcal{F}'$ as the armature 6''–1', and the magnetic pole of potential $\mathcal{F}_2$, the mapping function involves elliptic integrals and leads in the upper w-plane to two coplanar planes with infinitesimal gap, which has the solution (26).   With the armature

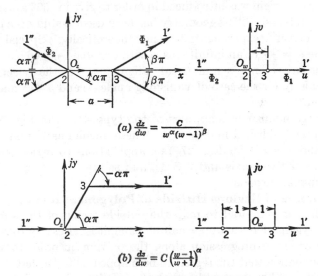

(a) $\dfrac{dz}{dw} = \dfrac{C}{w^{\alpha}(w-1)^{\beta}}$

(b) $\dfrac{dz}{dw} = C\left(\dfrac{w-1}{w+1}\right)^{\alpha}$

FIG. 27·14   Polygons with Other than Right Angles.

6''–1' omitted, the same geometry has been used to find in detail the magnetic field distribution in cyclotron magnets[38] with "shims" or pole shoes.

Polygons with Other than Right Angles.   The symmetrical arrangement of Fig. 27·14a is mapped upon the upper half w-plane by

$$z = C \int w^{-\alpha}(w-1)^{-\beta}\,dw + C_1 \tag{65}$$

which is an integral of the Euler type.[39]   The only scale parameter

[37] I. A. Terry and E. G. Keller, *Jl. I.E.E.*, **83**, p. 845 (1938).

[38] M. E. Rose, *Phys. Rev.*, **53**, p. 715 (1938).

[39] Jahnke and Emde, *Tables of Functions;* reprinted by Dover Publications, New York, 1943; originally published by B. G. Teubner, Leipzig, 1938.

a is determined by integration between 2 and 3, leading to

$$a = C \int_0^1 w^{-\alpha}(w - 1)^{-\beta} \, dw = C(-1)^\beta \frac{\Gamma(1 - \alpha)\Gamma(1 - \beta)}{\Gamma(3 - \alpha - \beta)} \quad (66)$$

where $\Gamma(q + 1) = q!$, so that C can be determined. The solution in the upper w-plane is given by (38) with $(2w - 1)$ replacing z/a; the shift in origin was introduced in order to give in (66) a standard form of integral. This geometry has been used to study the breakdown of oil[40] experimentally and theoretically. Special cases include $\alpha = \frac{1}{2}$, or an infinite plate with one sharp-edged electrode. Extension to non-symmetrical alignment of the electrodes, particularly for the case of vanishing angles α and β was made by Kehren.[41]

A large number of mappings of the type shown in Fig. 27·14*b* have been published in Japan.[42] These include particularly $\alpha = \pi/3$, and $\alpha = \pi/4$ for Fig. 27·14*b*, applications to regions formed by the positive x-axis and 2–3–1′, and solutions of flow problems in triangular regions.

Mapping of Regions Outside of Polygons. If in the general Fig. 27·3 it is desired to map the outside region of the straight-line polygon upon the upper half w-plane, it is necessary to reverse the direction of progression along the polygon in order to satisfy the convention that the region to be mapped be to the left; but in addition one has to consider that the infinite point of the z-plane is now a point of the region to be mapped and that there the function will certainly not be analytic. It can be shown that this results in a mapping function slightly modified as compared with (11), namely,

$$z = C \int \prod_{(\alpha)} (w - w_\alpha)^{-\gamma_\alpha} \frac{dw}{(w - w_0)^2 (w - \bar{w}_0)^2} \quad (67)$$

where the first product is to be extended over all vertices of the given polygon in the z-plane, and where w_0 is the image of $z = \infty$, $\bar{w}_0$ its conjugate complex value; see Bateman,[C1] p. 305, and

[40] L. Dreyfus, *Arch. f. Elektrot.*, **13**, p. 123 (1924); also Ollendorff,[A18] p. 209.

[41] E. Kehren, Dissertation; J. A. Barth, Leipzig, 1932.

[42] Y. Ikeda, *Jl. Faculty of Science, Hokkaido Univ.*, Series II (Physics), **2**, p. 1 (1938); A. Migadzu, *Technology Reports, Tôhoku Imperial Univ., Sendai*, **10**, No. 4, p. 51 (1932).

Kellogg,[C10] p. 374. The choice of w_0 is generally important because of the corresponding non-conformality of the mapping in the z-plane. The sum of the values γ_α is now -2 in contradistinction to (18), because the sum of the outside angles of a closed polygon is $(N + 2)\pi$.

An example is the simple straight line cut in the z-plane as in Fig. 27·15a. The contributions to the product function follow from the table

z-plane	1	3	(∞)	
Vertex location	$-b$	$+b$		
$\gamma_\alpha\pi$	$-\pi$	$-\pi$		($\Sigma\gamma_\alpha = -2$)
γ_α	-1	-1		
w_α	-1	$+1$	$w_0 = j$	

and the location of $z = \infty$ might be chosen at $w_0 = j$, so that

$$z = C \int \frac{w^2 - 1}{(w^2 + 1)^2} \, dw + C_1 = -C \frac{w}{1 + w^2} + C_1 \qquad (68)$$

The correspondence of the points 1 and 3 leads to $C = -2b$, $C_1 = 0$. Assuming the cut to represent a flat strip conductor with a total charge λ per unit length, then the field lines going out to infinity can be presumed to terminate there on $(-\lambda)$. In the w-plane the problem now becomes one of a line charge $(-\lambda)$ at $w = j$ above a plane conducting surface; the solution is from table 25·1, line 3,

$$P = +\frac{\lambda}{2\pi\varepsilon} \ln \frac{w - j}{w + j} + \Phi_0$$

if Φ_0 is the potential on the conductor surface. The electric field strength is, by (25·7),

$$E = -\overline{\left(\frac{dP}{dz}\right)} = j \frac{\lambda}{2\pi\varepsilon b} \overline{\left(\frac{1 + w^2}{1 - w^2}\right)} \qquad (69)$$

it becomes infinitely large at $w = \pm 1$. From (69) one obtains the surface charge density as εE with $w \equiv u$, real. By inversion, the straight line cut can be transformed into a circular arc as in Bateman,[C1] p. 306, where applications to hydrodynamic problems also are to be found.

A rectangular hole in an infinitely extended thin conducting sheet can be mapped upon the upper w-plane as in Fig. 27·15b, where again $z = \infty$ is mapped at $w = j$. If the electrodes are at

very large distance, one can consider them at $z = \infty$ and in the
w-plane they appear as a dipole line at $w = j$. In order to satisfy
the boundary conditions on the u-axis, i.e., to make it a field line,

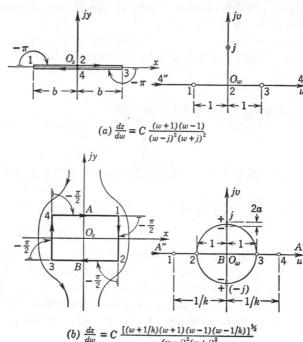

$$(a) \ \frac{dz}{dw} = C \ \frac{(w+1)(w-1)}{(w-j)^2(w+j)^2}$$

$$(b) \ \frac{dz}{dw} = C \ \frac{[(w+1/k)(w+1)(w-1)(w-1/k)]^{1/2}}{(w-j)^2(w+j)^2}$$

FIG. 27·15 Mapping of Regions Outside of Polygons.

a second dipole line must be located at $w = -j$, so that, in accordance with table 25·1, line 6, the solution in the w-plane is

$$P = -2aS \left(\frac{1}{w-j} - \frac{1}{w+j} \right) = -j \frac{2I}{\pi\gamma} \frac{a}{w^2+1} \qquad (70)$$

28· GENERAL LAPLACIAN POTENTIAL PROBLEMS AND CONFORMAL MAPPING

For cases of a more general geometry it becomes desirable to
have assurance of reaching a definite solution of the potential
problem. It has been shown that the interior of any simply
connected region[1] bounded by regular curves can be mapped upon

[1] A region in which any simple closed curve (without double points) can be
shrunk to a point without leaving the region; Kellogg,[C10] p. 74.

the interior of the unit circle in a one-to-one conformal manner;[2] this is Riemann's fundamental theorem.   It is, of course, difficult to find the particular mapping function for any general configuration of the original boundary curve, so that in practice several mappings might have to be performed or approximations by means of polynomials might have to be employed;   see Bateman,[C1] p. 322.   Several of the more general cases will be briefly outlined here as far as they have reached practical significance.

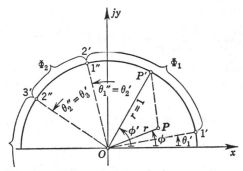

Fɪɢ. 28·1   Solution of First Boundary Value Problem on Unit Circle.

Solution of Boundary Value Problems of the First Kind.
If by some means the mapping into the unit circle has been accomplished, then it is possible to solve any potential problem for the unit circle, if the potential values on its periphery are given (boundary value problem of the *first kind* or *Dirichlet* problem), by means of Poisson's integral,

$$\Phi = \frac{1}{2\pi} \int_0^{2\pi} \frac{1 - r^2}{1 - 2r \cos (\phi - \phi') + r^2} \, \Phi(\phi') \, d\phi' \qquad (1)$$

where (r, ϕ) defines a point P within unit circle, and ϕ' a point on the unit circle as in Fig. 28·1; see Bateman,[C1] p. 238, or any of the references in Appendix 4, D, b.   For applications in the complex v plane one can also use the complex potential function of Schwarz

$$P = \frac{1}{2\pi} \int_0^{2\pi} \frac{e^{j\phi'} + z}{e^{j\phi'} - z} \, \Phi(\phi') \, d\phi' \equiv \Phi + j\Xi \qquad (2)$$

in which the real part is the form (1), since $z = re^{j\phi}$.

[2] B. Riemann, Inaugural Dissertation, Göttingen, 1851; P. Koebe, *Math. Annalen*, **67**, p. 146 (1909) and *Jl. of Math.*, **145**, p. 177 (1915); Frank and Mises,[C6] I, p. 718; Bateman,[C1] p. 275.

If, in particular, there are n potential values sectionally constant over the periphery of the unit circle, then for any one potential Φ_α extending from $\theta_\alpha{}'$ to $\theta_\alpha{}''$ ($\theta_1{}' > 0$ is taken closest to zero and $\theta_n{}'' = 2\pi + \theta_1{}'$), the integral gives

$$\Phi_\alpha \int_{\theta_\alpha'}^{\theta_\alpha''} \frac{e^{j\phi'} + z}{e^{j\phi'} - z}\, d\phi' = -\Phi_\alpha \left[2j \ln \frac{e^{j\theta_\alpha''} - z}{e^{j\theta_\alpha'} - z} + (\theta_\alpha{}'' - \theta_\alpha{}') \right]$$

For a total of n successive different potential sections, the total solution is then[3]

$$P = -\Phi_0 + \frac{j}{\pi} \sum_{\alpha=1}^{n} (\Phi_{\alpha+1} - \Phi_\alpha) \ln \left[e^{j\theta_\alpha''} - z \right] + 2\Phi_1 \qquad (3)$$

where in the summation $\Phi_{n+1} \equiv \Phi_1$. The last term compensates for summation in terms of $\theta_\alpha{}''$, the end angle of the section, and

$$\Phi_0 = +\frac{1}{2\pi} \sum_{\alpha=1}^{n} (\theta_\alpha{}'' - \theta_\alpha{}')\Phi_\alpha \qquad (4)$$

is the mean value of the potential over the periphery of the unit circle and, according to Gauss, identical with the potential at the center O of the circle (Gauss's mean value theorem). Thus, for $\Phi = \Phi_1$ along $0 \leqslant \phi' \leqslant \pi$ and $\Phi = -\Phi_1$ along $\pi \leqslant \phi' \leqslant 2\pi$, one has from (3) the simple result

$$P = -j\frac{2}{\pi}\Phi_1 \ln \frac{z+1}{z-1} + 2\Phi_1$$

Near the points of discontinuity of potential on the unit circle, the potential function (3) behaves like $(j \ln \zeta)$ if $\zeta = e^{j\theta_\alpha''} - w$; this is, in accordance with table $25 \cdot 1$, line 2, the complex potential of the magnetic field of a line current, so that the potential value right at the discontinuity is not analytic, but is regular in any arbitrarily close neighborhood.

Most mapping problems are simpler if mapping upon the upper half w-plane can be achieved, rather than upon unit circle. Since the function

$$w = j\frac{1-z}{1+z}$$

maps the unit circle of the z-plane upon the upper half w-plane,

[3] Bateman,[C1] p. 242; also H. Villat, *Bull. de soc. math. de France*, **39**, p. 443 (1911).

one can transform Schwarz's complex potential solution (2) with

$$z = -\frac{w-j}{w+j}, \qquad e^{j\phi'} = -\frac{u'-j}{u'+j}, \qquad d\phi' = \frac{2du'}{1+u'^2} \quad (5)$$

into

$$P = \frac{j}{\pi} \int_{-\infty}^{+\infty} \frac{1+u'w}{(1+u'^2)(w-u')} \Phi(u')\, du' = \Phi + j\Xi \quad (6)$$

which is the general solution of the first boundary value problem in the upper half w-plane. In (6), u' denotes the integration variable along the real u-axis, and w is the arbitrary point where

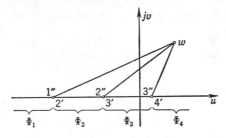

FIG. 28·2 Solution of First Boundary Value Problem in Upper Half Plane.

the potential P exists. The real part of (6) leads to the equivalent of Poisson's integral on the unit circle, (1), namely,

$$\Phi = \frac{1}{\pi} \int_{-\infty}^{+\infty} \frac{v}{(u-u')^2 + v^2} \Phi(u')\, du'$$

permitting the direct evaluation of the real potential distribution.

If, again, there are n potential values sectionally constant along the u-axis as indicated in Fig. 28·2, then for any one potential Φ_α extending from u_α' to u_α'', the integral in (6) can be separated into two simple integrals with the result

$$\Phi_\alpha \int_{u_\alpha'}^{u_\alpha''} \left[\frac{1}{w-u'} + \frac{u'}{(1+u'^2)} \right] du'$$

$$= \Phi_\alpha \left[-\ln \frac{w-u_\alpha''}{w-u_\alpha'} + \frac{1}{2}\ln \frac{1+u_\alpha''^2}{1+u_\alpha'^2} \right]$$

The sum of the n contributions can be contracted, since $u_\alpha'' = u_{\alpha+1}'$, into the rather simple form

$$P = \frac{j}{\pi} \sum_{\alpha=1}^{n-1} (\Phi_\alpha - \Phi_{\alpha+1}) \ln \frac{\sqrt{1+u_\alpha''^2}}{w-u_\alpha''} + \Phi_n \quad (8)$$

Use has been made of the fact that for $u_1' \to (-\infty)$ the term $\ln \dfrac{\sqrt{1 + u_1'^2}}{w - u_1'} \to 0$, whereas for $u_n'' \to (+\infty)$ the term $\ln \dfrac{\sqrt{1 + u_n''^2}}{w - u_n''} \to \ln (-1) = j\pi$. For only two potential values, namely, $\Phi = \Phi_1$ for $-\infty < u < 0$, and $\Phi = \Phi_2$ for $0 < u < +\infty$, (8) reduces immediately to the standard form $(25 \cdot 26)$ or $(27 \cdot 26)$ which has been used extensively.

The application to three parallel thin layers of transformer windings as in Fig. $27 \cdot 7c$ is now straightforward. Assume symmetry of potential distribution, namely, $\Phi_1 = -\Phi_3 = V$, and $\Phi_2 = 0$; then (8) becomes

$$P = \frac{j}{\pi} \left[V \ln \frac{\sqrt{2}}{w + 1} + V \ln \frac{\sqrt{1 + q^2}}{w - q} \right] - V$$

$$= V \left[\frac{j}{\pi} \ln \frac{\sqrt{2(1 + q^2)}}{(w + 1)(w - q)} - 1 \right] \quad (9)$$

The equipotential lines in the w-plane are actually two families of hyperbolas, one diverging from the point 3 and the other from the point 5. Transposing these into the z-plane shows that the outermost layer has the strongest field concentration near it[4] and must therefore be particularly well insulated. The field vector can be found again by $(25 \cdot 7)$ and becomes with (9) and the derivative of the mapping function from Fig. $27 \cdot 7c$,

$$E = - \overline{\left(\frac{dP}{dz} \right)} = - \frac{j}{\pi} V \overline{\left[\frac{(2w + 1 - q)}{Cw(w + p)(w - \tau)} \right]}$$

The field strength is infinitely high at the three sharp corners 2, 4, and 6; it is zero for $w = \frac{1}{2}(q - 1)$, i.e., on the center layer, the exact location depending on the relative geometric distances of the windings. In a similar manner can be treated Figs. $27 \cdot 12a$ and c, as well as problems in high-voltage transformers involving three separate windings of high, medium, and low voltage and the grounded core.[5]

Actually, the potential along windings is not constant but may vary linearly; similarly, the magnetostatic potential varies fre-

[4] W. Grösser, *Arch. f. Elektrot.*, **25**, p. 225 (1931).
[5] J. Labus, *Arch. f. Elektrot.*, **19**, p. 82 (1927).

quently along the iron surface either because of saturation or because of exciting windings.   In such cases one can make use of (6) directly if the variation of potential has been transposed from the original z-plane to the upper half w-plane, so that $\Phi(u')$ is known as a function of u'.   Unfortunately, the integrations can be carried out only in the simplest cases, so that either approximations or graphical or numerical methods become necessary.   A rather simple illustration is the evaluation of the magnetic field distribution in the air gap of an electrical machine if the rotor surface has a magnetomotive force distribution which is constant directly opposite the stator pole and decreases linearly from the edge of the pole to the plane of symmetry between poles.[6]

Solution of Second and Mixed Boundary Value Problems. If, again, the mapping of a simply connected region into unit circle has been accomplished, but the boundary conditions prescribe the values of the normal component of the field gradient, $E_r = -\partial\Phi/\partial r$, the boundary value problem is said to be of the *second kind* (or *Neumann* problem); if the boundary conditions prescribe over certain sections of the periphery of unit circle the potential values and over the remaining sections the normal component of the gradient, then the boundary value problem is said to be of the *mixed kind*.   It is not possible in these cases to deduce a general theorem of practical value comparable with the Poisson integral for the first boundary value problem; in fact, few problems of this type can be solved satisfactorily by conformal mapping alone.   The method of two-dimensional harmonics (see section 29) will generally prove to lead most quickly to the desired results.

In the special cases where the boundary is formed partly by fixed potential values and partly by field lines along which the normal component $E_n = -\partial\Phi/\partial n = 0$, conformal mapping gives quick solutions if the final map upon the upper half plane corresponds either to Fig. $27 \cdot 6b$ with $(27 \cdot 38)$ as complex potential solution, or to its correlate with equipotential lines and field lines interchanged where $(27 \cdot 38a)$ gives the complex potential, or, finally, to Fig. $27 \cdot 13a$ with $(27 \cdot 62)$ as complex potential solution. It is, therefore, advisable to utilize symmetries which define at least one field line so that one of these standard solutions can be applied.

[6] T. Nakamura, *Elektrotechn. Jl.*, **3**, p. 6 (1939).

An example of a general mixed boundary value problem is a wire carrying charge λ per unit length and located at P within a slotted cylindrical conductor[7] of potential Φ_0 as shown in Fig. 28·3; it is desired to find the field distribution around the slot 3–5.   Since the dielectric constant is the same within and outside the cylinder, one can only stipulate continuity of the electric field vector across the circular arc 3–5.   Mapping by the linear function

$$w = j\,\frac{a - z}{a + z} \tag{10}$$

produces a one-to-one correspondence between the entire z- and w-planes developing the cylinder into a flat strip of width $2p = (2 \sin \theta)/(1 - \cos \theta)$, where 2θ is the slot angle.   The point P, location of the wire, is imaged at

$$w_P = \frac{2\,\dfrac{a}{R}\,\sin \alpha + j\left[\left(\dfrac{a}{R}\right)^2 - 1\right]}{\left(\dfrac{a}{R}\right)^2 + 2\,\dfrac{a}{R}\,\cos \alpha + 1} \tag{11}$$

Further mapping by

$$\zeta = \cos^{-1}\left(\frac{w}{p}\right), \qquad w = p \cos \zeta \tag{12}$$

transforms the entire w-plane into a semi-infinite strip of width 2π, relating the four quadrants of the w-plane to the four semi-infinite strips of width $\pi/2$, each as indicated in Fig. 28·3, so that the upper side of the flat strip appears as $(-\pi) < \xi < 0$, the lower side as $0 < \xi < \pi$.   In the ζ-plane the problem is now that of an infinitely periodic grid of wires spaced 2π apart above a conducting plane, so that the complex potential solution becomes identical with (25·45) with appropriate change of notation, namely,

$$P = -\frac{\lambda}{2\pi\varepsilon}\,[\ln \sin \tfrac{1}{2}(\zeta - \zeta_P) - \ln \sin \tfrac{1}{2}(\zeta - \bar{\zeta}_P)] \tag{13}$$

Here, $\zeta_P = \cos^{-1}(w_P/p)$ with w_P from (11), and $\bar{\zeta}_P$ is the conjugate complex value of ζ_P; the factor $\tfrac{1}{2}$ arises from the fact that $\sin \zeta$ has period π, whereas the problem needs period 2π.   If the

[7] Ch. Snow, *Scient. Papers Bur. Stand.*, **21**, p. 631 (1926).

wire is located at the center as an approximation to certain photo-electric arrangements,[8] then

$$w_P = j, \qquad \zeta_P = \cos^{-1}\left(\frac{j}{p}\right) = \frac{\pi}{2} + j \sinh^{-1}\left(\frac{1}{p}\right) \qquad (14)$$

The same general solution (13) applies to the case where the wire is outside the cylinder; if it moves to $z = \infty$, the solution for the slotted cylinder is given in Bateman,[C1] p. 306.

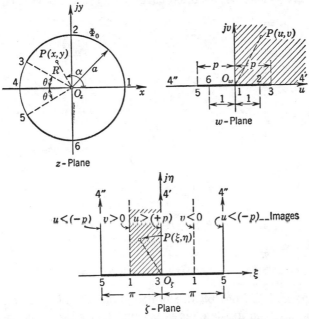

Fig. 28·3   Charged Wire within a Slotted Cylindrical Conductor.

A similar treatment solves the problem of a dielectric cylinder carrying one or more conducting layers on its surface,[9] Fig. 28·4. The linear mapping function

$$w = \frac{1 - ze^{j\alpha}}{z - e^{j\alpha}} \qquad (15)$$

transforms again the entire z-plane into the entire w-plane, but

[8] Th. C. Fry, *Am. Math. Monthly*, **39**, p. 199 (1932); also *Bell Tel. Monograph* No. 671.

[9] J. Hodgkinson, *Quart. Jl. Math.*, Oxford series, **9**, p. 5 (1938).

now the circular arc carrying the conducting layer with total charge λ per unit length is stretched into the positive u-axis, the upper half plane is filled with dielectric ε_2, the lower half plane with dielectric ε_1. The infinite point $z = \infty$ is mapped at $(-e^{j\alpha}) = e^{j(\alpha+\pi)}$, and since physically the charged layer sends its field lines into $z = \infty$, Ω will now represent a charged line carrying $(-\lambda)$; it is certainly a point of nonconformality. A further mapping upon a ζ-plane by $w = \zeta^2$ reduces the arrangement to the upper half ζ-plane with a line charge $(-\lambda)$ in ε_1 above a conduct-

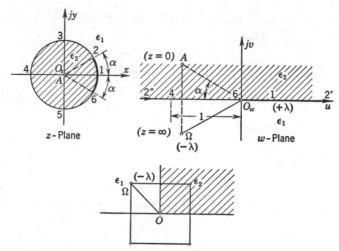

FIG. 28·4   Dielectric Cylinder with a Conducting Layer.

ing plane and in front of an infinite plane boundary of dielectric ε_2. The problem in the ζ-plane is thus reduced to a conventional image problem. The reference gives applications to two conducting layers of either like or opposite sign.

Mapping of Polygons Bounded by Circular Arcs.   A study of mappings obtained by various analytic functions discloses transformations from regions bounded by circular arcs into regions bounded by straight lines, so that further transformations utilizing the Schwarz-Christoffel mapping functions lead to the final solution of a potential problem. Thus, two conducting cylinders in contact carrying a total charge λ per unit length[10] and with radii a and b as in Fig. 28·5 can be mapped by complex inversion $w =$

[10] E. P. Adams, *Am. Philos. Soc. Proc.*, Philadelphia, **75**, 1, p. 11 (1935).

$2j/z$ upon the upper half w-plane.   Since the conductors have the same potential, the field lines in the z-plane will go to $z = \infty$, and in the w-plane they will converge upon its origin 0.   It is necessary only to consider the upper half z-plane which is mapped into a semi-infinite rectangular strip in the w-plane.   Further mapping by

$$\frac{dw}{d\zeta} = \frac{C}{\zeta} \left[(\zeta + p)(\zeta - 1) \right]^{-\frac{1}{2}} \tag{16}$$

produces a flat strip in the ζ-plane for which the solution was given in (27·38a).   With the appropriate shift of the origin to

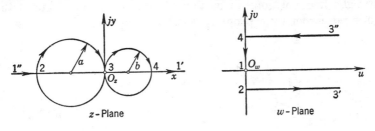

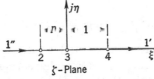

FIG. 28·5   Two Freely Charged Conducting Cylinders in Contact.

$(1 - p)/2$ and observing that the total width of the strip is $(1 + p)$, one has

$$P = + \frac{\lambda}{2\pi\varepsilon} \cosh^{-1} \frac{2\zeta - 1 + p}{1 + p} = \Phi + j\Xi \tag{17}$$

The electric field strength in the z-plane can be evaluated as in (25·7), except that now two successive mappings are involved, so that

$$E = -\overline{\left(\frac{dP}{dz}\right)} = -\overline{\left(\frac{dP}{d\zeta} \cdot \frac{d\zeta}{dw} \cdot \frac{dw}{dz}\right)} = j \frac{\lambda}{4\pi\varepsilon} \overline{\left(\frac{w^2}{C} \sqrt{\zeta(\zeta + p)}\right)} \tag{18}$$

Here, $dw/dz = -(2j/z^2) = j(w^2/2)$ has been introduced in the latter form but needs the knowledge of the complete mapping function (16).   Many other examples are found in the reference given, such as two parallel cylinders not in contact but connected by a conducting sheet along their center plane, and conductors made up of three or four intersecting cylinders.

The general theory for the mapping of polygons bounded by circular arcs upon the upper half plane was originally developed by Schwarz;[11] the resulting differential equation is, however, of second order and non-linear, so that rigorous solutions cannot be obtained in a practical manner.   If the problem involves the rounding off of an originally sharp corner, one can solve the field distribution for the sharp corner by the mapping procedure for straight line polygons in section 27 and then approximate the rounded corner by a properly selected equipotential line close to

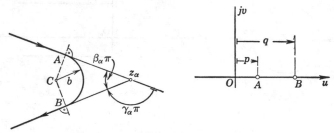

FIG. 28·6   Mapping of Rounded Corner.

the sharp corner with the desired smallest radius of curvature. This has been done for the rectangular corner opposite an infinite plane (see Fig. 27·9) in Rothe *et al.*,[D8] p. 136, and for a very thin plane winding opposite an infinite plane which is the same problem as the parallel plane condenser (Fig. 27·4*b*), by Grösser.[12]   It has to be observed, though, that the equipotential line generally has a shape different from that of the original electrodes, which may not make it a satisfactory approximation.

A much better procedure for replacing a sharp edge by a circular cylinder as in Fig. 28·6 is the substitution[13] of

$$[(w - p)^{-\gamma_\alpha} + \lambda(w - q)^{-\gamma_\alpha}] \tag{19}$$

for the vertex factor $(w - u_\alpha)^{-\gamma_\alpha}$ in the conventional polygonal mapping function (27·10).   In the form (19), the corresponding

[11] H. A. Schwarz, *Crelle's Jl.*, **70**, p. 105 (1869); also Bateman,[C1] p. 504.

[12] W. Grösser, *Arch. f. Elektrot.*, **25**, p. 211 (1931).

[13] J. Herlitz, referred to in L. Dreyfus, *Arch. f. Elektrot.*, **13**, p. 131 (1923).

change in direction of progression in the z-plane between $w < p$ and $w > q$ is $\gamma_\alpha\pi$, the same as produced by the normal vertex factor $(w - u_\alpha)^{-\gamma_\alpha}$; however, the change is now gradual rather than abrupt, and if λ is freely available for choice, can be made to approximate a circle rather closely. The locations p and q of the images of A and B have to be found by the correspondence of points in the z- and w-plane, as established by the mapping function. Instead of (19) one could also use the factor,

$$[w + \lambda\sqrt{w^2 - 1}]^{-\gamma_\alpha} \tag{20}$$

where the end points A, B of the circular arc are chosen at $w = \pm 1$.

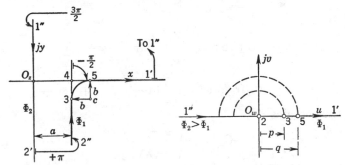

Fig. 28·7 Rounded Corner and Infinite Plane.

The solution for the rounded right-angle corner of Fig. 28·7 can be found by form (19) and this table:

α	1	2	3	5
Vertex locations	$1'\begin{cases}+\infty + j0 \\ 1'' \end{cases} \begin{cases} \\ 0 + j\infty\end{cases}$	$2'\begin{cases}0 - j\infty \\ 2''\end{cases}\begin{cases} \\ a - j\infty\end{cases}$	$a - jb$	$a + b$
$\gamma_\alpha\pi$	$+\dfrac{3\pi}{2}$	$+\pi$	$-\dfrac{\pi}{2}$	
γ_α	$+\dfrac{3}{2}$	$+1$	$-\dfrac{1}{2}$ ($\Sigma\gamma_\alpha = 2$)	
w_α	$\pm\infty$	0	p	q

The mapping function follows as

$$\frac{dz}{dw} = \frac{C_1}{w}[\sqrt{w - p} + \lambda\sqrt{w - q}] \tag{21}$$

where the factor $\sqrt{w - 1}$ of (27·42a) has been replaced by the form (19). Integration leads to the mapping function

$$z = 2C_1 \left\{ \sqrt{w-p} - \sqrt{p}\, \tan^{-1} \sqrt{\frac{w-p}{p}} \right.$$
$$\left. + \lambda \left[\sqrt{w-q} - \sqrt{q}\, \tan^{-1} \sqrt{\frac{w-q}{q}} \right] \right\} + C_2 \quad (22)$$

The constant C_1 can be determined by applying (27·17) to point 2, observing the equivalent definitions to establish one-valued branches of the functions,

$$\tan^{-1} \sqrt{\frac{w-p}{p}} = \frac{j}{2} \ln \frac{\sqrt{p} + \sqrt{p-w}}{\sqrt{p} - \sqrt{p-w}} = j \tanh^{-1} \sqrt{\frac{p-w}{p}} \quad (23)$$

so that

$$\text{for } w \to +0 \text{ (from right)}, \quad \frac{j}{2} \ln \frac{p}{w} \to +j\infty$$

$$\text{for } w \to -0 \text{ (from left)}, \quad \frac{j}{2} \ln \frac{p}{-|w|} \to +j\infty + \frac{\pi}{2}$$

One thus obtains

$$C_1 = \frac{a/\pi}{[\sqrt{p} + \lambda \sqrt{q}]} \quad (24)$$

At point z_3 one has $w = p$ and therefore

$$a - jb = 2j\lambda C_1 \left[\sqrt{q-p} - \sqrt{q}\, \tanh^{-1} \sqrt{\frac{q-p}{q}} \right] + C_2 \quad (25)$$

from where, since C_1 is real, one takes $C_2 = a$. At point z_4 one has $w = q$ and therefore

$$a + b = 2C_1 \left[\sqrt{q-p} - \sqrt{p}\, \tan^{-1} \sqrt{\frac{q-p}{p}} \right] + C_2 \quad (26)$$

The relations (25) and (26) connect p, q, and λ, so that one can either choose the location of a third point on the u-axis or select a value λ which gives the best approximation to a circular arc. Since the latter is rather difficult, one might choose

$$q - p = 1, \qquad q = 1 + p \quad (27)$$

since that simplifies (25) and (26) appreciably. Figure 28·8 gives the resultant values of p and λ as functions of b/a, the significant geometric ratio of radius of curvature b to distance of the parallel planes a. As b gets smaller, the value of p becomes large and thus approaches that of q, since for $b \to 0$ the case of the sharp corner should result, in which p and q merge. It is of interest

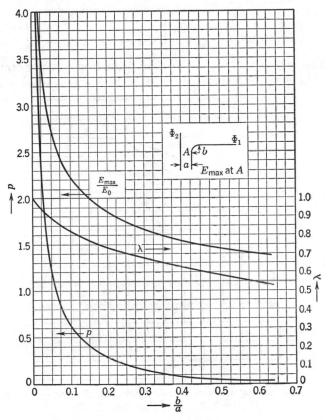

Fig. 28·8   Rounded Corner and Infinite Plate.

now to check the actual contour described by the mapping function (22). Figure 28·9 shows the contour for $b = a/8$ and a corresponding $\lambda = 0.787$; although not strictly circular, the deviation from the circular arc is nowhere larger than $0.1b$. A better approximation might be obtained by selecting by trial and error a specific value of λ for a given ratio b/a and leaving p and q to be determined from (25) and (26). This is, of course, a tedious process, since the entire computation must be repeated for each of the values of λ.

In the w-plane the complex potential solution is given by $(27 \cdot 26)$, so that the electric field strength follows from $(25 \cdot 7)$ with (21) and (24) as

$$E = -\overline{\left(\frac{dP}{dz}\right)} = -jE_0 \overline{\left[\frac{\sqrt{p} + \lambda\sqrt{q}}{\sqrt{w-p} + \lambda\sqrt{w-q}}\right]} \qquad (28)$$

Its value increases along the vertical plane from the uniform field $E_0 = (\Phi_2 - \Phi_1)/a$ somewhat below point 3 and reaches a maxi-

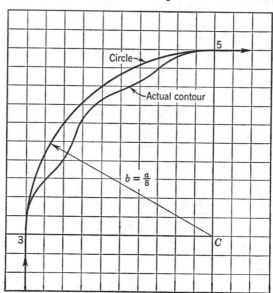

FIG. $28 \cdot 9$ Comparison between Actual Contour and Circular Arc; Geometry Fig. $28 \cdot 7$, Mapping Function $(28 \cdot 22)$.

mum value at point 3 where the circular arc begins; it then decreases again along the rounded corner but reaches E_0 only somewhere along the horizontal plane unless the radius $b > 0.38a$. The maximum value at $w = p$ follows from (28)

$$E_{\max} = E_0 \left[\frac{\sqrt{p}}{\lambda} + \sqrt{1+p}\right] \qquad (29)$$

It is plotted in Fig. $28 \cdot 8$ also as a function of b/a; in order to keep the maximum value to $2E_0$ or less, the radius of curvature must be at least $b \geqslant 0.15a$. The value of the field strength at point 5, the end point of the circular arc, follows with $w = q$ from (28) and is actually

$$|E|_{(5)} = \lambda \cdot E_{\max}$$

and is therefore larger than E_0 for $b \leqslant 0.38a$. Similar computations have been made to evaluate theoretically the electric breakdown between electrodes under oil.[14]

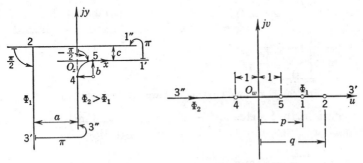

FIG. 28·10   Rounded Corner and Rectangular Corner.

For a rounded corner in a rectangular corner as in Fig. 28·10 the mapping function is found from

$$\frac{dz}{dw} = C_1 \frac{\sqrt{w + 1} + \lambda \sqrt{w - 1}}{(w - p)\sqrt{w - q}} \tag{30}$$

where again (19) was used to replace the vertex factor of the sharp corner. A complete discussion of the mapping for a value $\lambda = \sqrt{(q + 1)/(q - 1)}$, chosen because of most uniform distribution of the field strength over the arc, is given by Walker,[D10] p. 108; a graph shows also the actual contour, which is similar to Fig. 28·9.

Plane gratings with very large cylindrical wires can be treated by the same method.[15] Take one quarter of the periodic strips shown shaded in Fig. 28·11 as the mapping region; then the mapping derivative

$$\frac{dz}{dw} = C_1 \frac{(w + 1)^{\frac{1}{2}} + \lambda(w - 1)^{\frac{1}{2}}}{[(w + 1)(w - 1)(w + p)]^{\frac{1}{2}}} \tag{31}$$

---

[14] L. Dreyfus, *Arch. f. Elektrot.*, **13**, p. 131 (1923).

[15] Richmond, *Proc. London Math. Soc.*, Series 2, **22**, p. 389 (1923); also Smythe,[A22] p. 98.

transforms it into the upper half w-plane. Since the rounding only affects the corner 4 but leaves the right angles at points 3 and 5, the factors $(w + 1)$ and $(w - 1)$ appear twice, once for the existing right angles at 3 and 5 and the second time in additive

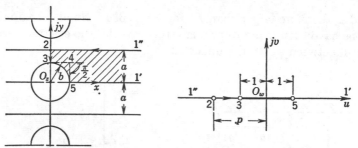

FIG. 28·11   Plane Grating of Large Cylindrical Wires.

combination to replace $(w - u_4)^{1/2}$ in accordance with (19). Separation of (31) into two terms and integration give

$$z = \frac{2a}{\pi(1 + \lambda)}\left[\tanh^{-1}\left(\frac{w - 1}{w + p}\right)^{1/2}\right.$$
$$\left. + \lambda \tanh^{-1}\left(\frac{w + 1}{w + p}\right)^{1/2}\right] \quad (32)$$

where $C_1 = \dfrac{a}{\pi(1 + \lambda)}$ was determined by applying (26·22) to point 1, and $C_2 = 0$ was found by correspondence of point z_2 and $w = -p$, observing

$$2 \tanh^{-1}\left(\frac{w \pm 1}{w + p}\right)^{1/2} = \ln\{(w \pm 1) + (w + p)$$
$$+ 2[(w \pm 1)(w + p)]^{1/2}\} - \ln(p \pm 1)$$

as the proper definition for one-valuedness. Having chosen the locations of three points in the w-plane, one must find the values of λ and p from the correspondence of the points 3 and 4. In this case, the deviation of the actual contour from the quarter circle is less than $0.02b$. The solution in the w-plane will depend on the stipulated boundary conditions; if the cylinders are all isolated and carry like potentials, then the contours $1''$–2–3 and 5–$1'$ are field lines and the solution in the w-plane is given by the complex potential function of a flat strip (27·38a). If the cylinders carry alternatingly positive and negative charges, then contours

2–3 and 5–1′ are field lines, contour 1″–2 is an equipotential line of zero potential, and the complex potential in the w-plane will be an elliptic integral which can be of the standard form (27·62) if a further transformation to the symmetrical arrangement of Fig. 27·13a is made.   Superposition of a uniform field and good graphs can be found in Richmond (*loc. cit.*).

Hydrodynamic Applications; the Hodograph.   With table 9·1 it is relatively simple to translate all Laplacian potential problems into solutions of hydrodynamic problems.   There are, however, problems which involve "free" surfaces, such as flow through various types of orifices with jet formation which cannot be treated as conventional boundary value problems.   In ideal fluids without effects of gravity, the Bernoulli equation[16] must hold along each stream line:

$$p + \tfrac{1}{2}\rho v^2 = \text{cons} \tag{33}$$

where p is the static pressure, ρ the mass density, and v the total velocity at any one point.   For a free surface it is assumed that pressure p is constant, usually atmospheric pressure, so that (33) also requires a constant velocity.   It is possible to solve two-dimensional flow problems involving free surfaces by means of conformal mapping of the velocity plane, or hodograph plane, rather than the actual geometry; see Lamb,[C22] p. 69; and Frank and Mises,[C6] II, p. 417; and Rothe et al.,[D8] p. 122.

Consider two planes P_1 and P_2 in Fig. 28·12 inclined towards each other with an angle $\beta\pi$ in the z-plane.   The ideal fluid issuing from the orifice AC will form a jet of unknown surface but with constant velocity v_0 on its surface.   If the complex potential solution $P = \Phi + j\Xi$ for the z-plane were known, the conjugate complex value of the velocity v could be found as

$$\bar{v} = \frac{dP}{dz} = v_x - jv_y \tag{34}$$

where the positive sign has been chosen for the potential gradient in accordance with prevailing custom in hydrodynamics.   If one now defines a new complex quantity

$$\zeta = \frac{1}{\bar{v}} = \frac{1}{|v|^2}(v_x + jv_y) \tag{35}$$

---

[16] For example Eshbach: *Handbook of Engineering Fundamentals*, p. 6-19; John Wiley, New York, 1936.

it will have the same direction but inverse value of the velocity at
each point in space, and a representation in the ζ-plane can at
least fix the boundaries of the hodograph map. Along the two
planes P_1 and P_2 the velocity will have the direction of the planes
and vary in value from v_0 at the orifice points A and C to value zero
at infinity on account of the divergence of the planes. Plotting
in the ζ-plane the locus of ζ, as defined in (35), gives the directions
OA and OC, with the points ζ_A and ζ_C of radial distance $1/v_0$ and
the infinite points corresponding to $|v| = 0$. The free surface of

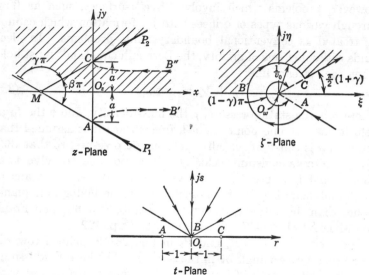

FIG. 28·12   Flow of Ideal Fluid through Orifice with Jet Formation.

the jet must then be represented by the circle $|\zeta| = 1/v_0$, the
infinitely distant point $B'B''$ of the z-plane corresponding to B
on the negative ξ-axis of the ζ-plane. The direction of the velocity
vector is towards 0 in the ζ-plane in accordance with flow from
infinity towards A and C.

Since all end points of ζ as representative of the velocity v lie
within the shaded area and its mirror image below the real axis,
one can find the solution for the velocity plane, or hodograph
plane, by conformal mapping. Thus, by the transformation
$\zeta' = \zeta^n$ one can change the angle $(1 - \gamma)\pi$ to π, i.e., compress or
expand into a half plane from which the interior of the circle $1/v_0$
is excluded.   The angle $\gamma\pi$ is in the conventional sense the change

in progression turning from plane P_1 to plane P_2 in the z-plane and is negative if in the clockwise sense; this gives $n = 1/(1 - \gamma)$. In order to have OC in the ζ-plane coincide with the positive ξ-axis, one must rotate the ζ-plane by $-(1 + \gamma)\dfrac{\pi}{2}$, and in order to make the semicircle of radius 1, one must multiply ζ by v_0, so that as better transformation one has

$$\zeta'' = \left[v_0 \zeta e^{-j(1+\gamma)\frac{\pi}{2}} \right]^n \tag{36}$$

This leads now to the upper half ζ''-plane with unit circle excluded. The further transformation $\zeta''' = \ln \zeta''$ gives, as shown in connection with $(26 \cdot 49)$ and in Fig. $26 \cdot 7$, a semi-infinite strip in the z'''-plane of width π. Finally, one can transform this strip into the complete upper half t-plane by

$$t = \cosh \zeta''' = \frac{1}{2} \left[\zeta'' + \frac{1}{\zeta''} \right] \tag{37}$$

In the t-plane the problem is that of a sink line located at B, the terminal of the free jet. The complex potential solution is, therefore, from table $25 \cdot 1$, line 1,

$$P = \Phi + j\Xi = -\frac{Q}{2\pi} \ln t \tag{38}$$

where Q is the total quantity of flow (per unit depth) taken positive. In particular, the free jet surface is given by the part of the real r-axis between (-1) and $(+1)$.

To transfer the solution (38) back into the z-plane it is necessary to integrate (34), which can be written with (35) to (37),

$$\frac{dz}{dP} = \frac{1}{\bar{v}} = \zeta = \frac{1}{v_0} e^{-j(1+\gamma)\frac{\pi}{2}} [t + \sqrt{t^2 - 1}]^{1/n} \tag{39}$$

Since from (38)

$$dP = -\frac{Q}{2\pi} \frac{dt}{t}, \qquad t = \exp\left(-2\pi \frac{P}{Q}\right) \tag{40}$$

one can integrate either with respect to P or with respect to t. The general integration cannot be performed, but several special cases have been evaluated.

Thus, one has for $\gamma = 0$ or $n = 1$ a slit in an infinite plate, the simplest type of orifice, and the integral becomes

$$z = jC_1 \int [1 + t^{-1}(t^2 - 1)^{1/2}] \, dt + C_2$$

$$= \begin{cases} jC_1 \left[t + \sqrt{t^2 - 1} - \cos^{-1} \left(\dfrac{1}{t} \right) \right] + C_2, & \text{for } |t| > 1 \quad (41a) \\ jC_1[t + j\sqrt{1 - t^2} + j\ln t - j\ln(1 + \sqrt{1 - t^2})] + C_2, \\ \qquad\qquad\qquad\qquad\qquad\qquad\qquad \text{for } |t| < 1 \quad (41b) \end{cases}$$

To assure one-valuedness, one has to observe carefully the sign of t. The value of $C_1 = Q/2\pi v_0$ follows from (40) and (39); the value of C_2 has to be determined from correspondence of points in z- and t-planes.   For

$$t = +1, \qquad z_C = jC_1(+1) + C_2$$
$$t = -1, \qquad z_A = jC_1(-1 - \pi) + C_2$$

so that, if one locates the origin of the z-plane as in Fig. $28 \cdot 12$ midway between A and C, the value of $C_2 = j(\pi/2)C_1$.   The asymptotic width of the jet is determined by

$$t = +0, \qquad z_B{}'' = \infty + C_2$$
$$t = -0, \qquad z_B{}' = \infty - j\pi C_1 + C_2$$

so that the contraction coefficient becomes

$$\frac{z_B{}'' - z_B{}'}{z_C - z_A} = \frac{\pi}{\pi + 2}$$

Good details of the solution with graphs are given in Lamb,[C22] p. 90, and Bewley,[D1] p. 146; see also Frank and Mises,[C6] II, p. 425.

For $\gamma = -1$ or $n = \frac{1}{2}$ one obtains the Borda mouthpiece, a long tube thrust deep into the fluid tank; good details are again found in Lamb,[C22] p. 88; Bewley,[D1] p. 143; and Frank and Mises,[C6] p. 424; see also Rothe *et al.*,[D8] p. 122.   Many other examples can be found in these references.

Since the general map of the hodograph in the ζ-plane upon the t-plane by (37) is independent of the original geometry in the z-plane, one can also study different types of complex potential solutions in the t-plane such as combination of source lines or vortex lines and transfer these back into the z-plane by means of

(39).   In this manner very interesting solutions for flow patterns in channels have been obtained by Migadzu.[17]   If a shift of the origin in the ζ-plane is made, curved profiles of channels result.

For electrical applications one might observe that the solutions describe the current distribution in thin conducting sheets; the free surface can be interpreted as a boundary along which constant current density is maintained.

29· TWO–DIMENSIONAL HARMONIC FUNCTION SYSTEMS

Though two-dimensional Laplacian potential problems can formally always be solved by conformal mapping and reduction to standard boundary value problems for the unit circle as indicated in section 28, the practical difficulties become rather great when the boundary conditions involve potential values that vary along the boundary (still a first boundary value problem), or involve potential values as well as conditions upon the field vector (mixed boundary value problems).   In these latter problems it is frequently simpler to express the solutions in terms of infinite series of "orthogonal" functions generated by the differential equations for the particular type of coordinate system best suited for the problem.   The first step will always be a separation of the two variables, say, u, v, and consequent reduction of the partial differential equation to two ordinary differential equations in u and v, respectively; practically any of the references in Appendix 4, C, a, describes the method and gives illustrations which will be presented here in connection with the individual coordinate systems.

Each of the ordinary differential equations will be of the second order and, if u is one of the general variables, will have the form

$$f''(u) + \eta_1(u)f'(u) + [\eta_2(u) + \lambda\eta_3(u)]f(u) = 0 \qquad (1)$$

where η_1, η_2, and η_3 are factors arising from the general coordinate relations and where λ is an unknown constant appearing in the process of separation of variables (see the later examples); the derivatives are designated by the primes.   Actually, one can rewrite (1) by multiplying through with $w(u) = \exp\left(\displaystyle\int \eta_1(u)\,du\right)$

---

[17] A. Migadzu, *Technology Report of Tohoku Imperial Univ.*, Sendai, Japan, **10**, No. 4, p. 51 (1932).

and combining the first two terms more conveniently as

$$\mathsf{L}f(u) = \frac{d}{du}\left[w(u)\,\frac{d}{du}f(u)\right] + [q(u) + \lambda p(u)]f(u) = 0 \quad (2)$$

Any solution of this equation has to satisfy boundary conditions at the extreme values a and b which u takes on within the region of the stated problem. Assuming *homogeneous*[1] boundary conditions such that

$$\left.\begin{array}{ll} \text{at } u = a, & a_1 f(a) + a_2 f'(a) = 0 \\ \text{at } u = b, & b_1 f(b) + b_2 f'(b) = 0 \end{array}\right\} \quad (3)$$

then these cover all possible types of homogeneous boundary value problems of the first kind (with $a_2 = b_2 = 0$), of the second kind (with $a_1 = b_1 = 0$), and of the third kind (with none of the coefficients zero); see Kellogg,[C10] pp. 236, 246, 314.

In general, the satisfaction of the homogeneous boundary conditions is possible only for selected values of the parameter λ, the *characteristic numbers* (or eigen values) λ_α leading to the *characteristic functions* (or eigen functions)[2] $\phi_\alpha(u)$. There exists, however, usually an infinite sequence of values λ_α, a *discrete spectrum*, and since an equation of the type (2) has to be solved for the second coordinate v, there will also be an infinite number of corresponding functions $\psi_\alpha(v)$. Each product $\phi_\alpha(u)\psi_\alpha(v)$ represents a solution of the Laplacian differential equation and therefore a harmonic function (see section 2), so that the general solution of the potential appears in the form

$$\Phi = \sum_{\alpha=1}^{\infty} A_\alpha \phi_\alpha(u)\,\psi_\alpha(v) \quad (4)$$

where the coefficients A_α have to be determined from the additional boundary conditions pertaining to the boundaries $v = c$ and $v = d$.

The homogeneous differential equation (2), together with the homogeneous boundary conditions (3), is called a Sturm-Liouville

---

[1] Homogeneous boundary conditions are defined in the same manner as homogeneous linear differential equations, i.e., each term is linear in the unknown function or one of its derivatives.

[2] A tabulation of the less usual function systems, associated differential equations, and characteristic numbers is given in E. Madelung: *Die Mathematischen Hilfsmittel des Physikers;* reprinted by Dover Publications, New York, 1943.

problem in honor of the original investigators, and it leads to a function system $\phi_\alpha(u)$ which is *orthogonal*, as can be demonstrated quite readily. Introducing into (2) successively two of the characteristic functions ϕ_α and ϕ_β for $f(u)$ and forming the difference of the products

$$\phi_\alpha \cdot \mathsf{L}\phi_\beta - \phi_\beta \cdot \mathsf{L}\phi_\alpha = 0$$

one can separate this with the complete right-hand sides of (2) into

$$(\lambda_\alpha - \lambda_\beta) p(u)\, \phi_\alpha \phi_\beta = \frac{d}{du}\left[w\phi_\alpha' \phi_\beta - w\phi_\beta' \phi_\alpha\right] \tag{5}$$

Integration in the boundary limits a and b of the variable u gives on the right-hand side of (5)

$$w(b)[\phi_\alpha'(b)\phi_\beta(b) - \phi_\beta'(b)\phi_\alpha(b)]$$
$$- w(a)[\phi_\alpha'(a)\phi_\beta(a) - \phi_\beta'(a)\phi_\alpha(a)] = 0$$

which vanishes if one substitutes for ϕ_α' and ϕ_β' the values resulting from (3). Thus, since $\lambda_\alpha \neq \lambda_\beta$, the integral on the left-hand side of (5) must vanish

$$\int_{u=a}^{u=b} p(u)\phi_\alpha(u)\phi_\beta(u)\, du = 0, \qquad \alpha \neq \beta \tag{6}$$

which constitutes the *condition of orthogonality of the function system* $\phi_\alpha(u)$ with $p(u)$ as *weight function*. One could, of course, define a different function system

$$h_\alpha(u) = \sqrt{p(u)}\, \phi_\alpha(u) \tag{7}$$

in which case the weight function is absorbed in $h_\alpha(u)$, and (6) reduces to

$$\int_{u=a}^{u=b} h_\alpha(u)h_\beta(u)\, du = 0, \qquad \alpha \neq \beta \tag{8}$$

The value of the integrals (6) or (8) for $\alpha = \beta$, namely,

$$\int_{u=a}^{u=b} p(u)\phi_\alpha{}^2(u)\, du = \int_{u=a}^{u=b} h_\alpha{}^2(u)\, du = N_\alpha \tag{9}$$

is a constant depending on α and called the *norm* of the function system. If one uses the modified functions

$$\frac{\phi_\alpha(u)}{\sqrt{N_\alpha}} \quad \text{or} \quad \frac{h_\alpha(u)}{\sqrt{N_\alpha}} \tag{10}$$

the integral (9) takes unit value; the functions (10) form then an *orthonormal* system: they are *normalized*. The latter modification is, of course, not necessary, but it can result in simplification. Good treatments of orthonormal function systems and their applications to boundary value problems are found[3] in Webster,[C16] in Byerly,[C2] in Courant and Hilbert,[C4] in Bateman,[C1] in Churchill,[C3] in Murnaghan.[C13] The advantage of orthonormal function systems is the fact that any reasonable function $G(u)$ can be represented within the interval $a \leqslant u \leqslant b$ uniquely in terms of a *generalized Fourier series*

$$G(u) = \sum_{\alpha=1}^{\infty} c_\alpha \phi_\alpha(u) = \sum_{\alpha=1}^{\infty} C_\alpha h_\alpha(u) \tag{11}$$

where

$$N_\alpha c_\alpha = \int_{u=a}^{u=b} G(u)\phi_\alpha(u)p(u)\,du;$$

$$N_\alpha C_\alpha = \int_{u=a}^{u=b} G(u)h_\alpha(u)\,du \tag{12}$$

with the assurance that everywhere in this interval the series converges towards $G(u)$, and that any first n coefficients represent the best approximation in the mean to $G(u)$ in the sense of least squares. One can also show that any such orthonormal function system is complete, i.e., that there is no function for which all coefficients vanish and which is yet different from zero. Finally, evaluating the deviation integrals for $\phi_\alpha(u)$ and $h_\alpha(u)$,

$$\int_{u=a}^{u=b} p(u)\left[G(u) - \sum_{\alpha=1}^{n} c_\alpha \phi_\alpha(u)\right]^2 du;$$

$$\int_{u=a}^{u=b} \left[G(u) - \sum_{\alpha=1}^{n} C_\alpha h_\alpha(u)\right]^2 du \tag{13}$$

with the aid of (6), (8), and (12), and letting $n \to \infty$, one obtains

---

[3] See also L. Bieberbach: *Theorie der Differentialgleichungen;* Dover Publications, New York, 1944; originally J. Springer, Berlin, 1930; E. L. Ince: *Ordinary Differential Equations*, Dover Publications, New York, 1944.

the *Parseval* theorem

$$\sum_{\alpha=1}^{\infty} N_\alpha c_\alpha{}^2 = \int_{u=a}^{u=b} p(u)[G(u)]^2 \, du;$$

$$\sum_{\alpha=1}^{\infty} N_\alpha C_\alpha{}^2 = \int_{u=a}^{u=b} [G(u)]^2 \, du \quad (14)$$

Returning now to the general solution (4) of the Laplacian potential problem, one can demonstrate that this infinite series of harmonic functions represents a convergent solution if one can apply to the function series $\psi_\alpha(v)$ the same argument as that just presented for the function series $\phi_\alpha(u)$. The actual demonstration for problems of direct physical significance is relatively simple, since one can restrict arguments to essentially analytic functions with only isolated singularities as pointed out in section 27. For details of existence and convergence proofs see Kellogg,[C10] Chapter X; Courant and Hilbert,[C4] Vol. II; Frank and Mises,[C6] Vol. I; and Evans.[C5]

Fourier Series in Cartesian Coordinates. In the Laplacian differential equation

$$\frac{\partial^2 \Phi}{\partial x^2} + \frac{\partial^2 \Phi}{\partial y^2} = 0 \quad (15)$$

the variables can be separated by defining $\Phi(x, y) = X(x)Y(y)$ as a product of functions of only one variable each, since (15) becomes

$$X''Y + XY'' = 0 \quad \text{or} \quad \frac{X''}{X} = -\frac{Y''}{Y} \quad (16)$$

Since in the last form the left-hand side can depend only on x and the right-hand side only on y for any combination of x and y whatsoever, none can contain the variable but must be a constant, say, m^2, so that

$$\frac{d^2X}{dx^2} + m^2X = 0, \qquad \frac{d^2Y}{dy^2} - m^2Y = 0 \quad (17)$$

For the function $X(x)$, comparison with (2) shows $w = 1$, $q = 0$, $p = 1$, $\lambda = m^2$. The obvious solutions are sin mx, cos mx; for $Y(y)$ the functions sinh my, cosh my are solutions, so that the harmonic function

$$XY = (C_1 \sin mx + C_2 \cos mx)(D_1 \sinh my + D_2 \cosh my) \quad (18)$$

as well as any sum of these products will satisfy (15). The selection of the spectrum of m-values is, however, possible only by specifying the boundary conditions. Since (15) contains only the second derivatives, it is always possible to add terms of the type $(k_1 + k_2 x + k_3 y)$ if required by the conditions of the problem.

Consider the rectangular region $0 \leqslant x \leqslant a$, $0 \leqslant y \leqslant b$ shown in Fig. 29·1a with potential values as indicated there. For the variable x both boundary conditions are homogeneous, of the type (3), requiring in (18)

$$X(0) = X(a) = 0 \qquad (19a)$$

Along $x = 0$ only $\sin mx$ vanishes, so that $C_2 = 0$; along $x = a$ it requires

$$\sin ma = 0, \qquad m = \frac{\alpha \pi}{a}, \qquad \alpha = \pm 1, \pm 2, \cdots \qquad (19b)$$

Thus, the conventional *Fourier sine series constitutes the natural orthogonal function system for Cartesian coordinates in finite regions,* with unity weight function, characteristic numbers $m_\alpha{}^2 = \lambda_\alpha$, and a norm from (9)

$$N_\alpha = \int_{x=0}^{x=a} \sin^2 \left(\frac{\alpha \pi}{a} x \right) dx = \frac{a}{2} \qquad (20)$$

which is in this case not dependent on the order number α. It is generally not customary to normalize this Fourier series; if desirable, it can be done by using amplitude factors $\sqrt{2/a}$. Since m is known by (19), the one homogeneous boundary condition $y(b) = 0$ leads in (18) to

$$D_{\alpha 1} \sinh m_\alpha b + D_{\alpha 2} \cosh m_\alpha b = 0, \qquad \frac{D_{\alpha 1}}{D_{\alpha 2}} = -\coth m_\alpha b$$

so that the potential solution takes the form in accordance with (4)

$$\Phi(x, y) = \sum_{\alpha=1}^{\infty} A_\alpha \sin \left(\alpha \pi \frac{x}{a} \right) \frac{\sinh \alpha \pi \, (b - y)/a}{\sinh \alpha \pi \, b/a} \qquad (21)$$

where the coefficients $C_{\alpha 1}$ and $D_{\alpha 2}$ have been merged into A_α and the negative values of α have been suppressed, since they leave the function unchanged except for sign. The final boundary condition requires

$$\Phi(x, 0) = \sum_{\alpha=1}^{\infty} A_\alpha \sin \alpha\pi \frac{x}{a} \equiv G(x) \tag{22}$$

or, essentially, that the A_α be the regular coefficients of a Fourier *sine* series representing the given function $G(x)$ in the interval $0 \leqslant x \leqslant a$, or

$$A_\alpha = \frac{2}{a} \int_{x=0}^{x=a} G(x) \sin \alpha\pi \frac{x}{a} \, dx \tag{22a}$$

in accordance with (12) and (20). This, of course, requires that $G(x)$ can be so expanded, demonstrating that this boundary value

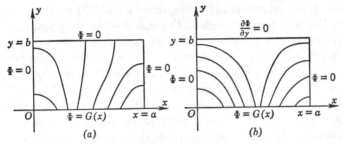

Fig. 29·1 Potential Solution in a Rectangle.

problem can be solved in all cases where $G(x)$ permits representation in terms of a Fourier sine series. This problem is used by Churchill,[C3] p. 137, to illustrate the proof of uniqueness of the solution; as a heat flow problem with the identical boundary conditions in temperature it is also solved by Churchill,[C3] p. 114, and by Byerly,[C2] p. 102.

Though this problem appears to be a rather special one because of the simple boundary conditions, any arbitrary potential distribution for example along $x = a$ can be treated in the same manner, namely, assuming $\Phi(a, y) = H(y)$ and $\Phi = 0$ on all other sides; the solution for simultaneously assuming this condition and $G(x)$ along $y = 0$ is simply the sum of the two independently found solutions according to the *principle of superposition* valid for all linear problems.

Changing the boundary conditions to the mixed kind of Fig. 29·1b leaves the solution $X(x)$ with the identical conditions (19a) and with the same series of characteristic numbers (19b). The boundary condition on $y = b$ is again homogeneous but of type $Y'(b) = 0$, so that with (18)

$$m_\alpha D_{\alpha1} \cosh m_\alpha b + m_\alpha D_{\alpha2} \sinh m_\alpha b = 0, \quad \frac{D_{\alpha1}}{D_{\alpha2}} = -\tanh m_\alpha b$$

and the potential solution becomes

$$\Phi(x, y) = \sum_{\alpha=1}^{\infty} A_\alpha \sin\left(\alpha\pi \frac{x}{a}\right) \frac{\cosh \alpha\pi (b - y)/a}{\cosh \alpha\pi b/a} \tag{23}$$

At $y = 0$ the same boundary condition as in (22) results. Physically, Fig. 29·1b can represent the stator of an electrical machine developed into a plane structure of height b, with pole pitch a and neutral zones at $x = 0$ and $x = a$ if $G(x)$ is a symmetrical distribution of the magnetostatic potential $\mathcal{F}$ along the air gap. Again, the principle of superposition can be applied in order to satisfy more complicated boundary conditions. Thus Zworykin,[C32] p. 369, applies this solution to a plane section of the electron multiplier, with one constant potential on two joining sides of the rectangle, and with a different potential on the other pair of joining sides.

It is, of course, also possible to join several regions, within each of which the potential solution has been found in general terms, by assuring continuity of the electric potential values (or the tangential components of **E**) and the normal components of **D** across the boundaries. In two-dimensional magnetic problems, the magnetic vector potential reduces to a single component parallel to the current flow (see section 6) and in the Cartesian system satisfies the Laplacian equation in regions free of current and the Poisson differential equation in regions with current flow. In the latter case, for uniform current density, the solution will be the sum of the Laplacian solution and of a particular integral which normally can be obtained by inspection. At the boundaries it is then required that the conditions (6·20) or (6·7) and (6·10) be satisfied. Many applications to rectangular current regions have been made in connection with leakage computations on transformer windings,[4] on conductors in slots of electrical machines,[5] and on pole windings located in the interpole space.[6]

Figure $29 \cdot 1a$ can also represent cooling of a fin with fixed temperature T_0 along $y = 0$ and the boundary conditions

$$k \frac{\partial T}{\partial n} + fT = 0 \tag{24}$$

along $x = 0$, $x = a$, and $y = b$, if n is the normal direction on any of these surfaces, k the thermal conductivity, and f the heat transfer coefficient for unit area.   Actually, because of symmetry, one can state $\partial T / \partial x = 0$ at $x = a/2$ as a more convenient boundary condition replacing (24) at $x = a$.   Take again the general form (18); the conditions which $X(x)$ must satisfy are

$$\text{at } x = 0, \qquad kX'(0) + fX(0) = 0 = mkC_1 + fC_2$$

$$\text{at } x = \frac{a}{2}, \qquad X'\left(\frac{a}{2}\right) = 0 = C_1 \cos m \frac{a}{2} - C_2 \sin m \frac{a}{2}$$

from which

$$C_2 = -mC_1 \frac{k}{f}, \qquad \tan m \frac{a}{2} = -\frac{f}{mk} \tag{25}$$

The second relation defines the characteristic numbers m_α as solutions of a transcendental equation, which is obtained best by graphical construction, finding the intersections of a *tangent* graph with the hyperbola on the right-hand side of $\tan q = -(af/2kq)$. With (25) one has then

$$X_\alpha(x) = C_{\alpha 1}\left(\sin m_\alpha x + \cot m_\alpha \frac{a}{2} \cos m_\alpha x\right)$$

$$= C_{\alpha\mathrm{r}} \frac{\cos m_\alpha(x - a/2)}{\sin m_\alpha\, a/2} \tag{26}$$

In spite of the fact that the m_α values are not harmonically related as in the conventional Fourier series, the function system (26) is orthogonal, as can be shown by applying either (C) with unit

[4] W. Rogowski, *Mitt. Forsch. V.D.I.*, No. 71 (1909); Bewley,[D1] p. 73; E. Roth, *Revue gén. de l'élec.*, **23**, p. 773 (1928); E. Roth and G. Kouskoff, *Revue gén. de l'élec.*, **23**, p. 1061 (1928); Hague,[B44] p. 302.

[5] E. Roth, *Revue gén. de l'élec.*, **22**, p. 417 (1927) and **24**, pp. 137 and 179 (1928); Bewley,[D1] p. 81; Hague,[B44] p. 314.

[6] A. R. Stevenson and R. H. Park, *Gen. Elec. Rev.*, **31**, p. 101 (1928); Hague,[B44] p. 310.

weight function, or (8), and by observing the second relation (25) in the result; one has

$$
\int_{x=0}^{x=a} \cos m \left(x - \frac{a}{2} \right) \cos n \left(x - \frac{a}{2} \right) dx
$$

$$
= \left\{ \begin{array}{l} 0 \quad \text{for } n \neq m \\ \dfrac{a}{2} \left(1 + \dfrac{\sin ma}{ma} \right) = N_\alpha \quad \text{for } n = m \end{array} \right\} \quad (27)
$$

where n and m are two values of m_α. The homogeneous condition (24) at $y = b$ gives the result

$$
kY'(b) + fY(b) = D_1(mk \cosh mb + f \sinh mb)
$$
$$
+ D_2(mk \sinh mb + f \cosh mb) = 0
$$

from which the ratio D_1/D_2 is found. The temperature at $y = 0$ is then subject to the final boundary condition

$$
T(x, 0) = \sum_{\alpha=0}^{\infty} A_\alpha \frac{\cos m_\alpha(x - a/2)}{\sin m_\alpha a/2} = T_0
$$

where $A_\alpha = C_{\alpha 1} D_{\alpha 2}$ as before. The expansion of T_0 into the non-conventional Fourier series follows exactly (12), so that

$$
A_\alpha = \frac{2T_0}{m_\alpha N_\alpha} \cdot \sin^2 m_\alpha \frac{a}{2}
$$

The final form of the temperature distribution[7] is

$$
T(x, y) = 4T_0 \sum_{\alpha=1}^{\infty} \frac{m_\alpha k \cosh m_\alpha(b - y) + f \sinh m_\alpha(b - y)}{m_\alpha k \cosh m_\alpha b + f \sinh m_\alpha b} \cdot
$$
$$
\frac{\sin m_\alpha a/2 \cos m_\alpha(x - a/2)}{m_\alpha a + \sin m_\alpha a} \quad (28)
$$

On account of the boundary conditions (24), this problem could not be solved by conformal mapping in any simpler manner.

As the height of the rectangle $b \to \infty$ in Fig. 29·1a, $D_1/D_2 \to (-1)$, so that the solution (21) goes over into

$$
\Phi(x, y) = \sum_{\alpha=1}^{\infty} A_\alpha e^{-\alpha \pi y/a} \sin \alpha \pi \frac{x}{a} \quad (29)
$$

This form of solution has been used[8] to compute the magnetic

---

[7] Bateman,[Cl] p. 213, where cosh $(s_m y)$ is a misprint of cos $(s_m y)$ in the final solution.

[8] R. Rüdenberg, *E.T.Z.*, **27**, p. 109 (1906); also Ollendorff,[A13] pp. 227, 235.

field distribution in armatures of infinite height, joining the magnetostatic potential at $y = 0$ to that of the air gap along which single- or multiphase current layers are assumed distributed.   The needed excitation can be found, as well as a theoretical shape of the pole form in synchronous machines.   Similarly can be evaluated the leakage field distribution surrounding transformer coils[9] or extending into the transformer core.

Fourier Integral in Cartesian Coordinates.   If, in Fig. $29 \cdot 1a$, the length of the rectangle $a \to \infty$, it affects the characteristic numbers; indeed, if the semi-infinite strip is considered, $X(0) = 0$ still insures $C_2 = 0$ in (18), but no other condition is available, since $\sin mx$ remains finite for $x \to \infty$.   The homogeneous condition $Y(b) = 0$ gives from (18)

$$\frac{D_1}{D_2} = - \coth mb$$

so that the product (18) becomes, with $C_1 D_2$ replaced by A,

$$XY = A \sin mx \frac{\sinh m(b - y)}{\sin mb} \tag{30}$$

Here, *any value of m is possible;* instead of a discrete spectrum of characteristic numbers one has now a *continuous spectrum.*   The boundary condition along $y = 0$ requires thus the representation of $G(x)$ over the infinite interval $0 \leqslant x \leqslant \infty$ in terms of $\sin mx$ which is possible with uniqueness by means of the *Fourier integral*[10] if $G(x)$ is bounded, at least sectionally continuous, and if

$$\int_{-\infty}^{+\infty} |G(x)| dx$$

exists.   Thus

$$\Phi(x, 0) = G(x) = \int_{m=0}^{\infty} [U(m) \sin mx + W(m) \cos mx] dm \tag{31}$$

---

[9] W. Rogowski, *Mitt. Forsch. V.D.I.,* No. 71 (1909); Ollendorff,[A18] p. 257; A. R. Stevenson, *Gen. Elec. Rev.,* **29,** p. 797 (1926); Bewley,[D1] p. 73.

[10] For details see particularly H. B. Carslaw: *Introduction to the Theory of Fourier Series and Integrals;* Macmillan, London, 1921; E. T. Whittaker and G. N. Watson: *Modern Analysis;* Cambridge University Press, 1935; N. Wiener: *The Fourier Integral and Certain of its Applications;* Cambridge University Press, 1933; E. C. Titchmarsh: *Introduction to the Theory of Fourier Integrals;* Oxford University Press, 1937.   For simpler accounts refer to almost any book in Appendix 4, C, a.

where the coefficient functions $U(m)$ and $W(m)$ are given in turn by the relations

$$U(m) = \frac{1}{\pi} \int_{x=-\infty}^{\infty} G(x) \sin mx \, dx,$$

$$W(m) = \frac{1}{\pi} \int_{x=-\infty}^{\infty} G(x) \cos mx \, dx \quad (32)$$

quite analogous to the Fourier series (22) and just a special case of the orthogonal function systems (11) and (12). In particular, $U(m)$ is the Fourier coefficient of an odd function in x, and $W(m)$ that of an even function in x, and, in turn, $U(m)$ itself is an odd function in m and $W(m)$ an even function. The particular form (30) implies an odd function of x with $W(m) = 0$ which might as well be assumed, since $x < 0$ is outside the region of the problem. Comparison of (30) for $y = 0$ with (31) shows because of the uniqueness that $A = U(m)$, and that the complete solution for the potential function as the most general superposition of all possible solutions must have the form

$$\Phi(x, y) = \int_{m=0}^{\infty} U(m) \sin mx \, \frac{\sinh m(b - y)}{\sinh mb} \, dm \quad (33)$$

with $U(m)$ from (32). The direct evaluation of this integral might be possible if $U(m)$ is actually known. One might also introduce (32) with a change of variable to x' directly into (33) and interchange the order of integration

$$\Phi(x, y) = \frac{2}{\pi} \int_{x'=0}^{\infty} G(x') \, dx' \int_{m=0}^{\infty} \sin mx \sin mx' \, \frac{\sinh m(b - y)}{\sinh mb} \, dm$$

Here the lower limit in x' has been replaced by zero, and a factor 2 applied because of the assumed odd character of $G(x')$. The inner integral can then be written in the form (see Byerly,[C2] p. 80, etc.).

$$\int_{m=0}^{\infty} \frac{\sinh q_1 m}{\sinh q_2 m} \cos q_3 \, m \, dm =$$

$$\frac{\pi}{2q_2} \frac{\sin (\pi q_1/q_2)}{\cosh (\pi q_3/q_2) + \cos (\pi q_1/q_2)} \quad (34)$$

where $q_1 = b - y$, $q_2 = b$, $q_3 = (x \pm x')$. This yields for the potential

$$\Phi(x, y) = \frac{1}{2b} \sin \frac{\pi y}{b} \int_{x'=-\infty}^{\infty} \frac{G(x') \, dx'}{\cosh \pi(x - x')/b - \cos \pi y/b} \quad (35)$$

where the original two terms were contracted into one on the basis that $G(x')$ is assumed odd.   Neither (33) nor (34) is generally of great practical value; both constitute formal solutions which are amenable to numerical or machine computations.   A number of examples are found in Byerly[C2]; some of them can be handled more simply by conformal mapping (section 26).

For practical applications, it is advantageous to use the complex form of the Fourier integral relationships

$$G(x) = \frac{1}{2\pi} \int_{m=-\infty}^{+\infty} F(m) \, e^{jmx} \, dm \qquad (36)$$

where the coefficient function

$$F(m) = \int_{x=-\infty}^{x=+\infty} G(x) \, e^{-jmx} \, dx \qquad (36a)$$

is definitely complex.   Actually, since $G(x)$ is a real function, one can expand e^{jmx} in (36a) and compare this relation with (32)

$$F(m) = \int_{-\infty}^{+\infty} G(x) \cos mx \, dx - j \int_{-\infty}^{+\infty} G(x) \sin mx \, dx$$
$$= \pi[W(m) - jU(m)] \qquad (37)$$

finding $F(m)$ simply a complex combination of the real Fourier coefficients.   Introducing this expression for $F(m)$ into (36) gives as real part directly (31); the imaginary parts $[W(m) \sin mx - U(m) \cos mx]$ vanish when integrated in the limits $(-\infty)$ to $(+\infty)$ because both of these are odd functions of m, as apparent from (31) and (32).   The form (37) also indicates that the real part of $F(m)$ must be an even function of m and the imaginary part an odd function, so that one can furthermore state: the absolute value $|F(m)|$ is always an even function of m, and the argument $\tan^{-1}[\operatorname{Im} F(m)/\operatorname{Re} F(m)]$ is always an odd function of m.

The complex form of the Fourier integral has the advantage that extensive tables[11] are available listing the dual Fourier integral

---

[11] Particularly G. A. Campbell and R. M. Foster: *Fourier Integrals for Practical Applications;* D. Van Nostrand, New York, 1947; first published as Monograph B-584, Bell Telephone Laboratories, New York, 1931.   These tables will be referred to as C.-F. tables.

coefficients in corresponding columns. From (36a) it is obvious that $F(m)$ will actually be a function of jm, since this is the only parameter in the integrand; the C.-F. tables (abbreviation for reference, *loc. cit.*) introduce therefore $jm = p$ as a new variable and list $F(m)$ as a function of p. In fact, the evaluation of most of the integrals (36) is simplified by completely changing to the variable p, thus

$$G(x) = \frac{1}{2\pi j} \int_{-j\infty}^{+j\infty} F(p) \, e^{px} \, dp \qquad (38)$$

In this form, the integral can be treated either as that of a real variable along the imaginary axis or, by considering p as a complex variable, as an integral in the complex p-plane. The latter interpretation leads directly into the theory of analytic functions and permits extensive use of the Cauchy integral theorem (26·14).

Assume that $F(p)$ is analytic in the entire p-plane except at a finite or possibly countably infinite[12] number of points where it has poles of the first order; then it can be represented as a finite or infinite sum of linear fractions

$$F(p) = \sum \frac{R_\alpha}{p - p_\alpha} \qquad (39)$$

where the p_α are the locations of the poles. The basis of this expansion is Gauss's fundamental theorem of algebra if $F(p)$ is a rational fraction,[13] or Weierstrass' product representation of trigonometric and hyperbolic functions; see any of the references, Appendix 4, D, b. The values R_α can be obtained either by direct comparison of coefficients on both sides of (39), or usually in simpler form by writing $F(p)$ as a proper fraction of positive power functions $N(p)/D(p)$ and then[14]

$$R_\alpha = \left[\frac{N(p)}{\dfrac{d}{dp} D(p)} \right]_{p = p_\alpha} \qquad (40)$$

[12] A series of points spaced at definite, known finite intervals, even though infinite in number, is called countably infinite.

[13] See any college textbook on algebra.

[14] See any book on Laplace transforms; for example M. F. Gardner and J. L. Barnes: *Transients in Linear Systems;* John Wiley, New York, 1942, Vol. I, p. 155.

Under the assumed conditions the value of the integral (38) can be shown to remain unchanged if the path is closed over the right-hand infinitely large semicircle (with reversed direction) for $x < 0$, and over the left infinitely large semicircle for $x > 0$; each of these closed integrals can further be contracted into very small circles surrounding each pole as in (26·13), and the result is a *sum of residues* (with proper sign) of the type (26·14), namely, the value of the integrand in (38) exclusive of the root factor $(p - p_\alpha)$ taken at $p = p_\alpha$; or with (39) and (40)

$$G(x) = \sum R_\alpha e^{p_\alpha x} = \sum \left(\frac{N(p)}{\frac{d}{dp} D(p)} e^{px} \right)_{p=p_\alpha} \tag{41}$$

If $F(p)$ possesses poles of order higher than the first, the modifications are those leading to the forms (26·15) at each such pole.

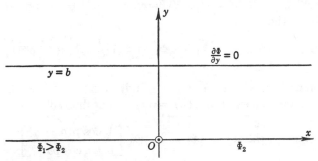

FIG. 29·2   Potential Solution in Infinite Strip.

As an example consider Fig. 29·2, with two potentials along the x-axis separated by an infinitesimal gap at the origin, and with $\partial\Phi/\partial y = 0$ on $y = b$. The basic solution of the Laplacian differential equation is (18), and therefore on $y = b$

$$Y'(b) = 0 = mD_1 \cosh mb + mD_2 \sinh mb, \qquad \frac{D_1}{D_2} = -\tanh mb$$

This gives the product solution

$$XY = A(m)e^{jmx} \frac{\cosh m(b - y)}{\cosh mb}$$

where the x-variation is assumed in the complex form in anticipation of the use of integral (36). Since $\cosh mb = \cos jmb = \cos pb$, one can readily write the potential function as a Fourier integral in the form of (38),

$$\Phi(x, y) = \frac{1}{2\pi j} \int_{-j\infty}^{+j\infty} A(p) \frac{\cos p(b - y)}{\cos pb} e^{px} \, dp \qquad (42)$$

In order to determine $A(p)$ one must compare $\Phi(x, 0)$ with the given boundary values. In turn, this requires a representation of the potential distribution along $x = 0$ as a Fourier integral. One can, of course, always add Φ_1 as a general constant and define the potential as zero along $x < 0$, as abrupt step of value $-(\Phi_1 - \Phi_2)$ at $x = 0$, and constant at this value for $x > 0$. Thus

$$G(x) = \Phi_1 - (\Phi_1 - \Phi_2) S_{-1}(x) \qquad (43)$$

where $S_{-1}(x)$ is the unit step of the C.-F. tables in pair 415 with the coefficient $F(p) = 1/p$. Therefore, at $y = 0$, the potential must have the form

$$G(x) \equiv \Phi(x, 0) = \Phi_1 - (\Phi_1 - \Phi_2) \frac{1}{2\pi j} \int_{-j\infty}^{+j\infty} \frac{1}{p} e^{px} \, dp$$

and comparison with (42) at $y = 0$ indicates the need of the additive constant Φ_1 as well as $A(p) = 1/p$. The final solution is, then,

$$\Phi(x, y) = \Phi_1 - (\Phi_1 - \Phi_2) \mathfrak{M} \left[\frac{1}{p} \frac{\cos p(b - y)}{\cos pb} \right] \qquad (44)$$

using the symbol $\mathfrak{M}$ or "mate" for the cumbersome integral notation. The Fourier "mate" can fortunately be found in C.-F. tables as pair 618, giving

$$\Phi(x, y) = G(x) + \frac{\Phi_1 - \Phi_2}{\pi} \tan^{-1} \left[\frac{\sin(\pi y/2b)}{\sinh(\pi x/2b)} \right] \qquad (45)$$

in closed form with $G(x)$ from (43). One easily verifies this as complete solution satisfying all boundary conditions. The C.-F. tables contain several similar forms in table II, section 2.

If the potential distribution along the x-axis is given as Φ_1 for $x < 0$ and $\Phi_1 e^{-\gamma x}$ for $x > 0$, then one can write

$$G(x) = \Phi_1 - (1 - e^{-\gamma x})\Phi_1 S_{-1}(x) = \Phi_1 - \gamma \Phi_1 \mathfrak{M} \left(\frac{1}{p(p + \gamma)} \right)$$

using coefficient pair 448 of the C.-F. tables. The potential solution becomes now

$$\Phi(x, y) = \Phi_1 - \gamma\Phi_1\mathfrak{M}\left[\frac{1}{p(p + \gamma)} \cdot \frac{\cos p(b - y)}{\cos pb}\right]$$

which cannot be found in the tables in closed form. However, the function has only first-order poles located at $p = 0$, $p = -\gamma$, and $p = \pm(2\nu - 1)\pi/2b$ with $\nu = 1, 2, \cdots$, so that (41) applies. The sum of the residues at the positive real poles taken with negative sign to maintain positive sense of integration constitutes then the solution for $x < 0$, whereas the sum of the residues at the negative real poles and at $p = 0$ constitutes the solution for $x > 0$.

For boundary conditions which prescribe potentials over finite sections of the boundary and tangential flow over the remainder, conformal mapping in accordance with section 27 can be employed to transform the geometry of the problem so that the boundary conditions can be more readily satisfied.

Circular Harmonics. The Laplacian differential equation in polar coordinates

$$\rho\frac{\partial}{\partial\rho}\left(\rho\frac{\partial\Phi}{\partial\rho}\right) + \frac{\partial^2\Phi}{\partial\phi^2} = 0 \tag{46}$$

permits direct separation of variables by defining $\Phi(\rho, \phi) = R(\rho)F(\phi)$ as a product of functions of only one variable each. One obtains

$$\rho F\frac{d}{d\rho}\left(\rho\frac{dR}{d\rho}\right) + R\frac{d^2F}{d\phi^2} = 0 \tag{47}$$

and, dividing by RF, one can argue as for (16), so that

$$\rho^2 R'' + \rho R' - m^2 R = 0, \qquad F'' + m^2 F = 0 \tag{48}$$

with the general solutions

$$R = C_1\rho^m + C_2\rho^{-m}, \qquad F = D_1\sin m\phi + D_2\cos m\phi \tag{49}$$

The selection of the spectrum of m-values is again only possible by specifying the boundary conditions. By inspection of (46) it is seen that one can add to any product RF, or sum of such products, terms of the type

$$k_1 + k_2\phi + k_3\ln\rho + k_4\phi\ln\rho \tag{50}$$

as special solutions if required; these last terms correspond to $m = 0$.

For integer values of m, the solutions (49) are called circular harmonics; for ρ constant, the functions $F_m(\phi)$ represent the conventional Fourier series for a circle and permit expansion of arbitrarily given bounded functions of physical significance in the same manner as (22) in a plane strip. For example, the solution of the Laplacian potential within unit circle for given potential values $\Phi(\psi)$ along unit circle is from (49)

$$\Phi(\rho, \phi) = k_1 + \sum_{m=1}^{\infty} \rho^m(a_m \sin m\phi + b_m \cos m\phi) \qquad (51)$$

with $C_2 = 0$ to avoid the singularity at $\rho = 0$ and with $C_1 D_1$ and $C_1 D_2$ contracted into a_m and b_m, respectively; these latter coefficients are determined in conventional manner as the Fourier coefficients along unit circle,

$$\left.\begin{array}{l} a_m = \dfrac{1}{\pi} \displaystyle\int_0^{2\pi} \Phi(\psi) \sin m\psi \, d\psi, \quad b_m = \dfrac{1}{\pi} \displaystyle\int_0^{2\pi} \Phi(\psi) \cos m\psi \, d\psi \\[2mm] k_1 = \dfrac{1}{2\pi} \displaystyle\int_0^{2\pi} \Phi(\psi) \, d\psi \end{array}\right\} \qquad (52)$$

Introducing these expressions into (51), one can establish the identities

$$1 + 2 \sum \rho^m \cos m \, (\phi - \psi) = \mathrm{Re}[1 + 2 \sum (\rho e^{j(\phi-\psi)})^m]$$

$$= \mathrm{Re}\left[\frac{1 + \rho e^{j(\phi-\psi)}}{1 - \rho e^{j(\phi-\psi)}}\right] = \frac{1 - \rho^2}{1 + \rho^2 - 2\rho \cos (\phi - \psi)}$$

and thus demonstrate that (51) with (52) represents actually the Poisson integral solution $(28 \cdot 1)$ in expanded form.

A cylindrical conductor covered with a dielectric layer of constant ε_2 and of finite thickness surrounded by air as in Fig. $29 \cdot 3$ might be exposed to a uniform electric field E_0. The potential corresponding to E_0 is

$$\Phi_0 = -E_0 x = -E_0 \rho \cos \phi$$

The modification of the potential distribution Φ_1 in air by the presence of the dielectric ε_2 is given in general form by (49) and so is the potential Φ_2 within ε_2, namely,

$$\Phi_1 = \sum b_{1m} \rho^{-m} \cos m\phi, \qquad \Phi_2 = \sum (a_{2m} \rho^m + b_{2m} \rho^{-m}) \cos m\phi \quad (53)$$

Since the effect of the dielectric must vanish at infinity, only negative powers in ρ have been retained in Φ_1, and in both cases the sine terms have been dropped because of the even symmetry in Φ_0.   The boundary conditions that have to be satisfied are

at $\rho = a$, $\Phi_2 = 0$

at $\rho = b$, $\Phi_1 + \Phi_0 = \Phi_2$, $\varepsilon_1 \dfrac{\partial}{\partial \rho} (\Phi_1 + \Phi_0) = \varepsilon_2 \dfrac{\partial \Phi_2}{\partial \rho}$

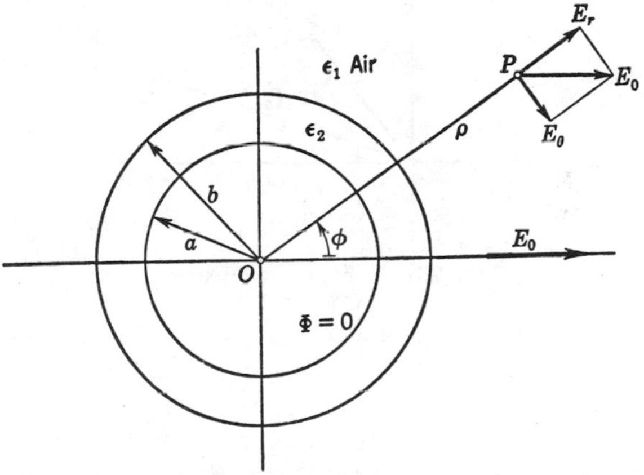

FIG. 29·3   Cylindrical Conductor Covered with Dielectric Layer.

From the conditions at $\rho = b$ it is obvious that only terms for $m = 1$ can occur as defined by Φ_0; the solution is then

$$\left.\begin{aligned}
\Phi_1 &= [\varepsilon_2(b^2 + a^2) - \varepsilon_1(b^2 - a^2)]E_0 \frac{b^2}{k\rho} \\[2mm]
\Phi_2 &= 2\varepsilon_1 E_0 \left(-\rho + \frac{a^2}{\rho}\right) \frac{b^2}{k}
\end{aligned}\right\} \tag{54}$$

with $k = [\varepsilon_2(b^2 + a^2) + \varepsilon_1(b^2 - a^2)]$.   This case is treated by Smythe,[A22] p. 65; it reduces for $a = 0$ at once to a solid dielectric cylinder in a uniform field as in (21·24), a solution obtained by the method of images.   In a quite similar manner could be treated the cylindrical dielectric shell with dielectric ε_1 in the core $\rho < a$, except that the boundary conditions at $\rho = a$ would be like those at $\rho = b$. For the magnetic cylindrical shell the solution is found in Moullin,[B48] p. 198; the solution for the magnetic solid cylinder obtained for $a = 0$ is the same as (22·20).

Slightly non-circular coaxial cables have been treated by assuming the outer conductor boundary as a periodic function of angle $b(\psi)$ and computing the effect upon capacitance at least in first approximation.[15]   The magnetic field distribution in unsaturated stators of electrical machines or in the air space with rotor removed has been evaluated by the general solutions (49), assuming a sinusoidal distribution of the radial magnetic field along the air gap boundary.[16]   Smythe,[A22] p. 275, also gives the axial com-

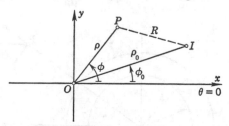

FIG. 29·4   Single Line Current.

ponent of the vector potential produced by a current distribution in a thin cylindrical shell, the current flowing only parallel to the cylinder axis.

The magnetic vector potential of a single line current at ρ_0, ϕ_0 from the origin of a coordinate system as shown in Fig. 29·4 is given by (13·23) as

$$A_z = -\frac{\mu}{2\pi} I \ln R$$

$$= -\frac{\mu}{4\pi} I \ln [\rho^2 + \rho_0{}^2 - 2\rho\rho_0 \cos (\phi - \phi_0)] \qquad (55)$$

where the last form takes as reference the origin instead of the current location.   One can write the logarithmand also as

$$\rho_0{}^2 \left[1 + \left(\frac{\rho}{\rho_0}\right)^2 - 2 \frac{\rho}{\rho_0} \cos (\phi - \phi_0) \right] = \rho_0{}^2 (1 - q)(1 - \bar{q})$$

where $q = (\rho/\rho_0) \exp [j(\phi - \phi_0)]$, and $\bar{q}$ is the conjugate complex value.   Thus, in (55),

$$\ln [\rho^2 + \rho_0{}^2 - 2\rho\rho_0 \cos (\phi - \phi_0)]$$
$$= 2 \ln \rho_0 + \ln (1 - q) + \ln (1 - \bar{q})$$

[15] P. Parzen, *Jl. Appl. Phys.*, **18**, p. 774 (1947).

[16] M. Schenkel, *Elektrot. und Masch.*, **27**, p. 201 (1909);   also Richter,[B49] I, p. 162.

and since $|q| < 1$, one can expand the last two logarithmic terms into a power series, add like powers of the two conjugate complex numbers, and obtain

$$A_z = -\frac{\mu}{2\pi} I \left[\ln \rho_0 - \Sigma \frac{1}{m} \left(\frac{\rho}{\rho_0} \right)^m \cos m(\phi - \phi_0) \right] \quad (56a)$$

which is valid for $\rho \leqslant \rho_0$, and by the appropriate modification

$$A_z = -\frac{\mu}{2\pi} I \left[\ln \rho - \Sigma \frac{1}{m} \left(\frac{\rho_0}{\rho} \right)^m \cos m(\phi - \phi_0) \right] \quad (56b)$$

which is valid for $\rho \geqslant \rho_0$. With these forms the magnetic fields of line currents can be treated if cylindrical iron shells or sheaths

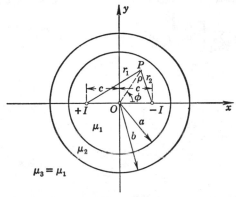

FIG. 29·5   Shielding Effect of Magnetic Cylindrical Shell.

are present, since outside of current regions the single vector potential component A_z in the two-dimensional polar coordinates also satisfies the Laplacian differential equation (46), as can be verified from Appendix 3, (37). The use of the scalar magnetic potential, as in Hague,[B44] p. 120, requires somewhat more care because of the necessary potential barrier (see section 6).

One can find the magnetic shielding effect of a cylindrical sheath within which two parallel wires are located as indicated in Fig. 29·5 by superimposing for region 1 the two line current potentials from (56) and a Laplacian potential solution of the type (51) with sine terms omitted because (56) will not contain them. In using (56a) or (56b), one must choose for ϕ_0 the values $\phi_1 = \pi$ and

$\phi_2 = 0$, respectively, for the two conductors, and also $\rho_1 = \rho_2 = c$ instead of ρ_0.   For region 2, the vector potential without sources has the character of the complete right-hand solution in (53), whereas in region 3, outside the sheath, one would have the left-hand form of (53).   The continuity conditions at both boundaries $\rho = a$ and $\rho = b$ apply to the normal component

$$B_\rho = \frac{1}{\rho} \frac{\partial A_z}{\partial \phi}$$

and the tangential component

$$H_\phi = -\frac{1}{\mu} \frac{\partial A_z}{\partial \rho}$$

The final result for the field just outside the sheath at $\rho = b$ is then

$$B_\rho = -\frac{4\mu_2}{\pi b} I \sum_{m=1}^{\infty} \left[(\mu_2 + \mu_1)^2 - (\mu_2 - \mu_1)^2 \left(\frac{a}{b}\right)^{4m-2} \right]^{-1}$$
$$\times \left(\frac{c}{b}\right)^{2m-1} \sin (2m - 1)\phi$$

$$\tag{57}$$

$$B_\phi = -\frac{4\mu_2}{\pi b} I \sum_{m=1}^{\infty} \left[(\mu_2 + \mu_1)^2 - (\mu_2 - \mu_1)^2 \left(\frac{a}{b}\right)^{4m-2} \right]^{-1}$$
$$\times \left(\frac{c}{b}\right)^{2m-2} \cos (2m - 1)\phi$$

Obviously, the shielding will be most effective when $a \ll b$ and $c \ll b$; the permeability influences the field only linearly.   For brief treatments see Smythe,[A22] p. 284; Zworykin et al.,[B32] p. 482; and Moullin,[B48] p. 209.   A similar treatment for line currents in a cylindrical air space between a solid inner magnetic cylinder and an outer magnetic cylindrical shell has been used extensively by Hague[B44] to simulate the field conditions in air gaps of electrical machines and to compute force actions on single coils and windings.

Elliptic Cylinder Coordinates.   As shown in (25·55), the inverse hyperbolic or trigonometric sine function of the complex variable z defines an orthogonal elliptic field geometry.   One can therefore actually use these functions to define elliptic cylinder coordinates; it has been customary, however, to use rather the analytic function $z = f \cosh \zeta$ for this purpose, where $\zeta = \xi + j\eta$ and

$$x = f \cosh \xi \cos \eta, \qquad y = f \sinh \xi \sin \eta \qquad (58)$$

or also

$$\cosh \xi = \frac{r_1 + r_2}{2f}, \qquad \cos \eta = \frac{r_1 - r_2}{2f} \qquad (59)$$

which are the equations of the confocal ellipses and hyperbolas in terms of the distances from the two foci F_1 and F_2 in Fig. 29·6. In the same manner as in section 26 one can demonstrate the

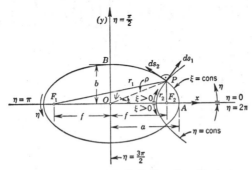

FIG. 29·6   Elliptic Cylinder Coordinates.

transformation of the Laplacian potential equation from the x-y-coordinate system to the orthogonal ξ-η-coordinate system and find

$$\frac{\partial^2 \Phi}{\partial x^2} + \frac{\partial^2 \Phi}{\partial y^2} = \frac{1}{f^2(\cosh^2 \xi - \cos^2 \eta)}\left(\frac{\partial^2 \Phi}{\partial \xi^2} + \frac{\partial^2 \Phi}{\partial \eta^2}\right) = 0 \quad (60)$$

Since this must hold for any value of ξ and η whatsoever and the first factor cannot vanish, one obtains again the Laplacian differential equation in terms of ξ, η and thus can solve it in just the same manner as (18) for x and y in the Cartesian system.

The simplest problem is that of two confocal elliptic cylinders of constant potentials.   If the major and minor axes of one cylinder are a_1 and b_1, those of the second a_2 and b_2, then $f = \sqrt{a_1{}^2 - b_1{}^2}$ defines the focal length, which must be the same for both.   The surfaces of the cylinders are defined from (59) as $\cosh \xi_1 = a_1/f$, $\cosh \xi_2 = a_2/f$, as one finds for the apex A of the major axis; or by $\xi_1 = \ln (a_1 + b_1)/f$, $\xi_2 = \ln (a_2 + b_2)/f$, as one finds from (58) for the points A and B. Because of the simple boundary condition, namely, $\Phi = \Phi_1$ on ξ_1 and $\Phi = \Phi_2$ on ξ_2, the solution of the problem is

$$\Phi = \Phi_1 - (\Phi_1 - \Phi_2)\frac{\xi - \xi_1}{\xi_2 - \xi_1} \tag{61}$$

analogous to (14·1) for the parallel plate condenser. The field vector has only a component in the ξ-direction; its value must also be found by means of the transformation equations (58) and can be best expressed as

$$E_\xi = (E_x^2 + E_y^2)^{1/2} = -\frac{\partial \Phi}{\partial \xi}\left[\left(\frac{\partial \xi}{\partial x}\right)^2 + \left(\frac{\partial \xi}{\partial y}\right)^2\right]^{-1/2}$$

since $E_x = -\dfrac{\partial \Phi}{\partial x} = -\dfrac{\partial \Phi}{\partial \xi}\dfrac{\partial \xi}{\partial x} - \dfrac{\partial \Phi}{\partial \eta}\dfrac{\partial \eta}{\partial x}$, but $\dfrac{\partial \Phi}{\partial \eta} = 0$; similarly for E_y. From (58) one has

$$\frac{\partial x}{\partial \xi} = f \sinh \xi \cos \eta, \qquad \frac{\partial y}{\partial \xi} = f \cosh \xi \sin \eta \tag{62}$$

so that with (61)

$$E_\xi = \frac{\Phi_1 - \Phi_2}{(\xi_2 - \xi_1)f}[\cosh^2 \xi - \cos^2 \eta]^{-1/2} \tag{63}$$

The charge density on cylinder ξ_1 with potential Φ_1 is

$$\sigma_1 = \varepsilon E_\xi = \frac{\varepsilon}{f}\frac{\Phi_1 - \Phi_2}{\xi_2 - \xi_1}[\cosh^2 \xi_1 - \cos^2 \eta]^{-1/2} \tag{64}$$

where η is variable. The total charge is the integral of σ_1 over the circumference of the ellipse and permits the definition of capacitance per unit depth for which the form is identical with (26·45), namely,

$$C_1 = 2\pi\varepsilon\left[\ln \frac{a_2 + b_2}{a_1 + b_1}\right]^{-1}$$

If the inner elliptic cylinder reduces to a flat strip of width $2f$, then $\xi_1 = 0$ and the charge density results from (64), with (58) for each side, as

$$\sigma_1 = \pm\frac{\varepsilon(\Phi_1 - \Phi_2)}{f\xi_2 \sin \eta} = \pm\frac{\varepsilon(\Phi_1 - \Phi_2)}{\sqrt{f^2 - x^2}\ln[(a_2 + b_2)/f]}$$

It obviously becomes infinitely large at $\eta = 0$ and $\eta = \pi$, the two ends, and must have the same sign on upper and lower surface.

For an arbitrary potential distribution on one of the elliptic cylinders, an infinite series of the Fourier type in functions $e^{-m\xi}$ sin $m\eta$ is possible, as in (29). For details see Bateman,[C1] p. 257, where also an application is given to a line charge paralleling an elliptic cylinder. A dielectric elliptic cylinder exposed to a uniform electric field is treated in Ollendorff,[A18] p. 182.

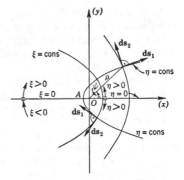

FIG. 29·7. Parabolic Cylinder Coordinates.

It is to be recognized that the use of these coordinates leads to more convenient expressions for the solutions and permits formulation of the boundary conditions in terms of simple parameters; the interpretation of the field structure is, however, usually against a Cartesian coordinate system as background unless one has prepared an elliptical orthogonal net on which he can read directly ξ- and η-values.

Parabolic Cylinder Coordinates. Parabolic cylinder coordinates (Stratton,[A23] p. 54, and Bateman,[C1] p. 486) are based upon the geometry defined by the analytic function $z = 2\zeta^2$ as in (25·57), where $\zeta = \xi + j\eta$ and

$$\left. \begin{array}{ll} \xi = \sqrt{2\rho}\cos\dfrac{\phi}{2}, & \xi^2 = \sqrt{x^2 + y^2} + x \\[2mm] \eta = \sqrt{2\rho}\sin\dfrac{\phi}{2}, & \eta^2 = \sqrt{x^2 + y^2} - x \end{array} \right\} \tag{65}$$

or also
$$x = \tfrac{1}{2}(\xi^2 - \eta^2), \qquad y = \xi\eta \tag{66}$$

Thus, constant values of ξ or of η lead to families of orthogonal parabolic cylinders as in Fig. 29·7.

Bipolar Coordinates. Bipolar coordinates (Stratton,[A23] p. 55, and Bateman,[C1] p. 260) are based on the analytic function $z = jc\cot(\zeta/2)$ as in (26·53), where

$$\xi = \phi_2 - \phi_1, \qquad \eta = \ln\frac{r_2}{r_1} \tag{67}$$

Referring to Fig. 12·5, $\xi = $ cons and $\eta = $ cons are the two families of orthogonal circles which represent the potential solution for two parallel wires of finite radii.[17]

PROBLEMS

1. N coplanar positively charged quasi lines, each with charge density λ and diameter d, are uniformly spaced a distance $2c$ apart and are located a height h above a grounded conducting plane. Find the capacitance of this finite grid. Let $N \to \infty$, and demonstrate that one obtains the solution for the "Maxwell grating."

2. In the triode of Fig. 25·5 find the distribution of the radial electric field along the grid circle $|z| = R_g$ between two grid wires. Assume $N = 20$, $N\rho_g/R_g = 0.1$, $R_a/R_g = 4$, $R_g/R_c = 2$ and (a) $V_a = 100$ volts, $V_g = 8$ volts; (b) $V_a = 100$ volts, $V_g = -8$ volts. Observe that $z_a{}^N = R_g{}^N$.

3. Find the mutual capacitance coefficients for a tetrode with two grids whose individual grid wires are lying along the same radius vectors.

4. Find the mutual capacitance coefficients for a tetrode with two grids if the individual wires of the one grid are lying midway between those of the other grid and (a) along the same circle, (b) along two different circles.

5. If the field vector $\mathbf{E}$ on the cathode surface is directed away from the cathode, no electrons can leave. Find the conditions for this cut-off of emission from parts of the cathode surface for the triode in problem 2 in terms of grid-cathode spacing.

6. The geometry in Fig. 25·5 might represent a thin copper sheet with small circular perforations and with radial current flow from an electrode forming the outer circular boundary to another concentric electrode forming the inner one. Find the total resistance to current flow if the conductivity is γ and the small thickness t. Assume uniform current densities at the electrodes.

7. Six wires are uniformly arranged on a circle to form a cylindrical grid. Find the electrostatic field distribution if successive wires alternatingly carry potentials $\pm V/2$. Assume the wire radii small compared with spacing, but finite.

8. In a three-phase four-wire transmission system, the three-phase wires are arranged in a plane parallel to ground, with mutual spacing $2b$. The ground wire is located a height h above the center phase wire. Find the mutual linkages for unbalanced current flow with currents I_1, $-I_1/2$, $-I_1/3$ in the phase wires.

9. A thin rectangular copper sheet of area $2a \times 2b$ has circular perforations along its center line parallel to the longer side $2a$. Two heavy electrodes are applied along the sides $2a$ with a potential difference V. Find the current, if the N perforations have equal spacing, and if the outermost ones have their centers a/N from the shorter sides of the sheet.

10. A very long and thin copper sheet of width $2a$ has applied two electrodes of small circular cross sections in a line transverse to the sheet and at distances $a/2$ from the edges. Find the resistance for a small thickness t.

[17] For an interesting application to a two-wire problem see G. Mie, *Ann. d. Physik*, **2**, p. 201 (1900).

11. The magnetic sheets (laminations) for an electromagnet are of rectangular shape and carry 2 bolt holes across the narrow side of width $2a$. Find the magnetic reluctance if the holes are spaced $a/2$ from the edges of the sheet and if the length of the sheet is $10a$, its small thickness t.

12. If the control grid wires in a vacuum tube are located very close to the cathode, one can treat the electric field distribution as a two-dimensional plane problem. Assume the grid wires as in Fig. $25 \cdot 6a$ with a spacing $h < a$ and carrying a negative line charge $-\lambda_g$; assume the anode plane at a distance b from the cathode and carrying a positive potential V_a with respect to the cathode. Find the field strength E along the cathode surface. Find the mutual capacitance coefficients.

13. A single long wire carrying current I is located between two parallel ideal magnetic boundary planes at distance $2a$ and of potentials $\mathcal{F}_1$ and $\mathcal{F}_2$. Find the variation of the magnetic flux density B along the closer surface. Find the variation of the maximum value of B as the wire approaches one of the surfaces.

14. Discuss the possible field solutions rendered by the function

$$\ln \left(\cot \frac{\pi z}{a} \right).$$

15. Discuss the possible field solutions rendered by the function

$$\ln \left(\tanh \frac{\pi z}{a} \right).$$

16. N parallel long wires each carrying current I are located in a plane parallel to two ideal magnetic boundary planes at distance $2a$ and of potentials $\mathcal{F}_1$ and $\mathcal{F}_2$. Find the variation of the magnetic flux density B along the closer boundary surface if the spacing between the wires is $a/4$.

17. A thin coaxial annular ring of copper is slit along one radius and heavy electrodes are applied there, impressing a potential difference V between the two opposite faces of that radius. Find the current distribution. Find the resistance of the sheet for a small thickness t.

18. In Fig. $26 \cdot 5$ find the current distribution along the diameter 1–3.

19. Discuss the conformal mapping obtained by the function $w = \ln \dfrac{z + a}{z - a}$.

20. Discuss the conformal mapping obtained by the function
$$w = \ln \left[(z + a)(z - a) \right].$$

21. Discuss the conformal mapping obtained by $w = \tan \dfrac{\pi z}{a}$.

22. A thin ring of copper sheet is bounded by two eccentric circles. Find the resistance if two circular electrodes of small area are applied with centers on the larger circle at the ends of the diameter bisecting the ring.

23. Consider a long cylindrical duct of semicircular cross section with radius R; within the duct extend two parallel wires of small radii ρ forming a transmission system. Find the capacitance of the system if the wires are located (a) symmetrical with respect to the center plane of the duct, at $R/2$ from it and close to the ceiling; (b) above each other in a plane normal to the plane base of the duct.

24. A solid cylindrical plastic base has six metal pins embedded, symmetrically spaced, along a coaxial cylindrical surface. Find the mutual capacitances per unit length between the pins.

25. A cylindrical cable has N conductors, each of small circular cross section, symmetrically distributed along a cylindrical surface coaxial with the grounded sheath. Find the mutual capacitance coefficients.

26. Assume in Fig. $27 \cdot 6b$ the gap $2a$ to be a rectangular orifice for the flow of an ideal fluid from large radial distance on the upper half to large radial distance on the lower half of the z-plane. Find the velocity distribution.

27. Assume in Fig. $27 \cdot 6b$ the two coplanar conducting planes to have the same potential $\Phi = 0$ and add a line charge $+\lambda$ at point B. Compute the surface charges induced in the two planes. Show that the total charge on each conducting plane is $-\lambda/2$.

28. In problem 27, if the line charge resides on a thin wire of radius ρ, compute its capacitance with respect to the conducting planes.

29. Two cylindrical electrodes of small radius ρ are placed upon a thin sheet of copper of the shape as shown in Fig. $27 \cdot 9c$; electrode A of potential Φ_2 is centered at O_z and electrode B of potential $\Phi_1 < \Phi_2$ is located with its center at distance $2a$ from O_z along the x-axis. Compute the resistance of the copper sheet if its small thickness is t.

30. The lower half of the z-plane in Fig. $27 \cdot 6b$ might represent an infinite-extent dielectric medium of dielectric constant ε, covered for $|x| > a$ by two grounded thin metal foils. Find the capacitance of a wire of radius ρ located along the y-axis at height h above the boundary plane.

31. For the symmetrical arrangement in Fig. $27 \cdot 7b$ find the end point of the field line emanating from the edge 2.

32. Consider a parallel thin wire of radius ρ located at $y = -2b$ in the geometry of Fig. $27 \cdot 7a$. Find its capacitance coefficients with respect to the two coplanar planes assumed at ground potential, and with respect to the plane $y = 0$ assumed to have potential difference V applied between it and the wire.

33. A thin copper sheet might have an abrupt change of width as in Fig. $27 \cdot 9b$. Assume one electrode located across the narrow part at a distance from the discontinuity where the current distribution is uniform to within $\pm 1\%$; assume the second electrode of semicylindrical shape and of such radius that along its periphery the current density is uniform within $\pm 1\%$. Find the resistance between the electrodes.

34. In Fig. $27 \cdot 9b$ assume the two right-angle electrodes to have the same potential Φ_1 and to have a third plane electrode of potential Φ_2 along the center plane from $y = \infty$ down to $y = -a$. Find the field distribution. Find the partial capacitance of the center plane for the sections from $y = +a$ to $y = -a$.

35. A two-wire transmission line is located at the height a above the plane $x < 0$ in Fig. $27 \cdot 9c$ and at the distance $x = -a$ from the discontinuity. Find the capacitance of the line per unit length, assuming the entire contour to have ground potential.

36. Plot in Fig. $27 \cdot 10a$ the potential lines and select a good approximation to a pole shoe configuration in electrical machines. Find the field line termi-

nating at point 2 to separate field lines entering the armature surface $y = 0$ from those passing to the neighboring pole shoe.

37. The geometry of Fig. $27 \cdot 10a$ might be considered as the flow of an ideal fluid from the channel between $y = 0$ and $y = a$ into the right corner and around the guide plate $3''-4-1'$ into the larger space above. Find the velocity distribution along the equipotential line extending from the corner point 2.

38. Find the resistance of a thin copper sheet having the shape of the right-angle bend in Fig. $27 \cdot 10b$. One electrode is applied across the vertical branch at a distance from the origin where the current density is uniform to within $\pm 1\%$; the other electrode is applied across the horizontal branch at a distance determined in the same manner. Find the resistance of the copper sheet of small thickness t.

39. Find the breakdown field strength for a shell winding of a transformer if it can be represented as in Fig. $27 \cdot 10d$, assuming b as the thickness of the winding with $b = 2a$, and taking the plane $y = 0$ as the grounded core.

40. Taking the plane $y = 0$ in Fig. $27 \cdot 10d$ as a plane of symmetry, the figure represents the upper half of two parallel long plates of finite thickness. Find the variation of the field vector E along the plane of symmetry $y = 0$ for the condition $b = a/4$. Compare these field-strength values with the case $b = 0$, shown in Fig. $27 \cdot 4$.

41. Carry through the mapping of the geometry, Fig. $27 \cdot 12b$, if the opposing right-angle equipotential surfaces are ideal magnetic boundary surfaces of potentials $\mathcal{F}_1$ and $\mathcal{F}_2$. Find the field lines starting at the corners 2 and 4. Compute the individual flux values bounded by these field lines. Determine the field line between $2-3'$ and $3''-4$ along which the field vector B is within $\pm 2\%$ of the uniform value $(\mathcal{F}_1 - \mathcal{F}_2)/b$.

42. Find the electric field distribution within the rectangle of Fig. $27 \cdot 13a$ by direct conformal transformation, if potential Φ_1 is applied to the two joining sides 1 2 and 2 3, and potential Φ_0 to the other two joining sides 3–4 and 4–1. (Section of plane electron multiplier, Zworykin,[C32] p. 369).

43. Find the charge distribution over the coplanar parallel strips in the w-plane of Fig. $27 \cdot 13a$.

44. Find the current distribution in a large thin copper sheet if two strip electrodes are applied as in the z-plane of Fig. $27 \cdot 13b$. Find the resistance for small thickness t of the copper sheet, assuming the electrodes to have equipotential contours.

45. Find the current distribution between the two coplanar strips of the w-plane of Fig. $27 \cdot 13b$. Find the resistance between the strips.

46. A thin wire of circular cross section carrying a linear charge density λ is located in a rectangular tunnel within a grounded conducting material. Find the capacitance per unit length of the wire of small radius ρ within the tunnel. Find the force upon the wire.

47. Replace the conducting material in problem 46 by a dielectric material. Find the force action upon the wire.

48. In the z-plane of Fig. $27 \cdot 13c$ consider the boundary line of the shaded region as representing ground with a rectangular long ditch. Assume a thin wire of potential difference V to ground located in the shaded area and find its capacitance to ground.

49. In the rectangular channel of Fig. 29·1a assume the potential $\Phi = \Phi_0$ along the base plate $y = 0$, and $\Phi = 0$ along the other three sides. Find the potential distribution within the channel. Find the charge density along all four sides.

50. Assume in Fig. 29·1a that the channel is made up of two sections with $\Phi = \Phi_0$ along the sides $y = 0$ and $x = a$, and with $\Phi = -\Phi_0$ along $x = 0$ and $y = b$. Find the potential distribution. Find the field line, starting at the corner $y = 0$ and $x = a$.

51. Find the current distribution in a thin rectangular copper sheet if one electrode is applied along $y = 0$ and the other electrode along $x = a$, and the potential difference is V. Find the resistance of the copper sheet for a small thickness t.

52. The base plate and the face $x = a$ of a rectangular bar are kept at constant temperature T_0; the top face loses heat so that the temperature gradient is proportional to the local temperature (as in 29·24); the face $x = 0$ is insulated so that on it $\partial T / \partial n = 0$. Find the thermal resistance of the bar per unit length.

53. A thin rectangular conducting sheet is one half copper and one half aluminum. Find the resistance if in Fig. 29·1a one electrode is applied over the left half of $y = 0$, which is of copper, and the other electrode is applied over the right half of $y = b$, which is of aluminum. Disregard contact potentials and assume both materials of the same small thickness t.

54. The armature of an electrical machine can be developed into an infinite slab of magnetic material of high permeability μ extending as in Fig. 29·2. Assume, as a first model, that the magnetostatic potential along $y = 0$ is constant and of value $\mathcal{F}_1$ for $-a < x < +a$, is constant and of value $\mathcal{F}_2 = -\mathcal{F}_1$ for $-3a < x < -a$ and for $a < x < 3a$, and continue in infinite alternation with the period $4a$; because of the high permeability, one can assume at $y = b$ that $\partial \mathcal{F} / \partial n = 0$. Find the magnetic reluctance per unit length for any periodic section. Find the distribution of the magnetic flux density along $y = 0$.

55. Assume in problem 54 that the magnetic field lines are refracted at $y = b$ and extend into the infinite air space above. Find the magnetic reluctance per unit length for any periodic section. Find the distribution of the magnetic flux density along $y = 0$ and along $y = b$.

56. Assume in problem 54 that the magnetostatic potential varies linearly along $y = 0$ with the same period $4a$, for example, having value $\mathcal{F} = M(x + a)/a$ for $0 < x < -2a$, and value $\mathcal{F} = M(a - x)/a$ for $0 < x < 2a$. Find the distribution of the magnetic flux density along $y = 0$.

57. An infinite strip of thin copper sheet of width b as in Fig. 29·2 has one electrode of potential $V/2$ applied at its lower edge along $-2a < x < -a$ and a second electrode of potential $-V/2$ along $a < x < 2a$. Find the resistance of the copper sheet if the small thickness is t. Describe this as a two-dimensional hydraulic flow problem.

58. Assume the cylindrical shell in Fig. 29·5 to represent the stator of an electrical machine with inner radius R_1 and outer radius R_2. On the inner surface, the magnetostatic potential is constant and of value $\mathcal{F}_1$ for $0 < \phi < \pi/2$ and $\pi < \phi < 3\pi/2$, and of value $\mathcal{F}_2 = -\mathcal{F}_1$ over the other two quadrants;

at the outer surface $\partial \mathcal{F} / \partial r = 0$. Find the reluctance per unit length for one periodic section. Find the distribution of the magnetic flux density along the inner surface.

59. In problem 58, find the magnetic field distribution in the air space for $r < R_1$. Find the reluctance per unit length of the air space for a periodic section.

60. If in problem 58 the condition $\partial \mathcal{F} / \partial r = 0$ on the outer surface is relaxed and replaced by the usual magnetic boundary conditions of refraction, find the distribution of the magnetic flux density just outside the magnetic shell. Find the value of the magnetic flux density at large distance from the shell.

61. A very long conductor of large rectangular cross section $2a \times 2b$ carries the uniformly distributed current I and is placed snugly at the bottom of an infinite rectangular slot formed by two parallel blocks of iron spaced $2a$. Find the distribution of the magnetic field if in good approximation the field lines can be taken as normal to all iron surfaces.

62. An infinite block of iron carries on its plane surface an infinitely periodic alternation of like conductors with large rectangular cross section, each carrying the same total current I but in alternatingly opposite directions. Find the magnetic field distribution within the conductors and the air space outside, assuming that the magnetic field lines enter the iron block perpendicularly.

63. A thin circular cylindrical shell is slotted so that its arc is $5\pi/3$ and carries potential V. Find the potential distribution by two-dimensional inversion. Find the charge distribution on the slotted cylinder.

64. A thin copper sheet of elliptical area with major axis $2a$ and minor axis $2b$ has two electrodes of small circular areas applied at the foci F_1 and F_2 (see Fig. 29·6). Find the resistance for a small thickness t of the sheet. Hint: in the neighborhood of F_1, ζ is small and η is close to π; in the neighborhood of F_2, ζ is small and η is small. Satisfy $\Phi = +V/2$ for $\eta = \pi - \rho_1$, $\Phi = -V/2$ for $\eta = \rho_2$, where ρ_1 and ρ_2 are the small radii of the electrodes. For the field vector observe (31·24). Check the result by conformal mapping.

65. A long solid bar has as cross section the right half of the ellipse in Fig. 29·6 with major axis $2a$ and minor axis $2b$. The base $\eta = \pi/2$ is kept at temperature T_1, and the cylinder surface is cooled so that its temperature is $T_2 < T_1$. Find the heat flow transmitted through the cylinder surface per unit length.

66. In problem 65 assume that the temperature of the cylinder surface varies linearly from T_1 at the base to $T_2 < T_1$ at A. Find the heat flow transmitted through the cylinder surface per unit length.

67. Transform the two-dimensional Laplacian differential equation from cartesian to (a) parabolic cylinder coordinates; (b) bipolar coordinates.

68. In Fig. 29·7 assume the infinite parabolic cylinder surface $\eta = 2$ to represent ground and to have a parallel line charge of density λ located at $\xi = 0$, $\eta = 4$. Find, by conformal mapping, the location of the image line charge and the distribution of the induced charge in ground.

8. THREE–DIMENSIONAL ANALYTIC SOLUTIONS

Admittedly among the most difficult group of boundary value problems, three-dimensional potential distributions require acquaintance with the less usual function systems, many of which have not been as extensively tabulated as might be desirable. It is seldom possible to arrive at solutions in closed forms, and, actually, most of these simpler cases have been treated in sections 14 and 15. In practically all cases treated here, therefore, infinite series expansions are necessary so that one can only speak of *formally* exact solutions if these are feasible at all; for all practical cases one must accept the approximations by finite sums. This holds also for the axially symmetrical field distributions, which are sometimes called two-dimensional because the axial symmetry eliminates one of the three variables; they belong, however, definitely to the three-dimensional class of solutions, involving the same types of function systems.

30· AXIALLY SYMMETRICAL POTENTIAL FIELDS

In terms of cylindrical coordinates the potential equation with axial symmetry has the form [Appendix 3, (37)]

$$\frac{1}{\rho} \frac{\partial}{\partial \rho} \left(\rho \frac{\partial \Phi}{\partial \rho} \right) + \frac{\partial^2 \Phi}{\partial z^2} = 0 \tag{1}$$

and permits readily separation of the variables by assuming $\Phi = R(\rho)Z(z)$, where R and Z are functions of only one variable each. Introducing this product into (1) and dividing by it give

$$\frac{1}{R} \frac{1}{\rho} \frac{d}{d\rho} \left(\rho \frac{dR}{d\rho} \right) = - \frac{1}{Z} \frac{d^2 Z}{dZ^2} = \pm m^2 \tag{2}$$

arguing as in (29·16) that each term can at most be a function of the indicated variable, and since the equation must hold for any combination of the independent variables, each term must actually be a constant. The possible values of m are selected by the boundary conditions and can form either a discrete or a continuous spectrum, as shown in section 29.

The fact that only two variables appear in the potential equation (1) just as in the two-dimensional case led early to attempts for utilization of two-dimensional field solutions and graphs. It has been shown,[1] however, that the only field geometries that are common for both types of problems are the orthogonal, confocal, conic sections, including circles; no other solutions can be translated.

An approximate utilization of two-dimensional solutions for axially symmetrical fields far from the axis was shown by Maxwell,[A17] I, p. 305. Assume that the analytic function $w = f(z)$ represents the complex solution of a potential problem in the x-y-plane by the method of conjugate functions as outlined in section 25. If $w = u + jv$, then $u(x, y)$ is the real potential solution and satisfies the Laplacian differential equation

$$\frac{\partial^2 u}{\partial x^2} + \frac{\partial^2 u}{\partial y^2} = 0$$

If it is desired to find the solution for the same cross section of electrodes but rotated about an axis parallel to the y-axis and y_0 to the left of it, then $u(x, y)$ must satisfy (1) with $(y + y_0)$ for ρ and x for z. Expanded, this becomes

$$\frac{\partial^2 u}{\partial y^2} + \frac{\partial^2 u}{\partial x^2} = -\frac{1}{y_0 + y}\frac{\partial u}{\partial y} \tag{3}$$

where use was made of $\partial/\partial y = \partial/\partial (y + y_0)$, so that the origin need not be shifted. This equation (3) has the form of a space charge potential equation (3·4) with space charge density

$$\rho(x, y) = \frac{\varepsilon}{y_0 + y}\frac{\partial u}{\partial y} \tag{4}$$

which can be taken as "correction." Obviously, inserting in (4) the two-dimensional solution $u(x, y)$ cannot give an exact solution;

[1] W. Gauster, *Arch. f. Elektrot.*, **15**, p. 89 (1926).

however, if y_0 is considerably larger than the region of y for which the field distribution is of real interest, a reasonably good approximation can be had.   One can further simplify by approximating $\partial u/\partial y$ to lead to simple results.   This method can best be used to evaluate the capacitance, since for that it is necessary only to compute the total space charge and add it to the surface charge of the same sign.   The total charge then defines the total capacitance for the axially symmetrical system of the same potential difference.   Maxwell applied this procedure to evaluate the effect of the guard ring for circular electrodes from the two-dimensional solution (27·40) referring to Fig. 27·7a.   He also converted the end effect at the edge of a plate parallel to and between two infinite plates, as in Fig. 27·7b, into a solution for concentric cylinders by rotation about an axis parallel to the y-axis, and into a solution for circular disks by rotation about an axis parallel to the x-axis.

Field Expansions near Axis.   In electron optical field problems one is mainly concerned with the potential and field values near and on the axis of symmetry.   Since the potential must be finite and continuous along the axis if it belongs to the field region and must be an even function of ρ, one can solve (1) by means of the power series

$$\Phi(\rho, z) = \sum_{\alpha = 0}^{\infty} f_{2\alpha}(z)\rho^{2\alpha} \tag{5}$$

where $\Phi(0, z) = f_0(z)$, the potential value along the axis.   Introducing (5) into (1), one obtains the recursion formula

$$(2\alpha + 2)^2 f_{2\alpha+2}(z) + f_{2\alpha}{}''(z) = 0 \tag{6}$$

for any power $\rho^{2\alpha}$.   Thus, all the coefficients $f_{2\alpha}(z)$ in (5) can be expressed in terms of $f_0(z)$, so that

$$\Phi(\rho, z) = \Phi(0, z) - \frac{\Phi''(0, z)(\rho/2)^2}{1!^2} + \frac{\Phi^{IV}(0, z)(\rho/2)^4}{2!^2} - \cdots \tag{7}$$

where the primes denote differentiations with respect to z; see Bateman,[C1] p. 406; Brüche and Scherzer,[B20] p. 66; Spangenberg,[B29] p. 339; and others.   The main problem is therefore the evaluation of the potential or of the field gradient $E_z(0, z) = f_0{}'(z)$ along the axis either analytically, if that is possible, or most expeditiously with the electrolytic trough (section 18).

Instead of the power series expansion in ρ, one can use Laplace's expression

$$\Phi(\rho, z) = \frac{1}{\pi} \int_{\psi=0}^{\psi=\pi} f_0(z + j\rho \cos \psi) \, d\psi \qquad (8)$$

where f_0 is again the potential function along the axis, but with z replaced by $(z + j\rho \sin \psi)$. This is verified by a Taylor series expansion of f_0 about $\rho = 0$ and integration term by term, which leads to (7); Bateman,[C1] p. 406, and also Myers,[B27] p. 89.

Though the potential function must be continuous along the axis, it can possess isolated singular points where the field vector vanishes, as discussed in section 10. Because of the continuity, one can develop $\Phi(0, z) = f_0(z)$ at any point z_0 on the axis into a Taylor series

$$\Phi(0, z) = f_0(z) = f_0(z_0) + f_0{}'(z_0)\frac{z - z_0}{1!} + f_0{}''(z_0)\frac{(z - z_0)^2}{2!} + \cdots$$

and introduce this for the first term in (7); the second derivative with respect to z near z_0 becomes

$$f_0{}''(z) = f_0{}''(z_0) + f_0{}'''(z_0)(z - z_0) + \cdots$$

and using this in the second term of (7), one obtains near z_0

$$\Phi(\rho, z) = f_0(z_0) + f_0{}'(z_0)(z - z_0)$$
$$+ f_0{}''(z_0)\frac{(z - z_0)^2}{2} - f_0{}''(z_0)\left(\frac{\rho}{2}\right)^2 \qquad (9)$$

if all terms involving higher than second derivatives in z_0 are discarded. Along an equipotential line near the axis one must then have

$$d\Phi(\rho, z) = 0 = f_0{}'(z_0) \, dz + f_0{}''(z_0)(z - z_0) \, dz - \tfrac{1}{2}f_0{}''(z_0)\, \rho \, d\rho \qquad (10)$$

which gives for the slope

$$\frac{d\rho}{dz} = 2\frac{f_0{}'(z_0) + f_0{}''(z_0)(z - z_0)}{\rho f_0{}''(z_0)}$$

As one approaches the point z_0 on the axis, $z \to z_0$ and $\rho \to 0$, so that $d\rho/dz \to \infty$ at all regular points A of Fig. 30·1, as it must be because of the axial symmetry. At a singular point B, however,

$f_0{}'(z_0) = 0$ and one finds

$$\left(\frac{d\rho}{dz}\right)_B = \tan \eta = \lim_{\substack{z \to z_0 \\ \rho \to 0}} \frac{2f_0{}''(z_0)(z - z_0)}{f_0{}''(z_0)\rho} = 2$$

by de l'Hospital's rule. Thus, only saddle points can occur as singular points, and at any such singularity the pair of equipotential lines intersects the axis at angles $\tan^{-1}(\pm 2) = \pm 54°44'$; see Myers,[B27] p. 95, and Zworykin *et al.*,[B32] p. 377.

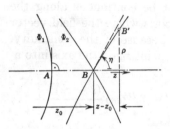

FIG. 30·1 Potential Values near the Axis for Axially Symmetrical System.

This is quite different from the two-dimensional field distribution, for which the general expansion corresponding to (7) in the neighborhood of an axis of symmetry, chosen as x-axis, is given by

$$\Phi(y, x) = f_0(x) - f_0{}''(x)\frac{y^2}{2!}$$
$$+ f_0{}^{\text{IV}}(x)\frac{y^4}{4!} + \dots \quad (11)$$

with $f_0(x) = \Phi(0, x)$ denoting the potential value along the axis. Using for it the same Taylor series near a point x_0 as above, introducing it into (11), and establishing the equipotential near x_0 analogous to (10) give now

$$d\Phi(y, x) = 0 = [f_0{}'(x_0) + \tfrac{1}{2}f_0{}''(x_0)(x - x_0)]\,dx - \tfrac{1}{2}f_0{}''(x_0)y\,dy$$

From this, the slope becomes

$$\frac{dy}{dx} = \frac{2f_0{}'(x_0) + f_0{}''(x_0)(x - x_0)}{f_0{}''(x_0)y}$$

which again shows the orthogonality of the equipotential lines to the axis, but gives at a singular point $\lim (dy/dx)_B = 1$; the intersection of the axis of symmetry by the equipotential lines at a singular point occurs at angles $\pm 45°$; see also Zworykin *et al.*,[B32] p. 375. This demonstrates clearly that substitution of two-dimensional fields for the axially symmetrical field near the axis is bound to give poor approximations.

Axially symmetrical magnetic fields are completely defined by only one component of the magnetic vector potential; since currents producing axially symmetrical fields must flow circularly around the axis, only A_ϕ will exist, as (13·25) shows. In regions free of current, as is usually true near the axis of the electron optical systems, the component A_ϕ will satisfy the differential equation

$$\frac{\partial}{\partial \rho}\left[\frac{1}{\rho}\frac{\partial}{\partial \rho}(\rho A_\phi)\right] + \frac{\partial^2 A_\phi}{\partial z^2} = 0 \tag{12}$$

which is obtained from Appendix 3, (37). In analogy to (5) one can assume a solution near the axis of the form

$$A_\phi(\rho, z) = \sum_{\alpha=0}^{\infty} f_{2\alpha+1}(z)\, \rho^{2\alpha+1} \tag{13}$$

where only odd powers of ρ can appear because A_ϕ encircles the axis. Introducing (13) into (12), one obtains the recursion formula

$$4\alpha(\alpha+1) f_{2\alpha+1}(z) + f_{2\alpha-1}''(z) = 0 \tag{14}$$

for any power $\rho^{2\alpha-1}$. Thus, all the coefficients $f_{2\alpha+1}(z)$ in (13) can be expressed in terms of derivatives of $f_1(z)$ so that

$$A_\phi(\rho, z) = f_1(z)\rho - f_1''(z)\left(\frac{\rho}{2}\right)^3$$
$$+ f_1^{IV}(z)\frac{1}{6}\left(\frac{\rho}{2}\right)^5 - \cdots \tag{15}$$

One can interpret the physical meaning of $f_1(z)$ if one also considers the field vector B whose components are given as in (13·26) by

$$B_\rho = -\frac{\partial A_\phi}{\partial z}, \qquad B_z = \frac{1}{\rho}\frac{\partial}{\partial \rho}(\rho A_\phi)$$

This gives with (15)

$$B_z = 2\left[f_1(z) - \frac{1}{(1!)^2}\left(\frac{\rho}{2}\right)^2 f_1''(z)\right.$$
$$\left. + \frac{1}{(2!)^2}\left(\frac{\rho}{2}\right)^4 f_1^{IV}(z) - \cdots\right] \tag{16}$$

where it is now apparent that $2f_1(z) = B_z(0, z)$ represents the axial component of the magnet field along the axis. With (16), the general form (15) becomes

$$A_\phi(\rho, z) = \frac{\rho}{2} B_z(0, z) - \frac{1}{1!\,2!}\left(\frac{\rho}{2}\right)^3 B_z''(0, z)$$

$$+ \frac{1}{2!\,3!}\left(\frac{\rho}{2}\right)^5 B_z^{IV}(0, z) \cdots \quad (17)$$

This form permits the utilization of experimental data; if one finds a good analytical approximation to the measured field dis-

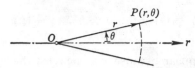

FIG. 30·2 Potential Values near the Axis for Spherical System.

tribution along the axis, one can construct a complete solution and use it for determination of electron paths or any other desired information. This is particularly important for magnetic fields because the analytical com-

putations quickly lead into difficult functions,[2] as pointed out in section 13. One can, of course, also use the magnetostatic potential function $\mathcal{F}$ which leads to forms quite similar to (7) and (8) as in Zworykin *et al.*,[B32] p. 474.

Occasionally it is also of interest to know potential solutions in a spherical system for small angles of opening as indicated in Fig. 30·2. From Appendix 3, (40) one has for axial symmetry in a spherical coordinate system

$$\frac{\partial}{\partial r}\left(r^2 \frac{\partial \Phi}{\partial r}\right) + \frac{1}{\sin\theta}\,\frac{\partial}{\partial\theta}\left(\sin\theta\,\frac{\partial\Phi}{\partial\theta}\right) = 0 \quad (18)$$

For small angles θ one can assume the solution of the type

$$\Phi(r, \theta) = \sum_{\alpha=0}^{\infty} f_{2\alpha}(r)\,\theta^{2\alpha} \quad (19)$$

Approximating in (18) $\sin\theta \approx \theta$, and collecting coefficients of the same powers in θ, one deduces the recursion formula

$$\frac{d}{dr}\left[r^2 f_{2\alpha}'(r)\right] + (2\alpha)^2 f_{2\alpha+2}(r) = 0 \quad (20)$$

[2] See W. Glaser, *Zeits. f. Physik*, **118**, p. 264 (1941).

which yields because $f_0(r) = \Phi(r, 0)$ the potential along the axis,

$$\Phi(r, \theta) = \Phi(r, 0) - \frac{1}{(1!)^2}\left(\frac{\theta}{2}\right)^2 [r^2\Phi'(r, 0)]$$

$$+ \frac{1}{(2!)^2}\left(\frac{\theta}{2}\right)^4 \{r^2[r^2\Phi'(r, 0)]\}' - \cdots \quad (21a)$$

where the primes denote differentiations with respect to r.   This development is particularly applicable to conical fields as exist in cathode-ray tubes and similar applications.

   Two Finite Equidiameter Coaxial Cylinders.   Two finite coaxial cylinders of equal diameters as in Fig. 30·3 with potentials

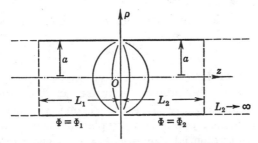

FIG. 30·3   Two Coaxial Cylinders of Equal Radii
(Two-cylinder Lens or Mirror).

Φ_1 and Φ_2, respectively, constitute a rather common electron lens of simple type.   Their lengths might be L_1 and L_2, with very small separation at the plane $z = 0$ and their end faces $z = -L_1$ of potential Φ_1 and $z = +L_2$ of potential Φ_2, disregarding any small apertures that might exist in these planes.   The solution of the potential distribution can be found from (2) where the variables have been separated.   For the upper, positive sign of m^2 one has at once as for $X(x)$ in (29·17) and (29·18)

$$Z(z) = C_1 \sin mz + C_2 \cos mz \quad (21b)$$

whereas the function $R(\rho)$ must satisfy

$$\frac{d^2R}{d\rho^2} + \frac{1}{\rho}\cdot\frac{dR}{\rho} - m^2R = 0 \quad (22)$$

which is the normal form of the differential equation for modified Bessel functions of zeroth order[3] [Appendix 5, (24)]

$$R(\rho) = D_1 I_0(m\rho) + D_2 K_0(m\rho) \tag{23}$$

The potential function must be continuous at all points except along the rim $\rho = a$ in the plane $z = 0$, where there exists an isolated singularity of the same type as in conformal mapping at the vertices of straight line polygons (section 27). This excludes the second term in (23) as a possible solution, since the function $K_0(m\rho)$ has a logarithmic singularity at $\rho = 0$. The potential solution is therefore the general product

$$(C_1 \sin mz + C_2 \cos mz) \, I_0(m\rho) \tag{24}$$

to which can be added by inspection of (1) the particular integrals

$$k_1 + k_2 z \tag{25}$$

The selection of the spectrum of m values is, as always, simplest with homogeneous boundary conditions of the type (29·3). Though these are not directly specified, one can allocate the inhomogeneous boundary conditions by placing the burden of satisfying the constant potential values at $z = -L_1$ and $z = +L_2$ upon the particular integrals (25)

$$k_1 - k_2 L_1 = \Phi_1, \qquad k_1 + k_2 L_2 = \Phi_2$$

or

$$k_1 = \frac{L_1 \Phi_2 + L_2 \Phi_1}{L_1 + L_2}, \qquad k_2 = \frac{\Phi_2 - \Phi_1}{L_2 + L_1} \tag{26}$$

and thus requiring of (24) the homogeneous conditions

$$Z(-L_1) = Z(+L_2) = 0$$

---

[3] Brief reviews of Bessel functions are given in Smythe,[A22] p. 168; Churchill,[C3] Chapter VIII; and almost any book on advanced calculus. Extensive treatises are Gray, Matthews and MacRobert;[C7] Byerly;[C2] N. W. McLachlan: *Bessel Functions for Engineers;* Oxford University Press, 1934; and G. N. Watson: *Theory of Bessel Functions;* Cambridge University Press, 1922. For tables see Jahnke and Emde: *Tables of Functions;* reprinted by Dover Publications, New York, 1943; originally by B. G. Teubner, Leipzig, 1938. See also Appendix 5.

This yields upon combination of the two equations the characteristic equation

$$C_2 \frac{\sin m(L_1 + L_2)}{\sin mL_1} = 0, \quad \text{or} \quad m_\alpha = \frac{\alpha\pi}{(L_1 + L_2)},$$

$$\alpha = \pm 1, \pm 2, \cdots \quad (27)$$

and therefore

$$\Phi(\rho, z) = k_1 + k_2 z + \sum_{\alpha=1}^{\infty} C_\alpha \frac{\sin\left(\alpha\pi \dfrac{L_1 + z}{L_1 + L_2}\right)}{\sin\left(\alpha\pi \dfrac{L_1}{L_1 + L_2}\right)} I_0\left(\frac{\alpha\pi\rho}{L_1 + L_2}\right) \quad (28)$$

where the negative values of α have been suppressed, since they lead to the same functional expressions. For $\rho = a$, the sum (28) is a conventional Fourier series in z and must represent the actual potential distribution on $\rho = a$ as well as the particular integral values. The coefficients A_α are therefore determined by

$$\begin{aligned}
A_\alpha &= C_\alpha \frac{I_0\left(\dfrac{\alpha\pi a}{L_1 + L_2}\right)}{\sin\dfrac{\alpha\pi L_1}{L_1 + L_2}} \\
&= \frac{2}{L_1 + L_2}\left[\int_{z=-L_1}^{z=0} (\Phi_1 - k_1 - k_2 z) \sin\left(\alpha\pi \frac{L_1 + z}{L_1 + L_2}\right) dz \right.\\
&\quad \left. + \int_{z=0}^{z=L_2} (\Phi_2 - k_1 - k_2 z) \sin\left(\alpha\pi \frac{L_1 + z}{L_1 + L_2}\right) dz\right]
\end{aligned} \quad (29)$$

analogous to $(29 \cdot 22)$ and $(29 \cdot 22a)$, with $(L_1 + L_2)$ as the half period. This expansion is definitely permissible and convergent, since the sine functions form an orthogonal system and since the potential values are bounded. The integrals in (29) can readily be evaluated and actually reduce to

$$A_\alpha = -\frac{2}{\alpha\pi} (\Phi_1 - \Phi_2) \cos \frac{\alpha\pi L_1}{L_1 + L_2}$$

so that the final solution for the potential becomes

$$\Phi(\rho, z) = \frac{(L_1 + z)\Phi_2 + (L_2 - z)\Phi_1}{L_1 + L_2}$$

$$- \frac{2}{\pi} (\Phi_1 - \Phi_2) \sum_{\alpha=1}^{\infty} \left\{ \frac{1}{\alpha} \cos\left(\frac{\alpha\pi L_1}{L_1 + L_2}\right) \cdot \right.$$

$$\left. \sin\left(\alpha\pi \frac{L_1 + z}{L_1 + L_2}\right) \frac{I_0\left(\frac{\alpha\pi\rho}{L_1 + L_2}\right)}{I_0\left(\frac{\alpha\pi a}{L_1 + L_2}\right)} \right\} \quad (30)$$

In the case of symmetry $L_1 = L_2 = L$, the Fourier series will contain only the terms for which α is even, since $\cos(\alpha\pi/2) = 0$ for α odd; in this case, the plane of symmetry $z = 0$ becomes an equipotential surface of potential $\frac{1}{2}(\Phi_1 + \Phi_2)$. Should, on the other hand, potential Φ_1 vary linearly or in any fashion along $\rho = a$ from a value zero at $z = -L_1$ identified as cathode surface, to a value Φ_1 at $z = 0$ as in the electrostatic image tube,[4] then the first integral in (29) would have to be appropriately modified by using the known function $\Phi_1(z)$ instead of the constant value Φ_1.

Two Equidiameter Coaxial Cylinders, One Infinitely Long. If L_2 is large compared with the diameter $2a$, it might as well be assumed infinitely long with the effect that the Fourier series goes over into a Fourier integral. Maintaining the same boundary conditions as in Fig. 30·3, except that $L_2 = \infty$, one can specify $Z(-L_1) = 0$ for (21), using the potential value Φ_1 as additive constant to satisfy the condition at $z = -L_1$; this gives

$$\frac{C_1}{C_2} = \cot mL_1$$

Therefore in accordance with (24)

$$\Phi(\rho, z) = \Phi_1 + \int_{m=0}^{\infty} C_2 \frac{\sin m(L_1 + z)}{\sin mL_1} I_0(m\rho) \, dm \quad (31)$$

since no discrete spectrum of m-values exists. The unknown coefficient C_2 must be obtained by representing the potential value

---

[4] V. K. Zworykin and G. A. Morton, *Jl. Optical Soc. Am.*, **26**, p. 181 (1936); Zworykin *et al.*,[B32] p. 46; also E. G. Ramberg and G. A. Morton, *Jl. Appl. Phys.*, **10**, p. 465 (1939).

along $\rho = a$ in Fourier integral form analogous to (29·31) and (29·32). Introducing a change of variable to $\zeta = z + L_1$, so that the origin of ζ is in the plane of the end face, one has from (31)

$$\Phi(a, \zeta) = \Phi_1 + \int_{m=0}^{\infty} C_2 \frac{\sin m\zeta}{\sin mL_1} I_0(ma) \, dm \qquad (32)$$

whereas the direct Fourier representation by (29·36) or (29·38) would read in the simpler complex form

$$\Phi(a, \zeta) - \Phi_1 = \frac{1}{2\pi} \int_{m=-\infty}^{\infty} F(m) e^{jm\zeta} \, dm$$

$$= \frac{1}{2\pi j} \int_{-j\infty}^{+j\infty} F(p) e^{p\zeta} \, dp, \qquad \zeta > 0 \qquad (33)$$

The potential values are referred to Φ_1 and are therefore zero for $0 < \zeta < L_1$ and equal to $(\Phi_2 - \Phi_1)$ for $\zeta > L_1$. However, this does not specify the character of the potential distribution for $\zeta < 0$; since (32) implies an odd function $U(m)$ as comparison with (29·31) indicates, one must assume *opposite* potentials at symmetrical locations with respect to $\zeta = 0$. The evaluation of $F(m)$ or $F(p)$ can now be made, keeping in mind a change in sign for $\zeta < 0$ as noted; the direct integration as in (29·36a) with $p = jm$ gives

$$F(p) = -\int_{-\infty}^{-L_1} (\Phi_2 - \Phi_1) e^{-p\zeta} \, d\zeta + \int_{L_1}^{\infty} (\Phi_2 - \Phi_1) e^{-p\zeta} \, d\zeta$$

$$= \frac{\Phi_2 - \Phi_1}{p} (e^{pL_1} + e^{-pL_1}) = \frac{2}{jm} (\Phi_2 - \Phi_1) \cos mL_1 \qquad (34)$$

From this one can get the function $U(m)$ by identifying it in accordance with (29·37) as related to the imaginary part of $F(m)$, so that

$$U(m) = -\frac{1}{\pi} \operatorname{Im} F(m) = -\frac{2}{\pi} \frac{\Phi_1 - \Phi_2}{m} \cos mL_1$$

This must now be identical with the integrand in (32) except for $\sin m\zeta$ and yields

$$\frac{C_2}{\sin mL_1} = -\frac{2}{\pi} \frac{\Phi_1 - \Phi_2}{m} \cdot \frac{\cos mL_1}{I_0(ma)}$$

which finally gives for (31) the solution

$$\Phi(\rho, z) = \Phi_1 - \frac{2}{\pi} (\Phi_1 - \Phi_2) \cdot$$

$$\int_{m=0}^{\infty} \frac{\cos mL_1}{m} \sin m(L_1 + z) \cdot \frac{I_0(m\rho)}{I_0(ma)} dm \quad (35)$$

Comparison of this Fourier integral with the Fourier series solution for finite values of L_2 in (30) demonstrates the very close similarity between them.   In many instances, (35) can readily be obtained by numerical or graphical methods with L_1 and a as parameters, and z and ρ as ultimate variables.   If again the potential on $\rho = a$ varies linearly over the distance $(-L_1) < z < 0$, as one might assume in the electrostatic image tube,[5] one need only to modify the integral (33) by introducing the variation along the distances $0 < \zeta < L_1$.

The analytical evaluation of the integral (35) is achieved best by replacing the real variable m by $p = jm$ and interpreting the integral as one in the complex p-plane as pointed out in connection with (29·38).   The poles of the integrand are located at $p = 0$ and at $I_0(ma) = J_0(jma) = J_0(pa) = 0$, the latter being the Bessel function of first kind and giving an infinite number of symmetrically located root values, of which the first six are

$$\begin{array}{ll}
p_1 a = \pm 2.4048 & p_4 a = \pm 11.7915 \\
p_2 a = \pm 5.5201 & p_5 a = \pm 14.9309 \\
p_3 a = \pm 8.6537 & p_6 a = \pm 18.0711
\end{array}$$

Thus, in the complex form (33) with (34)

$$\pm \Phi(\rho, z) = \Phi_1 - \frac{1}{2\pi j} (\Phi_1 - \Phi_2) \cdot$$

$$\int_{-j\infty}^{+j\infty} \frac{e^{pL_1} + e^{-pL_1}}{p} \frac{J_0(p\rho)}{J_0(pa)} e^{p(L_1+z)} dp, \quad z \gtrless (-L_1) \quad (36)$$

where the total potential values change sign as already assumed in the integral (34).   Combining the exponentials into e^{pz} and $e^{p(2L_1+z)}$, two integrals of the type (29·38) arise, each with poles of first order along positive and negative real axes.   In accordance

---

[5] G. A. Morton and E. G. Ramberg, *Phys.*, **7**, p. 451 (1936); also Zworykin et al.,[B32] p. 381.

with (29·41) and observing $(d/dp)\, J_0(pa) = -aJ_1(pa)$ one can now write the sums of residues in the following groups

$$
\left.
\begin{aligned}
R_{\mathrm{I}} &= 1 - \sum \frac{J_0(p_\alpha \rho)}{(p_\alpha a)\, J_1(p_\alpha a)}\, e^{-p_\alpha z} \quad \text{valid for } z > 0 \\[2ex]
R_{\mathrm{II}} &= + \sum \frac{J_0(p_\alpha \rho)}{(p_\alpha a)\, J_1(p_\alpha a)}\, e^{p_\alpha z} \qquad \text{valid for } z < 0 \\[2ex]
R_{\mathrm{III}} &= - \sum \frac{J_0(p_\alpha \rho)}{(p_\alpha a)\, J_1(p_\alpha a)}\, e^{-p_\alpha(2L_1+z)} \\
&\qquad\qquad\qquad\qquad \text{valid for } z > (-2L_1) \\[2ex]
R_{\mathrm{IV}} &= 1 + \sum \frac{J_0(p_\alpha \rho)}{(p_\alpha a)\, J_1(p_\alpha a)}\, e^{p_\alpha(2L_1+z)} \\
&\qquad\qquad\qquad\qquad \text{valid for } z < (-2L_1)
\end{aligned}
\right\}
\quad (37)
$$

where all sums are extended only over the *positive* root values of $J_0(p_\alpha a)$ listed in the table above. The total solution for the potential is thus

$$
\left.
\begin{aligned}
\Phi(\rho, z) &= \Phi_1 - (\Phi_1 - \Phi_2)[R_{\mathrm{I}} + R_{\mathrm{III}}] \;\text{valid for } z > 0 \\[1ex]
&= \Phi_1 - (\Phi_1 - \Phi_2)[R_{\mathrm{II}} + R_{\mathrm{III}}] \\
&\qquad\qquad\qquad \text{valid for } (-L_1) < z < 0
\end{aligned}
\right\}
\quad (38)
$$

the other ranges are of no interest, lying beyond the desired field region. The potential reduces to Φ_1 at $z = -L_1$, since the sums in R_{II} and R_{III} cancel, and it takes the proper values along $\rho = a$ as seen from (36) where only the positive unit step at $z = 0$ can be considered for $z > (-L_1)$. The unit step at $z = -2L_1$ is inverted because of the odd symmetry of potential values; its effect is therefore in R_{IV}. The values of the complete series in R_{I} and R_{II} have been computed and tabulated[6] in connection with a general attempt to solve the potential distribution for two equidiameter cylinders with a finite separation $2d$ as shown in Fig. 30·4. One can consider the right half of this arrangement as equivalent to the above case, except that the potential function is actually unknown for $\rho = a$ along $0 < z < d$; the assumption of

---

[6] S. Bertram, *Jl. Appl. Phys.*, **13**, p. 496 (1942); tabulation of values for ρ/a in steps of 0.1, for z/a in steps of 0.05 up to 1.75, beyond which exponential approximation is possible.

linear variation of the potential along this distance leads to results which check rather closely with data obtained with the electrolytic trough.   Analytically, one need only modify (34) in accordance with the assumed potential variation and enter this in (36) as a modification of the first factor under the integral sign.

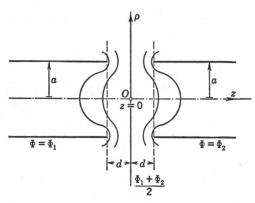

Fig. 30·4   Two Coaxial Equidiameter Cylinders with Finite Separation.

Two Infinite Coaxial Cylinders.   A simpler result obtains in the symmetrical case of Fig. 30·3, where the lengths of both equidiameter cylinders L_1 and L_2 are infinite.   One need only consider the right half with potential $\frac{1}{2}(\Phi_1 + \Phi_2)$ in the plane $z = 0$ and $\Phi = \Phi_2$ along $\rho = a$.   Though one could again use the Fourier integral method, it is simpler to formulate the solution directly in terms of the orthogonal Bessel function series.   For this purpose take the lower sign of m^2 in (2) where the variables have been separated.   For $Z(z)$ one has then hyperbolic or, better still, exponential functions as solution

$$Z(z) = C_1 e^{mz} + C_2 e^{-mz} \qquad (39)$$

Because of the infinite extension for $z > 0$, only the negative exponential function can be accepted as solution.   The function $R(\rho)$ must now satisfy

$$\frac{d^2R}{d\rho^2} + \frac{1}{\rho}\frac{dR}{d\rho} + m^2R = 0 \qquad (40)$$

which is the normal form of the differential equation for the

Bessel function $J_0(m\rho)$ of zeroth order[7]

$$R(\rho) = D_1 J_0(m\rho) + D_2 N_0(m\rho) \tag{41}$$

Again, $N_0(m\rho)$ has a logarithmic singularity at $\rho = 0$, so that it cannot be admitted as solution. Thus, one potential solution is the general product

$$ce^{-mz} J_0(m\rho) \tag{42}$$

where $D_1 C_2$ has been combined into c. To satisfy the boundary conditions, one can add a constant Φ_2 as particular integral and require of (42) that it vanish for $\rho = a$, which leads at once to the root values $(m_\alpha a)$ tabulated as $(p_\alpha a)$ for (36). The functions $J_0(m_\alpha \rho)$ now form an orthogonal system of a Sturm-Liouville problem, since the differential equation (40) can be rewritten in the form $(29 \cdot 2)$, namely,

$$\frac{d}{d\rho}\left[\rho \frac{d}{d\rho} R(\rho) \right] + m^2 \rho R(\rho) = 0 \tag{43}$$

which defines the characteristic numbers $\lambda = m^2$, the weight function $p(\rho) = \rho$, with respect to which orthogonality exists, and gives the norm N by the integration

$$\int_{\rho=0}^{\rho=a} \rho J_0(m_\alpha \rho) \, J_0(m_\beta \rho) \, d\rho$$
$$= \begin{cases} 0 & \text{for } \alpha \neq \beta \\ \dfrac{a^2}{2} J_1{}^2(m_\alpha a) = N_\alpha & \text{for } \alpha = \beta \end{cases} \tag{44}$$

One could, of course, normalize these Bessel functions as in $(29 \cdot 10)$ by dividing by $\sqrt{N_\alpha}$, and one can expand any bounded function into a Fourier-Bessel series in accordance with $(29 \cdot 11)$; for the more general forms see Appendix 5.

The total potential solution is now

$$\Phi(\rho, z) = \Phi_2 + \sum_{\alpha=1}^{\infty} c_\alpha e^{-m_\alpha z} J_0(m_\alpha \rho) \tag{45}$$

where the coefficients c_α are found from the remaining boundary

---

[7] See references. footnote 3.

condition which stipulates that $\Phi(\rho, 0)$ be constant and equal to the median potential value,

$$\Phi(\rho, 0) = \Phi_2 + \sum_{\alpha=1}^{\infty} c_\alpha J_0(m_\alpha \rho) \equiv \frac{1}{2} (\Phi_1 + \Phi_2)$$

Applying the first form of $(29 \cdot 12)$ in order to find the coefficients c_α, one has

$$N_\alpha c_\alpha = \frac{1}{2} (\Phi_1 - \Phi_2) \int_{\rho=0}^{\rho=a} \rho J_0(m_\alpha \rho) \, d\rho = \frac{1}{2} (\Phi_1 - \Phi_2) \frac{a}{m_\alpha} J_1(m_\alpha a)$$

With N_α from (44) this yields the final form for the potential

$$\Phi(\rho, z) = \Phi_2 + (\Phi_1 - \Phi_2) \sum_{\alpha=1}^{\infty} \frac{J_0(m_\alpha \rho)}{(m_\alpha a) \, J_1(m_\alpha a)} e^{-m_\alpha z} \quad (46)$$

The summation is identical with the one occurring in R_{I} of (37) and is tabulated as referred above.   Since one can deduce

$$\sum_{\alpha=1}^{\infty} \frac{J_0(\lambda_\alpha)}{\lambda_\alpha \, J_1(\lambda_\alpha)} = \frac{1}{2} \quad (47)$$

if λ_α are the root values of $J_0(\lambda) = 0$, one can readily show that $\Phi(\rho, 0) = \frac{1}{2}(\Phi_2 + \Phi_1)$.

In electron optical problems, one is mainly concerned with the value of the potential and its derivatives along the axis $\rho = 0$ as outlined in the first part of this section.   This makes an analytic expression practically necessary, yet makes it desirable to have a simple form to enter into the differential equation for the electron trajectories.   Introducing $\rho = 0$ into (46) gives

$$\Phi(0, z) = \Phi_2 - (\Phi_2 - \Phi_1) \sum_{\alpha=1}^{\infty} e^{-m_\alpha z} \, [(m_\alpha a) \, J_1(m_\alpha a)]^{-1} \quad (48)$$

for the axial potential variation for the two infinitely long equidiameter cylinders of Fig. $30 \cdot 3$ with $L_1 \rightarrow \infty$ and $L_2 \rightarrow \infty$.   The sum in (48) can be represented with very good accuracy by the much simpler form[8]

$$\sum_{\alpha=1}^{\infty} e^{-m_\alpha z} \, [(m_\alpha a) \, J_1(m_\alpha a)]^{-1} \approx \frac{1}{2}(1 - \tanh \omega z) \quad (49)$$

[8] F. Gray, *Bell System Techn. Jl.*, **18**, p. 25 (1939); also S. Bertram, *Proc. I.R.E.*, **28**, p. 418 (1940).

where $\omega = 1.32/a$, so that

$$\Phi(0, z) \approx \tfrac{1}{2}(\Phi_2 + \Phi_1) + \tfrac{1}{2}(\Phi_2 - \Phi_1) \tanh \omega z \qquad (50)$$

For graph of this and the first two derivatives see Zworykin et al.,[B32] p. 379. This approximation can be used with some modifications in other cases as well.

If the cylinders are not of equal diameters, the analytical method becomes well-nigh impossible, and approximations by a

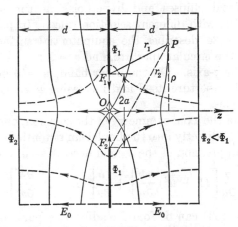

FIG. 30·5   Symmetrical Circular Aperture.

perturbation method using Green's function remain the only recourse. The electrolytic trough has been called upon extensively in such cases; see Spangenberg,[B29] p. 345.

Circular Aperture. Assume a circular hole of radius a in an infinite conducting plane of potential Φ_1 as in Fig. 30·5, which is called a *circular aperture* in electron optics, then the field lines must leave the conducting plane at right angles and tend to become parallel to the z-axis of revolution; at large distance the field must be nearly uniform so that one can place parallel planes of potentials Φ_2 at symmetrical distances d from the aperture plane. In order to describe the boundary condition on the aperture plane in the simplest terms one selects the orthogonal oblate spheroidal coordinate system from section 33 with a slight modification. Using instead of (33·60) the same transformation (32·52) as for the elliptic cylinder and introducing the auxiliary coordinates,

$$u = \sinh \xi, \qquad v = \sin \eta \qquad (51)$$

then the cylindrical coordinates ρ and z can be expressed as

$$z = a \sinh \xi \sin \eta = auv, \qquad \rho = a \cosh \xi \cos \eta = a\sqrt{u^2 + 1}\,\sqrt{1 - v^2}$$

$$(52)$$

where a is the radius of the aperture and identical with the focal distance f of the system. The coordinates ξ and η are similar to the elliptic cylinder coordinates in (29·59), and, indeed, constant values of u and v imply constant values of ξ and η and thus mean confocal ellipses and hyperbolas of the same shape as Fig. 29·6 but with different selection rules. In particular, $v = 0$ or $r_2 - r_1 = 2a$ describes the equipotential surface Φ_1, i.e., the plane with the circular aperture, and $v = 1$ or $\eta = \pi/2$ or $r_2 = r_1$ describes the z-axis. On the other hand, $u = 0$ or $r_2 + r_1 = 2a$ describes the aperture itself and increasing u gives the ellipses of increasing axes.

Because of the axial symmetry of the solution, one can introduce (52) and (51) directly into the Laplacian potential equation (33·2) and with suppression of the second derivative in ϕ obtain

$$\frac{\partial}{\partial u}\left[(1 + u^2)\frac{\partial \Phi}{\partial u}\right] + \frac{\partial}{\partial v}\left[(1 - v^2)\frac{\partial \Phi}{\partial v}\right] = 0 \qquad (53)$$

Solutions of (53) can be found readily by separation of variables; assuming $\Phi = M(u) \cdot N(v)$ and introducing into (53), one has

$$M^{-1}\frac{d}{du}\left[(1 + u^2)\frac{dM}{du}\right]$$

$$= -N^{-1}\frac{d}{dv}\left[(1 - v^2)\frac{dN}{dv}\right] = m^2 \quad (54)$$

Several solutions are feasible for specific values of m^2 which are of the type of particular integrals, since the boundary conditions are not yet utilized. Thus, for $m^2 = 2$ one finds as suggested by

$$\frac{d}{du}\tan^{-1} u = (1 + u^2)^{-1}$$

and

$$\frac{d}{dv}\tanh^{-1} v = (1 - v^2)^{-1}$$

that

$$MN = \{C_1 u + C_2\,[u \tan^{-1} u + 1]\} \cdot$$
$$\{D_1 v + D_2\,[v \tanh^{-1} v - 1]\} \quad (55)$$

satisfies (53). Since the boundary condition requires $\Phi = \Phi_1$ on $v = 0$, one can choose $D_2 = 0$ in (55) and add the constant Φ_1; since $v = 1$ along the z-axis, the potential remains finite there. The potential function is, therefore,

$$\Phi(u, v) = v \{C_1 u + C_2 [u \tan^{-1} u + 1]\} + \Phi_1$$

with D_1 discarded as superfluous. Actually, no other boundary conditions are available, but it is necessary that the solution be symmetrical to the plane $z = 0$, so that one must take $C_1 = 0$. It is also in the nature of the problem that a nearly uniform field should result for large values of z. Since $\tan^{-1} u \to (\pi/2)$ as $u \to \infty$, the potential becomes for large values of u

$$\lim_{u \to \infty} \Phi(u, v) \to C_2 v \left(u \frac{\pi}{2} + 1 \right) + \Phi_1 \approx \frac{\pi}{2} C_2 \frac{z}{a} + \Phi_1$$

if one disregards the value 1 and utilizes (52). Introducing $\Phi \approx \Phi_2$ at $z = d$ gives at once $C_2 = -\frac{2}{\pi} (\Phi_1 - \Phi_2) \frac{a}{d} = -\frac{2}{\pi} E_0 a$, if E_0 is the uniform field gradient at large distance from the aperture. Thus,

$$\Phi(u, v) = \Phi_1 - \frac{2}{\pi} a \left| E_0 \right| v[u \tan^{-1} u + 1] \tag{56}$$

and along the z-axis where $v = 1$ and therefore $u = z/a$ from (52), in cylindrical coordinates ρ and z

$$\Phi(0, z) = \Phi_1 - \frac{2}{\pi} a \left| E_0 \right| \cdot \left[\frac{z}{a} \tan^{-1} \frac{z}{a} + 1 \right] \tag{57}$$

The potential at the saddle point 0 with $z = 0$ is

$$\Phi(0) = \Phi_1 - \frac{2}{\pi} a \left| E_0 \right|$$

and can be made to vanish with proper choice of Φ_1. Good graphs of this symmetrical potential distribution are found in Spangenberg,[B29] p. 347, and in Zworykin et al.,[B32] p. 384. The problem is solved with more difficult notation in Ollendorff,[A18] p. 295, and in Brüche and Scherzer,[B20] p. 69; see also Lamb,[C22] p. 142, for hydrodynamic applications to the flow of an ideal fluid through a circular aperture.

In order to estimate the degree of approximation, one can consider that $\tan^{-1} 12 = 85.4°$ leads to $(u \tan^{-1} u) = 17.86 \gg 1$; this,

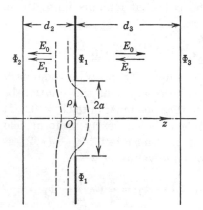

however, requires a distance along the z-axis of $(z/a) = u = 12$, or $d = 12a$ in accordance with (52), where $v = 1$. Admitting $(u \tan^{-1} u) \geqslant 10$ as tolerable approximation requires $d \geqslant 7a$.

One can also achieve solutions for unsymmetrical potential distributions by superimposing a uniform electric field gradient E_1, weakening to $(E_0 - E_1)$, and strengthening to $(E_0 + E_1)$, the respective sectional gradients. With the designations of Fig. 30·6, tak-

FIG. 30·6   Unsymmetrical Aperture Field.

ing all gradients with absolute values to avoid difficulties with signs, and observing (52) for z, one has

$$\Phi(u, v) = \Phi_1 - \frac{2}{\pi} a \left|E_0\right| v[u \tan^{-1} u + 1] + a \left|E_1\right| uv \quad (58)$$

The potentials at the electrode plates are given as

$$\Phi_2 = - (\left|E_0\right| + \left|E_1\right|)d_2 + \Phi_1$$

and

$$\Phi_3 = (\left|E_0\right| - \left|E_1\right|)d_3 + \Phi_1$$

they depend on the distances d_2 and d_3 and cannot be chosen freely, since the solution is approximated by superposition and is not an exact one. For $\left|E_1\right| = \left|E_0\right|$ one has a field free space to the right of the aperture plane and the equipotential lines bulge through the aperture.[9]   Good graphs are found in Spangenberg,[B29] p. 348, and in Zworykin,[B32] p. 384.

[9] Th. C. Fry, *Am. Math. Monthly*, **39**, p. 199 (1932); also *Bell Tel. Lab. Monograph* No. B-671; Ollendorff,[A18] p. 296; and Smythe,[A22] p. 161.

31 · GENERAL ORTHOGONAL COORDINATE SYSTEMS

For the solution of general potential problems in three-dimensional space it is desirable to choose coordinate systems which permit the simplest formulation of the boundary conditions, as pointed out previously. However, the coordinate system influences the form of the basic differential equations of potential, so that only such coordinate systems are of practical value which keep this form amenable to present-day mathematical treatments. This has restricted the choice to *orthogonal coordinate systems* in which the unit vectors in the three coordinate directions at any one point are mutually orthogonal, or, differently stated, in which the three families of surfaces defined by keeping the value of each coordinate constant in turn are mutually orthogonal.

It is customary to select the Cartesian system as fundamental, since in it the three coordinates play exactly equal roles and all relations involve the three coordinates in exactly symmetrical manner, so that any cyclic[1] interchange will not affect the form of any boundary value problem.

CARTESIAN COORDINATE SYSTEM

The Laplacian differential equation for the three-dimensional case is given by

$$\nabla^2 \Phi = \frac{\partial^2 \Phi}{\partial x^2} + \frac{\partial^2 \Phi}{\partial y^2} + \frac{\partial^2 \Phi}{\partial z^2} = 0 \tag{1}$$

In order to effect a solution in general terms one can readily separate the variables by assuming a product function

$$\Phi(x, y, z) = X(x)\, Y(y)\, Z(z) \tag{2}$$

in which each factor is a function of only one variable; this is obviously a direct extension of the two-dimensional case in section 29. Introducing (2) into (1) and dividing through by the product (2) will give

$$X^{-1}X'' + Y^{-1}Y'' + Z^{-1}Z'' = 0 \tag{3}$$

where the double primes indicate the second derivatives with respect to the pertinent variable. In (3) the variables are already

---

[1] A cyclic interchange is one in which the order of succession of the elements is preserved, as for example (x, y, z) to (y, z, x) to (z, x, y).

separated, so that in order to be an equation for any combination
of the variables x, y, and z, each term must by itself be a constant,
which is usually designated as *separation constant*, because it
enters on account of the reduction to ordinary differential equations.   One has, for example,

$$X'' = -m^2 X, \qquad Y'' = -n^2 Y, \qquad Z'' = (m^2 + n^2)Z \qquad (4)$$

where m^2 and n^2 are the *characteristic numbers* whose spectra are
defined by the boundary conditions; if the latter are homogeneous,
this leads to the classical Sturm-Liouville problem discussed more

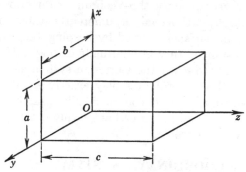

FIG. 31·1   Potential Distribution in Rectangular Parallelepiped.

extensively in section 29.   Of course, one can associate the
characteristic numbers m^2 and n^2 with any of the two variables
above; but the third one must then accept the negative sum of the
two.

To illustrate the procedure, determine the potential within a
rectangular box with the dimensions shown in Fig. 31·1 and a
potential distribution $\Phi = G(x, y)$ on the face $z = 0$ and $\Phi = 0$
on the other five faces.   This determines the boundary conditions
as homogeneous in x- and y-directions, so that m and n can be
found readily.   The typical solution in these variables is from (4)

$$X = C_1 \sin mx + C_2 \cos mx, \qquad Y = D_1 \sin ny + D_2 \cos ny \qquad (5)$$

with

$$X(0) = X(a) = 0, \qquad Y(0) = Y(b) = 0 \qquad (6)$$

Introducing these conditions into (5) yields

$$C_2 = 0, \quad \sin ma = 0, \qquad D_2 = 0, \quad \sin nb = 0 \qquad (7)$$

and therefore the characteristic numbers

$$m_\alpha = \frac{\alpha\pi}{a}, \qquad n_\beta = \frac{\beta\pi}{b}, \qquad \alpha, \beta = 1, 2, 3, \cdots \infty \qquad (8)$$

The negative values of m and n are suppressed, since they lead to no new functional forms. The typical solution for Z is from (4)

$$Z = P_1 \sinh \sqrt{m_\alpha{}^2 + n_\beta{}^2}\, z + P_2 \cosh \sqrt{m_\alpha{}^2 + n_\beta{}^2}\, z \qquad (9)$$

and since at $z = c$ one must satisfy $Z(c) = 0$, this gives

$$\frac{P_2}{P_1} = -\tanh \sqrt{m_\alpha{}^2 + n_\beta{}^2}\, c$$

with m_α and n_β known from (8). With all homogeneous boundary conditions satisfied, the potential has the form

$$\Phi(x, y, z) = \sum_\alpha \sum_\beta P_{\alpha,\beta} \frac{-\sinh \sqrt{m_\alpha{}^2 + n_\beta{}^2}(c - z)}{\cosh \sqrt{m_\alpha{}^2 + n_\beta{}^2}\, c} \sin m_\alpha x \sin n_\beta y$$

$$(10)$$

where the sums must extend over all the values of m_α and n_β as defined in (8); the coefficient $C_{1\alpha}$ and $D_{1\beta}$ have been merged with P_1 which therefore depends on α and β as indicated by the subscripts in (10). In a more general case one might have to add to (10) the solutions which correspond to the singular cases $m = 0$ and/or $n = 0$. If only $m = 0$, then (4) gives $X = C_1 x + C_2$, Y as before in (5) and Z as in (9), but with argument $(n_\beta z)$; this leads then to single summation in β. If only $n = 0$, a corresponding single summation in α will result. If both $m = n = 0$, then the product

$$(C_1 x + C_2)(D_1 y + D_2)(P_1 z + P_2)$$

will occur. In the present problem all these possibilities are excluded by the homogeneous boundary conditions in x and y.

The solution (10) represents a *double* Fourier series in the two variables x and y as is necessary in order to express the given distribution $G(x, y)$ defined over the finite area $0 < x < a$, $0 < y < b$. The extension from the one-dimensional Fourier series of section 29 is straightforward; general details on such series are found[2] in Churchill,[C3] p. 116; in Byerly,[C2] p. 139; and in Carslaw [C17] in conjunction with problems of conduction of heat. Assuming $G(x, y)$ an odd periodic function in x and y, bounded for all values of x and y in the region of definition and satisfying the Dirichlet conditions, then one can represent it as

$$G(x, y) = \sum_\alpha \sum_\beta A_{\alpha,\beta} \sin m_\alpha x \sin n_\beta y \tag{11}$$

where in turn the coefficients $A_{\alpha,\beta}$ are defined by

$$A_{\alpha,\beta} = \frac{2}{a} \cdot \frac{2}{b} \int_{x=0}^{x=a} \int_{y=0}^{y=b} G(x, y) \sin m_\alpha x \sin n_\beta y \, dx \, dy \tag{12}$$

Since $\alpha = 1$ and $\beta = 1$ in (8) define a and b as respective half fundamental periods of the distribution, $G(x, y)$ can well be assumed odd when extended beyond its region of definition. To satisfy the boundary condition at $z = 0$, comparison of (10) at $z = 0$ with (11) yields at once

$$-P_{\alpha,\beta} \tanh \sqrt{m_\alpha^2 + n_\beta^2} \, c = A_{\alpha,\beta}$$

so that the complete solution is

$$\Phi(x, y, z) = \sum_\alpha \sum_\beta A_{\alpha,\beta} \frac{\sinh \sqrt{m_\alpha^2 + n_\beta^2} \, (c - z)}{\sinh \sqrt{m_\alpha^2 + n_\beta^2} \, c} \sin m_\alpha x \sin n_\beta y$$

$$\tag{13}$$

with $A_{\alpha,\beta}$ from (12).

Any other boundary conditions with respect to the potential can be handled in analogous manner. If the potential is given over two or more of the faces, then the principle of superposition can be applied, solving for only one inhomogeneous boundary condition at a time as above and then taking the sum total of all partial solutions.

In addition to the spectral solutions determined by separation of the variables inclusive of the irregular cases $m = 0$ and/or $n = 0$, there are a considerable number of particular integrals which at times might lead to simpler overall solutions. Thus,

[2] See also H. S. Carslaw: *Fourier Series and Integrals;* Cambridge University Press, Cambridge, 1930.

any additive combination with suitable individual constants of the terms

$$x^2 - y^2, \qquad y^2 - z^2, \qquad z^2 - x^2 \tag{14}$$

and others presents a possible solution, as well as any general solution of the two-dimensional Laplacian differential equations in x and y or y and z or z and x; obviously, a constant Φ_0 can always be added. The selection of the most expeditious approach to a new problem is still an art, and the only reassurance that a solution does indeed exist and that a solution is the correct and only one comes from the existence and uniqueness theorems of pure and applied mathematics, as found in Kellogg,[C10] in Courant and Hilbert,[C4] and in Frank and Mises.[C6] If a solution satisfies the differential equation and all the boundary conditions in so far as these are compatible (or, perhaps better, correspond to some physical reality), the solution is the correct and only one no matter how it has been found.

If in the above problem $c \to \infty$, so that the rectangular box becomes a rectangular semi-infinite prism, then the solution (9) must be replaced by the exponential form

$$Z = P_1 \exp\left(-\sqrt{m_\alpha^2 + n_\beta^2}\, z\right) \tag{15}$$

in order to provide regularity at $z = \infty$. Keeping the same boundary conditions as before results then in

$$\Phi(x, y, z) = \sum_\alpha \sum_\beta A_{\alpha,\beta} \exp\left(-\sqrt{m_\alpha^2 + n_\beta^2}\, z\right) \sin m_\alpha x \sin n_\beta y \tag{16}$$

where the coefficients $A_{\alpha,\beta}$ are again determined by (12).

Boundary value problems involving the magnetic vector potential can be solved with the same facility, because in the Cartesian coordinate system—and in this alone—the identity (6·16) holds,

$$\nabla \times \nabla \times \mathbf{A} - \nabla(\nabla \cdot \mathbf{A}) = (\nabla \cdot \nabla)\mathbf{A}$$

with $\nabla \cdot \nabla = \nabla^2$ the conventional Laplacian operator. Since div $\mathbf{A} = 0$ as postulated in (6·17), the problem of finding solutions for the vector potential reduces to solving the scalar Laplacian differential equations for the components A_x, A_y, and A_z, which is the same procedure as just illustrated for the electrostatic potential.

GENERAL ORTHOGONAL COORDINATE SYSTEMS

Transformation of Scalar Potential Problems to General Orthogonal Coordinates. Assume a general orthogonal system of coordinates u_1, u_2, u_3 as given in Fig. 31·2; the mutual relation-

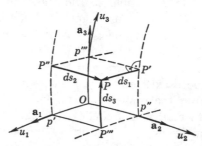

FIG. 31·2   Orthogonal Curvilinear Coordinate System.

ships between these coordinates and a Cartesian system can be expressed in terms of the functional relations

$$u_\alpha = u_\alpha(x, y, z), \qquad \alpha = 1, 2, 3 \tag{17}$$

and the inverse ones

$$x = f_1(u_1, u_2, u_3), \quad y = f_2(u_1, u_2, u_3), \quad z = f_3(u_1, u_2, u_3) \tag{18}$$

Obviously, these reciprocal relations must be one-valued or at least restricted to single values within the applicable ranges in order to provide the necessary uniqueness; they also must have no singularities within the ranges used.

For the transformation of differential relations from one system to the other, one takes from (17)

$$du_\alpha = \frac{\partial u_\alpha}{\partial x} dx + \frac{\partial u_\alpha}{\partial y} dy + \frac{\partial u_\alpha}{\partial z} dz, \qquad \alpha = 1, 2, 3 \tag{19}$$

and conversely,

$$dx = \sum_\alpha \frac{\partial f_1}{\partial u_\alpha} du_\alpha, \qquad dy = \sum_\alpha \frac{\partial f_2}{\partial u_\alpha} du_\alpha, \qquad dz = \sum_\alpha \frac{\partial f_3}{\partial u_\alpha} du_\alpha \tag{20}$$

Since the general line element in Cartesian coordinates is expressed in vector form (see Appendix 3)

$$\mathbf{ds} = \mathbf{i} \, dx + \mathbf{j} \, dy + \mathbf{k} \, dz$$

one has for its absolute value

$$ds^2 = \mathbf{ds} \cdot \mathbf{ds} = dx^2 + dy^2 + dz^2$$

Introducing into (20) the vector representation, as for example,

$$\mathbf{dx} = \mathbf{i}\, dx = \mathbf{i}\, \frac{\partial f_1}{\partial u_1}\, du_1 + \mathbf{i}\, \frac{\partial f_1}{\partial u_2}\, du_2 + \mathbf{i}\, \frac{\partial f_1}{\partial u_3}\, du_3 \tag{21}$$

and similarly for the other two coordinate directions, one can again form the scalar product $\mathbf{ds}\cdot\mathbf{ds}$ and obtains on account of the presumed orthogonality of the generalized curvilinear unit vectors, the normal form

$$ds^2 = h_1{}^2\, du_1{}^2 + h_2{}^2\, du_2{}^2 + h_3{}^2\, du_3{}^2$$

where

$$h_\alpha{}^2 = \left(\frac{\partial f_1}{\partial u_\alpha}\right)^2 + \left(\frac{\partial f_2}{\partial u_\alpha}\right)^2 + \left(\frac{\partial f_3}{\partial u_\alpha}\right)^2, \qquad \alpha = 1, 2, 3 \tag{22}$$

If now ds coincides successively with the coordinate directions, so that only one of the $du_\alpha \neq 0$, it gives the linear arc elements in Fig. 31·2

$$ds_\alpha = h_\alpha\, du_\alpha \tag{23}$$

where h_α can be a function of all three coordinates u_α, but usually is a rather simple expression adjusting for example in a simple case an angular coordinate to a linear measure. In some instances one can read the h_α values directly from the expression for the line element ds^2; usually one has to evaluate the h_α from (22) with the actual transformation equations (20). Good treatments of the transformation relations are found in Mason and Weaver,[A16] p. 116; in Planck,[A19] p. 59; in Stratton,[A23] p. 38; in Kellogg,[C10] p. 178; in Hobson,[C9] p. 1; in Byerly,[C2] p. 238; in Webster,[C16] p. 299; and in Murnaghan,[C13] p. 102; as well as in the advanced books on vector and tensor analysis. Though many authors, like Smythe[A22] and Stratton,[A23] use the definition of h_α as given in (22), about again as many use the exact reciprocal of it; caution is therefore necessary in comparing similar-looking forms.

The expressions for the first-order vector differentiations in generalized coordinates can best be obtained from the original definitions. Thus, the gradient of the scalar potential as the linear rate of change of the potential is

$$\nabla\Phi = \operatorname{grad}\Phi = \sum_\alpha \mathbf{a}_\alpha \frac{\partial\Phi}{\partial s_\alpha}$$

and its components are with (23)

$$\nabla\Phi = \operatorname{grad} \Phi = \frac{\mathbf{a}_1}{h_1}\frac{\partial\Phi}{\partial u_1} + \frac{\mathbf{a}_2}{h_2}\frac{\partial\Phi}{\partial u_2} + \frac{\mathbf{a}_3}{h_3}\frac{\partial\Phi}{\partial u_3} \qquad (24)$$

The divergence of a vector can be deduced from Gauss's theorem (Appendix 3) applied to a rectangular curvilinear parallelepiped formed by the coordinate surfaces as in Fig. 31·2. The flux, for example of vector **D**, through the opposite faces orthogonal to u_1, is by the use of first-order linear approximation

$$\left[D_1 \cdot ds_2\, ds_3 + \frac{\partial}{\partial s_1}\left(D_1 \cdot ds_2\, ds_3 \right) ds_1 \right] - D_1 \cdot ds_2\, ds_3$$

where $ds_2\, ds_3$ is the elemental area and where the bracket gives the flux out of the face $P{-}P''{-}p'{-}P'''$; it is, of course, important to observe the variation of the line elements ds_2 and ds_3 as defined by (23), along with that of the vector component D_1. Because of the mutual independence of du_1, du_2, and du_3, the resultant flux contribution becomes for the u_1-direction

$$\frac{\partial}{\partial u_1}\left(h_2 h_3 D_1 \right) du_2\, du_3\, du_1$$

and analogously for the other two directions. The sum total of this flux is then div **D** $d\tau$, where the volume element

$$d\tau = ds_1\, ds_2\, ds_3 = h_1 h_2 h_3\, du_1\, du_2\, du_3$$

so that

$$\nabla\cdot\mathbf{D} = \operatorname{div}\mathbf{D} = \frac{1}{h_1 h_2 h_3}\left[\frac{\partial}{\partial u_1}\left(h_2 h_3 D_1 \right) + \frac{\partial}{\partial u_2}\left(h_3 h_1 D_2 \right) + \left. \frac{\partial}{\partial u_3}\left(h_1 h_2 D_3 \right) \right] \right\} \qquad (25)$$

The general differential equation for the electrostatic potential is deduced from

$$\operatorname{div}\mathbf{D} = \operatorname{div}(\varepsilon\mathbf{E}) = \rho$$

as given in (2·1) and follows with the definition $\mathbf{E} = -\operatorname{grad}\Phi$ if one introduces the respective components from (24) into (25)

$$\frac{1}{h_1 h_2 h_3}\left[\frac{\partial}{\partial u_1}\left(\frac{h_2 h_3}{h_1}\varepsilon\frac{\partial\Phi}{\partial u_1} \right) + \frac{\partial}{\partial u_2}\left(\frac{h_3 h_1}{h_2}\varepsilon\frac{\partial\Phi}{\partial u_2} \right) + \frac{\partial}{\partial u_3}\left(\frac{h_1 h_2}{h_3}\varepsilon\frac{\partial\Phi}{\partial u_3} \right) \right] = -\rho$$

$$(26)$$

For constant ε as in homogeneous and isotropic media, one can take it outside and, if further no space charge is present, one has for the Laplacian of the scalar potential Φ

$$\nabla^2\Phi = \frac{1}{h_1 h_2 h_3}\left[\frac{\partial}{\partial u_1}\left(\frac{h_2 h_3}{h_1}\frac{\partial\Phi}{\partial u_1}\right)+\frac{\partial}{\partial u_2}\left(\frac{h_3 h_1}{h_2}\frac{\partial\Phi}{\partial u_2}\right)+\frac{\partial}{\partial u_3}\left(\frac{h_1 h_2}{h_3}\frac{\partial\Phi}{\partial u_3}\right)\right]=0$$

$$(27)$$

Transformation of Vector Potential Problems to General Orthogonal Coordinates. Applying the theorem of Stokes (Appendix 3) to the infinitesimal curvilinear rectangle O–p''–P'–p''' in Fig. 31·2, one has for the contribution to the line integral of the vector **V** in the mathematically positive sense

$$+\left\{V_2\,ds_2 - \left[V_2\,ds_2 + \frac{\partial}{\partial s_3}(V_2\,ds_2)\,ds_3\right]\right\}$$

$$-\left\{V_3\,ds_3 - \left[V_3\,ds_3 + \frac{\partial}{\partial s_2}(V_3\,ds_3)\,ds_2\right]\right\}$$

which reduces, because of the mutual independence of the du_α, to

$$\frac{\partial}{\partial u_2}(h_3 V_3)\,du_3\,du_2 - \frac{\partial}{\partial u_3}(h_2 V_2)\,du_2\,du_3$$

This must be curl_1 **V** integrated over the infinitesimal area $ds_2\,ds_3$, so that upon division by $ds_2\,ds_3$,

$$\mathrm{curl}_1\,\mathbf{V} = \frac{1}{h_2 h_3}\left[\frac{\partial}{\partial u_2}(h_3 V_3) - \frac{\partial}{\partial u_3}(h_2 V_2)\right] \qquad (28a)$$

and with cyclic rotation of the indices one obtains the other two components, namely,

$$\mathrm{curl}_2\,\mathbf{V} = \frac{1}{h_3 h_1}\left[\frac{\partial}{\partial u_3}(h_1 V_1) - \frac{\partial}{\partial u_1}(h_3 V_3)\right] \qquad (28b)$$

$$\mathrm{curl}_3\,\mathbf{V} = \frac{1}{h_1 h_2}\left[\frac{\partial}{\partial u_1}(h_2 V_2) - \frac{\partial}{\partial u_2}(h_1 V_1)\right] \qquad (28c)$$

For the magnetic vector potential **A** one actually needs the operation $\nabla\times\nabla\times\mathbf{A}$, which is obtained in the simplest manner by applying operation (28) once again to the components (28). No further general simplification is possible even if one assumes $\nabla\cdot\mathbf{A} = 0$ as customary, since the segregation

$$\nabla\times\nabla\times\mathbf{A} = \nabla(\nabla\cdot\mathbf{A}) - (\nabla\cdot\nabla)\mathbf{A}$$

as in (6·16) can be meaningful *only for the Cartesian system*[3] if one reserves $\nabla \cdot \nabla = \nabla^2$ for the conventional Laplacian operator, as appears the logical choice. In any case, it is necessary to reduce the vector equations to scalar differential equations in vector components to make them amenable to processes of solution similar to those employed for the Laplacian differential equation of the scalar potential.

Separation of Variables. Special solutions of the potential equation (27) can sometimes be obtained by inspection, but the systematic approach is the reduction to sets of ordinary differential equations in terms of single variables. This can be achieved best by the method of *separation of variables*, assuming first that the potential function can be expressed as the product

$$\Phi(u_1, u_2, u_3) = F(u_1)G(u_2)H(u_3) \tag{29}$$

similar to the simpler two-dimensional analogue in section 29. The Laplacian differential equation is then from (27) and, dividing through by FGH,

$$F^{-1}\frac{\partial}{\partial u_1}\left(\frac{h_2 h_3}{h_1}F'\right) + G^{-1}\frac{\partial}{\partial u_2}\left(\frac{h_3 h_1}{h_2}G'\right) + H^{-1}\frac{\partial}{\partial u_3}\left(\frac{h_1 h_2}{h_3}H'\right) = 0 \tag{30}$$

since the differentiations pertain only to one of the three factors. It depends now primarily upon the metric factors h_α whether or not complete separation is possible.

Assume, for example, that each h_α is only a product function of the coordinates,

$$h_\alpha = \xi_\alpha(u_1)\,\eta_\alpha(u_2)\,\zeta_\alpha(u_3) \tag{31}$$

then

$$\frac{\partial}{\partial u_1}\left(\frac{h_2 h_3}{h_1}F'\right) = \frac{\eta_2 \eta_3}{\eta_1}\frac{\zeta_2 \zeta_3}{\zeta_1}\frac{\partial}{\partial u_1}\left(\frac{\xi_2 \xi_3}{\xi_1}\frac{\partial F}{\partial u_1}\right)$$

and similarly for each of the other terms in (30). This will permit the separation of variables if also

$$\xi_2(u_1) = \xi_3(u_1), \qquad \eta_3(u_2) = \eta_1(u_2), \qquad \zeta_1(u_3) = \zeta_2(u_3) \tag{32}$$

---

[3] The identity $\mathbf{R} \times \mathbf{Q} \times \mathbf{P} \equiv \mathbf{R} \cdot \mathbf{P}\mathbf{Q} - \mathbf{R} \cdot \mathbf{Q}\mathbf{P}$ is established only for vectors and need not and does not hold for the above triple product involving the differential operator ∇.

because then (30) reduces to

$$(\xi_1 F)^{-1} \frac{\partial}{\partial u_1}\left(\frac{\xi_2{}^2}{\xi_1} F'\right) + (\eta_2 G)^{-1} \frac{\partial}{\partial u_2}\left(\frac{\eta_3{}^2}{\eta_2} G'\right)$$

$$+ (\zeta_3 H)^{-1} \frac{\partial}{\partial u_3}\left(\frac{\zeta_1{}^2}{\zeta_3} H'\right) = 0 \quad (33)$$

Introducing as in (3) two separation constants by equating the last term in (33) to m^2 and the middle term to n^2 gives three ordinary differential equations, each of the Sturm-Liouville type $(29 \cdot 2)$ in which the boundary conditions will define the spectral selection of the values m and n. Stratton,[A23] p. 198, gives a similar deduction with the assumption that

$$h_\alpha = M_\alpha \xi(u_1)\, \eta(u_2)\, \zeta(u_3) \quad (34)$$

where M_α does not contain u_α but might be any function of the other two variables; Smythe,[A22] p. 124, finds a form similar to (33) for axially symmetrical potential problems. More specific criteria for the separability will be established in the following two sections dealing with specific groups of coordinate systems.

The systems permitting separation of the three space variables with present-day methods can be grouped in accordance with their principal geometric aspects into

Cartesian coordinate system (section 31), only system symmetrical in all three coordinates

Cylindrical coordinate systems (section 32) with conic sections normal to the axis
Circular cylinder
Elliptic or hyperbolic cylinder
Parabolic cylinder

Confocal conicoid systems with axial symmetry (section 33) and with conic sections in the three Cartesian coordinate planes
Spherical system (and bipolar system)
Prolate spheroidal system (and possible inverse)
Oblate spheroidal system (and possible inverse)
Paraboloidal system
Toroidal system (and inverse of circular cylinder system)

Systems involving elliptic functions (section 31)
Ellipsoidal coordinates
Annular coordinates (with possible inverse)

Thus, there are eleven distinct, separable, orthogonal coordinate systems (or sixteen, counting inverse and related systems) useful for the solution of potential problems.

Because of the rather involved mathematical apparatus needed for the treatment of the last group of coordinate systems, a brief summary of the simpler relations will be given here, whereas the two larger and by far more widely used groups of cylindrical and axially symmetrical confocal systems will be taken up in separate sections.

Orthogonal coordinate systems in which the variables cannot be completely separated are still useful, but with present-day methods solutions can be obtained only in series form not identifiable with orthogonal function systems, so that examination of convergence becomes a primary concern. A good illustration is the biaxial cylindrical coordinate system, which can be used in two dimensions (see section 29) but does not permit inclusion of the axial z-coordinate[4] without loss of separability of the variables.

ELLIPSOIDAL COORDINATE SYSTEM

The equation of a general ellipsoid as in Fig. 31·3 with the semi-axes $a > b > c$ along the x-, y-, z-directions, respectively, is in normal form

$$\left(\frac{x}{a}\right)^2 + \left(\frac{y}{b}\right)^2 + \left(\frac{z}{c}\right)^2 = 1$$

One can describe a family of orthogonal and confocal ellipsoids and hyperboloids in analogous manner to the two-dimensional conic sections by introducing a parameter p such that

$$\frac{x^2}{a^2 + p} + \frac{y^2}{b^2 + p} + \frac{z^2}{c^2 + p} = 1 \tag{35}$$

This gives

for $+\infty > p > (-c^2)$:   ellipsoids
for $(-c^2) > p > (-b^2)$:   hyperboloids of one sheet
for $(-b^2) > p > (-a^2)$:   hyperboloids of two sheets

The ellipsoids are confocal; setting $z = 0$ in (35), one has ellipses of half focal distance $f_1 = (a^2 - b^2)^{1/2}$, therefore fixed; setting

[4] G. Mie, *Ann. d. Physik*, series IV, **2**, p. 201 (1900).

$x = 0$, one has ellipses with $f_2 = (b^2 - c^2)^{\frac{1}{2}}$; and setting $y = 0$, one has ellipses with $f_3 = (a^2 - c^2)^{\frac{1}{2}} > f_1$. One can consider $p \to \xi$ as coordinate, defining uniquely any particular ellipsoid of this confocal family, and to stress its range of values rewrite (35)

$$\frac{x^2}{a^2 + \xi} + \frac{y^2}{b^2 + \xi} + \frac{z^2}{c^2 + \xi} = 1, \qquad \xi > (-c^2) \qquad (36a)$$

As $\xi \to (-c^2)$, one must also have $z \to 0$, i.e., one obtains an infinitely thin elliptical disk in the x-y-plane of semiaxes f_3 and

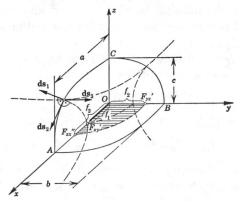

Fig. 31·3   Ellipsoidal Coordinates.

$f_2 < f_3$. The hyperboloids of one sheet can similarly be described by the coordinate η

$$\frac{x^2}{a^2 + \eta} + \frac{y^2}{b^2 + \eta} - \frac{z^2}{-(c^2 + \eta)} = 1, \qquad (-c^2) > \eta > (-b^2) \qquad (36b)$$

These hyperboloids are also confocal and have the same focal lengths as the ellipsoids. Setting $x = 0$ or $y = 0$ in (36b), one has hyperbolas; but setting $z = 0$, one has ellipses of major axis a' for which $f_0 > a' > f_1$, of minor axis $b' < f_2$, and of focal distance $2f_1$. This shows the hyperboloids to be of one sheet and to intersect the x-y-plane wholly within the limiting elliptic disk $\xi = -c^2$; their limit is $\eta \to -b^2$ and therefore $y \to 0$, a plane strip bounded by the hyperbolas in the x-z-plane

$$\frac{x^2}{a^2 - b^2} - \frac{z^2}{b^2 - c^2} = 1$$

Finally, the hyperboloids of two sheets are described by the coordinate ζ

$$\frac{x^2}{a^2 + \zeta} - \frac{y^2}{-(b^2 + \zeta)} - \frac{z^2}{-(c^2 + \zeta)} = 1, \qquad (-b^2) > \zeta > (-a^2) \tag{36c}$$

They are obviously confocal, and for $y = 0$ and $z = 0$ give hyperbolas in the z-x- and x-y-planes, respectively; for $x = 0$, however, they give imaginary intersection of the y-z-plane which is thus the plane of symmetry. These hyperboloids intersect the x-axis for $x < f_1$ and in the limiting case as $\zeta \to -b^2$ and $y \to 0$, become infinitely thin pencils and identical with the section of the x-axis for which $|x| > f_1$.

Solving for the coordinates x, y, z from the three relations (36) by direct elimination, one obtains

$$\left.\begin{aligned}
x^2 &= (f_3 f_1)^{-2} \left[(a^2 + \xi)(a^2 + \eta)(a^2 + \zeta) \right] \\
y^2 &= (f_1 f_2)^{-2} \left[(b^2 + \xi)(b^2 + \eta)(-b^2 - \zeta) \right] \\
z^2 &= (f_2 f_3)^{-2} \left[(c^2 + \xi)(-c^2 - \eta)(-c^2 - \zeta) \right]
\end{aligned}\right\} \tag{37}$$

with the focal distances f_α as defined above and with all factors positive within the proper ranges of ξ, η, ζ from (36). Differentiating both sides of the first line in (37), one has

$$2x \, dx = (f_3 f_1)^{-2} \left[(a^2 + \eta)(a^2 + \zeta) \, d\xi \right. $$
$$\left. + (a^2 + \zeta)(a^2 + \xi) \, d\eta + (a^2 + \xi)(a^2 + \eta) \, d\zeta \right] \tag{38}$$

in which x can be reintroduced from (37), and one thus has the explicit form (20); similarly for dy and dz. In accordance with (22) one can then formulate the metric factors h_α, which are after some considerable rearrangement[5] and use of (47) from below,

$$4h_1{}^2 = (\xi - \zeta)(\xi - \eta) \, g_1{}^{-2}(\xi);$$
$$g_1(\xi) = [(a^2 + \xi)(b^2 + \xi)(c^2 + \xi)]^{\frac{1}{2}}$$

$$4h_2{}^2 = (\xi - \eta)(\eta - \zeta) \, g_2{}^{-2}(\eta); \tag{39}$$
$$g_2(\eta) = [(a^2 + \eta)(b^2 + \eta)(-c^2 - \eta)]^{\frac{1}{2}}$$

$$4h_3{}^2 = (\eta - \zeta)(\xi - \zeta) \, g_3{}^{-2}(\zeta);$$
$$g_3(\zeta) = [(a^2 + \zeta)(-b^2 - \zeta)(-c^2 - \zeta)]^{\frac{1}{2}}$$

[5] For details see particularly Webster,[C16] p. 331; Hobson,[C9] p. 454; Murnaghan,[C13] p. 155; and Byerly,[C2] p. 251.

This yields then from (27) for the Laplacian potential equation, if one divides through with $(h_1 h_2 h_3)$ as indicated and observes the product character of h_α,

$$\nabla^2 \Phi = [(\xi - \zeta)(\xi - \eta)]^{-1} g_1(\xi) \frac{\partial}{\partial \xi}\left[g_1(\xi) \frac{\partial \Phi}{\partial \xi} \right]$$

$$+ [(\xi - \eta)(\eta - \zeta)^{-1} \cdot g_2(\eta) \frac{\partial}{\partial \eta}\left[g_2(\eta) \frac{\partial \Phi}{\partial \eta} \right]$$

$$+ [(\eta - \zeta)(\xi - \zeta)]^{-1} g_3(\zeta) \frac{\partial}{\partial \zeta}\left[g_3(\zeta) \frac{\partial \Phi}{\partial \zeta} \right] = 0 \quad (40)$$

Separation of the variables is possible and leads to the system of Lamé functions or ellipsoidal harmonics which, in general, involve elliptic integrals. A brief treatment of these is given in Jeans,[A10] p. 244, and in Webster,[C16] p. 333; more extensive treatments are found in Hobson,[C9] p. 459; in Byerly,[C2] p. 254; and in advanced treatises on elliptic functions.

Conducting Ellipsoid. Simple solutions result if the potential is dependent on only a single variable, for example ξ, which describes the confocal ellipsoids. If a conducting ellipsoid of semiaxes a, b, c is kept at a potential Φ_0, then (40) reduces for the outside field to

$$\frac{\partial}{\partial \xi}\left[g_1(\xi) \frac{\partial \Phi}{\partial \xi} \right] = 0, \qquad \frac{\partial \Phi}{\partial \xi} = \frac{A}{g_1(\xi)} \quad (41)$$

which yields with (39) the elliptic integral of the Weierstrass type

$$\Phi = B - A \int_\xi^\infty \frac{d\xi}{[(a^2 + \xi)(b^2 + \xi)(c^2 + \xi)]^{1/2}} \quad (42)$$

The limits have been chosen so as to secure the standard form of the integral;[6] the negative sign accounts for ξ appearing in the lower limit. If one selects $\Phi = 0$ for $\xi = \infty$, then $B = 0$. The constant A can be determined best from the total charge just as in the case of any single conductor (see section 10 or 11). The field vector is found from (24) with (39) and (41)

$$E_\xi = -h_1^{-1} \frac{\partial \Phi}{\partial \xi} = -2A[(\xi - \eta)(\xi - \zeta)]^{-1/2}$$

[6] For a summary of relations and some numerical values see E. Jahnke and F. Emde: *Tables of Functions*, p. 98; reprinted by Dover Publications, New York, 1943; originally published by B. G. Teubner, Leipzig, 1938.

For large values of ξ one can disregard η and ζ, since their values are definitely limited by (36b) and (36c), so that

$$\lim_{\xi \to \infty} E_\xi \to -\frac{2A}{\xi}$$

Since one also has from (36a) for $\xi \gg a^2$,

$$x^2 + y^2 + z^2 = r^2 \approx \xi$$

one finds that at large distance the field vector varies as $1/r^2$, as in the case of the single point charge (10·1), and one can therefore determine the constant A as

$$A = \frac{-Q}{8\pi\varepsilon}$$

This gives as final solution

$$\Phi(\xi) = \frac{+Q}{8\pi\varepsilon} \int_\xi^\infty [(a^2 + \xi)(b^2 + \xi)(c^2 + \xi)]^{-\frac{1}{2}} \, d\xi \qquad (43)$$

with the field vector from above as

$$E_\xi = \frac{+Q}{4\pi\varepsilon} \cdot [(\xi - \eta)(\xi - \zeta)]^{-\frac{1}{2}} \qquad (44)$$

On the surface of the conductor $\xi = 0$ and the respective potential Φ_0 determines the capacitance of the ellipsoid

$$C = \frac{Q}{\Phi_0} = \frac{8\pi\varepsilon}{\displaystyle\int_0^\infty [(a^2 + \xi)(b^2 + \xi)(c^2 + \xi)]^{-\frac{1}{2}} \, d\xi} \qquad (45)$$

The charge density distribution is then

$$\sigma = \varepsilon E_{\xi=0} = \frac{Q}{4\pi\sqrt{\eta\zeta}} = \frac{Q}{4\pi abc} \cdot \left[\frac{x^2}{a^4} + \frac{y^2}{b^4} + \frac{z^2}{c^4}\right]^{-\frac{1}{2}} \qquad (46)$$

where the last transformation is obtained by forming $[(x/a^2)^2 + (y/b^2)^2 + (z/c^2)^2]$ for $\xi = 0$ in (37), multiplying out the corresponding right-hand sides, collecting terms, and observing that

$$\left.\begin{aligned}
(f_3 f_1)^{-2} &- (f_1 f_2)^{-2} + (f_2 f_3)^{-2} \\
&= \left(\frac{a}{f_3 f_1}\right)^2 - \left(\frac{b}{f_1 f_2}\right)^2 + \left(\frac{c}{f_2 f_3}\right)^2 = 0 \\
(a f_3 f_1)^{-2} &- (b f_1 f_2)^{-2} + (c f_2 f_3)^{-2} = (abc)^{-2}
\end{aligned}\right\} \qquad (47)$$

For the numerical computations one can reduce the elliptic integrals to the Legendre type.[7]

Treatments of the conducting ellipsoid are found in Jeans,[A10] p. 247; in Kirchoff,[A13] p. 34; in Mason and Weaver,[A16] p. 126; in Smythe,[A22] p. 111; and in Stratton,[A23] p. 207, all of whom deduce several of the special cases below; also in Kellogg,[C10] p. 188; in Murnaghan,[C13] p. 155; in Byerly,[C2] p. 258; and in Lamb,[C22] p. 141, who considers hydrodynamic applications.

Application to the conducting ellipsoid in a uniform electric field is made in Stratton,[A23] p. 209; the dielectric ellipsoid in a uniform electric field is also treated there (p. 211), as well as in Jeans,[A10] p. 253, and in Mason and Weaver,[A16] p. 156. The analogous solution for the magnetic ellipsoid in a uniform magnetic field is given in Maxwell,[A17] II, p. 66, and in Frank and Mises,[C6] II, p. 720, and for fluid flow problems in Lamb,[C22] p. 143.

For $c = 0$ in (43), one obtains the potential produced by the infinitely thin *elliptic disk* in the plane $z = 0$. The capacitance can be obtained from (45) as elliptic integral. The charge density follows from (46) by taking c into the square root

$$\sigma = \frac{Q}{4\pi ab}\left[\left(\frac{cx}{a^2}\right)^2 + \left(\frac{cy}{b^2}\right)^2 + \left(\frac{z}{c}\right)^2\right]^{-\frac{1}{2}}$$

where now the first two terms vanish with c, whereas the last one must be replaced by its expression from (36a) with $\xi = 0$, so that

$$\sigma = \frac{Q}{4\pi ab}\left[1 - \left(\frac{x}{a}\right)^2 - \left(\frac{y}{b}\right)^2\right]^{-\frac{1}{2}} \tag{48}$$

This becomes infinitely large at the rim of the disk, as one would expect.

Axially Symmetrical Ellipsoids. For axial symmetry about the z-axis in Fig. 31·3 one has $a = b$, an *oblate spheroid*, and this reduces all the integrals to elementary ones. The potential (43) becomes

$$\Phi(\xi) = \frac{Q}{8\pi\varepsilon}\int_{\xi}^{\infty}[(a^2 + \xi)\sqrt{c^2 + \xi}]^{-1}\,d\xi$$

$$= \frac{Q}{4\pi\varepsilon\sqrt{a^2 - c^2}}\tan^{-1}\sqrt{\frac{a^2 - c^2}{c^2 + \xi}} \tag{49}$$

---

[7] See Jahnke and Emde, *loc. cit.*, p. 59, and the reference there listed: J. Honel: *Recueil de formules et de tables numériques;* Gauthier-Villars, Paris, 1901.

The capacitance is readily obtained as

$$C = \frac{Q}{\phi_{\xi=0}} = \frac{4\pi\varepsilon\sqrt{a^2 - c^2}}{\tan^{-1}\sqrt{(a/c)^2 - 1}} \tag{50}$$

and the charge density, if one introduces $x^2 + y^2 = \rho^2$, becomes

$$\sigma = \frac{Q}{4\pi a^2 c}\left[\frac{\rho^2}{a^4} + \frac{z^2}{c^4}\right]^{-\frac{1}{2}} \tag{51}$$

If $c \to 0$, one has the infinitely thin *circular disk* with

$$\Phi(\xi) = \frac{Q}{8\pi\varepsilon}\int_\xi^\infty \frac{d\xi}{(a^2 + \xi)\sqrt{\xi}} = \frac{Q}{4\pi\varepsilon a}\tan^{-1}\frac{a}{\sqrt{\xi}} \tag{52}$$

and from this for the capacitance

$$C = \frac{Q}{\Phi(0)} = 8\varepsilon a \tag{53}$$

The charge density follows directly from (48) with $a = b$ and $x^2 + y^2 = \rho^2$,

$$\sigma = \frac{Q/4\pi a}{\sqrt{a^2 - \rho^2}} \tag{54}$$

This value holds, of course, for each side of the disk; in the center where $\rho = 0$ one has the same density as on a uniformly charged sphere of radius a.   The value of ξ can readily be expressed in terms of Cartesian coordinates if one introduces the same simplifications into (36a).

For axial symmetry about the x-axis in Fig. 31·3 one has $b = c$, a *prolate spheroid*, and this again reduces all integrals to elementary ones.   The potential (43) becomes

$$\Phi(\xi) = \frac{Q}{8\pi\varepsilon}\int_\xi^\infty [(b^2 + \xi)\sqrt{a^2 + \xi}]^{-1}\,d\xi$$

$$= \frac{Q}{4\pi\varepsilon\sqrt{b^2 - c^2}}\tanh^{-1}\sqrt{\frac{a^2 - b^2}{a^2 + \xi}} \tag{55}$$

The capacitance is by definition from this

$$C = \frac{Q}{\Phi(0)} = \frac{4\pi\varepsilon\sqrt{a^2 - b^2}}{\tanh^{-1}\sqrt{1 - (b/a)^2}} \tag{56}$$

which is identical with (12·4), found there by direct integration in the Cartesian coordinate system. The charge density becomes, if one introduces $y^2 + z^2 = \rho^2$ and $b = c$ into (46),

$$\sigma = \frac{Q}{4\pi ab^2}\left[\frac{x^2}{a^4} + \frac{\rho^2}{b^4}\right]^{-\frac{1}{2}} \tag{57}$$

Though the extreme values for $x = 0$, $\rho = b$ and $x = a$, $\rho = 0$ had been given in section 12, this general expression could not be

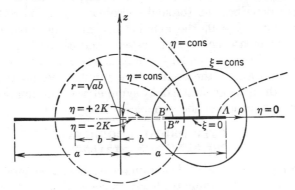

Fig. 31·4 Annular Coordinates.

found there in any simple way. The approximations for a *thin rod* with $b \ll a$ have been discussed in section 12 and need not be repeated.

ANNULAR COORDINATES

The circular annulus of inner radius b and outer radius a in Fig. 31·4 can be used as basis of an orthogonal coordinate system with axial symmetry, in which the relations between ξ, η, on the one hand, and z, ρ of the underlying cylindrical coordinate system, on the other hand, are given by the elliptic functions.[8] The sphere of radius $\sqrt{ab}$ is one member of the family of surfaces $\eta = $ cons, intersecting the z-axis at right angles and terminating orthogonally on the annulus proper. The confocal surfaces $\xi = $ cons have doughnut-like shapes surrounding the annulus. Separa-

[8] Ch. Snow: *The Hypergeometric and Legendre Functions with Applications to Integral Equations and Potential Theory*, p. 295; National Bureau of Standards, Washington, D.C., 1942.

tion of the variables ξ, η, and ϕ, the longitude angle, is possible, and the ensuing function systems are discussed in the reference.[9]

A bilinear conformal transformation of the meridian plane $w = z + j\rho$ into $w' = c(w - c)/(w + c)$ bends the axis $z = 0$ into a circle and therefore the annulus into a spherical zone. This can again be taken as basis of an orthogonal coordinate system which is, in fact, the inverse to the annular system and has the same function systems as solutions of potential problems.

If the annulus shrinks into a circular line, so that $a = b$, then the system describes the toroidal coordinates (section 33); if on the other hand, $b = 0$, the annulus becomes the circular disk, basis of the oblate spheroidal system, and treated in (52) as special case of the ellipsoidal coordinate system with axial symmetry with respect to the z-axis. The annular coordinate system is therefore the most general axially symmetrical coordinate system permitting separation of the variables.

32· CYLINDRICAL COORDINATE AND FUNCTION SYSTEMS

As a group, the cylindrical coordinate systems are characterized by the fact that any coordinate plane $z = $ cons, with z taken parallel to the cylindrical surfaces, intersects the other two coordinate surfaces along conic sections. These are circles and radial lines for the circular, ellipses and hyperbolas for the elliptical, and parabolas for the parabolic cylinder systems. If there is no variation of potential along the z-axis, the corresponding two-dimensional cases result (see section 29).

Separability of Variables. It is of interest to ascertain the conditions of separability of the variables because it will also serve as justification that only the three coordinate systems treated here have attained practical significance.

For any cylindrical coordinate system, the third coordinate is the longitudinal or axial coordinate z, so that from $(31 \cdot 23)$ one infers at once $h_3 = 1$. The requirement of orthogonality in the x-y-plane can be interpreted as meaning that any other plane coordinate pair (ξ, η) must be the result of a conformal transformation

$$w = x + jy = w(\zeta), \qquad \zeta = \xi + j\eta \qquad (1)$$

[9] Ch. Snow, *loc. cit.;* also N. Lebedev, *Techn. Physics of USSR,* **4,** p. 3 (1937).

so that $(31 \cdot 18)$ reduces to

$$x = f_1(\xi, \eta), \qquad y = f_2(\xi, \eta)$$

where x and y are conjugate functions of ξ and η (see section 25). This, in turn, implies that the Cauchy-Riemann equations hold for x and y, and, therefore, that $(31 \cdot 23)$ reduces to the simple form

$$h_1{}^2 = h_2{}^2 = h^2 = \left| \frac{dw}{d\zeta} \right|^2 \qquad (2)$$

The Laplacian of the scalar potential $(31 \cdot 27)$ becomes thus

$$\nabla^2 \Phi = \frac{1}{h^2} \left[\frac{\partial^2 \Phi}{\partial \xi^2} + \frac{\partial^2 \Phi}{\partial \eta^2} + \frac{\partial}{\partial z} \left(h^2 \frac{\partial \Phi}{\partial z} \right) \right] = 0 \qquad (3)$$

Since h must be independent of the axial coordinate z, one can introduce now the product function

$$\Phi(\xi, \eta, z) = \Xi(\xi) \, \mathsf{H}(\eta) \, Z(z) \qquad (4)$$

and rewrite (3) upon dividing through by (4), with primes denoting differentiation with respect to the pertinent variable,

$$h^{-2} \left[\frac{\Xi''}{\Xi} + \frac{\mathsf{H}''}{\mathsf{H}} \right] + \frac{Z''}{Z} = 0$$

This permits at once separation of the last term

$$\left. \begin{array}{l} Z'' = m^2 Z, \\ Z = D_1 \sinh mz + D_2 \cosh mz \end{array} \right\} \qquad (5)$$

where m^2 can be any constant value, real or complex. This leaves then

$$\Xi^{-1} \Xi'' + \mathsf{H}^{-1} \mathsf{H}'' = -m^2 h^2 \qquad (6)$$

It has been shown[1] that the necessary and sufficient condition of further separability is the fact that

$$h^2(\xi, \eta) \equiv g_1(\xi) + g_2(\eta) \qquad (7)$$

where g_1 and g_2 are functions of only ξ and η, respectively. This means, that $\left| \dfrac{dw}{d\zeta} \right|^2$ *must itself be separable* into a sum of functions

---

[1] Ch. Snow: *The Hypergeometric and Legendre Functions with Applications to Integral Equations and Potential Theory*, p. 202; National Bureau of Standards, Washington, D.C., 1942. Reference is made there to G. Haentzschel: *Studien über die Reduktion der Potentialgleichung auf gewöhnliche Differential Gleichungen*; G. Reimer, Berlin, 1893.

each of only one variable. This obviously limits the choice of practical cylinder coordinate systems to the conical sections, since only for the family of trigonometric (including exponential and hyperbolic) functions one has a clear separation as for example

$$\left|\frac{d}{d\zeta}\sin\zeta\right|^2 = \left|\cos(\xi+j\eta)\right|^2 = \cos^2\xi + \cosh^2\eta - 1$$

As a rather special case (parabolic cylinder), one also has

$$w = \zeta^2, \qquad \left|\frac{dw}{d\zeta}\right|^2 = 4\left|\zeta\right|^2 = 4(\xi^2+\eta^2)$$

Introducing (7) into (6), one obtains upon separation the two ordinary differential equations of the Sturm-Liouville type

$$\frac{d^2\Xi}{d\xi^2} + [m^2 g_1(\xi) - p^2]\Xi = 0$$

$$\frac{d^2\mathsf{H}}{d\eta^2} + [m^2 g_2(\eta) + p^2]\mathsf{H} = 0$$

(8)

where p^2 is the second separation constant.

CIRCULAR CYLINDER COORDINATES

The axial symmetry of the circular cylinder makes it simpler to proceed with the specific coordinate relations rather than to apply the preceding general deduction. Of course, one can employ the conformal mapping function $w = e^{-\zeta}$ and obtain (3) and (8) as shown in terms of the coordinates ξ and η; one can also define $\rho = e^{-\xi}$ with $-\infty < \xi < +\infty$, $\psi \equiv -\eta$ as suitable coordinates and systematically obtain the governing equations (8) in terms of the more usual coordinates ρ and ψ.

Conventionally, however, one chooses as coordinates directly the normal distance ρ from the cylinder axis, the angle ψ counted from the x-axis of the underlying Cartesian system and the distance z along the z-axis from an assumed origin 0. The coordinate surfaces are ρ = cons, giving coaxial right circular cylinders, ψ = cons, yielding planes through the z-axis, and z = cons, yielding planes normal to the axis. The line elements in the three coordinate directions are, for the point P in Fig. 32·1,

$$ds_1 = d\rho, \qquad ds_2 = \rho d\psi, \qquad ds_3 = dz \qquad (9)$$

so that by comparison with (31·23)

$$h_1 = 1, \qquad h_2 = \rho, \qquad h_3 = 1 \tag{10}$$

and thus for the components of the field vector in accordance with (31·24)

$$E_\rho = -\frac{\partial \Phi}{\partial \rho}, \qquad E_\psi = -\frac{1}{\rho}\frac{\partial \Phi}{\partial \psi}, \qquad E_z = -\frac{\partial \Phi}{\partial z} \tag{11}$$

The potential equation (31·27) becomes with (10) above

$$\nabla^2 \Phi = \frac{1}{\rho}\frac{\partial}{\partial \rho}\left(\rho \frac{\partial \Phi}{\partial \rho}\right) + \frac{1}{\rho^2}\frac{\partial^2 \Phi}{\partial \psi^2} + \frac{\partial^2 \Phi}{\partial z^2} = 0 \tag{12}$$

Introducing the product function

$$\Phi = R(\rho)\, P(\psi)\, Z(z) \tag{13}$$

and dividing through by it, one can readily separate the variables,

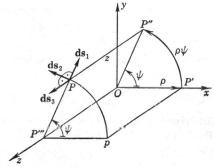

FIG. 32·1   Circular Cylinder Coordinates.

if one starts with the last term, leading to (5). The remaining part in (12) now reads

$$(\rho R)^{-1}\frac{d}{d\rho}\left(\rho \frac{dR}{d\rho}\right) + (\rho^2 P)^{-1}\frac{d^2 P}{d\psi^2} = -m^2$$

or also

$$\rho R^{-1}\frac{d}{d\rho}\left(\rho \frac{dR}{d\rho}\right) + m^2\rho^2 + P^{-1}\frac{d^2 P}{d\psi^2} = 0 \tag{14}$$

which permits further separation by assuming

$$\left.\begin{array}{c} P'' = -n^2 P \\[2mm] P = B_1 \sin n\psi + B_2 \cos n\psi \end{array}\right\} \tag{15}$$

With $(-n^2)$ for the last term, (14) gives finally

$$\frac{1}{\rho}\frac{d}{d\rho}\left(\rho\,\frac{dR}{d\rho}\right) + \left(m^2 - \frac{n^2}{\rho^2}\right) R = 0 \qquad (16)$$

which has as solution the *Bessel functions*[2] of first and second kind of order n

$$R = C_1 J_n(m\rho) + C_2 N_n(m\rho) \qquad (17)$$

These functions can form orthogonal systems of different types which can be used for expansions of inhomogeneous boundary values.

As special cases, one has to consider $n = 0$, for which the dependence on z remains as in (5) but $P = B_1\psi + B_2$ reduces to a linear form, and the Bessel functions become of zeroth order, as treated in (30·41) for axially symmetrical fields. If, on the other hand, $m = 0$, then $Z = D_1 z + D_2$ from (5), the dependence on ψ remains the same as (15), but (16) now reduces to the first of the forms (29·48), resulting in the two-dimensional circular harmonics. If, finally, $m = n = 0$, the solution of (16) degenerates into the logarithmic function, and the total contribution to the potential solution becomes

$$(C_1 \ln \rho + C_2)(D_1 z + D_2)(B_1\psi + B_2)$$

Hollow Cylindrical Ring. The hollow cylindrical ring of Fig. 32·2 with the indicated boundary potentials in (a) has axially symmetrical potential distribution, so that independence of ψ can be presumed, or $n = 0$. The homogeneous radial boundary conditions require from (17), since $n = 0$,

$$C_1 J_0(ma) + C_2 N_0(ma) = C_1 J_0(mb) + C_2 N_0(mb) = 0 \qquad (18)$$

which can only be satisfied by non-trivial values of C_1 and C_2 (non-vanishing) if their coefficient determinant vanishes, or

$$J_0(ma)\,N_0(mb) - J_0(mb)\,N_0(ma) = 0 \qquad (19)$$

---

[2] Brief reviews of Bessel functions are given in Smythe,[A22] p. 168; Churchill,[C3] Chapter VIII; and almost any book on advanced calculus. Extensive treatises are Gray, Matthews, and MacRobert[C7]; Byerly[C2]; N. W. McLachlan: *Bessel Functions for Engineers;* Oxford University Press, 1934; and G. N. Watson: *Theory of Bessel Functions;* Cambridge University Press, 1922. For tables see Jahnke and Emde: *Tables of Functions;* reprinted by Dover Publications, New York, 1943; originally published by B. G. Teubner, Leipzig, 1938. A brief summary of important relations is given in Appendix 5.

Setting $ma = x$, $mb = ma(b/a) = kx$, the first six roots of this relation for a large range of values k are given in Jahnke and Emde,[3] pp. 204–209. Since from (18) also

$$\frac{C_1}{C_2} = -\frac{N_0(m_\alpha a)}{J_0(m_\alpha a)} = \frac{N_0(m_\alpha b)}{J_0(m_\alpha b)}, \qquad \alpha = 1, 2, 3, \cdots \infty \qquad (20)$$

for the root values m_α as computed from the tables, and since further $D_2 = 0$ in (5) because of $\Phi = 0$ at $z = 0$, the solution for the potential is at this stage

$$\Phi(\rho, z) = \sum_\alpha C_\alpha \sinh m_\alpha z \left[J_0(m_\alpha \rho) - \frac{J_0(m_\alpha b)}{N_0(m_\alpha b)} N_0(m_\alpha \rho) \right] \qquad (21)$$

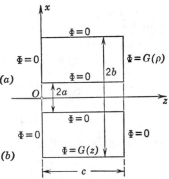

The only remaining boundary condition to be satisfied is for $z = b$, where it is required to expand the given function $G(\rho)$ into an orthogonal system of Bessel function combinations as contained in the brackets of (21). This can,

FIG. 32·2 Hollow Circular Cylindrical Ring with Two Typical Potential Applications: (a) radial, (b) longitudinal.

indeed, be done because the homogeneous boundary conditions in ρ specify the problem as of the Sturm-Liouville type; see section 29. Actually, with the abbreviation $R_0(m_\alpha \rho)$ for the bracketed function in (21), the coefficients C_α are defined by [Appendix 5,(43) and 5,(40)]

$$C_\alpha = \{b^2[R_1(m_\alpha b)]^2 - a^2[R_1(m_\alpha a)]^2\}^{-1} \cdot$$
$$\frac{2}{\sinh m_\alpha c} \int_{\rho = a}^{b} \rho G(\rho) R_0(m_\alpha \rho) \, d\rho \qquad (22)$$

where the first term $\{\ \} = 2N_\alpha$, with N_α the norm of the R_0 functions as given in Appendix 5,(40). The most salient difficulty with the Bessel functions is the lack of known integrals in closed form, so that many expressions like (22) remain purely formal unless numerical or machine computations are feasible. This

[3] E. Jahnke and F. Emde: *Tables of Functions;* reprinted by Dover Publications, New York, 1943; originally published by G. B. Teubner, Leipzig.

solution is given in Smythe,[A22] p. 183, and in Byerly,[C2] p. 230, for the equivalent temperature problem; Kellogg,[C10] p. 203, treats the similar case with $a = 0$, the hollow finite cylinder, and again Byerly,[C2] p. 226, gives the latter solution for the equivalent temperature distribution problem, modifying it also for $\partial T/\partial \rho = 0$ on $\rho = b$ and for $\partial T/\partial \rho + hT = 0$ on $\rho = b$. Churchill,[C3] Chapter VIII, solves several of the simpler problems involving time variation.

If, in the same problem, Fig. 32·2, the boundary potential distribution (b) is selected, then the boundary conditions in z are homogeneous, indicating trigonometric functions in z. It is therefore preferable to choose a negative sign in (5), so that

$$\left.\begin{array}{l} Z'' = -m^2 z \\[2mm] Z = D_1 \sin mz + D_2 \cos mz \end{array}\right\} \quad (23)$$

leading to the conditions

$$Z(0) = D_2 = 0, \qquad Z(c) = D_1 \sin mc = 0$$

with the spectrum of m-values

$$m_\alpha = \frac{\alpha\pi}{c}, \qquad \alpha = 1, 2, \cdots \infty \quad (24)$$

Since axial symmetry prevails, $n = 0$ and (16) becomes

$$\frac{1}{\rho} \frac{d}{d\rho}\left(\rho \frac{dR}{d\rho}\right) + m^2 R = 0 \quad (25)$$

with the solution in terms of Bessel functions of imaginary argument

$$R = C_1 J_0(jm\rho) + C_2 N_0(jm\rho)$$

or also in the form of the *modified Bessel functions*[4]

$$R = A_1 I_0(m\rho) + A_2 K_0(m\rho) \quad (26)$$

where these functions are defined so that they take on real values; this is merely a matter of convenience in order to keep the con-

---

[4] No uniformity exists with respect to the definition of the modified Bessel function of the second kind; see Appendix 5 for the interrelations between current usages. For the present example it does not matter which definition for K_0 is chosen.

stants A_1 and A_2 to real values, since the physical problem can tolerate only a real solution. The condition at $\rho = a$ requires $R = 0$ in (26), so that the total solution takes the form

$$\Phi(\rho, z) = \sum_\alpha A_\alpha \left[I_0(m_\alpha \rho) - \frac{I_0(m_\alpha a)}{K_0(m_\alpha a)} K_0(m_\alpha \rho) \right] \sin m_\alpha z \qquad (27)$$

This must then represent the conventional Fourier series expansion of $G(z)$ at $\rho = b$, so that the coefficients are found by

$$A_\alpha \left[I_0(m_\alpha b) - \frac{I_0(m_\alpha a)}{K_0(m_\alpha a)} K_0(m_\alpha b) \right]$$
$$= \frac{2}{c} \int_{z=0}^{z=c} G(z) \sin m_\alpha z \, dz \qquad (28)$$

The solution is given in Smythe,[A22] p. 195, and also in Byerly,[C2] p. 232, for the equivalent temperature problem; in both instances, the special case $a = 0$ is deduced by simply dropping the modified Bessel function of the second kind, since it has a logarithmic singularity at $\rho = 0$ and cannot contribute to the solution.

Again, if the boundary conditions require given potential variations over several of the boundary surface parts, then each one condition can be combined with zero potential over all other parts to make up a typical problem as illustrated. The sum total of all individual solutions will constitute the complete solution by superposition.

Finite Conducting Cylinder. A finite conducting cylinder of length $2c$, diameter $2a$, and conductivity γ, as shown in Fig. 32·3, has applied two electrodes at $z = \pm b$ for current supply and collection; the width of these electrodes is δ, and it is assumed that the current density normal to the electrode areas can be defined as $\pm I/2\pi a\delta$. The flow must be confined within the cylinder, so that on all surfaces the normal electric field must vanish except over the two bands where it has the specified value $\pm I/2\pi a\gamma\delta$. The solution for the potential and current distribution will be axially symmetrical, so that $n = 0$ in (8), and because of the finite length of the cylinder it will be preferable to choose (23) for the expression of Z. The boundary conditions in z are homogeneous and of the second kind, requiring at the ends $Z'(-c) = Z'(+c) = 0$, so that

$$m(D_1 \cos mc + D_2 \sin mc) = m(D_1 \cos mc - D_2 \sin mc) = 0 \qquad (29)$$

This can be satisfied only if $D_2 = 0$ and

$$\cos mc = 0, \qquad m_\alpha = \frac{(2\alpha + 1)\pi}{2c}, \qquad \alpha = 0, 1, 2, \cdots \infty \quad (30)$$

The solution for $R(\rho)$ will again be given by (26), but only the first kind of the modified Bessel function can be admitted, since

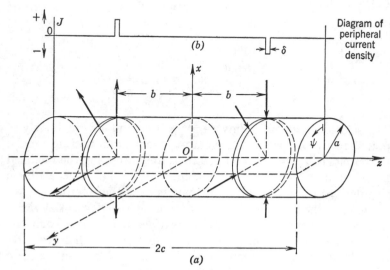

Fig. 32·3   Current Flow within Finite Cylinder.

$K_0(m\rho)$ has a logarithmic singularity at $\rho = 0$. The solution is therefore, up to this point, given by

$$\Phi(\rho, z) = \sum_\alpha A_\alpha I_0(m_\alpha\rho) \sin m_\alpha z \quad (31)$$

In order to determine the coefficients A_α, one must expand the assumed peripheral current distribution into the conventional Fourier series

$$J_\rho(\rho = a) = \sum_\alpha J_\alpha \sin m_\alpha z \quad (32)$$

where, because of the odd symmetry, the coefficients are given by

$$J_\alpha = -\frac{2}{c} \int_{z=b-\delta/2}^{z=b+\delta/2} \frac{I}{2\pi a\delta} \sin m_\alpha z \, dz$$

$$= -\frac{I}{\pi ac} \frac{\sin m_\alpha\delta/2}{m_\alpha\delta/2} \sin m_\alpha b \quad (33)$$

From the potential distribution (31) one has the radial current density

$$J_\rho = -\gamma \frac{\partial \Phi}{\partial \rho} = -\gamma \sum_\alpha m_\alpha A_\alpha I_1(m_\alpha \rho) \sin m_\alpha z$$

and comparing the coefficients of this Fourier series at $\rho = a$ with (33), one has

$$A_\alpha = \frac{I}{\pi a c \gamma} \left(\frac{\sin m_\alpha \delta/2}{m_\alpha \delta/2} \right) \frac{\sin m_\alpha b}{m_\alpha I_1(m_\alpha a)} \tag{34}$$

It is seen that as $\delta \to 0$ the factor in parentheses approaches unity so that no loss of generality results if one assumes $\delta = 0$, though justification would be needed for the application of the Fourier series. Since the potential difference is readily given from (31) as

$$V = \Phi_{(\rho=a,\, z=b)} - \Phi_{(\rho=a,\, z=-b)} = 2 \sum_\alpha A_\alpha I_0(m_\alpha a) \sin m_\alpha b \tag{35}$$

one can write for the total resistance with (34)

$$\frac{V}{I} = \frac{2}{\pi c \gamma} \sum_\alpha \frac{I_0(m_\alpha a)}{(m_\alpha a) I_1(m_\alpha a)} \left(\frac{\sin m_\alpha \delta/2}{m_\alpha \delta/2} \right) \sin^2 m_\alpha b \tag{36}$$

This problem was treated by Smythe,[A22] p. 236, and a similar method was used by Ollendorff,[A18] p. 341, to compute the amplification factor of a triode with a helical grid.

If the electrodes in Fig. 32·3 do not cover the entire circumference but extend only from $\psi = -(\pi/q)$ to $\psi = +(\pi/q)$, where q may be an arbitrary real number, then the axial symmetry will no longer hold and the potential function will be the double summation

$$\Phi(\rho, \psi, z) = \sum_n \sum_\alpha (A_{n,\alpha} \sin n\psi + B_{n,\alpha} \cos n\psi) I_n(m_\alpha \rho) \sin m_\alpha z \tag{37}$$

where the coefficients B_1 and B_2 of (15) were merged with D_1 of (23) and A_1 of (26) to give $A_{n,\alpha}$ and $B_{n,\alpha}$ and where the m_α are the same as in (24). This now represents a double Fourier series of same type as (31·10), and its coefficients must be determined by comparison of the expression for the radial current density from

(37), with the double Fourier series representing the given current density. From (37) one has at once

$$J_\rho = -\gamma \frac{\partial \Phi}{\partial \rho} = -\gamma \sum_n \sum_\alpha [A_{n,\alpha} \sin n\psi + B_{n,\alpha} \cos n\psi] \cdot$$

$$\left[-\frac{n}{m_\alpha \rho} I_n(m_\alpha \rho) + I_{n-1}(m_\alpha \rho) \right] m_\alpha \sin m_\alpha z \quad (38)$$

The double Fourier expansion of the given current density, defined as $\pm (qI/2\pi a\delta)$ over the electrode surface, is formally

$$J_\rho(\rho = a) = \sum_n \sum_\alpha J_{n,\alpha} \cos n\psi \sin m_\alpha z \quad (39)$$

where the coefficients are determined for $n \geqslant 1$ by the double integral

$$J_{n,\alpha} = -\frac{4}{c\pi} \int_{\psi=0}^{\pi/q} d\psi \int_{z=b-\delta/2}^{z=b+\delta/2} \frac{qI}{2\pi a\delta} \cos n\psi \sin m_\alpha z \, dz$$

$$= -\frac{2I}{\pi ac} \left(\frac{\sin n\pi/q}{n\pi/q} \right) \cdot \left(\frac{\sin m_\alpha \delta/2}{m_\alpha \delta/2} \right) \sin m_\alpha b \quad (40)$$

Use has been made of the two symmetries, namely, that J_ρ is an even function in ψ and an odd function in z. Comparison of (38) at $\rho = a$ with (39) indicates now

$$A_{n,\alpha} = 0, \qquad B_{n,\alpha} = \left[I_{n-1}(m_\alpha a) - \frac{n}{m_\alpha a} I_n(m_\alpha a) \right]^{-1} \frac{J_{n,\alpha}}{m_\alpha \gamma},$$

$$n \geqslant 1 \quad (41)$$

where $J_{n,\alpha}$ is to be taken from (40). The sums in (37), (38), and (39) must be taken from $n = 0$ to $n = \infty$; however, the expression (40) holds only for $n \geqslant 1$ because for $n = 0$

$$J_{0,\alpha} = -\frac{2}{c\pi} \frac{\pi}{q} \int_{z=b-\delta/2}^{b+\delta/2} \frac{qI}{2\pi a\delta} \sin m_\alpha z \, dz$$

$$= -\frac{I}{\pi ac} \left(\frac{\sin m_\alpha \delta/2}{m_\alpha \delta/2} \right) \sin m_\alpha b \quad (42)$$

which must be used for $B_{0,\alpha}$. The resistance between the electrodes can then be determined as before.

Point Charges and Dielectric Plate. The problem of a single point charge Q located in front of a finitely thick dielectric plate can be treated by the method of images as in section 21; however, this becomes very cumbersome and the results are not in practical form. A different approach is the expression of the point charge field in terms of cylindrical coordinates and satisfying the boundary conditions as in the conventional boundary value problem.

The point charge field alone is given by

$$\Phi(\rho, z) = \frac{Q}{4\pi\varepsilon_0 r} = \frac{Q}{4\pi\varepsilon_0 \sqrt{\rho^2 + z^2}} \tag{43}$$

in accordance with Fig. 32·4. This can be expressed as a Fourier integral

$$\Phi(\rho, z) = \frac{Q}{4\pi\varepsilon_0} \int_{m=0}^{\infty} J_0(m\rho) e^{-m|z|} \, dm \tag{44}$$

listed as pair 557 in the C.-F. tables[5] with m for the integration variable g there.

The total field in the three regions must be built up in terms of solutions (5), (15), and (17). Starting with $n = 0$ because of the obvious axial symmetry, and rejecting in (17) the second term because its logarithmic singularity on the axis $\rho = 0$, one has left only $C_1 J_0(m\rho)$, which must be the same for all three regions except for different constants. The solution of (5) must have $D_2 = +D_1$ for region 1 to provide decreasing values for $z < 0$, must have $D_1 = -D_2$ for region 3 to provide decreasing values for $z > 0$, and will contain both constants for region 2. Since no spectral selection of m values is possible, all final solutions must be in terms of Fourier integrals. Thus, the total solution for region 1 with superposition of (44) for the actual point charge there, and those

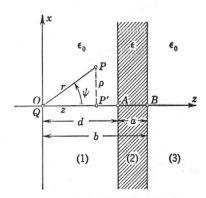

FIG. 32·4   Point Charge and Dielectric Plate.

[5] See reference, footnote 11 on p. 395; also Bateman,[C1] p. 409.

for the other regions are

$$\Phi^{(1)}(\rho, z) = \int_{m=0}^{\infty} \left[\frac{Q}{4\pi\varepsilon_0} e^{-m|z|} + D^{(1)}(m)e^{mz} \right] J_0(m\rho) \, dm$$

$$\Phi^{(2)}(\rho, z) = \int_{m=0}^{\infty} [D_1^{(2)}(m)e^{-mz} + D_2^{(2)}(m)e^{+mz}]J_0(m\rho) \, dm \quad (45)$$

$$\Phi^{(3)}(\rho, z) = \int_{m=0}^{\infty} [D^{(3)}(m)e^{-mz}]J_0(m\rho) \, dm$$

where the constants C_1 have been merged with the D constants. Because the Fourier integrals are unique representations, one can satisfy the boundary conditions in terms of the integrands in brackets. Continuity of the potentials and the normal components of dielectric flux density requires

$$\text{at } z = d, \qquad \Phi^{(1)} = \Phi^{(2)}, \qquad \varepsilon_0 \left(\frac{\partial \Phi}{\partial z} \right)^{(1)} = \varepsilon \left(\frac{\partial \Phi}{\partial z} \right)^{(2)}$$

$$\text{at } z = b, \qquad \Phi^{(2)} = \Phi^{(3)}, \qquad \varepsilon \left(\frac{\partial \Phi}{\partial z} \right)^{(2)} = \varepsilon_0 \left(\frac{\partial \Phi}{\partial z} \right)^{(3)} \tag{46}$$

from which one can solve for the constants, for example,

$$D^{(1)}(m) = \frac{e^{-2mb} - k_{12}{}^2 e^{-2md}}{1 - k_{12}{}^2 e^{-2ma}} \frac{Q}{4\pi\varepsilon_0},$$

$$D^{(3)}(m) = \frac{1 - k_{12}{}^2}{1 - k_{12}{}^2 e^{-2ma}} \frac{Q}{4\pi\varepsilon_0} \tag{47}$$

In these expressions,

$$k_{12} = -k_{23} = \frac{\varepsilon_0 - \varepsilon}{\varepsilon_0 + \varepsilon} \tag{48}$$

can be defined as reflection coefficients in analogy to optical problems or to transmission line theory. With the constants from (47), the integrals in (45) can actually be evaluated by the theorem of residues or by expansion into partial fractions leading to infinite sums related to the results obtained by image theory, though in much simpler form.

This problem is treated by Smythe,[A22] p. 181. With a finite radius of the point charge one can then compute the capacitance as influenced by the presence of the dielectric plate or one can translate this into a current flow problem exchanging dielectric constants against conductivities as in Maxwell,[A17] I, p. 443. For the point source located at A in Fig. 32·4, and assuming medium 1 to be non-conductive air, Smythe,[A22] p. 237, gives the solution to the current flow problem; this is of practical value in geophysical problems exploring the stratification of the earth by measurement of the potential distribution on its surface between two point electrodes.[6]

One can in similar manner solve for the potential distribution of a circular ring of charge found by direct integration in (12·58) and in the presence of ground in (12·65). Observe that the potential values of the point charge along the axis are obtained with $\rho = 0$ from (44) and that the potential values along the axis of the circular ring of radius a as found in (12·60) can be represented by introducing $\rho = a$ in (44), whereby

$$\frac{1}{\sqrt{a^2 + z^2}} = \int_{m=0}^{\infty} J_0(ma)e^{-m|z|}\, dm \tag{49}$$

Therefore, the potential anywhere in space should be

$$\Phi(\rho, z) = \frac{Q}{4\pi\varepsilon_0} \int_{m=0}^{\infty} J_0(ma)J_0(m\rho)e^{-m|z|}\, dm \tag{50}$$

introducing the same factor $J_0(m\rho)$ as for the point charge; see Bateman,[C1] pp. 410, 417. The form (50) can now be used to satisfy boundary conditions in analogous procedure as for the point charge.

For the circular disk with uniform charge distribution one can simply integrate (50) with respect to a from zero to the radius b of the disk. Thus, if the total charge is now Q, then for the elemental circular ring one has

$$dQ = \frac{Q}{b^2\pi} \cdot 2\pi a\, da$$

and therefore

$$\Phi(\rho, z) = \frac{Q}{2\pi\varepsilon_0 b} \int_{m=0}^{\infty} J_0(m\rho)e^{-m|z|}\, dm\left[\int_{a=0}^{b^2} J_0(ma)a\, da\right]$$

$$= \frac{Q}{2\pi\varepsilon_0} \int_{m=0}^{\infty} J_0(m\rho)e^{-m|z|}\, \frac{J_1(mb)}{mb}\, dm \tag{51}$$

[6] S. Stefanesco and C. and M. Schlumberger, *Jl. de physique*, **1**, p. 132 (1930).

This result[7] can again be used for the solution of problems involving a dielectric plate or plates parallel to the face of the disk as above.

Very Thin Cylindrical Coils. The electric fields of thin cylindrical coils can be computed by solving the scalar potential inside and outside in terms of the product functions (5), (15), and (17), where inside the coil only the first kind of Bessel function can be admitted, whereas in the outside space the two forms in (17) combine into the Hankel function to give vanishing results as $\rho \rightarrow \infty$. Ollendorff,[A18] p. 337, applies this to a short cylindrical coil with the simplifying assumption that the electric field in the end faces is purely radial.

The vector potential in idealized thin cylindrical coils with no axial current flow has only a peripheral component A_ψ, which, even for axial symmetry, does not satisfy Laplace's differential equation. Smythe,[A22] p. 290, finds the magnetic field distribution within the windows of an idealized shell-type transformer with very thin cylindrical windings and assuming the iron as infinitely permeable; he also gives several good field graphs, indicating the effect of the positioning of a thin cylindrical coil within the window.

ELLIPTIC CYLINDER COORDINATES

Here it is definitely advantageous to follow the generalized relations at the beginning of the section. Utilizing the conformal transformation (see 26·51)

$$w = x + jy = f \cosh (\xi + j\eta) \tag{52}$$

one obtains

$$x = f \cosh \xi \cos \eta, \qquad y = f \sinh \xi \sin \eta \tag{53}$$

which represent confocal ellipses and hyperbolas with the focal distance $2f$ as shown in Fig. 29·6. From (53),

$$\left(\frac{x}{f \cosh \xi}\right)^2 + \left(\frac{y}{f \sinh \xi}\right)^2 = 1, \qquad \left(\frac{x}{f \cos \eta}\right)^2 - \left(\frac{y}{f \sin \eta}\right)^2 = 1 \tag{54}$$

The first relation describes the ellipses with semiaxes $a = f \cosh \xi$, $b = f \sinh \xi$; the second relation gives the hyperbolas of semiaxes $a = f \cos \eta$, $b = f \sin \eta$. Specifically, ξ is analogous to the radial distance ρ of the circular cylinder, and $\xi = 0$ is the ellipse which

[7] A. Gray, *Phil. Mag.*, Series 6, **38**, p. 201 (1919); also Bateman,[Cl] p. 410.

has degenerated into the focal line $F_1 F_2$; $\eta = 0$ and $\eta = 2\pi$ are the hyperbolas which have degenerated into the positive x-axis from F_2 to the right, and $\eta = \pi$ is the hyperbola which has degenerated into the negative x-axis from F_1 to the left; $\eta = \pi/2$ is the plane of symmetry or y-z-plane in the underlying Cartesian system.

In accordance with (2) one has from (52)

$$h^2 = \left|\frac{dw}{d\zeta}\right|^2 = f^2 (\cosh^2 \xi - \cos^2 \eta) \qquad (55)$$

so that the components of the field vector become from (31·24), with $h_3 = 1$,

$$E_\xi = -\frac{1}{f}(\cosh^2 \xi - \cos^2 \eta)^{-\frac{1}{2}}\frac{\partial \Phi}{\partial \xi}, \quad E_\eta = -\frac{1}{f}(\cosh^2 \xi - \cos^2 \eta)^{-\frac{1}{2}}\frac{\partial \Phi}{\partial z},$$

$$E_z = -\frac{\partial \Phi}{\partial z} \qquad (56)$$

Defining in (55)

$$g_1(\xi) = f^2 \cosh^2 \xi, \qquad g_2(\eta) = -f^2 \cos^2 \eta,$$

one has directly from (8)

$$\frac{d^2 \Xi}{d\xi^2} + (m^2 f^2 \cosh^2 \xi - p^2)\Xi = 0 \qquad (57)$$

$$\frac{d^2 \mathsf{H}}{d\eta^2} + (p^2 - m^2 f^2 \cos^2 \eta)\mathsf{H} = 0 \qquad (58)$$

Both functions satisfy, therefore, differential equations of the same type which degenerate for $m \to 0$ into the standard differential equations for hyperbolic and trigonometric functions.

The more general form (58) with $m \neq 0$ possesses solutions which are called Mathieu functions;[8] these solutions are periodic in η with period 2π as required for the elliptic cylinder, if p^2 is selected for any given value m in accordance with a determinantal

---

[8] Brief treatments of Mathieu functions are given in E. T. Whittaker and G. N. Watson: *Modern Analysis*, Fourth Edition, Chapter XIX; Cambridge University Press, 1927; in Stratton,[A23] p. 376; and in Ince: *Ordinary Differential Equations*, Chapter XX; Longmans, 1927. Further details are given in M. J. O. Strutt: *Lamésche, Mathieusche und verwandte Funktionen in Physik und Technik;* J. Springer, Berlin, 1932. A summary of functional relations and graphical representations are given in E. Jahnke and F. Emde: *Tables of Functions;* reprinted by Dover Publications, New York, 1943; originally published by B. G. Teubner, Leipzig, 1939; the notation of Jahnke and Emde has been used here.

equation which leads to a denumerably infinite set of p_n values. As with the degenerate solution for $m = 0$, there are even and odd functions, so that the general solution is of the type

$$\mathsf{H}_n(\eta) = B_1^{(n)} \, ce_n(\eta, m) + B_2^{(n)} \, se_n(\eta, m) \tag{59}$$

where n is an order number starting from 0 for the ce functions (elliptic cosines) and from 1 for the se functions (elliptic sines).

TABLE 32·1

COMPARATIVE NOTATION FOR ELLIPTICAL COORDINATES

Coordinate	This Book	Bateman[C1]	Stratton[A23]	Whittaker and Watson (loc. cit.)	Strutt (loc. cit.)
u_1	ξ	ξ	$u = \cosh^{-1} \xi$	ξ	ξ
u_2	η	η	$v = \cos^{-1} \eta$	η	η
u_3	z	z	z	z	z
Focal distance	$2f$	$2c$	$2c_0$	$2c$	$2e$
Mathieu					
Elliptic sine	$se_n(\eta, m) \}$ *	$se_n \}$	$So_n(\cos v, \lambda) \}$ †	$se_n \}$	$S_n \}$
Elliptic cosine	$ce_n(\eta, m) \}$	$ce_n \}$	$Se_n(\cos v, \lambda) \}$	$ce_n \}$	$C_n \}$
Mathieu, associated radial			Re, Ro		$\mathcal{C}, \mathcal{S}$

* Same as Jahnke and Emde, loc. cit., p. 283.

† Actually, the order numbers n and m appear in interchanged positions in this reference.

As periodic functions, they can, of course, also be expanded into conventional Fourier series for which the recurrence formulas are found in Jahnke and Emde, loc. cit. These ce and se functions form a complete orthogonal system which can be normalized in the same general manner as the trigonometric functions.

For any solution $\mathsf{H}_n(\eta)$ with the parameters m and p_n there exists a solution $\Xi_n(\xi)$ of (57), called associated radial Mathieu functions by Stratton,[A23] p. 378, or modified Mathieu functions,[9] which are expressible as infinite sums of Bessel functions; choosing Bessel functions of first, second, or third (Hankel) kind, one has the respective kinds of associated radial Mathieu functions.

[9] H. Jeffreys, Proc. London Math. Soc., Series 2, **23**, pp. 437 and 455 (1925); also P. Humbert: Fonctions de Lamé et fonctions de Mathieu; Gauthiers-Villars, Paris, 1926.

The comparative notation of some references is given in Table 32·1.

As a simple illustration take the split elliptic cylinder of infinite length in Fig. 32·5. Because of homogeneity in the axial direc-

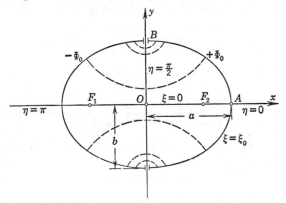

FIG. 32·5 Two Half Elliptic Cylinders.

tion, no dependence on z will exist, so that $m = 0$ and the solutions of (57), (58) become

$$\Xi(\xi) = C_1 \sinh p\xi + C_2 \cosh p\xi$$
$$\mathsf{H}(\eta) = B_1 \sin p\eta + B_2 \cos p\eta \tag{60}$$

There are two symmetry conditions which it is always good to utilize; namely, the major axis $\xi = 0$ must be a field line, so that along it

$$\left[\frac{\partial}{\partial \xi} \Xi(\xi)\right]_{\xi=0} = [pC_1 \cosh p\xi + pC_2 \sinh p\xi]_{\xi=0} = 0$$

which yields $C_1 = 0$; and along the minor axis $\eta = \pi/2$ and $\eta = 3\pi/2$ the potential is constant and equal to the median value, namely zero, so that

$$\mathsf{H}\left(\frac{\pi}{2}\right) = \mathsf{H}\left(\frac{3\pi}{2}\right) = \mathsf{U} = B_1$$

This leaves then for the potential

$$\Phi(\xi, \eta) = \sum_p B_p \cosh p\xi \cos p\eta \tag{61}$$

if the remaining constants C_2, B_2 are merged and made·dependent on p. The final boundary condition requires the potentials on

$\xi = \xi_0$ as given in Fig. 32·5, which can obviously be satisfied by considering (61) a Fourier series expansion in η. From Fig. 32·5 it is seen that $\Phi = \Phi_0$ for $-(\pi/2) < \eta < (\pi/2)$ and $\Phi = -\Phi_0$ for $(\pi/2) < \eta < (3\pi/2)$. The conventional Fourier series for this symmetrical rectangular function is

$$\Phi(\xi_0, \eta) = \frac{4}{\pi} \Phi_0 \sum_n \frac{(-1)^n}{2n + 1} \cos (2n + 1)\eta$$

so that comparison with (61) yields $p = 2n + 1$ and as final solution

$$\Phi(\xi, \eta) = \frac{4}{\pi} \Phi_0 \sum_{n=0}^{\infty} \frac{(-1)^n}{2n + 1} \frac{\cosh (2n + 1)\xi}{\cosh (2n + 1)\xi_0} \cos (2n + 1)\eta \quad (62)$$

The value of ξ_0 is determined by the given axes of the ellipse, since from (46) for point A one has $y = 0$, $x = a$ corresponding to $\eta = 0$, $\xi = \xi_0$, and similarly for the point B, so that

$$a = f \cosh \xi_0, \qquad b = f \sinh \xi_0, \qquad \xi_0 = \tanh^{-1} \frac{b}{a} \quad (63)$$

The field vector can be computed from (56) and with it the charge densities and capacitance for a small but finite gap between the halves.

PARABOLIC CYLINDER COORDINATES

The coordinates in the x-y-plane are chosen to describe orthogonal parabolas as in the case of the two-dimensional parabolic coordinates in section 29 with the additions of the third coordinate z. As seen in Fig. 29·7, the two families of parabolas can be defined by

$$\xi = \sqrt{2\rho} \cos \frac{\psi}{2}, \qquad \eta = \sqrt{2\rho} \sin \frac{\psi}{2} \quad (64)$$

Specifically, $\xi = 0$ is the parabola which has degenerated into the negative x-axis and $\eta = 0$ is the orthogonal parabola which has degenerated into the positive x-axis. The common focus is located at the origin 0, and the signs of ξ and η are uniquely defined by ψ in (64). In terms of a conformal transformation one can express (64) by

$$w = x + jy = \tfrac{1}{2}\zeta^2 \quad (65)$$

which gives parabolas as shown in section 29 and in particular

$$x = \tfrac{1}{2}(\xi^2 - \eta^2) = \rho \cos \psi, \qquad y = \xi\eta = \rho \sin \psi \quad (66)$$

Using (65) in (2), one obtains at once

$$h^2 = \left|\frac{dw}{d\zeta}\right|^2 = \xi^2 + \eta^2 \tag{67}$$

The components of the field vector are, therefore, from (31·24)

$$E_\xi = -(\xi^2 + \eta^2)^{-\frac{1}{2}}\frac{\partial \Phi}{\partial \xi}, \qquad E_\eta = -(\xi^2 + \eta^2)^{-\frac{1}{2}}\frac{\partial \Phi}{\partial \eta},$$

$$E_z = -\frac{\partial \Phi}{\partial z} \tag{68}$$

Separating in (67),

$$g_1(\xi) = \xi^2, \qquad g_2(\eta) = \eta^2$$

the individual differential equations (8) become in this case

$$\frac{d^2\Xi}{d\xi^2} + (m^2\xi^2 - p^2)\Xi = 0 \tag{69}$$

$$\frac{d^2\mathsf{H}}{d\eta^2} + (m^2\eta^2 + p^2)\mathsf{H} = 0 \tag{70}$$

Again, both functions satisfy differential equations of the same type which degenerate for $m \to 0$ into the standard differential equation for the hyperbolic and trigonometric functions.

The more general forms with $m \neq 0$ lead to the orthogonal function systems of the parabolic cylinder, thus, by defining in (69) a new variable $s = \sqrt{2jm}\xi$, and selecting for the available constant $p^2 = -2jm(n + \frac{1}{2})$, the differential equation results

$$\frac{d^2\Xi(s)}{ds^2} + \left[\left(n + \frac{1}{2}\right) - \frac{s^2}{4}\right]\Xi(s) = 0 \tag{71}$$

which has as solution the parabolic cylinder functions[10]

$$\Xi_n(\xi) \equiv \Psi_n(s) = (n!\,\sqrt{2\pi})^{-\frac{1}{2}}\exp\left(-\frac{s^2}{4}\right)H_n(s) \tag{72}$$

[10] Introduced by H. Weber, *Math. Annalen*, **1**, p. 1 (1869); brief treatment in E. T. Whittaker and G. N. Watson: *Modern Analysis*, Fourth Edition, p. 347; Cambridge University Press, 1927; and in Bateman,[C1] p. 488. A summary of functional relations and curves are given in E. Jahnke and F. Emde: *Tables of Functions;* reprinted by Dover Publications, New York, 1943; originally published by B. G. Teubner, Leipzig, 1939, whose notation has been used here.

The coefficients are so chosen that $\Psi_n(s)$ becomes normalized for real s in the range $s = -\infty$ to $s = +\infty$; the functions $H_n(s)$ are the Hermite polynomials[11] defined by the relation

$$\exp\left(-\frac{s^2}{2}\right) H_n(s) = \left(-\frac{d}{ds}\right)^n \exp\left(-\frac{s^2}{2}\right) \tag{73}$$

as they are used in (72). In analogous manner one obtains as solution of (70)

$$\mathsf{H}_n(\eta) \equiv \Psi_n(js) \tag{74}$$

since (70) becomes identical in form with (69) if one replaces η by $j\eta$.

The comparative notation of some references is given in Table 32·2.

TABLE 32·2

COMPARATIVE NOTATION FOR PARABOLIC COORDINATES

Coordinate	This Book	Bateman[C1]	Stratton[A23]
u_1	ξ	ξ	η
u_2	η	η	ξ
u_3	z	z	z
Hermite polynomial	$H_n(s)$	$U_n(s)$	—
(Generating exponential)	$\exp\left(-\dfrac{s^2}{2}\right)^*$	$\exp(-s^2)$	—

* Same as Jahnke and Emde, *loc. cit.*, p. 32.

33· CONFOCAL SPHEROIDAL COORDINATE AND FUNCTION SYSTEMS

The confocal spheroidal coordinate systems are characterized as a group by the fact that each of their coordinate surfaces is intersected by the three Cartesian coordinate planes $x = 0$, $y = 0$, and $z = 0$ along conic sections. Since the general ellipsoidal coordinate system is discussed in section 31, only coordinate

---

[11] Because of their importance in quantum mechanics, the Hermite polynomials with $\exp(-s^2)$ instead of $\exp\left(-\dfrac{s^2}{2}\right)$ are treated in practically any introduction to this topic, such as V. Rojansky: *Introductory Quantum Mechanics;* Prentice-Hall, New York, 1942; and L. Pauling and E. B. Wilson: *Introduction to Quantum Mechanics;* McGraw-Hill, New York, 1935; see also E. Madelung: *Mathematical Tools for the Physicist*, p. 59; reprinted by Dover Publications, New York, 1943; originally published by J. Springer, Berlin, 1936.

systems with axial symmetry will occur here; this will permit further generalization with respect to the separation of variables. It might be stressed that symmetry of the coordinate system does not imply symmetry of the potential fields.

Separability of Variables. One can establish basic conditions of separability quite similar to those demonstrated in section 32 and thus justify again the relatively small number of coordinate systems that have attained practical significance.

For any coordinate system with axial symmetry one will choose as one coordinate the angle ϕ of rotation about the axis of symmetry. Since the circular cylinder coordinate system has in a meridian plane the same rectangular reference grid as the Cartesian system normal to its z-axis, one can use it as background system and, indeed, introduce the complex notation $w = z + j\rho$ and consider any other orthogonal meridianal coordinate pair (ξ, η) as referred to it by a conformal transformation (Fig. 33·1)

$$w = z + j\rho = w(\zeta), \qquad \zeta = \xi + j\eta \tag{1}$$

The dependence of the geometric scale in the meridian plane upon the distance ρ from the axis of revolution is indicated in the Laplacian potential equation of the circular cylinder by the appearance of the first derivative in ρ, namely, from (32·12)

$$\frac{\partial^2 \Phi}{\partial \rho^2} + \frac{1}{\rho}\frac{\partial \Phi}{\partial \rho} + \frac{1}{\rho^2}\frac{\partial^2 \Phi}{\partial \phi^2} + \frac{\partial^2 \Phi}{\partial z^2} = 0 \tag{2}$$

It is convenient for the general discussion to define a modified potential function $\sqrt{\rho}\ \Phi$ and to separate at once the dependence on ϕ, so that one introduces

$$U(\rho, z)\cdot F(\phi) = \sqrt{\rho}\Phi(\rho, \phi, z) \tag{3}$$

into (2) which yields upon division by UF

$$\rho^2 \left[U^{-1}\left(\frac{\partial^2 U}{\partial \rho^2} + \frac{\partial^2 U}{\partial z^2}\right) + \frac{1}{4\rho^2} \right] + F^{-1}\frac{\partial^2 F}{\partial \psi^2} = 0 \tag{4}$$

Separation of the last term gives, therefore,

$$\left.\begin{aligned}
\frac{\partial^2 F}{\partial \phi^2} &= -m^2 F \\[2mm]
F &= A_1 \sin m\phi + A_2 \cos m\phi
\end{aligned}\right\} \tag{5}$$

where m is normally an integer, permitting conventional Fourier series expansions in ϕ. Though the coordinate systems in this section are axially symmetrical in their coordinate surfaces, it does not follow that all potential solutions must have the same symmetry!

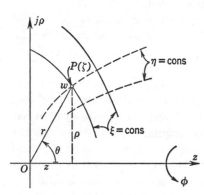

The reduced potential equation pertaining to the meridional distribution can now be written for the cylindrical system

$$\frac{\partial^2 U}{\partial \rho^2} + \frac{\partial^2 U}{\partial z^2} + \left(\frac{\frac14 - m^2}{\rho^2}\right) U = 0 \quad (6)$$

FIG. 33·1 General Coordinate System with Axial Symmetry.

which will be used as the rectangular background system. Any other pair of meridian plane coordinates (ξ, η) must be related to (z, ρ) by (1), which defines

$$z = f_1(\xi, \eta), \qquad \rho = f_2(\xi, \eta)$$

as conjugate functions (see section 25) in the same sense as in any two-dimensional geometry. Since the Cauchy-Riemann equations must hold for z and ρ, the two-dimensional metric factor from (31·23) becomes

$$h_1{}^2 = h_2{}^2 = h^2 = \left|\frac{dw}{d\zeta}\right|^2 \quad (7)$$

The Laplacian in ρ and z in equation (6) transforms in accordance with (26·5) if (x, y) is replaced by (ξ, η) here, so that (6) changes to

$$\frac{1}{h^2}\left(\frac{\partial^2 U}{\partial \xi^2} + \frac{\partial^2 U}{\partial \eta^2}\right) + \frac{\frac14 - m^2}{\rho^2} \cdot U = 0$$

For further separation of the variables, one introduces now the product function

$$U(\xi, \eta) = \Xi(\xi) \cdot \mathsf{H}(\eta) \quad (8)$$

which yields

$$\Xi^{-1}\, \Xi'' + \mathsf{H}^{-1}\, \mathsf{H}'' = -\left(\frac{1}{4} - m^2\right)\frac{h^2}{\rho^2} \quad (9)$$

It has been shown[1] that the necessary and sufficient condition of further separability is the fact that

$$h^2(\xi, \eta) = \rho^2[g_1(\xi) + g_2(\eta)] \tag{10}$$

where g_1 and g_2 are functions of only ξ and η, respectively. This means that $\left|\dfrac{dw}{d\zeta}\right|^2$ itself *must yield a factor* ρ^2 and the remainder *must be separable* into the sum of two individual functions of the variables. This obviously imposes severe limitations upon the choice of orthogonal families of surfaces which can serve as orthogonal coordinate systems with separability of the variables! Again, as in the cylindrical coordinate systems, it is primarily the family of conic sections which allows clear separability in the mapping function; there is an additional system employing elliptic functions for the relationship (z, ρ) to (ξ, η) which leads to the annular coordinate system briefly discussed in section 31.

If then (10) is valid, the separation of (9) leads to the two ordinary differential equations of the Sturm-Liouville type (see section 29)

$$\frac{d^2\Xi}{d\xi^2} + \left[\left(\frac{1}{4} - m^2\right)g_1(\xi) - p^2\right]\Xi = 0$$
$$\frac{d^2\mathsf{H}}{d\eta^2} + \left[\left(\frac{1}{4} - m^2\right)g_2(\eta) + p^2\right]\mathsf{H} = 0 \tag{11}$$

where p^2 is the second separation constant and can have any real or complex value. In addition to the solutions in terms of orthogonal function systems, one can always find particular solutions by inspection, such as indicated for the Cartesian system in section 31.

SPHERICAL COORDINATE SYSTEM

The spherical or polar coordinate system possesses such symmetry that it is simpler to proceed with the conventional and specific coordinate relations rather than to apply the above systematic approach. Of course, one can employ the conformal mapping function $w = e^{-\zeta} = e^{-\xi}(\cos\eta - j\sin\eta)$ and obtain (7) and (11) as shown; one can also introduce the more usual coordi-

---

[1] Ch. Snow: *The Hypergeometric and Legendre Functions with Applications to Integral Equations and Potential Theory*, p. 202; National Bureau of Standards, Washington, D.C., 1942; see also Hobson,[C9] Chapter X.

nates of Fig. 33·1, namely, $e^{-\xi} = r$ with $-\infty < \xi + \infty$ and $\theta = -\eta$ and systematically obtain the equations (11) in terms of these new coordinates.

Conventionally, however, one chooses as meridian coordinates directly the radial distance r from the origin 0 (pole) of the system and the colatitude θ measured from the positive direction of the axis of revolution so that $0 < \theta < \pi$. The coordinate surfaces $r = $ cons are then the concentric spheres with center at 0, and those $\theta = $ cons are the coaxial cones with apices at 0; $\phi = $ cons

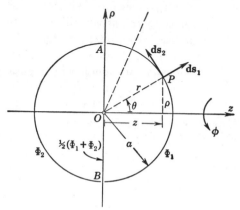

FIG. 33·2   Two Conducting Hemispherical Shells.

are, of course, the meridian planes as outlined previously. The line elements in the three coordinate directions are for the point P in Fig. 33·2

$$ds_1 = dr, \qquad ds_2 = r\,d\theta, \qquad ds_3 = \rho\,d\phi = r\sin\theta\,d\phi \qquad (12)$$

so that by comparison with (31·23)

$$h_1 = 1, \qquad h_2 = r, \qquad h_3 = r\sin\theta \qquad (13)$$

and thus for the components of the field vector by (31·24)

$$E_r = -\frac{\partial\Phi}{\partial r}, \qquad E_\theta = -\frac{1}{r}\frac{\partial\Phi}{\partial\theta}, \qquad E_\phi = -\frac{1}{r\sin\theta}\frac{\partial\Phi}{\partial\phi} \qquad (14)$$

The potential equation (31·27) becomes with (13) and deleting the factor $(h_1 h_2 h_3)^{-1}$

$$\nabla^2\Phi = \frac{\partial}{\partial r}\left(r^2\frac{\partial\Phi}{\partial r}\right) + \frac{1}{\sin\theta}\frac{\partial}{\partial\theta}\left(\sin\theta\frac{\partial\Phi}{\partial\theta}\right) + \frac{1}{\sin^2\theta}\frac{\partial^2\Phi}{\partial\phi^2} = 0 \qquad (15)$$

Introducing the product function

$$\Phi(r, \theta, \phi) = R(r) \cdot T(\theta) \cdot F(\phi) \qquad (16)$$

dividing through by it and multiplying by $\sin^2 \theta$ permit at once the separation of the last term as in (5). There remains, then,

$$\sin^2 \theta \, R^{-1} \frac{d}{dr}\left(r^2 \frac{dR}{dr}\right) + \sin \theta \, T^{-1} \frac{d}{d\theta}\left(\sin \theta \frac{dT}{d\theta}\right) - m^2 = 0$$

from which one can separate the first term after clearing $\sin^2 \theta$, so that

$$\frac{d}{dr}\left(r^2 \frac{dR}{dr}\right) = p^2 R \qquad (17)$$

This can be satisfied by r^n which yields

$$n(n + 1) = p^2 \qquad (18)$$

for $n \geqslant 0$; or also by $r^{-(n+1)}$ with $n \neq -1$ which also yields (18), so that one uses (18) as definition of the second separation constant for integer values of n and has as general solution of (17)

$$R = C_1 r^n + C_2 r^{-(n+1)}, \qquad n = 0, 1, 2, \cdots \qquad (19)$$

The differential equation for $T(\theta)$ thus becomes

$$\frac{1}{\sin \theta} \frac{d}{d\theta}\left(\sin \theta \frac{dT}{d\theta}\right) + \left[n(n + 1) - \frac{m^2}{\sin^2 \theta}\right] T = 0 \qquad (20)$$

which has as solution the *associated Legendre functions*[2] or tesseral harmonics of first and second kind, of order n, and of degree $m \leqslant n$

$$T(\theta) = D_1 P_n{}^m (\cos \theta) + D_2 Q_n{}^m (\cos \theta), \qquad n \geqslant m \qquad (21)$$

One frequently denotes $\cos \theta = \mu$ (or also x) because of the simpler forms that result in functional relations; in particular,

---

[2] These functions are rather uniformly designated in the manner indicated; good treatments can be found in practically any one of the references in Appendix 4, C, a, as well as in Smythe,[A22] p. 128; in Stratton,[A23] p. 172; and in Jeans,[A10] p. 206. Excellent summaries of definitions and interrelations as well as graphs and numerical values are given in E. Jahnke and F. Emde: *Tables of Functions;* reprinted by Dover Publications, New York, 1943; originally published by B. G. Teubner, Leipzig, 1939. Some of the simpler relations are given in Appendix 6.

for $m = 0$ this gives for the differential equation (20)

$$\frac{d}{d\mu}\left[(1 - \mu^2)\frac{dT(\mu)}{d\mu}\right] + n(n + 1)\,T(\mu) = 0 \qquad (22)$$

which is clearly of the Sturm-Liouville type (29·2) with characteristic number $\lambda = n(n + 1)$ and weight function $p(\mu) = 1$. The solutions of (22) are valid for problems with axial symmetry and are of two kinds, the *Legendre polynomials* or zonal harmonics of the first kind $P_n(\cos\theta)$, which are continuous for all values $0 \leqslant \theta \leqslant \pi$ or $-1 \leqslant \mu \leqslant 1$; and the zonal harmonics of the second kind $Q_n(\cos\theta)$, which have logarithmic singularities at $\theta = 0$ and $\theta = \pi$ or $\mu = \pm 1$, so that they cannot constitute solutions for problems which include the axis of revolution. The Legendre polynomials $P_n(\mu)$ are orthogonal polynomials in μ for all values of the variable; in the range $(-1) \leqslant \mu \leqslant +1$ they can be used to represent any bounded function in terms of a *Legendre series*, as shown in Appendix 6, (24) to 6, (28). For $m \neq 0$ and with $\mu = \cos\theta$, the differential equation (20) becomes

$$\frac{d}{d\mu}\left[(1 - \mu^2)\frac{dT(\mu)}{d\mu}\right] + \left[n(n + 1) - \frac{m^2}{1 - \mu^2}\right]T(\mu) = 0 \quad (23)$$

leading to the *associated Legendre functions* which also are of two kinds. In particular, the functions $P_n{}^m(\mu)$ of the first kind are again orthogonal with weight function unity in the range $(-1) \leqslant \mu \leqslant (+1)$. If these associated Legendre functions of the first kind are combined with their respective trigonometric factors in ϕ from (5), namely,

$$S_n{}^m(\theta, \phi) = P_n{}^m(\cos\theta)\cdot[A_1 \sin m\phi + A_2 \cos m\phi] \qquad (24)$$

they are frequently called *surface harmonics* or *tesseral harmonics* and constitute an orthogonal function system with respect to both order numbers n and m.

Conducting Spherical Shells. If two hemispherical shells of infinitesimal thickness and potentials Φ_1 and Φ_2 are given as in Fig. 33·2, axial symmetry will prevail. In accordance with (16), the general type of solution must be the product of (19) and (21) for $m = 0$,

$$[C_1 r^n + C_2 r^{-(n+1)}]\,[D_1 P_n(\cos\theta) + D_2 Q_n(\cos\theta)] \qquad (25)$$

For the interior space $r < a$ one cannot admit negative powers in r, and for the exterior space $r > a$ no positive powers in r can appear; furthermore, the second kind of Legendre function must be discarded because of its singularity along the axis. This reduces the solutions with appropriate contraction of the amplitude factors to

$$\left.\begin{array}{ll} \Phi(r, \theta) = \sum_{n=0}^{\infty} M_n r^n P_n(\cos \theta), & r \leqslant a \\[3mm] \Phi(r, \theta) = \sum_{n=0}^{\infty} N_n r^{-(n+1)} P_n(\cos \theta), & r \geqslant a \end{array}\right\} \quad (26)$$

On the sphere $r = a$ these expressions must represent the expansion of the given potential values $\Phi = \Phi_1$ for $0 \leqslant \theta < \pi/2$, and $\Phi = \Phi_2$ for $\pi/2 < \theta \leqslant \pi$ into a Legendre series for which the coefficients for the internal potential are now found with $\cos \theta = \mu$ from Appendix 6,(24) and 6,(25),

$$\frac{2}{2n+1} [M_n a^n] = \int_{\mu=-1}^{\mu=0} \Phi_1 P_n(\mu) \, d\mu + \int_{\mu=0}^{\mu=+1} \Phi_2 P_n(\mu) \, d\mu \quad (27)$$

Because of the general integral form [Appendix 6,(21)]

$$(2n+1) \int_{\mu_1}^{\mu_2} P_n(\mu) \, d\mu$$
$$= [P_{n+1}(\mu_2) - P_{n-1}(\mu_2)] - [P_{n+1}(\mu_1) - P_{n-1}(\mu_1)] \quad (28)$$

the values of the integrals in (27) can readily be determined. For n even, say, $n = 2k$, Appendix 6,(5) and 6,(6) give

$$P_{2k}(0) = (-1)^k \frac{1 \cdot 3 \cdot 5 \cdots (2k-1)}{2 \cdot 4 \cdot 6 \cdots (2k)},$$
$$P_{2k}(-1) = P_{2k}(+1) = +1 \quad (29)$$

and for n odd, say, $n = 2k + 1$,

$$P_{2k+1}(0) = 0, \qquad P_{2k+1}(+1) = -P_{2k+1}(-1) = +1 \quad (30)$$

One finds, therefore, that $n = 0$ gives the only even contribution, and for $n > 0$ only odd functions remain, just as one would expect with the conventional Fourier series. Introducing the results into (26), one obtains

$$
\left.
\begin{aligned}
\Phi(r, \theta) &= \frac{1}{2} \left(\Phi_1 + \Phi_2 \right) - \left(\Phi_1 - \Phi_2 \right) \left[\frac{3}{4} \frac{r}{a} P_1 \right. \\
&\left. - \frac{7}{8} \cdot \frac{1}{2} \left(\frac{r}{a} \right)^3 P_3 + \frac{11}{12} \frac{1 \cdot 3}{2 \cdot 4} \left(\frac{r}{a} \right)^5 P_5 - \cdots \right], r \leqslant a \\
\Phi(r, \theta) &= \frac{1}{2} \left(\Phi_1 + \Phi_2 \right) \frac{a}{r} - \left(\Phi_1 - \Phi_2 \right) \left[\frac{3}{4} \left(\frac{a}{r} \right)^2 P_1 \right. \\
&\left. - \frac{7}{8} \frac{1}{2} \left(\frac{a}{r} \right)^4 P_3 + \frac{11}{12} \frac{1 \cdot 3}{2 \cdot 4} \left(\frac{a}{r} \right)^6 P_5 - \cdots \right], r \geqslant a
\end{aligned}
\right\} \quad (31)
$$

This solution holds also for the temperature distribution within a *solid sphere* if the temperature is kept constant over each of the two hemispheric caps, (see Byerly,[C2] p. 173); it also describes the current distribution through a *solid conducting sphere* with hemispherical electrode caps. Since the plane $\theta = \pi/2$ is an equipotential plane with $\Phi = \frac{1}{2}(\Phi_1 + \Phi_2)$, one can use the same solution for the internal potential distribution between one hemisphere shell $r = a$ and $0 \leqslant \theta < \pi/2$ of potential Φ_1 and the circular base plate AB in Fig. 33·2 of potential $\frac{1}{2}(\Phi_1 + \Phi_2)$. Choosing $\Phi_2 = -\phi_1$ gives to the base plate the potential zero.

Similar applications can be made to concentric spherical shells of arbitrary potential distributions; in this case the complete solution for $R(r)$ in (19) must be used as in Byerly,[C2] p. 176. The case of a uniformly charged circular ring within a closed spherical shell is treated in Smythe,[A22] p. 138, by finding the potential produced by the ring along the spherical surface and compensating it by a solution of the type (26) for $r \leqslant a$ so as to produce a constant potential for $r = a$. This method can be used where the original charge distribution is a fixed one, as in the case of line charges, and is not disturbed by the presence of other conductors.

Solid Spherical Conductor. Assume two small electrodes to bring current to, and to collect current from, a solid sphere as in Fig. 33·3. If these electrodes are located at A and B, at diametrically opposite points, the current distribution will have axial symmetry and the potential solution within the sphere will be given by the first line in (26). The boundary conditions require a vanishing normal component of the field vector over the entire surface except for $\theta \leqslant \tau$ and for $(\pi - \tau) < \theta < \pi$, where it must have the value necessary to maintain the current density at the electrodes. In accordance with (14), the radial field vector component is from (26)

$$E_r = -\frac{\partial \Phi}{\partial r} = -\sum_{n=0}^{\infty} n M_n r^{n-1} P_n(\cos \theta) \tag{32}$$

and at $r = a$ this must be the Legendre series expansion [Appendix 6,(24)], so that the coefficients become similar to (27)

$$-\frac{2}{2n+1}[n M_n a^{n-1}] =$$
$$+ \int_{\mu=-1}^{\mu=-\cos\tau} \frac{J}{\gamma} P_n(\mu)\, d\mu - \int_{\mu=\cos\tau}^{\mu=+1} \frac{J}{\gamma} P_n(\mu)\, d\mu \tag{33}$$

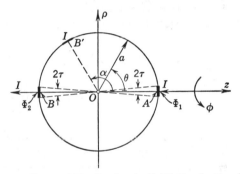

Fig. 33·3   Current Distribution in Solid Conducting Sphere.

where J is the current density (positive, if radially out)

$$J = \frac{I}{(a\tau)^2 \pi}$$

if τ is a small angle. The integrals are evaluated again by (28), since the current densities are constant;[3] because of (29) and (30) only the odd functions contribute, so that one can restrict $n = 2k + 1$ and thus

$$[n M_n a^{n-1}] = +\frac{J}{\gamma} \cdot [P_{2k}(\cos\tau) - P_{2k+2}(\cos\tau)] \tag{34}$$

[3] Smythe,[A22] p. 234, treats the same problem but assumes in (33) $P_n(\mu) \approx P_n(1)$ which leads to infinite potentials at the electrodes and does not permit evaluation of the resistance between electrodes.

The complete potential solution is, therefore,

$$\Phi(r, \theta) = \frac{aJ}{\gamma} \sum_{k=0}^{\infty} \frac{1}{2k+1} \left(\frac{r}{a}\right)^n$$
$$[P_{2k}(\cos \tau) - P_{2k+2}(\cos \tau)]P_{2k+1}(\cos \theta) \quad (35)$$

Defining the voltage between the electrodes

$$V = \Phi(a, \theta = 0) - \Phi(a, \theta = \pi) = RI$$

and observing (30) as well as the definition of the current density, (35) yields for the resistance R between the electrodes

$$R = \frac{2}{a\pi\gamma} \sum_{k=0}^{\infty} \frac{1}{2k+1} \frac{1}{\tau^2} [P_{2k}(\cos \tau) - P_{2k+2}(\cos \tau)] \quad (36)$$

If the second electrode is shifted from B at $\theta = \pi$ to B' at $\theta = \alpha$, the axial symmetry no longer holds and the potential solution becomes

$$\Phi(r, \theta, \phi) = \sum_{n=0}^{\infty} \left[\sum_{m=1}^{\infty} M_{m,n} r^n P_n{}^m (\cos \theta) \cos m\phi \right.$$
$$\left. + N_n r^n P_n(\cos \theta) \right] \quad (37)$$

where the last term holds for $m = 0$ and where advantage has been taken of the even symmetry in ϕ with respect to the plane through the centers of the two electrodes by dropping the sine terms.   The coefficients must be determined from the boundary conditions on the electrodes as previously.   There is no change at A, where the electrode is defined by $0 < \theta < \tau$, $0 < \phi < 2\pi$; however, at B' the electrode cannot easily be described as round: it is more convenient to define it as a small square by $(\alpha + \tau) > \theta > (\alpha - \tau)$ and $-\tau < \phi < \tau$ with an area $(2a\tau)^2$, which one could, of course, make equal to that at A.   Computing the radial derivative of the potential (37) and letting it be zero everywhere except on the electrode surfaces where constant values are assumed, one has for the coefficients expressions similar to (33).   Since no such simple integral relations exist for the associated Legendre functions as (28) for the Legendre polynomials, further simplifying assumptions become necessary.

Dielectric Spheres.   The dielectric spherical shell of finite thickness in a uniform electric field E^0 as in Fig. 33·4 is a very simple application of the Legendre functions. Expressing the given field as in section 21 by

$$E_r{}^0 = E^0 \cos \theta, \qquad E_\theta{}^0 = -E^0 \sin \theta \qquad (38)$$

it becomes obvious that the potential functions for the various regions can only contain terms $n = 0$ and $n = 1$ in the general

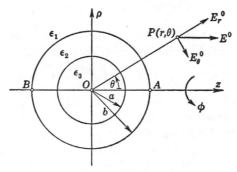

FIG. 33·4   Dielectric Spherical Shell in Uniform Electric Field.

axially symmetrical solution (26), since boundary conditions would render all other coefficients equal to zero. For the three regions one would therefore have

$$
\begin{aligned}
\text{for } r \geqslant b: \quad & \Phi_1 = N_0 r^{-1} P_0(\cos \theta) + N_1 r^{-2} P_1(\cos \theta) \\
\text{for } a \leqslant r \leqslant b: \quad & \Phi_2 (C_{01} + C_{02} r^{-1}) P_0(\cos \theta) \\
& \qquad + (C_{11} r + C_{12} r^{-2}) P_1(\cos \theta) \\
\text{for } r \leqslant a: \quad & \Phi_3 = M_0 P_0(\cos \theta) + M_1 r P_1(\cos \theta)
\end{aligned}
\right\} \quad (39)
$$

and as boundary conditions

$$
\begin{aligned}
\text{at } r = b: \quad & \varepsilon_1 \left(E_r{}^0 - \frac{\partial \Phi_1}{\partial r} \right) = -\varepsilon_2 \left(\frac{\partial \Phi_2}{\partial r} \right), \\
& \qquad\qquad E_\theta{}^0 - \frac{1}{r} \frac{\partial \Phi_1}{\partial \theta} = -\frac{1}{r} \frac{\partial \Phi_2}{\partial \theta} \\
\text{at } r = a: \quad & -\varepsilon_3 \frac{\partial \Phi_3}{\partial r} = -\varepsilon_2 \frac{\partial \Phi_2}{\partial r}, \\
& \qquad\qquad -\frac{1}{r} \frac{\partial \Phi_3}{\partial \theta} = -\frac{1}{r} \frac{\partial \Phi_2}{\partial \theta}
\end{aligned}
\right\} \quad (40)
$$

Introducing the gradients from (39) and the external field from (38), the constants can all be evaluated, giving $C_{02} = N_0 = C_{01} = M_0 = 0$, and

$$M_1 = - \left\{ \frac{2}{9} \frac{\varepsilon_2 - \varepsilon_1}{\varepsilon_1} \frac{\varepsilon_2 - \varepsilon_3}{\varepsilon_2} \left[1 - \left(\frac{a}{b} \right)^3 \right] \right.$$
$$\left. + \frac{1}{3} \frac{2\varepsilon_1 + \varepsilon_3}{\varepsilon_1} \right\}^{-1} \cdot E_0 \quad (41)$$

where terms have been collected to lead to this simpler expression. Since the electric field inside the spherical shell follows from (39) as

$$E_r{}^{(3)} = -M_1 \cos \theta, \qquad E_\theta{}^{(3)} = +M_1 \sin \theta$$

it is definitely a *uniform* field like the impressed field (38) and has the *same* direction as E^0. Its intensity is decreased by the factor within the brackets of (41), so that this factor k_s defines directly the shielding efficiency of the dielectric shell. If one assumes $\varepsilon_1 = \varepsilon_3 = \varepsilon_0$ and $\varepsilon_2 = \varepsilon$, then

$$k_s = \left\{ \frac{2}{9} \left(\frac{\varepsilon}{\varepsilon_0} - 1 \right)^2 \left[1 - \left(\frac{a}{b} \right)^3 \right] + 1 \right\}^{-1} \quad (42)$$

For a value $\varepsilon = 5\varepsilon_0$ and $b/a = 2$, one has $k_s = (1.62)^{-1} = 0.617$, so that dielectric shielding can be made effective only with special materials with very large dielectric constants. Solutions are given briefly in Smythe,[A22] p. 139, and more extensively in Ollendorff,[A18] p. 55; Maxwell,[A17] I, p. 438, solves the analogous current distribution for conductors of like geometry and conductivities γ_1, γ_2, γ_3, respectively.

The completely analogous case of a *magnetic shell* in a uniform magnetic field is obtained by appropriate substitutions; it is treated in Maxwell,[A17] II, p. 59; in Moullin,[B48] p. 205; in Smythe,[A22] p. 288; and in Frank and Mises,[C6] II, p. 718.

If one lets $a \to 0$, the spherical shell becomes a solid sphere. The solution for Φ_1 remains the same as in (39); Φ_2 reduces to

$$\Phi_2 = C_{11} r P_1(\cos \theta) = C_{11} r \cos \theta \quad (43)$$

It has, therefore, the same form as Φ_3 before, and one finds

$$C_{11} = - \frac{3\varepsilon_1}{\varepsilon_2 + 2\varepsilon_1} E^0$$

again a uniform field throughout the sphere. The application to the analogous magnetic case is obvious. The dielectric sphere is treated well in Jeans,[A10] p. 228; in Harnwell,[A9] p. 67; in Mason and Weaver,[A16] p. 151; in Ramsay,[A21] p. 135; and in Stratton,[A23] p. 205; the magnetic sphere in Moullin,[B48] p. 205; in Planck,[A19] p. 99; and in Frank and Mises,[C6] II, p. 716. If one lets $\varepsilon_2 \to \infty$, the solution becomes identical with that of the conducting sphere in a uniform field (see section 21). It is worth noting that at the pole $\theta = 0$ the electric field strength has the largest radial value; for the dielectric it follows from (43)

$$E^{(2)} = -\frac{\partial \Phi_2}{\partial r} = \frac{3\varepsilon_1}{\varepsilon_2 + 2\varepsilon_1} E^0$$

and for air because of the continuity of the dielectric flux density D,

$$E^{(1)} = \frac{\varepsilon_2}{\varepsilon_1} E^{(2)} = \frac{3\varepsilon_2}{\varepsilon_2 + 2\varepsilon_1} E^0 \qquad (44)$$

If $\varepsilon_1 \gg \varepsilon_2$, then $E^{(2)} \to \frac{3}{2}E^0$, and if $\varepsilon_2 \gg \varepsilon_1$, $E^{(1)} \to 3E^0$; the dielectric of lower dielectric constant always carries a larger local field strength than the impressed uniform field E^0! Spherical air bubbles in transformer oil correspond to the first alternative, and water drops in transformer oil to the second alternative; both can readily ionize under field strength values considered moderate for the oil.

It had been stressed in section 21 that no image treatment exists for a point charge and a dielectric sphere. Assume the point charge located at Q as in Fig. 33·5; then its potential is given by

$$\Phi_Q = \frac{Q}{4\pi\varepsilon_1 r'} \qquad (45)$$

In order to be able to satisfy the boundary conditions on the surface of the sphere, the potential must be expressed in terms of the spherical coordinates r and θ, which can be done by the classical expansion

$$(r')^{-1} = [r^2 + b^2 - 2rb \cos \theta]^{-\frac{1}{2}}$$
$$= \frac{1}{b} \sum_{n=0}^{\infty} \left(\frac{r}{b}\right)^n P_n(\cos \theta), \qquad r < b \quad (46)$$

which has led to the designation *Legendre coefficients* for the polynomials $P_n(\cos \theta)$. Taking for the total external potential the combination $(\Phi_1 + \Phi_Q)$, where Φ_1 is the reaction potential of the dielectric sphere and is identical with the second line in (26),

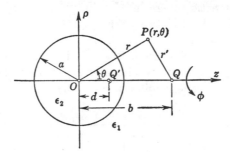

FIG. 33·5   Dielectric Sphere and Point Charge.

and for the internal potential Φ_2 the first line in (26), one can satisfy the boundary conditions

at $r = a$: $\varepsilon_1 \dfrac{\partial}{\partial r}(\Phi_1 + \Phi_Q) = \varepsilon_2 \dfrac{\partial}{\partial r}\Phi_2,$ $\Phi_1 + \Phi_Q = \Phi_2$ (47)

and actually finds as in Stratton,[A23] p. 204, for the coefficients of (26):

$$N_n = \frac{Q}{4\pi} \frac{-n(\varepsilon_2 - \varepsilon_1)}{\varepsilon_1[n(\varepsilon_2 + \varepsilon_1) + \varepsilon_1]} \frac{a^{2n+1}}{b^{n+1}}$$

$$M_n = \frac{Q}{4\pi} \frac{2n + 1}{[n(\varepsilon_2 + \varepsilon_1) + \varepsilon_1]} \frac{1}{b^{n+1}}$$

(48)

As $\varepsilon_2 \rightarrow \infty$, the inner potential Φ_2 becomes a constant and the potential solution Φ_1 can be shown to be identical with a Legendre series of the type (46) for a point charge $-Q(a/b)$ located at a distance $d = a^2/b$ from the center of the sphere; it therefore reduces to the solution of a point charge and an isolated conducting sphere given in section 21. No such simple interpretation is possible for the dielectric sphere.

Admitting a small but finite radius a_1 of the point charge Q permits the determination of its capacitance as influenced by the presence of the dielectric sphere. The total potential on the surface of the given quasi point charge is now the value of Φ_Q from (45) at $r' = a_1$ and that of Φ_1 at $r \approx b$ and $\theta = 0$, since $a_1 \ll b$; thus with N_n from (48)

$$\Phi(a_1) = \frac{Q}{4\pi\varepsilon_1}\left[\frac{1}{a_1} - \frac{1}{b}\sum_{n=0}^{\infty} \frac{n(\varepsilon_2 - \varepsilon_1)}{n(\varepsilon_2 + \varepsilon_1) + \varepsilon_1}\left(\frac{a}{b}\right)^{2n+1}\right] = \frac{Q}{C} \quad (49)$$

since $P_n(1) = 1$. For $\varepsilon_2 \to \infty$ this expression for capacitance becomes identical with (11·23), the capacitance of a quasi point

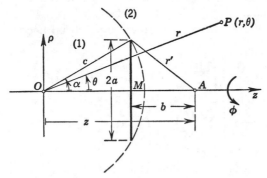

FIG. 33·6   Circular Ring of Charge.

charge Q near an isolated conducting sphere. Numerically, the effect upon the capacitance of the quasi point charge caused by the dielectric sphere is much smaller than that caused by the conducting sphere, though both tend to increase it.

Uniformly Charged Circle and Disk. Though the circular ring of charge has been treated in section 12, a more convenient formulation can be obtained by the use of Legendre polynomials. As obtained in (12·60), the potential along the axis where $\theta = 0$ can be written $Q/4\pi\varepsilon r'$, where r' is the distance of any point on the circle of charge to the point of observation A on the axis, as indicated in Fig. 33·6. But one can expand

$$(r')^{-1} = [z^2 + c^2 - 2zc\cos\alpha]^{-\frac{1}{2}}$$

into the Legendre series (46), so that the potential along the axis is also

$$\Phi_{\theta=0} = \frac{Q}{4\pi\varepsilon}\frac{1}{c}\left[\sum\left(\frac{z}{c}\right)^n P_n(\cos\alpha)\right]_{z<c};$$

$$\left[\sum\left(\frac{c}{z}\right)^{n+1} P_n(\cos\alpha)\right]_{z>c} \quad (50)$$

where the first bracket is used for $z < c$, and the second bracket for $z > c$. From (50) one can at once construct the solution anywhere in space by replacing z by r and adding the factors $P_n(\cos \theta)$, which formally reproduces the expansions (26) but now with known coefficients basically obtained by coefficient comparison along the axis of rotation. That this method is generally applicable in systems with axial symmetry where the axis belongs completely to the field region is demonstrated in Byerly,[C2] p. 157; in Kellogg,[C10] p. 255; in Webster,[C16] p. 346; and in Bateman,[C2] p. 406. The solution for the potential becomes thus

$$
\left. \begin{array}{l}
\Phi(r, \theta) = \dfrac{Q}{4\pi\varepsilon} \dfrac{1}{c} \left[\displaystyle\sum_{n=0}^{\infty} \left(\dfrac{r}{c}\right)^n P_n(\cos \alpha)\, P_n(\cos \theta) \right]_{r<c} ; \\[4ex]
\dfrac{Q}{4\pi\varepsilon} \dfrac{1}{c} \left[\displaystyle\sum_{n=0}^{\infty} \left(\dfrac{c}{r}\right)^{n+1} P_n(\cos \alpha)\, P_n(\cos \theta) \right]_{r>c}
\end{array} \right\} \quad (51)
$$

Shifting the origin 0 in Fig. 33·6 to the center M of the circle, where $\alpha = \pi/2$ and $r' = \sqrt{z^2 + c^2}$, one sees that the expansion follows the binomial theorem. The more general forms (50) and (51) are, however, useful, since they permit extension to disks, cylinders, spherical caps and zones, by simply integrating the axial potential of the circle over the given geometry in terms of c and α. For gravitational potentials such applications are given in Byerly[C2]; Jeans,[A10] p. 226, solves the uniformly charged spherical cap.

Thus the extension to a uniformly charged circular disk of radius a is readily made by first determining the potential along the axis. Integrating the potential produced along the axis by the circle above, with the origin chosen at the center of the disk, one has simply

$$
\Phi_{\theta=0} = \frac{Q}{4\pi\varepsilon} \frac{2}{a^2} [\sqrt{z^2 + a^2} - z]
$$

for example from Attwood,[A2] p. 67. Expanding into positive or negative powers of z by the binomial theorem, replacing z by r and applying the appropriate Legendre factor, one can then construct the complete solution

$$\Phi(r, \theta) = \frac{Q}{4\pi\varepsilon} \frac{2}{a} \left[\frac{1}{2} \left(\frac{a}{r} \right) - \frac{1}{2 \cdot 4} \left(\frac{a}{r} \right)^3 P_3(\cos \theta) \right.$$

$$\left. + \frac{1 \cdot 3}{2 \cdot 4 \cdot 6} \left(\frac{a}{r} \right)^5 P_5(\cos \theta) - \cdots \right], \quad r > a \quad (52)$$

and similarly for $r < a$, as given also in Webster,[C16] p. 346, and in Churchill,[C3] p. 198, for the gravitational analogue.

Circular Currents. For axially symmetrical magnetic fields, the vector potential **A** reduces to the single component A_ϕ parallel to the circular currents; even so, it does not satisfy the Laplacian differential equation in the spherical coordinate system, but rather from $(6 \cdot 15)$ with $\mathbf{J} = 0$ the equation

$$\nabla \times \nabla \times \mathbf{A}_\phi = \frac{1}{r} \left\{ \frac{\partial^2}{\partial r^2} (rA_\phi) \right.$$

$$\left. + \frac{1}{r} \frac{\partial}{\partial \theta} \left[\frac{1}{\sin \theta} \frac{\partial}{\partial \theta} (\sin \theta \, A_\phi) \right] \right\} \mathbf{u}_3 = 0 \quad (53)$$

which is obtained by applying twice Appendix 3, (41). Upon separation of variables, one finds the solution in r identical with (19), but in θ one obtains the associated Legendre function of order n and first degree $(m = 1)$. Thus, the general solution becomes, disregarding Q_n^1 as singular on the axis,

$$A_\phi = \sum_n (C_{1n}r^n + C_{2n}r^{-(n+1)}) P_n^1 (\cos \theta) \quad (54)$$

The radial magnetic field component is from Appendix 3, (41)

$$B_r = \frac{1}{r \sin \theta} \cdot \frac{\partial}{\partial \theta} (\sin \theta \, A_\phi)$$

Because one has from Appendix 6, (31),

$$P_n^1 (\cos \theta) = \sin \theta \, \frac{d}{d \cos \theta} P_n (\cos \theta) = \frac{d}{d\theta} P_n (\cos \theta)$$

one can use this in (54) and introduce it for differentiation into B_r. This leads to

$$- \frac{1}{\sin \theta} \frac{\partial}{\partial \theta} \left(\sin \theta \, \frac{dP_n}{d\theta} \right) = n(n + 1) P_n$$

on account of (20) for $m = 0$, since P_n is just a special case of the general spherical harmonic $T(\theta)$.   Thus, the radial field component becomes

$$B_r = \sum_{n=0}^{\infty} n(n+1)(C_{1n}r^{n-1} + C_{2n}r^{-n-2})P_n(\cos\theta) \quad (55a)$$

The meridian component B_θ is, then, from Appendix 3, (41) and using (54) directly,

$$B_\theta = -\frac{1}{r}\frac{\partial}{\partial r}(rA_\phi)$$

$$= -\sum_{n=0}^{\infty}[(n+1)C_{1n}r^{n-1} - nC_{2n}r^{-n-2}]P_n^{1}(\cos\theta) \quad (55b)$$

Assuming now an infinitely thin circular current located as in Fig. 33·6, one can evaluate the field distribution by using (54) in a manner similar to (26).   For this one will expand the locally concentrated current distribution along the sphere $r = c$ into a series of associated Legendre functions and then satisfy the boundary conditions which require (see section 6)

$$\text{at } r = c: \qquad B_{r1} = B_{r2}, \qquad B_{\theta 2} - B_{\theta 1} = \mu K_\phi \qquad (56)$$

where $K_\phi = I/c\delta\theta$, if the total current of the circular loop is I. Obviously, in all three forms (54) and (55), one has to use only the positive powers of r for $r < c$, and only the negative powers for $r > c$.   Introducing the respective parts of (55a) into the first boundary condition (56) gives at once for each value n,

$$C_{1n}c^{n-1} = -C_{2n}c^{-n-2}$$

Introducing the respective parts of (55b) into the second boundary condition (56) gives

$$\sum_n nC_{2n}c^{-n-2}P_n^{1}(\cos\theta)$$

$$-\sum_n(n+1)C_{1n}c^{n-1}P_n^{1}(\cos\theta) = \mu K_\phi = \frac{\mu I}{c\delta\theta}$$

This requires now the expansion of K_ϕ into a similar series of associated functions $P_n^{1}(\cos\theta)$,

$$K_\phi = \sum_n D_n P_n^{1}(\cos\theta)$$

where the coefficients can be found as for any orthogonal function system by (29·12), with the norm $N_n(1) = \dfrac{2}{2n+1} \dfrac{(n+1)!}{(n-1)!}$ from Appendix 6, (48) and weight function $p = 1$. Thus, observing that the current is restricted to $\delta\theta$ at $\theta = \alpha$, one obtains in good approximation

$$N_n(1)D_n = \int_{\theta=0}^{\pi} K_\phi P_n^{\,1}\,(\cos\theta)\,\sin\theta\,d\theta \approx \frac{I}{c\delta\theta}\,P_n^{\,1}\,(\cos\alpha)\,\sin\alpha\delta\theta$$

With this expression for the coefficients in K_ϕ one can reduce the second boundary condition to individual relations for each value n; this also permits the evaluation of the constants C_{1n} and C_{2n}.

The field components become, then, finally,

$$B_r = \pm \frac{\mu I}{2c} \sin\alpha \sum_{n=0}^{\infty} \begin{bmatrix} (r/c)^{n-1} \\ (c/r)^{n+2} \end{bmatrix} \cdot$$
$$P_n^{\,1}\,(\cos\alpha)\,P_n(\cos\theta), \qquad r \lessgtr a$$

$$\tag{57}$$

$$B_\theta = -\frac{\mu I}{2c} \sin\alpha \sum_{n=0}^{\infty} \begin{bmatrix} (r/c)^{n-1} \cdot 1/n \\ (c/r)^{n+2} \cdot (n+1)^{-1} \end{bmatrix} \cdot$$
$$P_n^{\,1}\,(\cos\alpha)\,P_n^{\,1}(\cos\theta), \qquad r \lessgtr a$$

where the signs and terms in the brackets are related to the ranges of r as indicated on the right. Obviously, these expressions could be converted to cylindrical coordinates and compared with the elliptic integrals in (13·26). The major advantage of the formulation with Legendre functions lies in the fact that one can now again integrate with respect to c and α over various current distributions on cylindrical[4] or spherical surfaces. Solutions for the circular loop are given in Maxwell,[A17] II, p. 304, and in Smythe,[A22] pp. 263 and 270, who also considers general spherical surface distributions.

Conical Boundaries. If it is desired to solve the potential distribution in a conical space as in Fig. 33·7 with the given boundary values, then one has in θ a homogeneous boundary value problem of axial symmetry, so that the solution of (22) is subject to

$$D_1 P_n\,(\cos\alpha) + D_2 Q_n\,(\cos\alpha) = D_1 P_n\,(\cos\beta) + D_2 Q_n\,(\cos\beta) = 0$$

---

[4] See H. B. Dwight, *Trans. A.I.E.E.*, **61**, p. 327 (1942) for comparative practical forms of field expressions for cylindrical coils.

This condition can be satisfied only if the determinant of the Legendre functions vanishes

$$P_n (\cos \alpha) Q_n (\cos \alpha) - P_n (\cos \beta) Q_n (\cos \beta) = 0 \quad (58)$$

which in turn means that this relation defines the order n as a real but non-integral number, since the Legendre functions can be considered as analytic and continuous functions of their order numbers; see particularly Hobson,[C9] Chapter IX, on the discus-

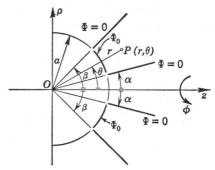

FIG. 33·7   Conical Boundaries.

sion of the zeros of Legendre functions. Having the order numbers, one can then write the potential

$$\Phi(r, \theta) = \sum_n D_n r^{-(n+1)} \left[P_n (\cos \theta) - \frac{P_n (\cos \alpha)}{Q_n (\cos \alpha)} Q_n (\cos \theta) \right] \quad (59)$$

and must determine the coefficients D_n such that for $r = a$ one has $\Phi = \Phi_0$.

On the other hand, if the boundary value problem is homogeneous with respect to two spherical surfaces $r = a$ and $r = b$, then from (19) follows

$$C_1 a^n + C_2 a^{-(n+1)} = C_1 b^n + C_2 b^{-(n+1)} = 0$$

which defines the order number as

$$a^n b^{-(n+1)} = a^{-(n+1)} b^n, \qquad 2n + 1 = \frac{\ln 1}{\ln a/b}$$

and admitting $\ln 1 = \ln (\exp j2\pi p)$, one has the complex order numbers $n = -\frac{1}{2} + jq$ with $q = \pi p/(\ln a/b)$, leading to the *cone functions*.[5]

Dipole Coordinates. The function $w = e^{-\varsigma}$ has been shown to define the spherical coordinate system; the conformal transformation to the w'-plane

$$w = e^{-\varsigma} = \frac{w' - f}{w' + f}, \qquad w' = f \coth \frac{\varsigma}{2} = z' + j\rho'$$

also gives

$$\xi = \ln \left| \frac{w' + f}{w' - f} \right| = \ln \frac{r_1}{r_2}, \qquad \eta = \phi_1 - \phi_2$$

or, as shown in Fig. 33·8 and already discussed in (26·53), the biaxial family of circles such as the field picture of two parallel line

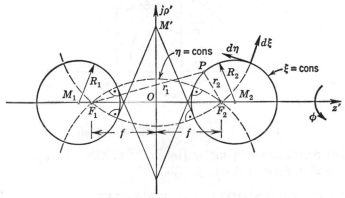

FIG. 33·8   Dipolar Coordinates.

charges $\pm\lambda$. Because of the axial symmetry, this coordinate system actually provides two families of orthogonal spheres and is called the *dipolar coordinate system*. Solving for the coordinates of the w'-plane, one has

$$z' = f \frac{\sinh \xi}{\cosh \xi - \cos \eta}, \qquad \rho' = f \frac{\sin \eta}{\cosh \xi - \cos \eta}$$

[5] Introduced by F. G. Mehler, *Math. Ann.* **18**, p. 161 (1881); see also rather extensive treatment in Heine,[C8] II, p. 217, and in Hobson,[C9] p. 444.

and from (7)

$$h'^2 = \left| \frac{dw'}{d\zeta} \right| = \frac{f}{(\cosh \xi - \cos \eta)^2}$$

Thus,

$$\frac{h'^2}{\rho'^2} = [\sin \eta]^{-2}$$

defines the system as clearly separable in its coordinates in accordance with the condition (10). It is definitely related to the polar or spherical coordinate system and leads also to tesseral harmonics.

The problem of two finite spheres, which was treated with an infinite number of images in section 21, has been solved by means

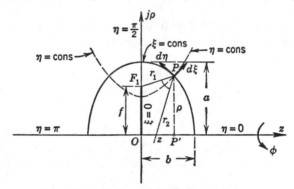

FIG. 33·9   Oblate Spheroidal Coordinates.

of this coordinate system by Hobson,[C9] p. 448. Further details are found in Snow, *loc. cit.*, p. 235.

OBLATE SPHEROIDAL COORDINATES

The oblate spheroidal coordinate system is an axially symmetrical ellipsoidal system in which the minor axis is the axis of revolution as shown in Fig. 33·9. In accordance with the general discussion at the beginning of the section, one obtains the meridian coordinates ξ, η by the conformal transformation from the underlying cylinder system

$$w = z + j\rho = f \sinh (\xi + j\eta) \tag{60}$$

which is similar to the one used for the elliptic cylinder in (32·52). From (60) one obtains

$$z = f \sinh \xi \cos \eta, \qquad \rho = f \cosh \xi \sin \eta \tag{61}$$

which represent confocal ellipses and hyperbolas with $2f$ as the focal distance. This is shown explicitly by

$$\left(\frac{z}{f \sinh \xi}\right)^2 + \left(\frac{\rho}{f \cosh \xi}\right)^2 = 1, \qquad -\left(\frac{z}{f \cos \eta}\right)^2 + \left(\frac{\rho}{f \sin \eta}\right)^2 = 1$$

The first relation describes the ellipsoids $\xi = $ cons with semiaxes $a = f \cosh \xi$ along the ρ-direction and minor axes $b = f \sinh \xi$ along the axis of revolution; these degenerate into the circular area $\rho \leqslant f$ in the $z = 0$ plane for $\xi = 0$. The second relation gives the orthogonal and confocal hyperboloids $\eta = $ cons, degenerating into the plane $z = 0$ with a circular hole for $\eta = \pi/2$. The ranges of values are $0 < \xi < \infty$, $0 < \eta < \pi$, quite analogous to the spherical coordinate pair r, θ.

In accordance with (7) one has

$$h^2 = \left|\frac{dw}{d\zeta}\right|^2 = f^2 \left|\cosh^2 \zeta\right| = f^2 \left(\cosh^2 \xi - \sin^2 \eta\right) \qquad (62)$$

so that

$$\frac{h^2}{\rho^2} = \frac{\cosh^2 \xi - \sin^2 \eta}{\cosh^2 \xi \sin^2 \eta} = \frac{1}{\sin^2 \eta} - \frac{1}{\cosh^2 \xi}$$

and therefore

$$g_1(\xi) = \frac{-1}{\cosh^2 \xi}, \qquad g_2(\eta) = \frac{1}{\sin^2 \eta} \qquad (63)$$

One can thus write down at once the separated Sturm-Liouville equations (11). It is advantageous at this point to transform these equations (11) by a change of variables and redefinition of the functions, namely,

$$\left.\begin{array}{ll} u = \sinh \xi, & \Xi(\xi) = \sqrt{\cosh \xi}\, W_1(u) \\[2mm] v = \cos \eta, & \mathrm{H}(\eta) = \sqrt{\sin \eta}\, W_2(v) \end{array}\right\} \qquad (64)$$

into equations of the type (20) or (22), namely,

$$\left.\begin{array}{l} \dfrac{d}{du}\left[(u^2 + 1)\dfrac{dW_1}{du}\right] + \left[-\left(p^2 - \dfrac{1}{4}\right) + \dfrac{m^2}{u^2 + 1}\right]W_1 = 0 \\[4mm] \dfrac{d}{dv}\left[(1 - v^2)\dfrac{dW_2}{dv}\right] + \left[+\left(p^2 - \dfrac{1}{4}\right) - \dfrac{m^2}{1 - v^2}\right]W_2 = 0 \end{array}\right\} \qquad (65)$$

The solutions for W_2 are the conventional associated Legendre functions if one writes $(p^2 - \frac{1}{4}) = (p - \frac{1}{2})(p + \frac{1}{2})$ and defines $(p - \frac{1}{2}) = n$, so that

$$W_2(v) = D_1 P_n{}^m (\cos \eta) + D_2 Q_n{}^m (\cos \eta) \qquad (66)$$

Since a substitution ju for u makes the differential equation for W_1 identical with that for W_2, one can write with the same values of $(p^2 - \frac{1}{4}) = n(n + 1)$ the solutions for W_1 in analogy to (66) (see also Appendix 6)

$$W_1(u) = C_1 \overline{P}_n{}^m(j \sinh \xi) + C_2 \overline{Q}_n{}^m(j \sinh \xi) \qquad (67)$$

It is, however, customary to define these modified associated Legendre functions of imaginary (or complex) argument, say $t = r + js$, by [Appendix 6, (33) and 6, (39)]

$$\left.\begin{array}{l} \overline{P}_n{}^m(t) = (t^2 - 1)^{m/2} \dfrac{d^m}{dt^m} P_n(t) \underset{|t|>>1}{\longrightarrow} \dfrac{n!}{(n-m)!} \dfrac{(2t)^n}{\sqrt{n\pi}} \\[3ex] \overline{Q}_n{}^m(t) = (t^2 - 1)^{m/2} \dfrac{d^m}{dt^m} Q_n(t) \underset{|t|>>1}{\longrightarrow} \dfrac{(n+m)!}{n!} \dfrac{\sqrt{\pi}(-1)^m}{\sqrt{n}(2t)^{n+1}} \end{array}\right\} \quad (68)$$

which assures that for imaginary argument the combinations

$$\exp\left(-jn\,\frac{\pi}{2}\right) \overline{P}_n{}^m(js), \qquad j \exp\left(+jn\,\frac{\pi}{2}\right) \overline{Q}_n{}^m(js)$$

take on real values. The asymptotic expressions in (68) demonstrate the analogy of these functions to the radial functions (19) for the spherical coordinate system.

Returning to the original definition of the product solution for the potential in (3) and introducing (8), (61), and (64) yield now

$$\Phi(\xi, \eta, \phi) = \sum_n \sum_m f^{-\frac{1}{2}} W_1 (j \sinh \xi) \cdot W_2(\cos \eta) \cdot F(\phi) \qquad (69)$$

where the constant $f^{-\frac{1}{2}}$ can, of course, be absorbed in the other constants. Treatments of this coordinate system, solutions in it, and in particular discussion of the various system functions are found in several references, and for convenience table $33 \cdot 1$ gives the comparative notations used.

Conducting Spheroids. Ascribe to a solid conducting spheroid of semiaxes a and b the constant potential Φ; then the potential distribution in space will be axially symmetrical so that $m = 0$ and W_1, W_2 reduce to the plain Legendre functions. The surface of the spheroid is defined by the semiaxes as

$$a = f \cosh \xi_0, \qquad b = f \sinh \xi_0, \qquad \xi_0 = \tanh^{-1}\left(\frac{b}{a}\right)$$

TABLE 33·1

COMPARATIVE NOTATION FOR OBLATE SPHEROIDAL COORDINATES

Coordinate	This Book	Bateman[C1]	Byerly[C2]	Hobson[C9]	Lamb[C22]	Smythe[A22]
u_1	$u = \sinh \xi$	$\theta = \sinh \eta$	$\tanh \eta f$	$\sinh \eta$	$\zeta = \sinh \eta$	ζ
u_2	$v = \cos \eta$	$\mu = \sin \xi$	$\tan \xi f$	$\cos \theta$	$\mu = \cos \theta$	ξ
u_3	ϕ	ϕ	ϕ	ϕ	ω	ϕ
Focal distance	$2f$	$2k$	$2f$	$2c$	$2k$	$2c_1$
Distance from axis	ρ	$\tilde{\omega}$	$\sqrt{x^2+y^2}$	ρ	$\tilde{\omega}$	ρ
Distance along axis	z	z	z	z	z	x

On account of the asymptotic behavior of the functions $\overline{P}_n{}^m$ and $\overline{Q}_n{}^m$ given in (68), the former must be excluded because the potential must at least remain finite at infinite, distance. One thus has left

$$\Phi(\xi, \eta) = \sum_{n=0}^{\infty} [D_{1n}P_n(\cos \eta) + D_{2n}Q_n(\cos \eta)]\overline{Q}_n(j \sinh \xi)$$

This, then, must represent the expansion of the potential function for $\xi = \xi_0$ into the conventional Legendre series; because Q_n has a logarithmic singularity for $\eta = 0$, π or for $\cos \eta = \pm 1$, it also must be excluded if the z-axis belongs to the field region. For the assumed constant potential the series thus reduces to a constant, i.e., $n = 0$, so that

$$\Phi(\xi) = \Phi_0 \frac{\overline{Q}_0(j \sinh \xi)}{\overline{Q}_0(j \sinh \xi_0)} = \Phi_0 \frac{\coth^{-1}(j \sinh \xi)}{\coth^{-1}(j \sinh \xi_0)}$$

$$= \Phi_0 \frac{\cot^{-1}(\sinh \xi)}{\cot^{-1}(\sinh \xi_0)} \quad (70)$$

where the definition of $\bar{Q}_0$ from Appendix 6 has been used; see Byerly,[C2] p. 247.

The charge distribution is readily found from the normal component of the field vector, which is from the general definition $(31\cdot24)$ with (62)

$$E_\xi = -\frac{1}{h}\frac{\partial \Phi}{\partial \xi} = \Phi_0[f \cosh \xi \sqrt{\cosh^2 \xi - \sin^2 \eta}\ \cot^{-1}(\sinh \xi_0)]^{-1}$$

$$= \Phi_0[f\sqrt{u^2 + 1}\sqrt{u^2 + v^2}\ \cot^{-1} u_0]^{-1} \tag{71}$$

where one might use for quicker computation from (61) and (64)

$$z = fuv, \qquad \rho = f\sqrt{u^2+1}\sqrt{1-v^2}$$

On the surface of the spheroid one has $u = u_0 \sinh \xi_0$, so that

$$\sigma = (\varepsilon E_\xi)_{\xi_0} = \varepsilon \Phi_0[f\sqrt{u_0^2+1}\sqrt{u_0^2+v^2}\ \cot^{-1} u_0]^{-1} \tag{72}$$

The total charge can be found best as for the ellipsoid in section 31 by letting ξ become very large, so that the equipotential surfaces approach spheres. From (61) one has

$$z = fu \cos \eta, \qquad \rho \approx fu \sin \eta, \qquad z^2 + \rho^2 = r^2 \approx f^2 u^2$$

and for the field vector in (71) this gives

$$\lim_{\xi \to \infty} E_\xi \approx \Phi_0[fu^2 \cot^{-1} u_0]^{-1} = \frac{f\Phi_0}{r^2 \cot^{-1} u_0}$$

which is the same as that of a point charge Q at the origin. The value of the charge itself is found by integrating (εE_ξ) over a large sphere. The capacitance of the spheroid follows then as

$$C = \frac{Q}{\Phi_0} = \frac{4\pi\varepsilon f}{\cot^{-1} u_0} \tag{73}$$

With the charge value from (73) one can replace Φ_0 in the expressions of field vector and charge density. The maximum charge exists for $u = u_0$ and $v = 0$ and the minimum charge for $v = 1$, so that (72) yields

$$\sigma_{\max} = \frac{Q}{4\pi ab}, \qquad \sigma_{\min} = \frac{Q}{4\pi a^2}$$

or the ratio is (a/b), directly the ratio of the semiaxes of the spheroid.

In the limit as $\xi_0 \to 0$, the spheroid becomes a *circular disk* of radius f. Since $\cot^{-1} 0 = \pi/2$, one gets at once the same values for charge density and capacitance as found in (31·54) and (31·53), respectively. Ollendorff,[A18] p. 280, solves this case and applies it to the capacitance of an umbrella antenna above ground. Smythe,[A22] p. 160, treats the uncharged circular disk in a uniform electric field of arbitrary angle with the plane of the disk and also computes the torque exerted on it. Byerly,[C2] p. 153, expresses the potential along the z-axis by setting $\eta = 0$ in (61), and by replacing $\sinh \xi = z/f$ in (70), where also $\xi_0 = 0$,

$$\Phi(z) = \frac{2}{\pi} \Phi_0 \cot^{-1} \frac{z}{f} = \frac{2}{\pi} \Phi_0 \left[\frac{\pi}{2} - \left(\frac{z}{f} \right) + \frac{1}{3} \left(\frac{z}{f} \right)^3 - \frac{1}{5} \left(\frac{z}{f} \right)^5 + \cdots \right]$$

Replacing now z^n by r^n and multiplying each term by $P_n (\cos \theta)$, one has the alternative form for the potential

$$\left. \begin{array}{ll} \Phi(r, \theta) = \Phi_0 - \dfrac{2}{\pi} \Phi_0 \sum_n \dfrac{(-1)^n}{2n + 1} \left(\dfrac{r}{f} \right)^n P_n (\cos \theta), & r < a \\[4mm] \qquad = \dfrac{2}{\pi} \Phi_0 \sum_n \dfrac{(-1)^n}{2n + 1} \left(\dfrac{f}{r} \right)^{2n+1} P_{2n} (\cos \theta), & r > a \end{array} \right\} \quad (74)$$

where the value for $r > a$ follows from the corresponding expansion of the potential.

If the potential along $\xi = \xi_0$ is a prescribed function, for example for two hemispheroidal shells where $\Phi = \Phi_1$ for $0 < \eta < \pi/2$ and $\Phi = \Phi_2$ for $\pi/2 < \eta < \pi$, as in the corresponding case of two hemispheres in Fig. 33·2, one can take the development for the outside potential directly from (27), replacing $[M_n a^n]$ by $[D_{1n} \bar{Q}_n (j \sinh \xi_0)]$. For the inside field one would have to substitute $P_n{}^m (j \sinh \xi)$ for the second kind of the modified Legendre function; see Byerly,[C2] p. 248, who solves the analogous case of a temperature field between two hemispheroidal caps. The hydrodynamic problem of a spheroid moving through an infinite ideal fluid is treated in Lamb,[C22] p. 135.

Dielectric Spheroids. In analogy to the dielectric sphere in a uniform electric field, one can treat the dielectric spheroid $\xi = \xi_0$ in a uniform electric field; here, however, one has to observe the direction of the impressed field and can obviously consider two principal orientations: parallel to the axis of revolution and normal to it. The first case is by far the simpler one, since it retains axial symmetry in the field distribution. Expressing the impressed potential as

$$\Phi^0 = -E^0 z = -E^0 f uv = -E^0 f \sinh \xi \cos \eta \qquad (75)$$

and forming the local potential solutions Φ_1 outside the spheroid in dielectric constant ε_1 and Φ_2 inside the spheroid of dielectric constant ε_2, then one has from (69) with $m = 0$ and using u and v as abbreviations from (64),

$$\Phi_1(\xi, \eta) = \sum D_n P_n(v) \cdot \overline{Q}_n(ju), \qquad u > u_0$$

$$\Phi_2(\xi, \eta) = \sum C_n P_n(v) \cdot \overline{P}_n(ju), \qquad u < u_0$$

$$(76)$$

where $\overline{P}_n$ is suppressed in the outside potential because it increases beyond all limits as $\xi \to \infty$, and $\overline{Q}_n$ is suppressed in Φ_2 since it has a logarithmic singularity at ± 1. As in the spherical case, the form of (75) requires similar forms of (76) because of the boundary conditions. Noting $\cos \eta$ in (75) restricts the sums to $n = 1$, since only $P_1 (\cos \eta) = \cos \eta$. The boundary conditions can now be set down as

$$\text{at } \xi = \xi_0, \qquad \Phi^0 + \Phi_1 = \Phi_2, \qquad \varepsilon_1 \left(\frac{\partial \Phi^0}{\partial \xi} + \frac{\partial \Phi_1}{\partial \xi} \right) = \varepsilon_2 \frac{\partial \Phi_2}{\partial \xi} \quad (77)$$

where in the second form the factor $1/h$ has been omitted. With the functional forms of Appendix 6, (4) and 6, (16) one finds from the boundary conditions (77), observing $\partial / \partial \xi = (du/d\xi)(\partial / \partial u) = \cosh \xi \cdot (\partial / \partial u)$,

$$\left. \begin{aligned} \Phi_2 &= -E^i f uv = \frac{-zE^0}{\Delta} \\ \Delta &= 1 + \left(\frac{\varepsilon_2}{\varepsilon_1} - 1 \right) (u_0{}^2 + 1)(1 - u_0 \cot^{-1} u_0), \\ u_0 &= \sinh \left(\tanh^{-1} \frac{b}{a} \right) \end{aligned} \right\} \quad (78)$$

The field within the spheroid is again *uniform* in the same direction as E^0 and for $\varepsilon_2 > \varepsilon_1$ weaker than the impressed field. For $b/a = \frac{1}{2}$, one finds $\Delta = 1 + 0.53(\varepsilon_2/\varepsilon_1 - 1)$, and as b decreases, $\Delta \to \varepsilon_2/\varepsilon_1$, so that for a very flat spheroidal disk the inner field strength becomes $E^i \approx E^0 \varepsilon_1/\varepsilon_2$. This solution is given with considerable detail in Ollendorff,[A18] p. 289; he also treats the second orientation of E^0 normal to the axis, which requires the use of the associated Legendre function of degree $m = 1$ but otherwise is yet simple. In the case $\varepsilon_2 \to \infty$ one obtains again the solution of the conducting spheroid in a uniform electric field.

Obviously, this analysis can be transposed to solve the analogous problem of an iron spheroid in a uniform magnetic field. In turn, one can solve for the proper azimuthal current distribution in a spheroidal coil to give a uniform magnetic field within.[6]

Inverse Coordinate System. By the inversion

$$w' = \frac{-f^2}{(w - z_0)} = z' + j\rho'$$

where $z_0 = f \sinh \xi_0$, the w-plane is transformed so that the ρ-axis in Fig. 33·9 is bent into a circle, and the part OF_1 becomes a

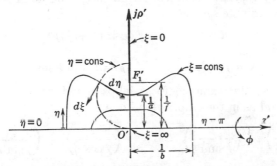

Fig. 33·10   Inverse to Oblate Spheroidal Coordinate System.

finite circular arc which upon rotation about the z-axis forms a spherical cap. The confocal ellipses then transform into shells about this spherical cap and about a pole at the origin where the base circle intersects. For $z_0 = 0$, the ρ-axis inverts into itself with OF_1 transforming into the complementary part of the ρ-axis, thus leading to the circular aperture in an infinite conductive plane but with the pole at the center of the aperture as shown in Fig. 33·10. The function systems involved in the solution are identical with those above, since the same metric factor applies, so that it can be classed with the oblate spheroidal system.

[6] J. P. Blewett, *Jl. Appl. Phys.*, **18**, p. 968 (1947).

PROLATE SPHEROIDAL COORDINATES

The prolate spheroidal coordinate system is an axially symmetrical ellipsoidal system in which the major axis is the axis of revolution as shown in Fig. 33·11. The meridian coordinates ξ, η are

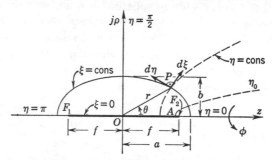

FIG. 33·11   Prolate Spheroidal Coordinates.

obtained by the same conformal transformation as in the elliptic cylinder coordinate system

$$w = z + j\rho = f \cosh (\xi + j\eta)$$

so that

$$z = f \cosh \xi \cos \eta, \qquad \rho = f \sinh \xi \sin \eta \qquad (79)$$

which represents again confocal ellipses and hyperbolas. Specifically, and as in the elliptical cylinder,

$$\left(\frac{z}{f \cosh \xi}\right)^2 + \left(\frac{\rho}{f \sinh \xi}\right)^2 = 1; \qquad \left(\frac{z}{f \cos \eta}\right)^2 - \left(\frac{\rho}{f \sin \eta}\right)^2 = 1$$

The prolate spheroids generated by the revolution of the ellipses about their major axis degenerate into the focal line F_1F_2 for $\xi = 0$ and approach spheres as $\xi \to \infty$. The two-sheeted hyperboloids generated by the revolution of the hyperbolas about the z-axis degenerate for $\eta = 0$ and $\eta = \pi$ into the respective sections of the z-axis outside the focal points F_1 and F_2, and become identical with the plane of symmetry $z = 0$ for $\eta = \pi/2$. The ranges of values $0 < \xi < \infty$, $0 < \eta < \pi$ are quite analogous to the spherical coordinate pair r, θ.

In accordance with (7) the metric coefficient h^2 is identical with (32·55), so that

$$\frac{h^2}{\rho^2} = \frac{\cosh^2 \xi - \cos^2 \eta}{\sinh^2 \xi - \sin^2 \eta} = \frac{1}{\sinh^2 \xi} + \frac{1}{\sin^2 \eta}$$

and therefore

$$g_1(\xi) = \frac{1}{\sinh^2 \xi}, \qquad g_2(\eta) = \frac{1}{\sin^2 \eta} \qquad (80)$$

This permits one immediately to utilize the separated Sturm-Liouville equations (11); but as in the case of the oblate spheroidal coordinates it is advantageous to transform these equations by a change of variables and redefinition of functions

$$u = \cosh \xi, \qquad \Xi(\xi) = \sqrt{\sinh \xi}\, W_1(u)$$
$$\qquad (81)$$
$$v = \cos \eta, \qquad \mathsf{H}(\eta) = \sqrt{\sin \eta}\, W_2(v)$$

This results in the differential equations

$$\frac{d}{du}\left[(u^2 - 1)\frac{dW_1}{du}\right] + \left[-\left(p^2 - \frac{1}{4}\right) + \frac{m^2}{u^2 - 1}\right] W_1 = 0$$
$$\qquad (82)$$
$$\frac{d}{dv}\left[(1 - v^2)\frac{dW_2}{dv}\right] + \left[+\left(p^2 - \frac{1}{4}\right) - \frac{m^2}{1 - v^2}\right] W_2 = 0$$

Setting again $p^2 - \frac{1}{4} = n(n+1)$, both equations are of the type (20) or (22), so that for W_2 one has the solution (66), whereas for W_1 because of $u^2 > 1$, one must choose the modified associated Legendre functions (see Appendix 6), namely,

$$W_1(u) = C_1 \overline{P}_n{}^m(j\cosh \xi) + C_2 \overline{Q}_n{}^m(j\cosh \xi) \qquad (83)$$

Returning to the original definition of the product solution for the

TABLE 33·2

Comparative Notation for Prolate Spheroidal Coordinates

Coordinate	This Book	Bateman[C1]	Byerly[C2]	Hobson[C9]	Lamb[C22]	Smythe[A22]
u_1	$u = \cosh \xi$	$\theta = \cosh \eta$	$\coth \xi f$	$\cosh \eta$	$\zeta = \cosh \eta$	η
u_2	$v = \cos \eta$	$\mu = \cos \zeta$	$\tanh \eta f$	$\cos \theta$	$\mu = \cos \theta$	ξ
u_3	ϕ	ϕ	ϕ	ϕ	ω	ϕ
Focal distance	$2f$	$2k$	$2f$	$2c$	$2k$	$2c_2$
Distance from axis	ρ	$\tilde{\omega}$	$\sqrt{x^2+y^2}$	ρ	$\tilde{\omega}$	ρ
Distance along axis	z	z	z	z	x	z

potential in (3) and introducing (8), (79), and (81), this yields now

$$\Phi(\xi, \eta, \phi) = \sum_n \sum_m f^{-\frac{1}{2}} W_1 (\cosh \xi) \, W_2 (\cos \eta) \, F(\phi) \quad (84)$$

where the constant $f^{-\frac{1}{2}}$ can, of course, be absorbed in the other constants. Treatments of this coordinate system, solutions in it, and discussions of the function systems appearing in these solutions are found in several references, and for convenience table $33 \cdot 2$ gives the comparative notations used.

Conducting Spheroids. With the suitable modifications, the applications of the oblate spheroidal system can readily be transposed into solutions for the prolate spheroids. Since the asymptotic forms (68) apply also for real arguments $|\mu| > 1$, the potential outside a conducting spheroid of semiaxes $a = f \cosh \xi_0$, $b = f \sinh \xi_0$, is by transposition of (70)

$$\Phi = \Phi_0 \frac{\overline{Q}_0 (\cosh \xi)}{\overline{Q}_0 (\cosh \xi_0)} = \Phi_0 \frac{\coth^{-1} (\cosh \xi)}{\coth^{-1} (\cosh \xi_0)}$$

$$= \Phi_0 \frac{\ln (u + 1)/(u - 1)}{\ln (u_0 + 1)/(u_0 - 1)} \quad (85)$$

where the definition of $\overline{Q}_0$ from Appendix 6 has been used. The normal component of the field vector is from the general definition $(31 \cdot 24)$ with h^2 from $(32 \cdot 55)$

$$E_\xi = -\frac{1}{h} \frac{\partial \Phi}{\partial \xi} = \Phi_0 [f \sinh \xi \sqrt{\cosh^2 \xi - \cos^2 \eta} \, \coth^{-1} (\cosh \xi_0)]^{-1}$$

$$= \Phi_0 [f \sqrt{u^2 - v^2} \sqrt{u^2 - 1} \, \coth^{-1} u_0]^{-1} \quad (86)$$

where one might use for quicker computations

$$z = fuv, \qquad \rho = f \sqrt{u^2 - 1} \sqrt{1 - v^2} \quad (87)$$

On the surface of the spheroid $u = u_0 = \cosh \xi_0$, so that the charge density becomes

$$\sigma = (\varepsilon E_\xi)_{\xi_0} = \varepsilon \Phi_0 [f \sqrt{u_0^2 + 1} \sqrt{u_0^2 + v^2} \, \coth^{-1} u_0]^{-1} \quad (88)$$

The total charge can be found in analogous manner as for (73), so that the capacitance follows:

$$C = \frac{Q}{\Phi_0} = \frac{4\pi\varepsilon f}{\coth^{-1} u_0} \quad (89)$$

With the charge value from this expression one can replace Φ_0 in (86) for the field vector and (88) for the charge density. The maximum and minimum values of charge density exist for $u = u_0$ and $v = 1$, $v = 0$, respectively, so that (88) yields

$$\sigma_{\max} = \frac{Q}{4\pi b^2}, \qquad \sigma_{\min} = \frac{Q}{4\pi ab}$$

or the ratio is again a/b, as for the oblate spheroid; however, the respective maximum values as well as the minimum values in the two cases bear the same ratios a/b, with the larger values occurring in the prolate spheroid.

In the limit as $\xi_0 \to 0$, the spheroid becomes an ellipsoidal rod of length $2f$ which has been treated rather completely in section 12. A general solution with the rod as special case is given in Kirchhoff,[A13] p. 37; in Ollendorff,[A18] p. 308, who also applies the solution to the current flow from a grounding electrode reaching below the level of ground water; and in Byerly,[C2] p. 155, in terms of zonal Legendre harmonics, and p. 250 for gravitational potential applications. Smythe,[A22] p. 167, solves the field near a semispheroidal mound on an infinite ground plane; see also Bateman,[C1] p. 436.

If the potential along $\xi = \xi_0$ is a prescribed function, then it can be readily expressed from (84) as a normal Legendre series if axial symmetry prevails, or as series of surface harmonics (24) in the more general case.

Dielectric Spheroids. The prolate dielectric spheroid in a uniform electric field E^0 can be treated in exact analogy to the oblate spheroid. Two principal orientations are possible; the electric field can be either parallel to the axis z or normal to it. The first case retains axial symmetry, and its solution proceeds exactly as with the oblate spheroid, leading again to the uniform internal field of value

$$E^i = \frac{E^0}{\Delta}, \quad \Delta = 1 + \left(\frac{\varepsilon_2}{\varepsilon_1} - 1\right)(u_0^2 - 1)(u_0 \coth^{-1} u_0 - 1) \quad (90)$$

where $u_0 = \cosh \xi_0 = a/f$. Here one finds for $b/a = \frac{1}{2}$ the value $\Delta = 1 + 0.177(\varepsilon_2/\varepsilon_1 - 1)$, and as b decreases, $\Delta \to 1$, so that the very thin rod has a uniform inner field which is equal to the impressed outer field, $E^i \approx E^0$. However, the continuity of the normal component of $\mathbf{D}$ requires then that at the pole of the spheroid a local field strength exist of value

$$E_1 = \frac{\varepsilon_2}{\varepsilon_1} E^i \approx \frac{\varepsilon_2}{\varepsilon_1} E^0$$

causing a very strong concentration of the electric field on dielectric objects, as masts, poles, or sharp mountain peaks. This solution is given for the analogous magnetic case with considerable detail in Ollendorff,[A18] p. 315; Lamb,[C22] p. 132, also solves the motion of a spheroid through an ideal fluid.

If the uniform electric field is oriented normal to the axis z and parallel to the plane $\phi = 0$, then its potential can be expressed in the form

$$\Phi^0 = -E^0 x = -E^0 \rho \cos \phi$$
$$= -E^0 f \sqrt{u^2 - 1} \sqrt{1 - v^2} \cos \phi, \qquad u < u_0 \quad (91)$$

where the x-direction is taken from the Cartesian system, converted to cylindrical coordinates ρ, ϕ, and with (87) finally to the spheroidal system. Now, the general solution (84) has to satisfy the boundary conditions which are identical with (77) and which relate only to ξ or u; one surmises that in (5) only $m = 1$ can occur and only the cosine term; further, that in (66) only $n = 1$ can lead to the requisite term $\sqrt{1 - v^2} = \sin \eta$ and that the second kind of associated Legendre functions must be avoided, since the axis $y = 0$ belongs to the field region. One can therefore write for the local potential solutions inside and outside

$$\Phi_1(\xi, \eta, \phi) = D_1 P_1^{\ 1}(v) \overline{Q}_1^{\ 1}(u) \cos \phi, \qquad u > u_0$$
$$\Phi_2(\xi, \eta, \phi) = C_1 P_1^{\ 1}(v) \overline{P}_1^{\ 1}(u) \cos \phi, \qquad u < u_0 \quad (92)$$

With the functional forms from Appendix 6, one finds then the inner potential

$$\Phi_2 = -E^i f P_1^{\ 1}(v) \overline{P}_1^{\ 1}(u) \cos \phi$$

where

$$E^i = \frac{E^0}{\Delta}, \quad \Delta = 1 + \left(\frac{\varepsilon_2}{\varepsilon_1} - 1\right) \frac{u_0}{2} [u_0 - (u_0^2 - 1) \coth^{-1} u_0] \quad (93)$$

There is again a uniform field inside the spheroid in the same direction as the impressed field, and for $\varepsilon_2 > \varepsilon_1$ weaker than it. For $b/a = \frac{1}{2}$ one finds here $\Delta = 1 + 0.412 \ (\varepsilon_2/\varepsilon_1 - 1)$, and as b

decreases, $\Delta \to \frac{1}{2}(\varepsilon_2/\varepsilon_1 + 1)$. This solution is given in detail by Ollendorff,[A18] p. 319, for the analogous magnetic problem; he applies it also to evaluate the error in long-range radio navigation caused by the body of the ship.

Conducting Hyperboloids. Selecting one of the hyperboloids in Fig. 33·11 as a conductor surface of potential Φ_0 in combination with either the symmetrical one of potential $-\Phi_0$, or the center plane $z = 0$ with zero potential, gives solutions for needle electrodes[7] which might be applied to high-voltage rectifiers.[8] Assume axial symmetry; then variation of the potential occurs only with $v = \cos \eta$, and the analogous solution to (85) is in this case

$$\Phi = \Phi_0 \frac{Q_0(\cos \eta)}{Q_0(\cos \eta_0)} = \Phi_0 \frac{\tanh^{-1}(\cos \eta)}{\tanh^{-1}(\cos \eta_0)} \qquad (94)$$

where $\eta_0 = \tan^{-1} b/a$ is defined by the semiaxes of the hyperboloid electrode. The field vector can be evaluated from the general definition (30·24) with h^2 from (32·55), so that

$$E_\eta = -\frac{1}{h}\frac{\partial \Phi}{\partial \eta} = \Phi_0[f \sin \eta \sqrt{\cosh^2 \xi - \cos^2 \eta} \, \tanh^{-1}(\cos \eta_0)]^{-1}$$
$$(95)$$

The maximum field strength exists for $\xi = 0$ and $\eta = \eta_0$, at the apex of the hyperboloid; its value becomes from (95)

$$E_{\max} = \frac{\Phi_0}{f}\left[\left(\frac{b}{f}\right)^2 \tanh^{-1}\left(\frac{a}{f}\right)\right]^{-1}$$

where the focal distance $f = (a^2 - b^2)^{1/2}$; this can be plotted entirely as a function of a/f or b/f, indicating the rapid increase of $E_{\max}$ with the decrease of the angle η_0.

Inverse Coordinate System. By the inversion

$$w' = \frac{-f^2}{w - z_0} = z' + j\rho'$$

where $z_0 = f \cosh \xi_0$, the w-plane is transformed so that the focal length $2f$ moves along the axis to points F_1' and F_2' and the origin becomes a pole, the image of $z = \infty$. The confocal ellipses thus transform into odd-shaped surfaces of revolution and in the limit

---

[7] J. Müller, *Arch. f. Elektrot.*, **29**, 568 (1935).

[8] R. Strigel, *Fachberichte, V.D.E.*, 1929; see also Ollendorff,[A18] p. **311**.

for $z_0 \to 0$ represent essentially hyperboloids about the z-axis with ellipsoid-shaped surfaces close to the pole and surrounding it as shown in Fig. $33 \cdot 12$. The function systems involved in the

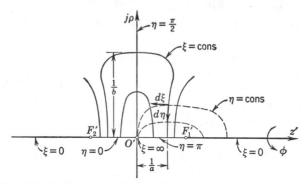

FIG. $33 \cdot 12$ Inverse to Prolate Spheroidal Coordinate System.

solution are identical with those above; this coordinate system can be classed therefore with the prolate spheroidal coordinate system.

PARABOLOIDAL COORDINATES

The paraboloidal coordinate system can be considered a singular case of the spheroidal system where one of the foci has moved into infinity. One obtains the meridian coordinates ξ, η as in the parabolic cylinder coordinates by the conformal transformation

$$w = z + j\rho = \tfrac{1}{2}(\xi + j\eta)^2$$

so that

$$z = \tfrac{1}{2}(\xi^2 - \eta^2), \qquad \rho = \xi\eta \tag{96}$$

These represent confocal parabolas with focus at the origin as shown in Fig. $33 \cdot 13$. The ranges of the variables are $0 < \xi < \infty$ and $0 < \eta < \infty$.

In accordance with (7) one has

$$h^2 = \left| \frac{dw}{d\zeta} \right|^2 = (\xi^2 + \eta^2)$$

and therefore from (10) with (96)

$$g_1(\xi) = \frac{1}{\xi^2}, \qquad g_2(\eta) = \frac{1}{\eta^2} \tag{97}$$

One can therefore write down at once the separated Sturm-Liouville equations (11) and identify them as belonging to the class of Bessel equations with solutions[9]

$$\Xi(\xi) = \sqrt{\xi}[C_1 I_m(p\xi) + C_2 K_m(p\xi)] = \sqrt{\xi} B_1(\xi)$$

$$\mathsf{H}(\eta) = \sqrt{\eta}[D_1 J_m(p\eta) + D_2 N_m(p\eta)] = \sqrt{\eta} B_2(\eta)$$

$$(98)$$

where p is an arbitrary separation parameter, and J_m, N_m are the conventional and I_m, K_m the modified Bessel functions of first and second kind; see also Appendix 5.

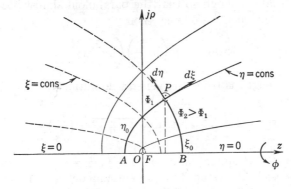

FIG. 33·13 Paraboloidal Coordinates.

Returning to the original definition of the product solution for the potential in (3) and introducing (8), (96), and (98) yield now

$$\Phi(\xi, \eta, \phi) = \sum_m \sum_p B_1(\xi)\, B_2(\eta)\, F(\phi) \qquad (99)$$

Treatments of this coordinate system are less frequent; see, however, Bateman,[C1] p. 449, and references there.

Paraboloidal Conductors. Ascribe to a solid conducting paraboloid $\xi = \xi_0$ the potential Φ_0; then the potential distribution must be axially symmetrical and, moreover, can depend only on ξ. For this singular case, $m = p = 0$, so that both equations (11) reduce to the same form

$$\frac{d^2\Xi}{d\xi^2} + \frac{1}{4\xi^2}\,\Xi = 0$$

[9] Jahnke and Emde, *loc. cit.*, p. 146.

which has as solution for ξ

$$\Xi(\xi) = \sqrt{\xi}(C_1 + C_2 \ln \xi), \qquad B_1 = C_1 + C_2 \ln \xi$$

and similarly for η

$$\mathsf{H}(\eta) = \sqrt{\eta}(D_1 + D_2 \ln \eta), \qquad B_2 = D_1 + D_2 \ln \eta$$

so that the potential function (99) becomes, suppressing the variation with η,

$$\Phi(\xi) = C_1 + C_2 \ln \xi \tag{100}$$

Defining the boundary conditions $\Phi(\xi_0) = \Phi_0$ and $\Phi(\xi_1) = 0$, and choosing ξ_1 large enough so that the paraboloid almost becomes a plane as a convenient reference, then

$$\Phi(\xi) = \Phi_0 \left(\ln \frac{\xi}{\xi_0}\right)\left(\ln \frac{\xi_1}{\xi_0}\right)^{-1} \tag{101}$$

The field strength is from the general definition $(31\cdot24)$ with h^2 from above

$$E_\xi = -\frac{1}{h}\frac{\partial \Phi}{\partial \xi} = \Phi_0 \left[\xi\sqrt{\xi^2 + \eta^2}\ln\left(\frac{\xi_1}{\xi_0}\right)\right]^{-1}$$

which has its maximum value at $\eta = 0$, $\xi = \xi_0$. Ollendorff,[A18] p. 204, has used this system to represent a model of a pin insulator.

Another special case is indicated in Fig. $33\cdot13$, where the paraboloid generated by AP carries potential Φ_1 and that generated by PB potential $\Phi_2 > \Phi_1$. The internal potential distribution will show axial symmetry, so that $m = 0$. Since the second kind of Bessel functions possess logarithmic singularities at the origin which is included in the field region, they must be suppressed and the solution becomes, from (99) with (98),

$$C_1 I_0(p\xi) J_0(p\eta)$$

To satisfy the boundary conditions one might best add the constant Φ_1 to the potential solution and thus make the condition at $\eta = \eta_0$ homogeneous, namely, $\Phi = 0$. This requires then

$$J_0(p\eta_0) = 0$$

leading to an infinite number of root values p_n as discussed in sections 30 and 32. The potential solution is now

$$\Phi = \Phi_1 + \sum_n C_n I_0(p_n\xi) J_0(p_n\eta), \qquad J_0(p_n\eta_0) = 0 \tag{102}$$

and the coefficients C_n must be evaluated by interpreting the summation as the Fourier-Bessel series expansion of the potential $(\Phi_2 - \Phi_1)$ at $\xi = \xi_0$ in terms of the orthogonal system $J_0(p_n\eta)$ between the limits $0 < \eta < \eta_0$. From Appendix 5,(43) and 5,(40) the coefficients are, therefore

$$C_n I_0(p_n\xi_0) \; \tfrac{1}{2}[\eta_0 J_1(p_n\eta_0)]^2 = (\Phi_2 - \Phi_1) \int_0^{\eta_0} \eta \, J_0(p_n\eta) \, d\eta$$

where the brackets on the left-hand side indicate the norm $2N_n$. Since $(\Phi_1 - \Phi_2)$ is constant, the integration can be performed and gives simply $(\eta_0/p_n) \, J_1(p_n\eta_0)$, so that the final complete solution for the internal potential is

$$\Phi = \Phi_1 + 2(\Phi_2 - \Phi_1) \sum_n \frac{I_0(p_n\xi)}{I_0(p_n\xi_0)} \frac{J_0(p_n\eta)}{(p_n\eta_0) \, J_1(p_n\eta_0)} \quad (103)$$

Because of the axial symmetry, this can represent a paraboloidal electron lens system with focussing action for which the field vector is found by the application of $(31 \cdot 24)$ as before.

For potential distributions in external regions it is usually necessary to formulate Fourier integrals rather than Fourier series in the parameter p, since the ranges of both variables ξ and η extend to infinity.

TOROIDAL COORDINATES

The toroidal coordinate system represents in any meridian plane the same cross section as the two-dimensional biaxial system with two orthogonal families of circles as produced by the potential distribution between two parallel charged lines in section 12. One obtains the meridian coordinates ξ and η by the conformal transformation discussed in $(26 \cdot 53)$ and again in connection with the dipolar coordinates in this section with the appropriate modification for the different axis of rotation

$$w = z + j\rho = jf \coth [\tfrac{1}{2}(\xi + j\eta)] \quad (104)$$

Explicitly, from this one has

$$z = f \frac{\sin \eta}{\cosh \xi - \cos \eta}, \qquad \rho = f \frac{\sinh \xi}{\cosh \xi - \cos \eta} \quad (105)$$

which represent the circles shown in Fig. $33 \cdot 14$, namely,

$$z^2 + (\rho - f \coth \xi)^2 = \left(\frac{f}{\sinh \xi}\right)^2, \qquad (z - f \cot \eta)^2 + \rho^2 = \left(\frac{f}{\sin \eta}\right)^2$$

The first relation describes the circles $\xi = $ cons with centers along the ρ-axis and radii $a = f/\sinh \xi$, degenerating for $\xi = 0$ into the z-axis and for $\xi = \infty$ into the point F; by rotation, each circle generates a toroid, shrinking to the circle of radius f for $\xi = \infty$. The second relation gives the orthogonal circular arcs $\eta = $ cons, which generate spherical caps with the circle of radius f as common

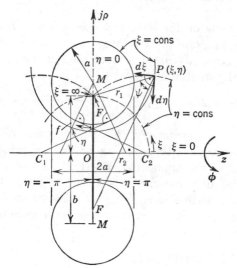

Fig. 33·14 Toroidal Coordinates.

base; the line OF describes a barrier surface where the values $\eta = -\pi$ and $\eta = +\pi$ join back to back.

In accordance with (7) one has

$$h^2 = \left| \frac{dw}{d\zeta} \right|^2 = \frac{f^2}{(\cosh \xi - \cos \eta)^2} \tag{106}$$

so that with (105)

$$\frac{h^2}{\rho^2} = \frac{1}{\sinh^2 \xi} \equiv g_1(\xi), \qquad g_2(\eta) = 0 \tag{107}$$

One can, therefore, write down at once the separated Sturm-Liouville equations (11). Since $g_2(\eta) = 0$, the solutions for $\mathsf{H}(\eta)$ are simply trigonometric functions,

$$\mathsf{H}(\eta) = D_1 \sin p\eta + D_2 \cos p\eta \tag{108}$$

The value of $g_1(\xi)$ is the same as in (80) for the prolate spheroids so that the same substitution for $\Xi(\xi)$ as in (81) will be indicated; the solution is, therefore, given by (83), or also, with $n = p - \frac{1}{2}$, as defined there and in (66),

$$\Xi(\xi) = \sqrt{\sinh \xi}\, W_1(\cosh \xi)$$
$$= \sqrt{\sinh \xi}\,[C_1 \overline{P}_{p-\frac{1}{2}}{}^m (\cosh \xi) + C_2 \overline{Q}_{p-\frac{1}{2}}{}^m (\cosh \xi)] \quad (109)$$

Returning to the original definition of the product solution for the potential in (3) and introducing (105), (108) and (109) yield now

$$\Phi(\xi, \eta, \phi) = \sum_m \sum_p f^{-\frac{1}{2}} \sqrt{\cosh \xi - \cos \eta}$$
$$W_1(\cosh \xi)\, \mathsf{H}(\eta)\, F(\phi) \quad (110)$$

where, of course, $f^{-\frac{1}{2}}$ can be absorbed in the other constants. Treatments of this coordinate system, solutions in it, and discussions of the function systems are found in several references, and for convenience, table 33·3 gives the comparative notations used.

TABLE 33·3

COMPARATIVE NOTATION FOR TOROIDAL COORDINATES

Coordinate	This Book	Bateman[C1]	Byerly[C2]	Hobson[C9]
u_1	$\xi = \cosh^{-1} u$	$\sigma = \cosh^{-1} s$	α	η
u_2	η	ψ	β	θ
u_3	ϕ	ϕ	γ	ϕ
Radius of base circle	f	a	a	c
Distance from axis	ρ	ρ	r	ρ
Distance along axis	z	z	z	z

Conducting Toroid. Ascribe to a solid conducting toroid as in Fig. 33·14 of center diameter $2b$ and of cross-sectional radius a a potential Φ_0; the potential distribution in space will be axially symmetrical, so that $m = 0$. To determine the value ξ_0 for the surface of the toroid, one can use the relations from the definition of the circles above

$$a = \frac{f}{\sinh \xi_0}, \qquad b = \overline{OM} = f \coth \xi_0$$

so that

$$\cosh \xi_0 = \frac{b}{a}, \qquad f = \sqrt{b^2 - a^2}$$

For the external potential $\xi > \xi_0$ one can use only the second kind of modified Legendre function in (109) in accordance with the asymptotic forms (68); then (110) reduces to the single summation

$$\Phi(\xi, \eta) = f^{-\frac{1}{2}} \sqrt{\cosh \xi - \cos \eta}$$
$$\times \sum_p (D_{1,p} \sin p\eta + D_{2,p} \cos p\eta) \, \bar{Q}_{p-\frac{1}{2}} (\cosh \xi) \quad (111)$$

Since at $\xi = \xi_0$ the potential must give the constant value Φ_0, the series (111) must actually represent there the Fourier expansion of $\Phi_0 (\cosh \xi_0 - \cos \eta)^{-\frac{1}{2}}$, which permits coefficient comparison and complete solution of the problem. Since $\sqrt{\cosh \xi_0 - \cos \eta}$ is even symmetrical about $\eta = 0$, only cosine terms will occur, so that in conventional Fourier coefficient determination

$$D_{2,p} \bar{Q}_{p-\frac{1}{2}} (\cosh \xi_0) = \Phi_0 \frac{2\sqrt{f}}{\pi} \int_0^\pi \frac{\cos p\eta}{\sqrt{\cosh \xi_0 - \cos \eta}} \, d\eta \quad (112)$$

For any other potential variation with η the modification of the integral is rather obvious. If the potential is also a function of ϕ, then a double Fourier series results. The toroidal coordinates were introduced by C. Neumann;[10] brief treatments are in Bateman,[C1] p. 461, and in Byerly,[C2] p. 266; also in Hobson,[C9] p. 433, who calls the special type of Legendre functions occurring here "ring functions." Obviously, as $a \to 0$ one approaches the solution for the circular ring of charge in (12·58).

The field vector and charge density can again be found by the application of (31·24) with (106).

Related Coordinate Systems. The toroidal coordinate system can be considered a special case of the annular coordinate system in section 31 if in Fig. 31·4 one takes $b = a = f$; the oval rings then go over into the circular ones of Fig. 33·14.

If, on the other hand, one lets $f \to 0$ in Fig. 33·14, the circles all pass through the origin, as in the potential solution for the dipole line in section 12, Fig. 12·7. This coordinate system is then actually the *inverse* to the circular cylindrical coordinate

---

[10] C. Neumann: *Theorie der Elektrizitäts- und der Wärme- Verteilung in einem Ringe;* Halle, 1864; see also G. Szegö, *Bull. Am. Math. Soc.,* **51,** 325 (1945).

system of section 32 and leads to the same function systems, thus demonstrating the close inner relationship of all these coordinate systems.

34· USE OF GREEN'S FUNCTIONS

Starting with the second identity of Green (see Appendix 3),

$$\iiint_\tau (\Phi\nabla^2\Psi - \Psi\nabla^2\Phi)\, d\tau = \iint_S \left(\Phi\frac{\partial\Psi}{\partial n} - \Psi\frac{\partial\Phi}{\partial n}\right) dS \qquad (1)$$

where both Φ and Ψ are harmonic or potential functions and where the volume τ is bounded by a regular surface S (which can be contracted to a point without intersecting itself), choose for $\Psi = 1/r$ with r the distance from an arbitrary point $P(x, y, z)$ within the volume τ. Obviously, $\Psi \to \infty$ as $r \to 0$, so that the point P must be excluded by a very small volume τ' of surface S'. Since $\nabla^2(1/r) = 0$ as the solution of the Laplacian potential equation, the identity (1) becomes

$$-\iiint_\tau \frac{1}{r}\nabla^2\Phi\, d\tau = \iint_S \left[\Phi\frac{\partial}{\partial n}\left(\frac{1}{r}\right) - \frac{1}{r}\frac{\partial\Phi}{\partial n}\right] dS$$
$$+ \iint_{S'} \left[\Phi\frac{\partial}{\partial n}\left(\frac{1}{r}\right) - \frac{1}{r}\frac{\partial\Phi}{\partial n}\right] dS' \qquad (2)$$

Since S' is very small and can as well be assumed to be a small sphere around point P at $r = 0$, one has also, observing that the outward normal on S' is directed towards point P,

$$-\frac{\partial}{\partial n}\left(\frac{1}{r}\right) = -\frac{1}{r^2}, \qquad -\frac{\partial\Phi}{\partial n} = \frac{\partial\Phi}{\partial r}, \qquad dS' = r^2\, d\Omega$$

with $d\Omega$ the element of the solid angle from P, so that the last integral becomes

$$4\pi\,\Phi(P) + \iint_\Omega r\frac{\partial\Psi}{\partial r}\, d\Omega$$

Here, $\Phi(P)$ is the average potential value over the surface S', and as $r \to 0$, it becomes identical with the potential value at P itself; the remaining integral vanishes as $r \to 0$, assuming that $\partial\Phi/\partial r$ remains finite as in any regular region.

The identity (2) yields now finally an expression for the potential $\Phi(P)$ itself,

$$\Phi(P) = -\frac{1}{4\pi} \iiint_\tau \frac{1}{r} \nabla^2\Phi \, d\tau + \frac{1}{4\pi} \iint_S \frac{1}{r} \frac{\partial\Phi}{\partial n} \, dS$$

$$-\frac{1}{4\pi} \iint_S \Phi \frac{\partial}{\partial n}\left(\frac{1}{r}\right) dS \quad (3)$$

With the general interpretation (see section 2) (again observing the proper direction of the normal)

$$\nabla^2\Phi = -\frac{\rho}{\varepsilon}, \qquad \sigma = +\varepsilon\frac{\partial\Phi}{\partial n}$$

the first term constitutes the integral expression for the electrostatic potential as given in $(2\cdot5)$ in terms of space charge within the volume τ. Having assumed S to be a regular surface, the other two integrals in (3) constitute fictitious charge effects; the first represents the potential of an equivalent surface charge distribution σ on the inside of S as in $(2\cdot3)$, the second the potential of an equivalent dipole moment distribution with moment $\varepsilon\Phi \, dS$ per element dS (directed into the volume τ) as comparison with $(10\cdot33)$ shows. Thus the potential inside S is defined completely by the actual space charge within τ and by charge distributions on the inside of S which replace the effect of all charges actually located outside of S and which reduce the potential outside of S everywhere to zero. An excellent detailed interpretation of this integral representation (3) and the physical meaning of its parts is given in Stratton,[A23] pp. 185–192.

The representation (3) can still be maintained if conductors are located within the surface S; in this case, however, the conductor surfaces must be considered as part of the bounding surface of τ and the first surface integral in (3) will then include the real charge densities on these conductor surfaces.

GREEN'S FUNCTION FOR THE FIRST BOUNDARY VALUE POTENTIAL PROBLEM

It is seen that the potential at any point of a regular region can be found by integrations over the boundary of the region. If no space charge is present, the first term in (3) disappears. If, furthermore, only surfaces with known potential values form the boundaries of the electrostatic field, so that the boundary conditions state $\Phi = \Phi_\alpha,\ \Phi_\beta \cdots$ on surfaces $\alpha,\ \beta, \cdots$, then the boundary value problem is called of the *first kind*, as stated in sections 2 and 6 and, more particularly, section 28. The potential solution is then in integral form

$$\Phi(P) = -\frac{1}{4\pi} \iint_S \left[\Phi \frac{\partial}{\partial n}\left(\frac{1}{r}\right) - \frac{1}{r}\frac{\partial \Phi}{\partial n} \right] dS \qquad (4)$$

In general, if Φ and Ψ are solutions of the Laplacian potential problem, the left-hand side of (1) vanishes completely, and one also has

$$-\iint_S \left[\Phi \frac{\partial \Psi}{\partial n} - \Psi \frac{\partial \Phi}{\partial n} \right] dS = 0 \qquad (5)$$

Adding (4) and (5) shows that, if one can select Ψ in such a manner that anywhere on the surface S the value of

$$\left[\Psi + \frac{1}{r} \right]_{\text{on } S} = 0 \qquad (6)$$

the second terms drop out, and one has

$$\Phi(P) = -\frac{1}{4\pi} \iint_S \Phi(Q) \frac{\partial}{\partial n} G(P, Q)\, dS \qquad (7)$$

where $G(P, Q)$ is called *Green's function of the first kind* and is the combination (6). It will, therefore, generally be a function of the point $P(x, y, z)$ of observation where the potential value is to be found, and of the point $Q(\bar{x}, \bar{y}, \bar{z})$ on the surface S where the potential value is known. See Kellogg,[C10] p. 236; Bateman,[C1] p. 240; and many other textbooks on advanced mathematics.

The use of Green's function for the solution of potential problems of the first kind, then, requires that one assume at a point P in the region τ bounded by surfaces of known potential values, a point charge of unit charge value and with $1/r$ as reduced potential function (stripped of all constant factors), and that one find the suitable set of *image charges* with respect to the bounding surfaces which renders all of them of zero potential value. The sum total of potentials of the original and all image charges then constitutes $G(P, Q)$, which can be used to find the potential functions by (7) for any point P in the region τ. It is clear that the use of Green's function demands the complete solution of a related boundary value problem, even if not quite as complex as the whole original problem might be! Moreover, it then requires a further surface integration. For this reason, there are only a few instances in which Green's function actually has been used for the potential evaluation; however, many specific Green's functions of the first kind have been computed: indeed, every one of the image problems involving a point charge can be interpreted as a Green function.

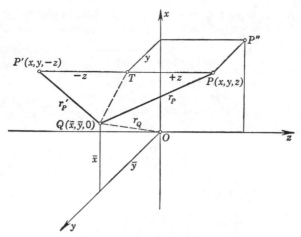

FIG. 34·1 Green's Function for the Plane $z = 0$.

Green's Function for Planes. For the infinite conducting plane located at $z = 0$, the potential solution (10·15) gives Green's function when referred to Fig. 10·2 as

$$G(P, Q) = \frac{1}{r_P} - \frac{1}{r_{P'}} \tag{8}$$

where r_P and $r_{P'}$ are the distances between *any* point $P(x, y, z)$ or its image point $P'(x, y, -z)$ and *any* point in the conducting plane $Q(\bar{x}, \bar{y}, 0)$ as in Fig. 34·1, so that

$$r_P{}^2 = [(\bar{x} - x)^2 + (\bar{y} - y)^2 + (-z)^2],$$
$$r_{P'}{}^2 = [(\bar{x} - x)^2 + (\bar{y} - y)^2 + (+z)^2] \tag{9}$$

since the image must be located symmetrically with respect to the plane $\bar{z} = 0$. The normal derivative at $\bar{z} = 0$ is then

$$\frac{\partial}{\partial z} G(P, Q) = -2z[(\bar{x} - x)^2 + (\bar{y} - y)^2 + z^2]^{-\frac{3}{2}} \tag{10}$$

so that for any general potential distribution in the plane $\bar{z} = 0$ one has in accordance with (7) the potential solution

$$\Phi(x, y, z) = \frac{z}{2\pi} \int_{-\infty}^{+\infty} d\bar{x} \int_{-\infty}^{+\infty} [(\bar{x} - x)^2 + (\bar{y} - y)^2 + z^2]^{-\frac{3}{2}} \Phi(\bar{x}, \bar{y}) \, d\bar{y} \quad (11)$$

Complete results for $\Phi = \Phi_0$ within the rectangle $-a < \bar{x} < +a$, $-b < \bar{y} < +b$, and $\Phi = 0$ outside of it, are given in Byerly,[C2] p. 138.

This method can, of course, readily be extended to a metallic corner formed by two perpendicularly intersecting conducting planes, as by (10·19), or for intersection at any other angle, π/n, where n is integer. Obviously, the amount of labor rapidly grows prohibitive if one keeps in mind the integration (7), which might be performed numerically or by machine methods in special cases.

For two parallel planes, Green's function can be represented by a Fourier integral[1] in axial distance ρ, since axial symmetry prevails; the relation to the solution by means of images as in section 21 is given in Bateman,[C1] p. 414, who also gives, p. 472, Green's function for a conducting wedge, i.e., in the outside space of two conducting planes intersecting at π/n with $n > 1$ and integer as well for the semi-infinite single plane. Smythe,[A22] p. 210, gives the results for a rectangular prism and a rectangular box in terms of Fourier double series expansions.

Green's Function for Spherical Surfaces. For the single sphere of radius a the potential solution in the presence of a point charge is given by (10·26), where b is the distance of the point charge from the center of the sphere. In order to get Green's function one has to make the spherical coordinates of P more general, say, $P(r, \theta, \phi)$ and those of $Q(\bar{r} = a, \bar{\theta}, \bar{\phi})$ as in Fig. 34·2. Thus one has

$$G(P, Q) = \left(\frac{1}{r_P} - \frac{a}{r} \frac{1}{r_{P'}} \right) \quad (12)$$

where, then

$$r_P{}^2 = [r^2 + \bar{r}^2 - 2r\bar{r} \cos \gamma],$$
$$r_{P'}{}^2 = \left[\left(\frac{a^2}{r} \right)^2 + \bar{r}^2 - 2 \frac{a^2}{r} \bar{r} \cos \gamma \right] \quad (13)$$

---

[1] C. Fox, *Phil. Mag.*, **6**, 7, p. 994 (1928); also Bateman,[C1] p. 413.

are the respective distances of the point charge at P and its image at P', which is located on the same radius vector but at a distance a^2/r from the center. The angle between the radius vectors to P (or P') and Q is given by

$$\cos \gamma = \cos \theta \cos \bar{\theta} + \sin \theta \sin \bar{\theta} \cos (\phi - \bar{\phi}) \tag{14}$$

The normal derivatives with respect to $\bar{r}$ can now be evaluated and give

$$\frac{d}{d\bar{r}} \left(\frac{1}{r_P}\right) = \frac{r \cos \gamma - \bar{r}}{r_P{}^3}, \qquad \frac{d}{d\bar{r}} \left(\frac{1}{r_{P'}}\right) = \frac{(a^2/r) \cos \gamma - \bar{r}}{r_P{}^3}$$

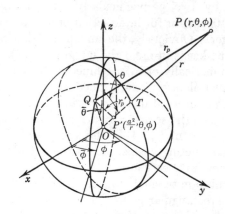

Fig. 34·2   Green's Function for the Sphere.

Since now for $\bar{r} = a$, $G(P, Q) = 0$ as boundary condition, one can replace $r_{P'}$ from (12) so that

$$\left[\frac{\partial}{\partial \bar{r}} G(P, Q)\right]_{\bar{r}=a} = \frac{1}{r_P{}^3} \left(-a + \frac{r^2}{a}\right)$$

and therefore

$$\Phi(r, \theta, \phi) =$$

$$-\frac{r^2 - a^2}{4\pi a} \int_{\bar{\theta}=0}^{\bar{\theta}=\pi} d\bar{\theta} \int_{\bar{\phi}=0}^{\bar{\phi}=2\pi} \frac{1}{r_P{}^3} \Phi(\bar{\theta}, \bar{\phi}) a^2 \sin \bar{\theta} \, d\bar{\theta} \, d\bar{\phi} \tag{15}$$

where

$$r_P{}^2 = r^2 + a^2 - 2ra \cos \gamma \tag{16}$$

and cos γ from (14).   The integral (15) is the celebrated *Poisson integral* for the sphere; see Kellogg,[C10] p. 241; Bateman,[C1] p. 367; and many other textbooks on advanced mathematics.

Green's functions for a circular disk and a spherical bowl are also given in Bateman,[C1] p. 465.

The solution for the potential of a point charge in an earthed cone of semiopening $\theta = \alpha$ can be obtained in spherical coordinates by means of the general product functional expansion (33·16). The point charge, which is confined to the volume element $d\tau$, must be expressed as a double Fourier series in θ and ϕ.   Smythe,[A22] p. 154, gives the complete solution for the conical space as well as for the conical box.

Green's Function for the Cylinder.   For the circular cylinder, the potential of a point charge cannot be found by any image theory.   One has to use the complete functional solution from section 32 and expand the point charge, as distributed over a small volume $\delta\tau$, into a Fourier-Bessel series.   A solution which is symmetrical about the plane through the point charge and the axis of the cylinder and also symmetrical about the plane through the point charge and normal to the axis of the cylinder is given by the double series (see section 32)

$$G(P, Q) = \sum_n \sum_m C_{n,m} e^{-p_n|\bar{z}-z_0|} J_m(p_n\bar{\rho}) \cos m(\bar{\phi} - \phi_0) \quad (17)$$

if a is the radius of the cylinder; the point charge is located at point P with coordinates $\rho_0 < a$, $z = z_0$, and $\phi = \phi_0$, and the point Q at $(\bar{\rho} = a, \bar{z}, \bar{\phi})$.   The values p_n are obtained from the condition that

$$J_m(p_n a) = 0$$

In the plane $\phi = \phi_0$ the field lines have no axial component except right at the point charge, which is assumed as an infinitesimal area $\delta S = \rho_0 \delta\rho\delta\phi$, over which the integral gives one half the total electric flux in the positive z-direction and one half in the negative z-direction.   The Fourier coefficients $C_{n,m}$ in the derivative $(\partial G/\partial z)$ are, therefore,

$$-p_n C_{n,m} \left\{ \frac{1}{2} [aJ_{m+1}(p_n a)]^2 \right\}$$
$$= \left(\frac{\partial G}{\partial z} \right)_{z=z_0} \cdot J_m(p_n\rho_0)\rho_0\delta\rho\delta\phi \left(\frac{1}{\pi} \quad \text{or} \quad \frac{1}{2\pi} \right) \quad (18)$$

where the bracket on the left-hand side is the norm of the Bessel function of order m, and where on the right-hand side $1/\pi$ holds for $m > 0$, $1/2\pi$ for $m = 0$. In accordance with the definition of $G(P, Q)$ one has, then,

$$\left(\frac{\partial G}{\partial z}\right)_{z=z_0} \rho_0 \delta \rho \delta \phi = -\frac{1}{2} \tag{19}$$

so that with this and (18), one obtains

$$G(P, Q) = \frac{1}{2\pi a^2} \sum_{n=1}^{\infty} \frac{1}{p_n} \exp\left(-p_n |\bar{z} - z|\right) \left\{ \frac{J_0(p_n \bar{\rho}) \, J_0(p_n \rho)}{[J_1(p_n a)]^2} \right.$$
$$\left. + 2 \sum_{m=1}^{\infty} \frac{J_m(p_n \bar{\rho}) \, J_m(p_n \rho)}{[J_{m+1}(p_n a)]^2} \cos m(\bar{\phi} - \phi) \right\} \tag{20}$$

This function, as required, is symmetrical in the coordinates of the points P and Q; actually the zero subscripts have been dropped, since they are no longer necessary. To use (20), one must differentiate with respect to $\bar{\rho}$; in the result set $\bar{\rho} = a$ and introduce it again into the general form (7), which becomes here

$$\Phi(\rho, \phi, z) = -\frac{1}{\pi} \int_0^\infty d\bar{z} \int_\phi^{\phi+\pi} \left[\frac{\partial G(P, Q)}{\partial \bar{\rho}}\right]_{\bar{\rho}=a} \Phi(\bar{\phi}, \bar{z}) a \, d\bar{\phi} \tag{21}$$

The Green function is deduced[2] in Smythe,[A22] p. 174, for the cylinder as well as for the cylindrical box. For the somewhat simpler case of a point charge on the axis the solution can be given in terms of a Fourier integral to which reasonable approximations[3] can be made so as to allow further integrations.

GREEN'S FUNCTIONS FOR OTHER BOUNDARY VALUE POTENTIAL PROBLEMS

Potential Problems of the Second Kind. If the normal component of the field gradient or the charge distribution is specified on the boundary surfaces, rather than the potential values, one calls the boundary value problem of the *second kind*, as stated in sections 2 and 6 and, more particularly, in section 28. Starting again from the two relations (4) and (5), one observes

---

[2] C. J. Bouwkamp and N. G. de Bruijn, *Jl. Appl. Phys.*, **18**, p. 573 (1947).
[3] E. Weber, *Jl. Appl. Phys.*, **10**, p. 663 (1939); also Bouwkamp and de Bruijn, *loc. cit.*

that, if one can find a function Ψ such that the combination

$$G^{(2)}(P, Q) = \frac{1}{r} + \Psi(P, Q)$$

has a normal derivative on the boundary surfaces which is at most a constant but preferably zero, then the sum of (4) and (5) gives

$$\Phi(P) = \frac{1}{4\pi} \iint_S \frac{\partial \Phi}{\partial n} \cdot G^{(2)}(P, Q) \, dS + \frac{k}{4\pi} \iint_S \Phi(Q) \, dS \qquad (22)$$

The function $G^{(2)}$ is called Green's function of the second kind; it determines the potential function except for the constant second term (k is an arbitrary constant), which is as expected, since only the normal derivative of the potential is known; see Kellogg,[C10] p. 246.

Rather few explicit solutions have been given for this second kind of Green's function, so that the usual terminology "Green's function" without qualification is assumed to apply to the first kind only.

For the interior of the sphere of radius a, the second kind of Green's function in terms of the coordinates of $P(r, \theta, \phi)$, $P'(r' = a^2/r, \theta, \phi)$, and $Q(\bar{r} = a, \bar{\theta}, \bar{\phi})$ is

$$G^{(2)}(P, Q) = \frac{1}{r_P} + \frac{a}{r} \frac{1}{r_{P'}} + \frac{1}{a} \ln \frac{2a^2}{a^2 + rr_{P'} - r\bar{r} \cos \gamma} \qquad (23)$$

where r_P and $r_{P'}$ are defined as in (13) but with $r < a$, and $\cos \gamma$ is given by (14). On the surface of the sphere $\bar{r} = a$, and $r_{P'} = (a/r)r_P$, so that the form (22) becomes explicitly

$$\Phi(r, \theta, \phi) = \frac{1}{4\pi} \int_0^\pi d\bar{\theta} \int_0^{2\pi} \left(\frac{\partial \Phi}{\partial r} \right)_{r=a}$$
$$\times \left[\frac{2}{r_P} + \frac{1}{a} \ln \frac{2a}{a + r_P - r \cos \gamma} \right] a \, d\bar{\phi} + \Phi(0) \qquad (24)$$

where $\Phi(0)$ is the potential at the center of the sphere in accordance with the mean theorem of Gauss (Bateman,[C1] p. 369). The above solution is given in Kellogg,[C10] p. 247.

Other Potential Problems. It is possible to construct formally Green's function for many other types of problems, notably those in which boundary conditions of the first and second kind are mixed. Similarly, one can deduce a formulation for the third kind of boundary value problem, as in Bateman,[C1] p. 141. In many cases, however, the direct solution of the boundary value problem is less involved.

One might surmise that Green's function for *two-dimensional problems* would be much simpler to formulate and that, indeed, it should have close relation to the complex potential theory. As a matter of fact, there exists a unique relationship between Green's function for a regular region and the conformal transformation of that region upon the unit circle which was discussed in section 28.   Whenever one can perform the latter, one has the explicit solution for the former and vice versa, so that Green's function will give no advantage.   For the details see Kellogg,[C10] p. 365.

PROBLEMS

1. Two infinitely long coaxial cylinders of equal diameters and potentials $\Phi = 0$ and $\Phi = V$ have finite separation $2d$ as in Fig. $30 \cdot 4$.   Assuming the potential to vary as $\frac{1}{2}V \sin (\pi z/2d)$ along $\rho = a$ across the gap, find the potential distribution near the axis $\rho = 0$.

2. A semi-infinite cylindrical bar of circular cross section with radius a extends for $z > 0$.   The base at $z = 0$ is kept at a high temperature T_0 and heat is transferred from the cylindrical boundary surface in accordance with $(29 \cdot 24)$.   Find the temperature gradient along the axis $\rho = 0$.   Find the amount of heat transferred to the ambient medium.

3. Express the solution $(30 \cdot 46)$ for two semi-infinite coaxial cylinders near the axis $\rho = 0$ in the series form $(30 \cdot 7)$ and identify the first three terms.

4. Formulate the solution for the potential distribution between two semi-infinite coaxial cylinders of different radii R_1 and $R_2 > R_1$, both starting at $z = 0$ and forming there an electron lens similar to Fig. $30 \cdot 3$.   Point out the basic difficulty of an exact solution.

5. Demonstrate the validity of the expressions $(30 \cdot 16)$ and $(30 \cdot 17)$ for vector potential and magnetic flux density near the axis of a single circular loop of current.

6. Find the best spacing of three coaxial circular current loops lying in parallel planes in order to produce nearly uniform magnetic field close to the axis, if (a) the loops are identical and carry the same current I, (b) the loops are identical but carry conveniently chosen different currents.

7. For the two semi-infinite coaxial cylinders in Fig. $30 \cdot 3$ determine the values of z for which the potential along the axis is within 2% of the respective cylinder potential.   Check this with the approximation form $(30 \cdot 50)$.

8. A very large number of coaxial cylinders of equal diameters are arranged with infinitesimal gaps similar to the two cylinders shown in Fig. $30 \cdot 3$.   Assuming that the voltage increment between any two neighboring cylinders is ΔV, find the potential distribution along the axis.   Choose the length to diameter ratio $L/2a$ so that the potential increases nearly linearly along the axis.

9. A circular cylinder of length L, radius a, and completely closed except for a coaxial circular aperture of radius $b < a$ in one of the end faces can be considered a collector of electrons or ions. Find the potential distribution inside, if the cylinder is at ground potential and the aperture has an arbitrary radial potential distribution $\Phi(r)$. Plot some equipotential surfaces if $b = a/2$ and the aperture potential is a linear function of the radius.

10. In a solid cube of side a, one face is kept at temperature T_0, the opposite face is ideally insulated, and all the other faces transfer heat to the ambient medium of zero temperature in accordance with (29·24), namely, $k(\partial T/\partial n) + fT = 0$. Find the thermal resistance of the cube.

11. A rectangular metal box as shown in Fig. 31·1 has the face $x = 0$ kept at potential difference V with respect to all other faces. Find the potential distribution. Find the surface charge on the face $x = a$.

12. Assume in problem 11 that the two opposite faces $x = 0$ and $x = a$ are kept at the same potential difference with respect to all the other faces. Find the potential distribution. Find the charge distribution on face $x = 0$ and its total charge.

13. The solid conducting rectangular block in Fig. 31·1 has two electrodes with potential difference V applied, one covering the left half top face $x = a$, the other covering the right half of the lower face $x = 0$. Find the resistance of the block. Hint: divide the block into two halves by the plane $z = c/2$ and establish the boundary conditions in this plane.

14. Find the capacitance between two confocal ellipsoids of semiaxes $A > B > C$, and $a > b > c$, respectively.

15. Find the gravitational potential produced by an ellipsoid of mass density ρ and with semiaxes $a > b > c$. Show that at large distance the mass can be considered as concentrated at the center of the ellipsoid.

16. A dielectric ellipsoid with semiaxes $a > b > c$ and of dielectric constant ε becomes uniformly polarized in a uniform electric field $E^{(0)}$ which is parallel to the largest axis. If the polarization is P, parallel to $E^{(0)}$ and in opposite direction, find the resultant potential distribution. Plot some resultant equipotential and field lines. Find the resultant potential at large distance from the ellipsoid. Find the equivalent dielectric constant in terms of P and $E^{(0)}$.

17. A conducting ellipsoid of semiaxes $a > b > c$ is introduced into a uniform electric field $E^{(0)}$ with its axis b parallel to it. Find the resultant potential distribution. Find the charge distribution over the surface of the ellipsoid.

18. Find the approximations for a thin long rod for which $a \gg b$ and $b = c$ by utilizing the solution for the conducting ellipsoid. Verify the results with the values obtained in section 12.

19. Deduce the Laplacian differential equation and its separation into ordinary differential equations for the circular cylinder coordinates by means of the generalized theory in section 32.

20. A solid cylindrical ring as in Fig. 32·2 has the base $z = c$ kept at high temperature T_1, the opposite end face $z = 0$ is cooled to a low temperature T_0, and the cylinder surfaces $\rho = a$ and $\rho = b$ transfer heat to the surrounding medium in accordance with (29·24) in the form $k(\partial T/\partial n) + f(T_1 - T_2) = 0$, where T_2 is the fixed temperature of the ambient and $T_1 > T_2 > T_0$. Find

the temperature distribution in the ring.   Find the total heat transferred from the heated base $z = c$.

21. All the walls of a hollow cylindrical ring as in Fig. 32·2 are kept at zero potential except an annular ring $a_1 < \rho < b_1$ on the face $z = 0$, which is at potential V and separated by infinitesimal gaps from the rest of the surface. Find the charge distribution on the annular ring.   Find its capacitance with respect to the walls of the cylinder.

22. A solid cylindrical ring as in Fig. 32·2 has two thin ring electrodes applied in its center plane $z = c/2$, one at the outer surface $\rho = b$, the other at the inner surface $\rho = a$.   Find the current distribution if the total current entering is I, the small width of the electrodes w, and the current distribution can be assumed as uniform.   Find the resistance of the ring.

23. A solid cylinder of finite length is heated internally by distributed sources of space density h such as joule heat.   Find the temperature distribution if the heat loss on all surfaces is given by (29·24) in the form $k(\partial T/\partial n) + f(T - T_0) = 0$, where T_0 is the ambient temperature.   Find the maximum temperature.   Find the temperature distribution along the axis.

24. A hollow cylinder of finite length is grounded.   Find the potential distribution if a quasi sphere with charge Q is placed on the axis at the center of the cylinder.   Find its capacitance.   Hint: divide the cylinder space by the plane of symmetry into two halves and consider that in this plane the normal dielectric flux is injected like current from an electrode.   (See also Smythe, [A 22] p. 175.)

25. A very long conducting cylinder of radius a is covered with a dielectric of thickness $a/2$.   Find the distribution of the potential and the electric field within the dielectric if the conductor surface has a potential value given by $V \sin(2\pi z/L)$ and the outer surface of the dielectric is kept at zero potential.

26. A solid conducting cylinder of radius a and finite length has one cylindrical electrode of small radius ρ applied at one end face with center at $r = a/2$ and the second, like electrode at the opposite face again with center at $r = a/2$ but in diametrically opposite position.   Find the resistance to the current flow.

27. A hollow cylinder of radius a and finite length L has a narrow slot cut in its cylindrical surface parallel to the axis and of length $L/2$.   Assuming that the cylinder is grounded and that the slot is covered with a strip of potential V, find the capacitance of the strip with respect to the cylinder walls.   Assume the slot symmetrically located and the strip fitting into the slot with infinitesimal clearances.

28. A point charge Q is located at a distance d from an infinite plane dielectric boundary.   Find the potential distribution by means of (32·44) for the potential of the point charge and the complete solution of the boundary value problem.   Demonstrate that the result can be interpreted in terms of the image method in section 21.

29. Find the capacitance between two small spheres of radii ρ_1 and ρ_2 carrying charges $\pm Q$ and being located symmetrically with respect to the dielectric plate in Fig. 32·4.

30. A circular loop of current of radius R is located in a plane parallel to an infinite magnetic plate of thickness a and permeability μ, analogous to Fig. 32·4.   Find the inductance of the loop.

Problems 529

31. A circular ring of charge of loop radius R and small wire radius ρ is located in a plane parallel to an infinite plane dielectric boundary and at distance a from it. Find its capacitance. Find the charge distribution on its surface.

32. Two small semispherical electrodes with centers in the surface of ground and buried in it are a distance $2c$ apart. Find the resistance between them if the ground has uniform conductivity γ_1 to a depth a_1, and uniform conductivity γ_2 for the additional depth a_2, beyond which the conductivity is so large that it can be assumed infinite.

33. Verify the solution (32·62) for the two half elliptic cylinders in Fig. 32·5 by means of conformal mapping.

34. Find the charge distribution on the two half cylinders of Fig. 32·5 and evaluate the capacitance.

35. Deduce the Laplacian differential equation and the equivalent ordinary differential equations in the coordinates r and θ for the spherical coordinate system from the general theory at the beginning of section 33.

36. Find the temperature distribution in a solid sphere of radius a if the two diametrically opposite caps $0 < \theta < \pi/4$ and $3\pi/4 < \theta < \pi$ are kept at high temperature T_1 and the zone of the surface $\pi/4 < \theta < 3\pi/4$ is kept at low temperature T_0. Find the thermal resistance.

37. A solid hemisphere of large radius a is set with its flat surface upon conducting ground of potential $\Phi = 0$. Find the current distribution in the sphere, if an electrode of potential V is applied over $0 < \theta < \pi/6$ with pole $\theta = 0$ located on the normal to ground.

38. A solid conducting sphere has two electrodes of small area S applied at the points A and B' as in Fig. 33·3. Find the resistance between the electrodes. Hint: use for the associated Legendre functions a Taylor series approximation near B'.

39. A conducting thin hemispherical shell of radius a is placed with its large circle a small distance above a conducting plane. Find the capacitance between the shell and the plane. Find the charge distribution induced in the plane if the shell carries a total charge Q.

40. The dielectric spherical shell of finite thickness as in Fig. 33·4 with $\varepsilon_2 = \varepsilon$ and $\varepsilon_3 = \varepsilon_0$ carries two hemispherical electrodes of potential difference V on its outer surface. Find the internal capacitance between the hemispheres. Compare it with the case of a single dielectric of constant ε_0.

41. A uniformly charged circular ring of radius R is coaxial with a dielectric sphere with constant ε_2 and radius a. Find the resultant field distribution if the plane of the ring is at distance b from the center of the sphere. Find the capacitance of the ring for a small wire radius ρ.

42. Find the potential solution for a point charge Q located within the dielectric sphere at $b < a$ in Fig. 33·5. Find its capacitance for a small radius ρ. Find the approximate charge distribution on the surface of the sphere.

43. Find the mutual inductance of two coaxial parallel circular current loops of equal radii a and center distance d in terms of spherical harmonics.

44. A circular current loop of radius R is coaxial with a magnetic sphere of permeability μ and radius a. Find the resultant magnetic field distribution if the plane of the loop is at distance b from the center of the sphere. Find the inductance of the loop for a small wire radius ρ.

45. Find the potential distribution within the cone $\theta = \pi/6$ and $r \geqslant a$ if the potential difference between the cone surface and the spherical zone is V. Find the capacitance.

46. A point charge Q is located at the axis of a grounded cone with angle $\theta = \pi/6$. Find the induced charge distribution on the cone. Assuming the charge to reside on a small sphere of radius ρ, find its capacitance.

47. A thin circular metallic disk of radius R is located at the center of an oblate conducting spheroid of semiaxes a and $b = 3a/4$. Find the potential distribution if the disk belongs to the family of spheroids. Find the capacitance of the disk.

48. Find the potential distribution within a dielectric, oblate spheroidal shell of finite thickness in a uniform electric field E^0 parallel to the axis of rotation.

49. A very small sphere with charge Q is located in the center of a circular aperture of an infinite conducting plane. Find the field distribution. Find the capacitance of the sphere.

50. A thin metallic rod of length $2c$ is located at the center of a prolate conducting spheroid of semiaxes a and $b = 3a/4$. Find the potential distribution if the rod belongs to the family of the spheroids. Find the capacitance of the rod for a small radius ρ.

51. Find the potential distribution within a dielectric prolate spheroidal shell of finite thickness in a uniform field E^0 parallel to the axis of rotation.

52. The inside of a tank of insulating material filled with conducting fluid can be approximated by a prolate spheroid of semiaxes a and $b = a/2$. Two electrodes are inserted at the opposite ends along the axis of revolution; their lengths are $a/10$. Find the total resistance of the fluid if the uniform conductivity is γ.

53. A small sphere is located with its center in the surface plane of ground. At a distance c directly below the sphere is a very long thin rod extending perpendicular to the surface of the ground. Find the resistance between the sphere and the rod if a potential difference V is applied and if the conductivity of ground can be assumed uniform. Use the inverse to the prolate spheroidal coordinate system.

54. Show that the integrals in $(33 \cdot 112)$ are reducible to elliptic integrals. Demonstrate that the solution in $(33 \cdot 111)$ actually becomes that for the circular ring of charge if a is very small and $b \to f$. Observe that as ξ_0 becomes very large, one can approximate $(\cosh \xi_0 - \cos \eta)^{1/2} \to \sqrt{\cosh \xi_0} - (\frac{1}{2} \cos \eta / \sqrt{\cosh \xi_0})$.

55. The infinite plane $z = 0$ has zero potential everywhere except for a circular area of radius R where the potential is V. Find the potential distribution for $z > 0$. Find the charge distribution in the plane $z = 0$.

56. Two conducting planes intersect at an angle $\pi/6$. Find the potential distribution between their halves if they are bisected by a plane normal to both, and one half of the intersecting planes carries potential zero, the other half potential V. Find the charge distributions on the planes.

57. Find Green's function for the interior of a cubical box.

58. A thin spherical shell is bisected into two hemispherical shells with a potential difference V between them. Find the potential distribution inside the shells by Green's function, and verify the solution $(33 \cdot 31)$.

Appendix 1

LETTER SYMBOLS FOR
ELECTRICAL QUANTITIES

The letter symbols for electrical quantities have been chosen in close correspondence with the latest "Proposed American Standard," prepared in 1947 by the Committee Z10.8 on Letter Symbols for Electrical Quantities of the American Standard Association under the chairmanship of Professor Edward Bennett. To make reference more convenient, table 1·2 gives an alphabetical list of the quantities, their symbols, and their units in the now most frequently used rationalized MKSC system (the extended Giorgi system of units), which has as fundamental units the meter, kilogram-mass, second, and coulomb. Where the standards proposal allows alternative symbols or designations, a choice has been made here which leads to minimum conflicts. The only major discrepancy is the symbol **K**, used here for the current sheet density instead of A, since the latter would conflict with **A**, the symbol

TABLE 1·1

<small>Alphabetical List of Symbols with Item Number of Table 1·2</small>

Symbol	Item No. Table 1·2	Symbol	Item No. Table 1·2	Symbol	Item No. Table 1·2
A	37	**M**	34	γ	7
B	22	**m**	28	ε	11
C	1	$\mathcal{P}$	29	ε_r	13
c	41	**P**	33	ε_v	12
D	14	P	38	Λ	20
				λ	3
E	24	p	27	μ	30
$\mho$	30, 20	Q	2	μ_r	32
F	21	$\mathcal{R}$	39	μ_v	31
G	6	R	40	ρ	5
H	25	S	16	σ	4
I	8	V	17	Φ	35
J	9	W	42, 18	Φ_m	19
K	10			Ψ	15
L	23				

531

for magnetic vector potential, and both quantities occur simultaneously in several of the relations in section 6.

As an additional assistance for the identification of the symbols used, table 1·1 gives the alphabetic listing of the symbols with the respective item numbers of table 1·2.

TABLE 1·2

ALPHABETICAL LIST OF THE NAMES OF QUANTITIES WITH THEIR SYMBOLS AND UNITS

Item	Quantity	Symbol	MKSC Unit	Remarks
1	Capacitance	C	Farad	Notes 1, 2
2	Charge, electric	Q	Coulomb	
	Charge density			
3	line d. of charge	λ	Coulomb per meter	
4	surface d. of charge	σ	Coulomb per meter^2	
5	volume d. of charge	ρ	Coulomb per meter^3	
6	Conductance	G	Mho	Notes 1, 2
7	Conductivity	γ	Mho per meter	
8	Current	I	Ampere	
9	Current density	$\mathbf{J}$	Ampere per meter^2	
10	sheet c.d. (linear c.d.)	$\mathbf{K}$	Ampere per meter (width)	Note 3
11	Dielectric constant	ε	Farad per meter	
12	of evacuated space	ε_v		$= (c^2\mu_v)^{-1} \approx$ $(10^{-9}/36\pi)$ farad per meter
13	relative d.c.	ε_r	A ratio	relative to evacuated space
14	Displacement, electric	$\mathbf{D}$	Coulomb per meter^2	
15	Displacement flux	Ψ	Coulomb	
16	Elastance	S	Daraf	Notes 1, 2
17	Electromotive force or electric potential difference	V	Volt	Note 4 on subscripts
18	Energy	W	Joule	
19	Flux, magnetic	Φ_m	Weber	
20	Flux linkage	Λ	Weber-turn	Notes 1, 2
21	Force	$\mathbf{F}$	Newton	
22	Induction, magnetic, or magnetic flux density	$\mathbf{B}$	Weber per meter^2	
23	Inductance	L	Henry	Notes 1, 2
24	Intensity, electric, or electric field strength	$\mathbf{E}$	Volt per meter	
25	Intensity, magnetic, or magnetizing force	$\mathbf{H}$	Ampere-turn per meter	

TABLE 1·2 *Continued*

Item	Quantity	Symbol	MKSC Unit	Remarks
26	Magnetomotive force or magnetic potential difference	$\mathcal{F}$	Ampere-turn	Note 4 on subscripts
27	Moment, electric	**p**	Coulomb-meter	
28	Moment, magnetic	**m**	Weber-meter	
29	Permeance	$\mathcal{P}$	Henry	Or weber per ampere-turn
30	Permeability, magnetic	μ	Henry per meter	
31	of evacuated space	μ_v		$= 4\pi \times 10^{-7}$ henry per meter relative to evacuated space
32	relative permeability	μ_r	A ratio	
33	Polarization, electric	**P**	Coulomb per meter^2	
34	Polarization, magnetic, or magnetization	**M**	Weber per meter^2	
35	Potential, electric	Φ	Volt	
36	Potential, magnetic scalar or magnetostatic potential	$\mathcal{F}$	Ampere-turn	Note 4 on subscripts
37	Potential, magnetic vector	**A**	Weber per meter	
38	Power, active	P	Watt	
39	Reluctance	$\mathcal{R}$	Ampere-turn per weber	Notes 1, 2
40	Resistance	R	Ohm	Notes 1, 2
41	Velocity of light	c	Meter per second	
42	Work	W	Joule	

Note 1. Quantities per unit length, area, or volume are generally designated by the capital letters from the table with the subscript 1 unless a specific symbol is listed in the table.

Note 2. For mutual coefficients (partial capacitances, inductances, resistances, etc.) double subscripts are used in the sense of determinant notation, i.e., the first index indicates row, the second column of the square array of coefficients.

Note 3. Current sheet density cannot be designated by **A** as proposed in the standards, since it occurs in the same equation with **A**, the magnetic vector potential; the notation **K** if also used by Stratton.[A48]

Note 4. Potential differences usually carry a double subscript, the order indicating the direction in which the difference is to be taken.

Appendix 2

CONVERSION TABLES FOR UNITS

For the conversion of units from one system to another it is well to keep in mind a few basic concepts pertaining to physical quantities[1] which tend to minimize misinterpretations.

Any mathematical equation defines a relation between numerical values, whereas physical laws relate physical quantities whose values are expressed with reference to specifically chosen units. A physical quantity Q is best conceived as the product of a numerical value N and the chosen unit U,

$$Q = NU \tag{1}$$

which merely reiterates the fact that measurement is basic to any quantitative knowledge about the physical quantity Q. Conversion from a unit U_1 to another unit U_2,

$$Q = N_1 U_1 = N_2 U_2 \tag{2}$$

involves the knowledge of the *conversion factor*

$$U_1 = N_{12} U_2 \tag{3}$$

which relates relative magnitudes of units but which obviously itself must be a pure number for any two consistent unit systems; thus,

$$Q = N_1 U_1 = (N_1 N_{12}) U_2, \qquad N_2 = N_1 N_{12} \tag{4}$$

The following conversion table gives these values $N_{1\alpha}$ with the MKSC system of units chosen as system 1, since it has been used throughout this monograph; $\alpha = 2$ is chosen as the CGS electrostatic, $\alpha = 3$ the CGS electromagnetic, and $\alpha = 4$ the symmetrical Gaussian, system of units, respectively.

Any relation between physical quantities given in the MKSC system of units, as for example equation (6·3)

$$\oint \mathbf{H} \cdot \mathbf{ds} = I \quad \text{MKSC units} \tag{5}$$

---

[1] *Handbook of Engineering Fundamentals*, section 3, "Physical Units and Standards," edited by O. Eshbach; published by John Wiley, New York, 1936.

will retain exactly the same form in any other unit system in which

$$U^H U^s = U^I$$

or in which all units are connected by "unitary" relations. There are, however, very few such desirably consistent and logical unit systems besides the MKSC system which utilize well-established units. All the systems in table 2·1 for $\alpha = 2, 3, 4$ contain several units which are rather arbitrarily defined and therefore lead to extra numerical factors in equations like (5) which must be committed to memory.

To establish the general procedure of converting relations like (5) from one unit system 1 to another system α, assume a simple equation given in system 1

$$A \cdot B = C \tag{6}$$

where A, B, C are physical quantities defined by (1), so that in systems 1 and α, respectively,

$$\left. \begin{array}{lll} A = N_1{}^a U_1{}^a, & B = N_1{}^b U_1{}^b, & C = N_1{}^c U_1{}^c \\ A = N_\alpha{}^a U_\alpha{}^a, & B = N_\alpha{}^b U_\alpha{}^b, & C = N_\alpha{}^c U_\alpha{}^c \end{array} \right\} \tag{7}$$

with conversion factors $N_{1\alpha}$ such as listed in table 2·1. In system 1 for which (6) is valid, it is obvious that with (7)

$$N_1{}^a N_1{}^b = N_1{}^c, \qquad U_1{}^a U_1{}^b = U_1{}^c \tag{8}$$

In the system α such an assumption is not generally warranted, and the units might be related by

$$U_\alpha{}^a U_\alpha{}^b = k U_\alpha{}^c \tag{9}$$

where k must be a numeric for any self-consistent unit system which claims to be useful for dimensional analysis or model theory. But in order to maintain (6) as equation, it must now read

$$A_{(\alpha)} B_{(\alpha)} = \frac{1}{k} C_{(\alpha)} \tag{10}$$

so that with the units of system α the numerical values are corrected for the non-unitary relation (9). To determine k one needs only to convert (9) to system 1 by the relations,

$$U_1{}^a = N_{1\alpha}{}^a U_\alpha{}^a, \qquad U_1{}^b = N_{1\alpha}{}^b U_\alpha{}^b, \qquad U_1{}^c = N_{1\alpha}{}^c U_\alpha{}^c$$

so that

$$\frac{U_1{}^a}{N_{1\alpha}{}^a} \cdot \frac{U_1{}^b}{N_{1\alpha}{}^b} = k \frac{U_1{}^c}{N_{1\alpha}{}^c} \tag{11}$$

TABLE 2·1

CONVERSION FACTORS FROM MKSC SYSTEM

Unit in MKSC System (1)	Item in Table 1·2	To CGS Electrostatic System (2)		To CGS Electromagnetic System (3)		To Symmetrical Gaussian System (4)	
U_1		N_{12}	U_2 (esu)	N_{13}	U_3 (emu)	N_{14}	U_4 (sgu)
Meter		10^2	Centimeter	10^2	Centimeter	10^2	Centimeter
Kilogram mass		10^3	Gram	10^3	Gram	10^3	Gram
Joule	18, 42	10^7	Erg	10^7	Erg	10^7	Erg
Newton	21	10^5	Dyne	10^5	Dyne	10^5	Dyne
Ampere	8, 37	3×10^9	Statampere	10^{-1}	Abampere	3×10^9	Statampere
Ampere-turn	26, 36	$12\pi \times 10^9$	esu of MMF	$4\pi \times 10^{-1}$	Gilbert	$4\pi \times 10^{-1}$	Gilbert
Ampere-turn per meter	25	$12\pi \times 10^7$	esu of H	$4\pi \times 10^{-3}$	Oersted	$4\pi \times 10^{-3}$	Oersted
Coulomb	2, 15	3×10^9	Statcoulomb	10^{-1}	Abcoulomb	9×10^{11}	Statcoulomb
Farad	1	9×10^{11}	Statfarad	10^{-9}	Abfarad	9×10^{11}	Statfarad
Henry	23, 29	$\frac{1}{9} \times 10^{-11}$	Stathenry	10^9	Abhenry	10^9	Abhenry
Mho	6	9×10^{11}	Statmho	10^{-9}	Abmho	9×10^{11}	Statmho
Ohm	40	$\frac{1}{9} \times 10^{-11}$	Statohm	10^9	Abohm	$\frac{1}{9} \times 10^{-11}$	Statohm
Volt	17, 35	$\frac{1}{3} \times 10^{-2}$	Statvolt	10^8	Abvolt	$\frac{1}{3} \times 10^{-2}$	Statvolt
Weber	19	$\frac{1}{3} \times 10^{-2}$	Statweber	10^8	Maxwell	10^8	Maxwell
Weber-turn	20	$\frac{1}{3} \times 10^{-2}$	Statweber-turn	10^8	Maxwell-turn	10^8	Maxwell-turn
Weber per meter²	22, 34	$\frac{1}{3} \times 10^{-6}$	Statweber per centimeter²	10^4	Gauss	10^4	Gauss

$\mu_v = 4\pi 10^{-7}$ henry/m
$\varepsilon_v = (c^2 \mu_v)^{-1}$ farad/m

$\mu_v = \frac{1}{9} \times 10^{-20}$ stathenry/cm
$\varepsilon_v = 1$ statfarad/cm

$\mu_v = 1$ abhenry/cm
$\varepsilon_v = \frac{1}{9} \times 10^{-20}$ abfarad/cm

$\mu_v = 1$ abhenry/cm
$\varepsilon_v = 1$ statfarad/cm

and with the unit equation (8) this gives at once

$$k = \frac{N_{1\alpha}{}^c}{N_{1\alpha}{}^a N_{1\alpha}{}^b}, \qquad \frac{1}{k} = \frac{N_{1\alpha}{}^a N_{1\alpha}{}^b}{N_{1\alpha}{}^c} \qquad (12)$$

to be used in (10).

Applying this conversion to equation (5) and expressing it in the CGS electromagnetic system, one has, with $\alpha = 3$ from table 2·1,

$$\frac{1}{k} = \frac{N_{13}{}^H N_{13}{}^s}{N_{13}{}^I} = 4\pi \times 10^{-3} \times \frac{10^{+2}}{10^{-1}} = 4\pi$$

$$\oint \mathbf{H} \cdot \mathbf{ds} = 4\pi I \quad \text{(CGS emu)}$$

Similarly, for the symmetrical Gaussian system with $\alpha = 4$, follows

$$\frac{1}{k} = \frac{N_{14}{}^H N_{14}{}^s}{N_{14}{}^I} = 4\pi 10^{-3} \times \frac{10^{+2}}{3 \times 10^{+9}} = \frac{4\pi}{3 \times 10^{10}}$$

$$\oint \mathbf{H} \cdot \mathbf{ds} = \frac{4\pi}{V} I \quad \text{(CGS Gaussian)}$$

where $V = 3 \times 10^{10}$ is the value of the velocity of light but not the velocity itself.

This treatment can readily be extended to any mixture of units such as the poor compromises that were made rather early in magnetic computations by expressing the left-hand side in (5) in CGS electromagnetic units and the right-hand side in "practical" or now MKSC units. One obtains

$$\oint \mathbf{H} \cdot \mathbf{ds} = \frac{4\pi}{10} I, \qquad H, s \text{ in emu; } I \text{ in MKS}$$

and it should be felt as the author's obligation to indicate clearly the hybrid units used.

Appendix 3

REVIEW OF FUNDAMENTALS OF VECTOR ANALYSIS

A distinction is made between a physical quantity which is uniquely given by numerical value and unit and called a *scalar quantity*, and one that requires in addition the specification of direction in space, a *vector quantity*. The notation of a vector, **V**, therefore implies the fact that one must know all three components in a coordinate system, say V_x, V_y, V_z in Cartesian coordinates, in order to be able to construct the vector.

If there is associated with every point in space a vector quantity describing a physical phenomenon, such space is called a *vector field;* the electrostatic field, for example, is described by the electric field strength **E**.

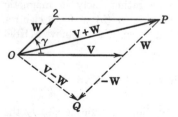

FIG. A·1 Addition and Subtraction of Vectors.

Vector Algebra. A vector **V** may be displaced parallel to itself in space as long as it retains both length and direction. A vector of the same length but opposite direction is designated as the *negative vector* −**V**. The length of the vector is usually designated as absolute value $|\mathbf{V}| = V$: it is a scalar value; the direction is usually designated by $\mathbf{u}_v = \mathbf{V}/V$, the *unit vector* of length 1. A vector of the same direction as **V** but of length V^{-1} is called the *inverse vector* $\mathbf{V}^{-1}$ to **V**.

Two vectors **V** and **W** referred to a common starting point 0 determine a plane. The sum of the two vectors is the directed diagonal of the parallelogram formed by them as in Fig. A·1 with the same starting point 0. The difference $(\mathbf{V} - \mathbf{W})$ of two vectors is obtained by adding −**W** to **V**; it is the second diagonal in the same parallelogram. For more than two vectors the corresponding extensions hold, since one can always combine two vectors at one time, their resultant with the third, etc. The order is irrelevant, since the commutative, associative, and distributive laws of algebra are valid.

Though vector operations as such are entirely independent of specific coordinate systems, it is convenient to introduce orthogonal reference coordinates and the simplest is the rectangular Cartesian system as in Fig. A·2. The vector can then be expressed

$$V = iV_x + jV_y + kV_z \tag{1}$$

where V_x, V_y, and V_z are the projections of V upon the three coordinate axes. The sum and difference of two vectors W and V are then simply

$$V \pm W = i(V_x \pm W_x) + j(V_y \pm W_y) + k(V_z \pm W_z) \tag{2}$$

indicating the obvious extension to any number of vectors.

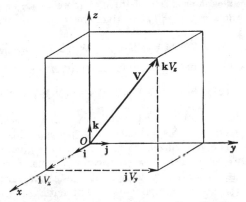

FIG. A·2 Cartesian Reference Coordinates.

The *scalar* or *dot product* of two vectors (also inner product) is defined as

$$
\begin{aligned}
V \cdot W &= VW \cos \gamma = V(W \cos \gamma) = W(V \cos \gamma) \\
&= (V_x W_x + V_y W_y + V_z W_z)
\end{aligned}
\tag{3}
$$

It is a scalar and can be interpreted in two different ways: as the product of V and the projection of W upon V or vice versa, valuable when *work* is to be computed; and as the sum of the products of corresponding vector components, valuable as concept because of its feasible extension to n dimensions or even infinite orthogonal systems (see sections 29 and 31). Application to the unit vectors, already used in (3), gives

$$i \cdot i = j \cdot j = k \cdot k = 1, \qquad i \cdot j = j \cdot k = k \cdot i = 0 \tag{4}$$

The *vector* or *cross product* of two vectors (also outer product) is defined as

$$\mathbf{V} \times \mathbf{W} = \begin{vmatrix} \mathbf{i} & \mathbf{j} & \mathbf{k} \\ V_x & V_y & V_z \\ W_x & W_y & W_z \end{vmatrix} = \mathbf{n}VW \sin \gamma = \left\{ \begin{matrix} \mathbf{i}(V_y W_z - V_z W_y) \\ +\mathbf{j}(V_z W_x - V_x W_z) \\ +\mathbf{k}(V_x W_y - V_y W_x) \end{matrix} \right\} \quad (5)$$

It is a vector directed normal to the plane defined by $\mathbf{V}$ and $\mathbf{W}$ and so that it forms the third direction in a right-handed triplet with them; obviously interchange of $\mathbf{V}$ and $\mathbf{W}$ changes the direction of $\mathbf{n}$. If the cross product of two vectors vanishes, they must have the same direction. One can interpret the magnitude of (5) as the area of the parallelogram formed by $\mathbf{V}$ and $\mathbf{W}$. Application to the unit vectors gives

$$\mathbf{i} \times \mathbf{i} = \mathbf{j} \times \mathbf{j} = \mathbf{k} \times \mathbf{k} = 0 \qquad \mathbf{i} \times \mathbf{j} = \mathbf{k}, \quad \mathbf{j} \times \mathbf{k} = \mathbf{i}, \quad \mathbf{k} \times \mathbf{i} = \mathbf{j} \quad (6)$$

Several significant products of three or more vectors are summarized below; the proofs can readily be given by direct expansion with (4) and (6):

$$\mathbf{U} \cdot (\mathbf{V} \times \mathbf{W}) = \mathbf{V} \cdot (\mathbf{W} \times \mathbf{U}) = \mathbf{W} \cdot (\mathbf{U} \times \mathbf{V}) \quad \text{cyclic change} \quad (7)$$

$$\mathbf{U} \times (\mathbf{V} \times \mathbf{W}) = (\mathbf{U} \cdot \mathbf{W})\mathbf{V} - (\mathbf{U} \cdot \mathbf{V})\mathbf{W} \quad (8)$$

$$(\mathbf{T} \times \mathbf{U}) \cdot (\mathbf{V} \times \mathbf{W}) = (\mathbf{T} \cdot \mathbf{V})(\mathbf{U} \cdot \mathbf{W}) - (\mathbf{T} \cdot \mathbf{W})(\mathbf{U} \cdot \mathbf{V}) \quad (9)$$

Formulation of vector algebra in any other specific orthogonal coordinate system requires primarily the pertinent definition of the unit vectors. The generalized forms for these are given in section 31.

Vector Differentiation. In physical problems, vectors are functions of the space coordinates which enter as scalar variables into the definition of the vector components. Differentiation with respect to one of these scalar variables follows exactly the rules of differentiation of scalar quantities.

On the other hand, in the vector field it is important to obtain the differential variation with respect to all three space variables. It is convenient and economical, then, to introduce a vectorial combination of the derivative symbols in the form of the *vector differential operator*

$$\nabla \equiv (\text{``del'' or ``nabla''}) = \mathbf{i} \frac{\partial}{\partial x} + \mathbf{j} \frac{\partial}{\partial y} + \mathbf{k} \frac{\partial}{\partial z} \quad (10)$$

Application of this operator to a scalar space function $\Phi(x, y, z)$ gives

$$\nabla \Phi = \mathbf{i} \frac{\partial \Phi}{\partial x} + \mathbf{j} \frac{\partial \Phi}{\partial y} + \mathbf{k} \frac{\partial \Phi}{\partial z} = \text{grad } \Phi \quad (11)$$

which is known as the *gradient* of the scalar function; it is actually a vector pointing everywhere in the direction of largest space variation of $\Phi(x, y, z)$ and therefore is always normal to the surfaces $\Phi(x, y, z) = $ cons, which are called niveau or level surfaces of Φ.

As a vector, ∇ can be applied to a field vector either in scalar or in vector product form in accordance with (3) and (5), respectively. The results in these two cases are

$$\nabla \cdot \mathbf{V} = \frac{\partial V_x}{\partial x} + \frac{\partial V_y}{\partial y} + \frac{\partial V_z}{\partial z} = \text{div } \mathbf{V} \tag{12}$$

$$\nabla \times \mathbf{V} = \begin{vmatrix} \mathbf{i} & \mathbf{j} & \mathbf{k} \\ \dfrac{\partial}{\partial x} & \dfrac{\partial}{\partial y} & \dfrac{\partial}{\partial z} \\ V_x & V_y & V_z \end{vmatrix} = \begin{cases} \mathbf{i}\left(\dfrac{\partial V_z}{\partial y} - \dfrac{\partial V_y}{\partial z}\right) \\ +\mathbf{j}\left(\dfrac{\partial V_x}{\partial z} - \dfrac{\partial V_z}{\partial x}\right) \\ +\mathbf{k}\left(\dfrac{\partial V_y}{\partial x} - \dfrac{\partial V_x}{\partial y}\right) \end{cases} = \text{curl } \mathbf{V} \tag{13}$$

The physical significance of (12) is obvious from the fact that div $\mathbf{V} = 0$ is nothing but the law of continuity of fluid flow, characterizing the fluid as incompressible; if the fluid is compressible, div $\mathbf{V}$ is then related to the local change in mass density. The physical significance of (13) can also be seen best by considering curl $\mathbf{V} = 0$, in which case each component must be zero, which can only be if in turn

$$V_x = \frac{\partial \Phi}{\partial x}, \qquad V_y = \frac{\partial \Phi}{\partial y}, \qquad V_z = \frac{\partial \Phi}{\partial a}, \quad \mathbf{V} = \text{grad } \Phi \tag{14}$$

or also if

$$V_x dx + V_y dy + V_z dz = d\Phi$$

is a complete differential whose integral over any closed path must vanish. If $\mathbf{V}$ is taken as a force vector, then (14) expresses the law of conservation of energy and curl $\mathbf{V} = 0$ characterizes the force field $\mathbf{V}$ as a conservative one with a force function or "potential" $\Phi(x, y, z)$. Since integration over a closed path is involved, one calls the value curl $\mathbf{V}$ also a measure of the "circulation" of the vector $\mathbf{V}$.

With the definitions given, one can now deduce

$$\nabla \cdot (\nabla \Psi) = \frac{\partial^2 \Phi}{\partial x^2} + \frac{\partial^2 \Phi}{\partial y^2} + \frac{\partial^2 \Phi}{\partial z^2} = \nabla^0 \Psi = \text{Laplace } \Phi \tag{15}$$

$$\nabla \cdot (\nabla \times \mathbf{V}) = 0 \tag{16}$$

$$\nabla \times (\nabla \Phi) = 0 \tag{17}$$

In a formal sense one can write with (8)

$$\nabla \times (\nabla \times \mathbf{V}) = (\nabla \cdot \mathbf{V})\nabla - (\nabla \cdot \nabla)\mathbf{V} \tag{18}$$

which is not very sensible; but one can interpret by direct expansion in the Cartesian system the first part as meaning $\nabla(\nabla \cdot \mathbf{V}) = \mathrm{grad\ div\ } \mathbf{V}$, and the second part as $\nabla^2 \mathbf{V}$. However, the latter contraction is permissible only in the Cartesian system, where it can be identified with the Laplacian from (15); in no other coordinate system is any explicit definition possible, and one certainly must beware of confusing it with the well-established operation (15).

Again, with (7) and (8) one can interpret ∇ applied to products, such as

$$\nabla(\Phi\Psi) = \Psi\nabla\Phi + \Phi\nabla\Psi \tag{19}$$

$$\nabla(\mathbf{V}\cdot\mathbf{W}) = (\mathbf{V}\cdot\nabla)\mathbf{W} + (\mathbf{W}\cdot\nabla)\mathbf{V} + \mathbf{V}\times(\nabla\times\mathbf{W}) + \mathbf{W}\times(\nabla\times\mathbf{V}) \tag{20}$$

$$\nabla\cdot(\Phi\mathbf{V}) = (\nabla\Phi)\cdot\mathbf{V} + \Phi(\nabla\cdot\mathbf{V}) \tag{21}$$

$$\nabla\cdot(\mathbf{V}\times\mathbf{W}) = \mathbf{W}\cdot(\nabla\times\mathbf{V}) - \mathbf{V}\cdot(\nabla\times\mathbf{W}) \tag{22}$$

$$\nabla\times(\Phi\mathbf{V}) = (\nabla\Phi)\times\mathbf{V} + \Phi(\nabla\times\mathbf{V}) \tag{23}$$

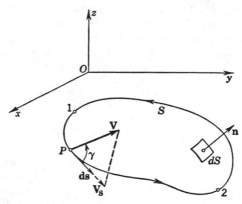

FIG. A·3   Line Integral of a Vector; Stokes's Theorem.

Vector Integral Theorems. The line integral of a vector $\mathbf{V}$ is defined as

$$\int_1^2 \mathbf{V}\cdot\mathbf{ds} = \int_1^2 V_s ds = \int_1^2 V \cos \gamma\, ds \tag{24}$$

If the path is a closed one and regular, so that it can be contracted to a point without intersecting itself, as for example in Fig. A·3, then one can transform

$$\oint \mathbf{V}\cdot\mathbf{ds} = \iint_S (\nabla\times\mathbf{V})\cdot\mathbf{dS} = \iint_S \mathrm{curl}_n\, V\, dS \tag{25}$$

This is *Stokes's theorem*, and S is the surface bounded by the closed path with $\mathbf{dS} = \mathbf{n}\, dS$ so chosen that, from the top of the normal direction, the closed line integral appears counterclockwise; the surface S can have any convenient shape whatsoever. If the closed line integral vanishes for any regular path in a continuous volume τ, then from (25) and (17)

and
$$\left.\begin{array}{c} \text{in } \tau: \oint \mathbf{V}\cdot\mathbf{ds} = 0, \qquad \nabla\times\mathbf{V} = \text{curl }\mathbf{V} = 0 \\[2mm] \mathbf{V} = \nabla\Phi = \text{grad }\Phi \end{array}\right\} \qquad (26)$$

This means that a vector field with no circulation is derivable in accordance with (17) from a scalar function usually called *potential*: it is a potential field; it is also called a *lamellar field* because the equipotential surfaces subdivide space into non-intersecting lamellas.

The surface integral of a vector $\mathbf{V}$ is defined as flux of the vector,

$$\iint_S \mathbf{V}\cdot\mathbf{dS} = \iint_S V_n\, dS = \iint_S V \cos\gamma\, dS \qquad (27)$$

where $\mathbf{dS} = \mathbf{n}\, dS$ is the vector representation of the surface element as shown in Fig. A·4. If the surface S becomes the closed one S' which

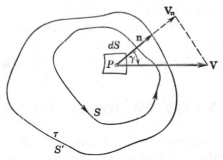

FIG. A·4   Surface Integral of a Vector; Gauss's Theorem.

is regular, so that it can be contracted to a point without intersecting itself, then one can transform

$$\oint\oint \mathbf{V}\cdot\mathbf{dS} = \iiint_\tau (\nabla\cdot\mathbf{V})\, d\tau = \iiint_\tau \text{div } V\, d\tau \qquad (28)$$

where τ is the volume bounded by the closed surface S'. This is usually called *Gauss's theorem* or, better, the *divergence theorem*. If the closed surface integral vanishes for any closed surface within a volume τ', then from (28) and (16)

$$\text{in } \tau': \oint\!\!\oint \mathbf{V}\cdot d\mathbf{S} = 0, \qquad \nabla\cdot\mathbf{V} = \text{div } \mathbf{V} = 0 \left.\vphantom{\begin{matrix}0\\0\end{matrix}}\right\}$$

and

$$\mathbf{V} = \nabla\times\mathbf{A} = \text{curl } \mathbf{A} \qquad (29)$$

This means that a vector field without divergence is derivable from another vector function **A**, usually called *vector potential;* it is a *solenoidal* field because the vector has no sources and no sinks; the field lines defined as everywhere tangential to the vector are closed lines.

Substituting in (28) for the vector **V** the product $\Phi(\nabla\Psi)$ and using (21) in the right-hand integral, one has

$$\oint\!\!\oint \Phi(\nabla\Psi)_n \, dS = \iiint_\tau \nabla\Phi\cdot\nabla\Psi \, d\tau + \iiint_\tau \Phi\nabla^2\Psi \, d\tau \qquad (30)$$

This is *Green's first theorem*, which can be used for many formal deductions in the theory of potential fields. Interchanging Φ and Ψ and subtracting this second relation from the above, one obtains (since the center term cancels)

$$\oint\!\!\oint [\Phi\nabla\Psi - \Psi\nabla\Phi]_n \, dS = \iiint_\tau [\Phi\nabla^2\Psi - \Psi\nabla^2\Phi] \, d\tau \qquad (31)$$

which is *Green's second theorem*.

Substituting in (28) for the vector **V** the vector product $\mathbf{V}\times(\nabla\times\mathbf{W})$ and using the identity (22)

$$\nabla\cdot\mathbf{V}\times(\nabla\times\mathbf{W}) = (\nabla\times\mathbf{W})\cdot(\nabla\times\mathbf{V}) - \mathbf{V}\cdot[\nabla\times(\nabla\times\mathbf{W})]$$

one has

$$\oint\!\!\oint (\mathbf{V}\times\nabla\times\mathbf{W})\cdot d\mathbf{S} = \iiint_\tau (\nabla\times\mathbf{W})\cdot(\nabla\times\mathbf{V}) \, d\tau - \iiint_\tau \mathbf{V}\cdot(\nabla\times\nabla\times\mathbf{W}) \, d\tau \qquad (32)$$

which is the *vector analogue* to Green's first theorem (30); see Stratton,[A23] p. 250. By interchange of **V** and **W** and subtracting this second relation from (32), one obtains

$$\oint\!\!\oint [\mathbf{V}\times(\nabla\times\mathbf{W}) - \mathbf{W}\times(\nabla\times\mathbf{V})]\cdot d\mathbf{S} =$$

$$\iiint_\tau [\mathbf{V}\cdot(\nabla\times\nabla\times\mathbf{W}) - \mathbf{W}\cdot(\nabla\times\nabla\times\mathbf{V})] \, d\tau \qquad (33)$$

which is the vector analogue to Green's second theorem (31).

General Curvilinear Coordinates. All the vector operations can readily be expressed in any orthogonal coordinate system by using the general forms of metric factors deduced in section 31 and specifically illustrated in the various coordinate systems of significance in applications. Because of frequent references in the text to the cylindrical and spherical coordinate systems, the most important vector operations are repeated below for these systems only.

Cylindrical coordinates ρ, ψ, z:

$$\nabla\Phi = \left(\frac{\partial\Phi}{\partial\rho},\ \frac{1}{\rho}\frac{\partial\Phi}{\partial\psi},\ \frac{\partial\Phi}{\partial z}\right) \tag{34}$$

$$\nabla\cdot\mathbf{V} = \frac{1}{\rho}\frac{\partial}{\partial\rho}(\rho V_\rho) + \frac{1}{\rho}\frac{\partial V_\psi}{\partial\psi} + \frac{\partial V_z}{\partial z} \tag{35}$$

$$\nabla\cdot\nabla\Phi = \nabla^2\Phi = \frac{1}{\rho}\frac{\partial}{\partial\rho}\left(\rho\frac{\partial\Phi}{\partial\rho}\right) + \frac{1}{\rho^2}\frac{\partial^2\Phi}{\partial\psi^2} + \frac{\partial^2\Phi}{\partial z^2} \tag{36}$$

$$\nabla\times\mathbf{V} = \left[\left(\frac{1}{\rho}\frac{\partial V_z}{\partial\psi} - \frac{\partial V_\psi}{\partial z}\right),\ \left(\frac{\partial V_\rho}{\partial z} - \frac{\partial V_z}{\partial\rho}\right),\right.$$
$$\left.\left(\frac{1}{\rho}\frac{\partial}{\partial\rho}(\rho V_\psi) - \frac{1}{\rho}\frac{\partial V_\rho}{\partial\psi}\right)\right] \tag{37}$$

Spherical coordinates r, θ, ϕ:

$$\nabla\Phi = \left(\frac{\partial\Phi}{\partial r},\ \frac{1}{r}\frac{\partial\Phi}{\partial\theta},\ \frac{1}{r\sin\theta}\frac{\partial\Phi}{\partial\phi}\right) \tag{38}$$

$$\nabla\cdot\mathbf{V} = \frac{1}{r^2}\frac{\partial}{\partial r}(r^2 V_r) + \frac{1}{r\sin\theta}\frac{\partial}{\partial\theta}(\sin\theta V_\theta) + \frac{1}{r\sin\theta}\frac{\partial V_\phi}{\partial\phi} \tag{39}$$

$$\nabla\cdot\nabla\Phi - \nabla^2\Phi = \frac{1}{r^2}\frac{\partial}{\partial r}\left(r^2\frac{\partial\Phi}{\partial r}\right) + \frac{1}{r^2\sin\theta}\frac{\partial}{\partial\theta}\left(\sin\theta\frac{\partial\Phi}{\partial\theta}\right) + $$
$$\left.\frac{1}{r^2\sin^2\theta}\cdot\frac{\partial^2\Phi}{\partial\phi^2} \right\} \tag{40}$$

$$\nabla\times\mathbf{V} = \left\{\frac{1}{r\sin\theta}\left[\frac{\partial}{\partial\theta}(\sin\theta V_\phi) - \frac{\partial V_\theta}{\partial\phi}\right],\right.$$
$$\left.\frac{1}{r}\left[\frac{1}{\sin\theta}\frac{\partial V_r}{\partial\phi} - \frac{\partial}{\partial r}(rV_\phi)\right],\ \frac{1}{r}\left[\frac{\partial}{\partial r}(rV_\theta) - \frac{\partial V_r}{\partial\theta}\right]\right\} \tag{41}$$

References. Practically all the references in Appendix 4, A, where use of vector notation is mentioned, also give considerable detail on vector analysis; in addition, many books on advanced calculus contain chapters on vector analysis. Particular references not mentioned in Appendix 4 are:

L. Brand: *Vector and Tensor Analysis;* John Wiley & Sons, New York, 1947.
J. F. Coffin: *Vector Analysis,* Second Edition; John Wiley & Sons, New York, 1924.

J. W. Gibbs: *Vector Analysis*, edited by E. B. Wilson; Yale University Press, New Haven, 1901.

L. Page and N. I. Adams: *Electrodynamics*, Chapter I; D. Van Nostrand Co., New York, 1940.

H. B. Phillips: *Vector Analysis*; John Wiley & Sons, New York, 1933.

H. H. Skilling: *Fundamentals of Electric Waves*, Second Edition; John Wiley & Sons, New York, 1948.

J. Spielrein: *Vektorrechnung;* C. Wittwer, Stuttgart, 1927.

A. P. Wills: *Vector Analysis with an Introduction to Tensor Analysis;* Prentice-Hall, New York, 1931.

Appendix 4

GENERAL BIBLIOGRAPHY

A. BOOKS ON ELECTROMAGNETIC THEORY WITH PARTICULAR REFERENCE TO ELECTRIC AND MAGNETIC FIELD PROBLEMS

1. M. Abraham and R. Becker: *The Classical Theory of Electricity;* Blackie and Sons, London, 1932.
   Most readable presentation of the classical theory in vector notation; uses CGS units.
2. S. S. Attwood: *Electric and Magnetic Fields,* Third Edition; John Wiley & Sons, New York, 1949.
   Very good introduction with excellent illustrations and field maps of simpler types; uses MKS units.
3. E. Bennett and H. M. Crothers: *Introductory Electrodynamics for Engineers;* McGraw-Hill, New York, 1926.
   Very clear exposition of basic facts, hypotheses, and deductions, with many applications; uses a practical unit system.
4. F. Breisig: *Theoretische Telegraphie;* F. Vieweg & Son, Braunschweig, 1924.
   Gives many practical applications of simple field problems; uses vector notation and CGS units.
5. E. Cohn: *Das elektromagnetische Feld;* J. Springer, Berlin, 1927.
   Very good and clear treatment with many applications; uses vector notation and a practical unit system.
6. E. G. Cullwick: *The Fundamentals of Electromagnetism;* Macmillan, New York, 1939.
7. J. Fischer: *Einführung in die klassische Elektrodynamik;* J. Springer, Berlin, 1936.
   Good presentation with many practical examples; uses vector notation and a practical unit system.
8. *Handbuch der Physik,* Vol. 10: *Theorien der Elektrizität, Elektrostatik* (1927); Vol. 15: *Magnetismus, Elektromagnetisches Feld* (1927); J. Springer, Berlin.
   Very comprehensive treatment with extensive bibliographies.
9. G. P. Harnwell: *Principles of Electricity and Magnetism;* McGraw-Hill, New York, 1938.
   Very good introduction, using vector notation and MKS units.
10. J. Jeans: *Electricity and Magnetism;* Cambridge University Press, 1927.
    Very comprehensive treatment, particularly of electrostatics; uses long notation and CGS units.

547

11. V. Karapetoff: *The Electric Circuit;* McGraw-Hill, New York, 1910.
    Simple treatment, from engineering viewpoint; uses a practical unit system.
12. V. Karapetoff: *The Magnetic Circuit;* McGraw-Hill, New York, 1910.
    Simple treatment from engineering viewpoint; uses a practical unit system.
13. G. Kirchhoff: *Vorlesungen über Elektrizität und Magnetismus;* B. G. Teubner, Leipzig, 1891.
    Many detailed solutions of static fields in long notation; uses CGS units.
14. K. Küpfmüller: *Einführung in die theoretische Elektrotechnik;* J. Springer, Berlin, 1932.
    Very clear treatment with emphasis on technical applications; uses vector notation and a practical unit system.
15. G. H. Livens: *The Theory of Electricity;* Cambridge University Press, London, 1926.
    Very thorough and rigorous presentation of theory in vector notation; uses CGS units; no practical applications.
16. M. Mason and W. Weaver: *The Electromagnetic Field;* Chicago University Press, 1929. Dover reprint.
    Excellent advanced presentation of static fields in media; uses vector notation and CGS units.
17. J. C. Maxwell: *A Treatise on Electricity and Magnetism*, Third Edition; Clarendon Press, Oxford, 1892. Dover reprint.
    The original presentation; many detailed solutions of static field problems with excellent field graphs; uses long notation and CGS units.
18. F. Ollendorff: *Potentialfelder der Elektrotechnik;* J. Springer, Berlin, 1932.
    Large collection of solutions of field problems in different coordinate systems; uses vector notation and a practical unit system.
19. M. Planck: *Theory of Electricity and Magnetism;* Macmillan, London, 1932.
    Very clear basic presentation, few applications; uses vector notation and CGS units.
20. R. W. Pohl: *Physical Principles of Electricity and Magnetism;* Blackie and Son, London, 1933.
    Best presentation of experimental evidence and very clear exposition of the physical concepts; uses a practical unit system.
21. A. S. Ramsay: *Electricity and Magnetism;* Cambridge University Press, London, 1937.
    Clear presentation with simpler applications; uses vector notation and CGS units.
22. W. R. Smythe: *Static and Dynamic Electricity;* McGraw-Hill, New York, 1939.
    Very extensive mathematical treatment and many applications; largest collection of problems; uses vector notation and CGS units.
23. J. A. Stratton: *Electromagnetic Theory;* McGraw-Hill, New York, 1941.
    Very advanced treatment, very clear and comprehensive; uses vector notation and MKS units.

24. J. B. Whitehead: *Electricity and Magnetism;* McGraw-Hill, New York, 1939.

B. BOOKS ON APPLICATIONS OF ELECTRIC AND MAGNETIC FIELDS

(a) Fields in Cables and Lines

1. E. Clarke: *Circuit Analysis of A-C Power Systems,* Vol. I; John Wiley & Sons, New York, 1943.
2. L. J. Corbett: *Inductive Coordination of Electric Power and Communication Circuits;* J. H. Neblett Press Room, San Francisco, 1936.
   Discusses all phases of line interference.
3. W. A. Del Mar; *Electric Cables;* McGraw-Hill, New York, 1934.
   Excellent bibliography.
4. P. Dunsheath: *High Voltage Cables;* I. Pitman & Sons, London, 1929.
5. H. B. Dwight: *Transmission Line Formulas;* D. Van Nostrand, New York, 1925.
   Gives derivations of capacitance and inductance formulas for conventional lines and cables.
6. L. Emanueli: *High Voltage Cables;* John Wiley & Sons, New York, 1930.
7. A. E. Kennelly: *Applications of Hyperbolic Functions to Electrical Engineering;* New York, 1912.
8. W. Nesbit: *Electrical Characteristics of Transmission Circuits;* E. Pittsburgh, 1926.
9. F. E. Pernot: *Electrical Phenomena in Parallel Conductors:* New York, 1918.
10. D. M. Robinson: *Dielectric Phenomena in High Voltage Cables;* Instruments Publishing Company, Pittsburgh, 1936.
    Very good bibliography; descriptive.
11. A. Russell: *The Theory of Alternating Currents;* Cambridge University Press, England, 1914.
12. L. F. Woodruff: *Principles of Electric Power Transmission,* Second Edition; John Wiley & Sons, New York, 1938.
    Gives derivations of capacitances and inductances for conventional and *n*-wire lines and cables.

(b) General Dielectric Fields

13. A. Gemant: *Elektrophysik der Isolierstoffe;* J. Springer, Berlin, 1931.
    Very good presentation of physics of dielectrics.
14. A. Gemant: *Liquid Dielectrics;* John Wiley & Sons, New York, 1933.
    Monograph on physical characteristics of liquid insulators.
15. F. W. Peek, Jr.: *Dielectric Phenomena in High-Voltage Engineering;* McGraw-Hill, New York, 1929.
    Extensive empirical data from engineering viewpoint.
16. A. Roth: *Hochspannungstechnik;* J. Springer, Berlin, 1927.
    Most comprehensive treatment of theory and design of insulating materials; extensive bibliography.
17. A. Schwaiger: *Theory of Dielectrics,* Second Edition, translated by R. W. Sorensen; John Wiley & Sons, New York, 1932.

Contains many solutions of practical field problems and correlation with break-down data.

18. N. Semenoff and A. Walter: *Die physikalischen Grundlagen der elektrischen Festigkeitslehre;* J. Springer, Berlin, 1928.
    Very good survey of experimental methods.

19. J. B. Whitehead: *Lectures on Dielectric Theory and Insulation;* McGraw-Hill, New York, 1923.

(c) Electrons in Electric and Magnetic Fields

20. E. Brüche and O. Scherzer: *Geometrische Elektronenoptik;* J. Springer, Berlin, 1934.
    Original treatise on the subject; rather comprehensive.

21. E. L. Chaffee: *Theory of Thermionic Vacuum Tubes;* McGraw-Hill, New York, 1933.
    Classical treatise on vacuum tube characteristics with several electrostatic field problems.

22. V. E. Cosslett: *Introduction to Electron Optics;* Oxford University Press, England, 1946.
    Good introductory presentation of principles and applications.

23. W. G. Dow: *Fundamentals of Engineering Electronics;* John Wiley & Sons, New York, 1937.
    Very detailed treatment of basic concepts; good bibliography.

24. O. Klemperer: *Electron Optics;* Cambridge University Press, England, 1939.
    Very concise and advanced monograph.

25. I. G. Maloff and D. W. Epstein: *Electron Optics in Television;* McGraw-Hill, New York, 1938.
    Good basic treatment with particular applications to cathode-ray tubes.

26. J. Millman and S. Seely: *Electronics;* McGraw-Hill, New York, 1941.
    Good general presentation of applications.

27. L. M. Myers: *Electron Optics;* D. Van Nostrand, New York, 1939.
    Very comprehensive treatment of field solutions and electron trajectories; very extensive bibliography.

28. J. Picht: *Einführung in die Theorie der Elektronenoptik;* J. A. Barth, Leipzig, 1939.
    Concise and very advanced treatment.

29. K. R. Spangenberg: *Vacuum Tubes;* McGraw-Hill, New York, 1948.
    Very extensive treatment of electric fields in vacuum tubes of all types, including space charge effects and electron optics.

30. M. J. O. Strutt: *Moderne Mehrgitter—Elektronenröhren*, Vol. 2; J. Springer, Berlin, 1938.
    Excellent but brief treatise of field problems.

31. V. K. Zworykin and G. A. Morton: *Television; The Electronics of Image Transmission;* John Wiley & Sons, New York, 1940.
    Excellent exposition of principles of axially symmetrical fields and electron trajectories; good bibliography.

32. V. K. Zworykin, G. A. Morton, E. G. Ramberg, J. Hillier, and A. W. Vance: *Electron Optics and the Electron Microscope;* John Wiley & Sons, New York, 1945.

Very comprehensive and authoritative treatise with many design principles and illustrative applications.

(d) Electric Discharges in Gases

33. J. D. Cobine: *Gaseous Conductors;* McGraw-Hill, New York, 1941. Dover reprint.

34. M. Knoll, F. Ollendorff, and R. Rompe: *Gasentladungstabellen;* J. Springer, Berlin, 1935.

Comprehensive tables of all physical quantities relating to gaseous conduction.

35. L. B. Loeb: *Fundamental Processes of Electrical Discharge in Gases;* John Wiley & Sons, New York, 1939.

Good basic treatment.

36. F. A. Maxfield and R. R. Benedict: *Theory of Gaseous Conduction and Electronics;* McGraw-Hill, New York, 1941.

Clear presentation of basic principles; uses MKS units.

37. W. O. Schumann: *Elektrische Durchbruchsfeldstärke von Gasen;* J. Springer, Berlin, 1923.

38. R. Seeliger: *Einführung in die Physik der Gasentladungen;* J. Springer, Berlin, 1933.

39. J. Slepian: *Conduction of Electricity in Gases;* Educ. Dept., Westinghouse Electric Corporation, 1933.

Good advanced treatment.

40. J. J. Thomson and G. P. Thomson: *Conduction of Electricity through Gases;* Cambridge University Press, 1928.

Classical treatise on subject, very detailed.

41. J. S. Townsend: *Motions of Electrons in Gases;* Oxford University Press, 1923.

(e) Magnetic Fields

42. A. M. Gray: *Electrical Machine Design;* McGraw-Hill, New York, 1926.

Gives practical details of magnetic circuit computations.

43. F. W. Grover: *Inductance Calculations;* D. Van Nostrand, New York, 1948. Dover reprint.

Large collection of formulas for the inductances of simple circuits and coils with many tables.

44. B. Hague: *Electromagnetic Problems in Electrical Engineering;* Oxford University Press, London, 1929. Dover reprint as *The Principles of Electromagnetism.*

Presents basic theory and many advanced solutions of magnetic field problems involving iron; also gives good field graphs.

45. J. Hak: *Eisenlose Drosselspulen;* K. F. Koehler, Leipzig, 1938.

Gives many computations of inductances of coils without iron and a very comprehensive bibliography.

46. E. Jasse: *Die Elektromagnete;* J. Springer, Berlin, 1930.

Magnetic circuit and force actions are treated from designer's viewpoint.

47. M. Liwschitz: *Die elektrischen Maschinen*, Vol. 3: *Design Principles;* J. Springer, Berlin, 1934.

Gives practical design principles with very clear engineering viewpoint.

48. E. B. Moullin: *The Principles of Electromagnetism;* Oxford University Press, London, 1932.

Good introduction with many practical solutions of simpler problems.

49. R. Richter: *Elektrische Maschinen*, Vol. 1: *Fundamentals and D-c Machines* (1924); Vol. 2: *Synchronous Machines and Converters* (1930); Vol. 3: *Transformers* (1932); Vol. 4: *Asynchronous Machines* (1936); J. Springer, Berlin.

In each volume extensive computations of magnetic circuits and field distributions are included; treatment from viewpoint of development engineer.

C. BOOKS ON POTENTIAL THEORY

(a) General Potential Theory

1. H. Bateman: *Partial Differential Equations of Mathematical Physics;* Dover Publications, New York, 1944.

Generalized treatment of boundary value problems in many coordinate systems; applications to all fields of physics.

2. W. E. Byerly: *Fourier's Series and Spherical, Cylindrical, and Ellipsoidal Harmonics;* Ginn, Boston, 1902. Dover reprint.

Gives many physical applications, particularly to problems of electric and temperature fields.

3. R. V. Churchill: *Fourier Series and Boundary Value Problems;* McGraw-Hill, New York, 1941.

Excellent introduction into solution of boundary value problems from all fields of physics.

4. R. Courant and D. Hilbert: *Methoden der mathematischen Physik*, Vol. I (1931); Vol. II (1937); J. Springer, Berlin.

Very comprehensive and rigorous mathematical treatise with many applications to physical problems.

5. G. C. Evans: *The Logarithmic Potential, Discontinuous Dirichlet, and Neumann Problems;* American Mathematical Society, Colloquium Publications, Vol. VI, New York, 1927.

6. Ph. Frank and R. V. Mises: *Die Differential- und Integralgleichungen der Mechanik und Physik*, Vol. I (1930); Vol. II (1935); F. Vieweg & Sohn, Braunschweig. Dover reprint.

Very comprehensive volumes of applications to all fields of physics.

7. A. Gray, G. B. Matthews, and T. M. MacRobert: *A Treatise on Bessel Functions and Their Applications in Physics;* Macmillan, London, 1931. Dover reprint.

Many applications to temperature fields.

8. E. Heine: *Anwendungen der Kugelfunktionen;* Berlin, 1881.

Many applications involving spherical, ellipsoidal, and Bessel harmonics.

9. E. W. Hobson: *Spherical and Ellipsoidal Harmonics;* Cambridge University Press, Cambridge, 1931.
Most extensive treatise on these harmonic functions with many applications to potential problems.

10. O. D. Kellogg: *Foundations of Potential Theory;* J. Springer, Berlin, 1929. Dover reprint.
Classical volume on potential theory in all fields of physics; rigorous establishment of methods of solutions.

11. A. Korn: *Lehrbuch der Potentialtheorie;* Berlin, 1899.

12. T. M. MacRobert: *Spherical Harmonics;* E. P. Dutton, New York, 1927.
Gives also applications to electrical problems.

13. F. D. Murnaghan: *Introduction to Applied Mathematics;* John Wiley & Sons, New York, 1948. Dover reprint.
Modern advanced treatment of potential equation with application to electrostatics, and of general boundary value problems by Green's function and by integral equations.

14. B. O. Peirce: *Newtonian Potential Function;* Ginn, Boston, 1902.
Gives the mathematical theory of the gravitational potential with some applications to electrostatics.

15. W. Sternberg: *Potentialtheorie;* W. de Gruyter, Leipzig, 1925.
Brief mathematical treatise on existence of solutions.

16. A. G. Webster: *Partial Differential Equations;* G. B. Teubner, Leipzig, 1927. Dover reprint.
General exposition of methods of solution with many applications to all fields of physics.

(b) Temperature Fields

17. H. S. Carslaw and J. C. Jaeger: *Conduction of Heat in Solids;* Oxford University Press, New York, 1947.
Successor to *Introduction to Mathematical Theory of the Conduction of Heat in Solids* by H. S. Carslaw, a classical reference on heat boundary value problems with many solutions of value in practical applications.

18. J. B. J. Fourier: *Théorie analytique de la chaleur;* Paris, 1822; English translation by Freeman, Cambridge University Press, England, 1878. English translation, Dover reprint.
Original treatise formulating the theory of heat with many illustrative applications.

19. L. R. Ingersoll and O. J. Zobel: *Mathematical Theory of Heat Conduction with Engineering and Geological Applications;* Ginn, Boston, 1913.
Excellent treatment by rigorous and approximation methods with much practical information on conduction of heat in materials.

(c) Fluid Dynamic Fields

20. B. Eck: *Einführung in die technische Strömungslehre,* Vol. I: *Theory* (1935); Vol. II: *Laboratory Methods* (1936); J. Springer, Berlin.
Excellent studies of flow lines.

21. Th. V. Karman and J. M. Burgers: *General Aerodynamic Theory, Perfect Fluids,* Vol. II of *Aerodynamic Theory,* edited by W. F. Durand; J. Springer, Berlin, 1935. Dover reprint.
Excellent advanced theory of fluid flow with many applications.

22. H. Lamb: *Hydrodynamics*, Sixth Edition; Cambridge University Press, England, 1932. Dover reprint.
   Advanced classical treatise with many practical solutions.
23. W. Müller: *Mathematische Strömungslehre;* J. Springer, Berlin, 1928.
   Basic treatise with many illustrative graphs.
24. L. Prandtl and O. G. Tietjens: *Applied Hydro- and Aeromechanics;* McGraw-Hill, New York, 1934. Dover reprint.
   Excellent and comprehensive treatment.
25. T. G. Whitlock: *Elementary Applied Aerodynamics;* Oxford University Press, London, 1931.

(d) Gravitational Fields

26. A. R. Clarke: *Geodesy;* Oxford, 1880.
27. G. Kirchhoff: *Vorlesungen über Mechanik;* B. G. Teubner, Leipzig, 1897.
   Many detailed solutions.
28. R. B. Lindsay: *Physical Mechanics;* D. Van Nostrand, New York, 1933.
   See also references 2, 10, 14, and 15 of section a.

(e) Elastic Potential Problems

29. A. Clebsch: *Theorie der Elastizität fester Körper;* Leipzig, 1862; · French translation by St. Venant and Flamant, Paris, 1883.
   Comprehensive and basic treatise with advanced solutions.
30. A. E. H. Love: *Theory of Elasticity*, Fifth Edition; Cambridge University Press, England, 1934. Dover reprint.
   Advanced classical treatise on theory of elasticity.
31. A. Nadai: *Die elastischen Platten;* J. Springer, Berlin, 1925.
32. S. Timoshenko: *Theory of Elasticity;* McGraw-Hill, New York, 1934.

D. BOOKS ON COMPLEX FUNCTION THEORY AND CONFORMAL MAPPING

(a) Brief and Introductory Books

1. L. V. Bewley: *Two-dimensional Fields in Electrical Engineering;* Macmillan, New York, 1948. Dover reprint.
2. L. Bieberbach: *Einführung in die konforme Abbildung;* Sammlung Göschen, Leipzig, 1915.
3. R. E. Doherty and E. G. Keller: *Mathematics of Modern Engineering,* Vol. 1, Chapter IV, p. 242; John Wiley & Sons, New York, 1936.
4. S. L. Green: *The Theory and Use of the Complex Variable;* I. Pitman & Sons, London, 1939.
5. K. Knopp: *Funktionentheorie;* Sammlung Göschen, Leipzig, 1918. English translation, Dover reprint.
6. L. Lewent: *Konforme Abbildung;* B. G. Teubner, Leipzig, 1912.
7. H. W. Reddick and F. H. Miller: *Advanced Mathematics for Engineers,* Chapter X, Second Edition; John Wiley & Sons, New York, 1947.
8. R. Rothe, F. Ollendorff, and K. Pohlhausen: *Theory of Functions as Applied to Engineering Problems;* Technology Press, Cambridge, Mass., 1933. Dover reprint.
9. I. S. Sokolnikoff and E. S. Sokolnikoff: *Higher Mathematics for Engineers and Physicists,* Chapter XV; McGraw-Hill, New York, 1934.

10. M. Walker: *Conjugate Functions for Engineers;* Oxford University Press, 1933. Dover reprint.

(b) Extensive and Advanced Books

11. L. Bieberbach: *Lehrbuch der Funktionentheorie,* 2 Vols.; reprint by Chelsea Publishing Company, New York, 1945; originally published by B. G. Teubner, Leipzig.

12. E. Borel: *Leçons sur les fonctions entières;* Paris, 1900.

13. E. Goursat: *Cours d'analyse mathématique;* A. Hermann, Paris, 1910, 1911. Dover reprint.

14. A. Hurwitz: *Vorlesungen über allgemeine Funktionentheorie;* J. Springer, Berlin, 1929.

15. W. F. Osgood: *Lehrbuch der Funktionentheorie;* B. G. Teubner, Leipzig, 1912.

16. J. Pierpont: *Functions of a Complex Variable;* Ginn, Boston, 1914. Dover reprint.

17. E. Study and W. Blaschke: *Konforme Abbildung einfach zusammenhängender Bereiche;* B. G. Teubner, Leipzig, 1913.

18. E. C. Titchmarsh: *Theory of Functions;* Oxford University Press, 1932.

19. E. T. Whittaker and G. N. Watson: *A Course of Modern Analysis,* Chapters 5 and 6 on analytic functions; Cambridge University Press, 1927.

Appendix 5

ON BESSEL FUNCTIONS

The Bessel differential equation

$$\rho \frac{d}{d\rho}\left(\rho \frac{dR}{d\rho}\right) + (m^2\rho^2 - p^2)R = 0 \tag{1}$$

can be solved by a power series in $m\rho = x$ multiplied by $(m\rho)^p$, so that the most direct result for real argument x and any real value $p > 0$ is

$$J_p(x) = \frac{(x/2)^p}{p!}\left\{1 - \frac{(x/2)^2}{1!\,(p+1)} + \frac{(x/2)^4}{2!\,(p+1)(p+2)} - + \cdots\right\},$$
$$p > 0 \tag{2}$$

Actually, this solution, the *first kind of Bessel functions*, can be continued into the complex domain as $J_p(z)$ by replacing x in (2) by the complex variable $z = x + jy$. The function $J_p(x)$ is regular at $x = 0$ and at $x = \infty$ and possesses an infinite number of zeros for real values of the argument which are not harmonically spaced but approach a spacing of π for values of the argument which are large compared with the order number p. For small and large values of the argument, the approximations hold

$$J_p(x) \approx \frac{(x/2)^p}{p!}, \qquad J_0(x) \approx 1, \qquad\qquad x \ll 1 \tag{3}$$

$$J_p(x) \approx \sqrt{\frac{2}{\pi x}} \cdot \cos\left[x - (p + \tfrac{1}{2})\frac{\pi}{2}\right], \qquad x \gg p \tag{4}$$

For integer values n of the order, the functional values are real for positive or negative values of the argument, as well as of order, and actually

$$J_n(-x) = (-1)^n J_n(x) = J_{-n}(x), \qquad n > 0, \text{integer} \tag{5}$$

For non-integer values $p > 0$ one interprets

$$p! = \Gamma(p+1)$$

556

where $\Gamma(p + 1)$ is the gamma function[1] of Euler. For negative values of the argument, the function takes on in this case complex values, which can be written best

$$J_p(j^{2m}x) = j^{2mp}J_p(x) \tag{6}$$

For *negative, non-integer* orders, the Bessel function (2) becomes

$$J_{-p}(x) = \frac{1}{(-p)!}\left(\frac{2}{x}\right)^p \left\{1 + \frac{(x/2)^2}{1!\,(p-1)} + \frac{(x/2)^4}{2!\,(p-1)(p-2)} + \cdots\right\},$$

$$p > 0 \tag{7}$$

where

$$(-p)! = \Gamma(-p + 1) = \frac{p\pi}{p!\,\sin p\pi} \tag{8}$$

This Bessel function approaches infinite values as $x \to 0$, so that for small values of the argument with $p = n + \eta$, n being the nearest integer,

$$J_{-p}(x) \approx (-1)^n (p-1)! \frac{\sin \eta\pi}{\pi} \left(\frac{2}{x}\right)^p \qquad x \ll 1 \tag{9}$$

The general solution of the equation (1) could, therefore, be represented by

$$AJ_p(x) + BJ_{-p}(x)$$

as long as p is non-integer; for integer values, (5) shows that $J_{-n}(x)$ is not a different solution from $J_n(x)$. In order to have a more general second solution, it is customary to define a *Bessel function of the second kind (Neumann* function)

$$N_p(x) = \frac{J_p(x)\cos p\pi - J_{-p}(x)}{\sin p\pi} \tag{10}$$

which clearly is related to (7) for p non-integer; this solution can be continued into the complex domain as $N_p(z)$ in the same manner as $J_p(z)$. For integer values of the order number n one takes

$$N_n(x) = \lim_{\eta \to 0} \left\{\frac{J_{n+\eta}(x)\cos(n+\eta)\pi - J_{-(n+\eta)}(x)}{\sin(n+\eta)\pi}\right\} \tag{11}$$

which is formally written

$$N_n(x) = \frac{J_n(x)\cos n\pi - J_{-n}(x)}{\sin n\pi} \tag{12}$$

[1] E. Jahnke and F. Emde, *Tables of Functions*, p. 9; reprinted by Dover Publications, New York, 1943; originally published by B. G. Teubner, Leipzig, 1938.

and can be expressed as a rather unwieldy series expansion[2] by the usual process of evaluating indeterminate forms. This function always approaches infinite values as $x \to 0$, in fact for small values of x, the following approximations hold:

$$N_0(x) \approx -\frac{2}{\pi} \ln \frac{2}{\gamma x} \tag{13}$$

$$N_n(x) \approx -\frac{(n-1)!}{\pi} \left(\frac{2}{x}\right)^n \tag{14}$$

$$N_p(x) \approx -\frac{(p-1)!}{\pi} \cdot \frac{\sin \eta\pi}{\eta\pi} \left(\frac{2}{x}\right)^p (1+\varepsilon), \qquad n < p < n+1 \tag{15}$$

where $\ln \gamma = C = 0.5772$, the Euler constant, and where with $p = n + \eta$,

$$\varepsilon = \eta[\psi(-\eta) + \psi(n-\eta)], \qquad \psi(\alpha) = \sum_{\nu=1}^{\infty} \left(\frac{1}{\nu} - \frac{1}{\nu + \alpha}\right)$$

For very large values of the argument,

$$N_p(x) \approx \sqrt{\frac{2}{\pi x}} \sin\left[x - (p + \tfrac{1}{2})\frac{\pi}{2}\right], \qquad x \gg p \tag{16}$$

For *negative* order numbers, one has with (10)

$$N_{-p}(x) = \frac{-J_{-p}(x)\cos p\pi + J_p(x)}{\sin p\pi} = J_p(x)\sin p\pi + N_p(x)\cos p\pi \tag{17}$$

so that no new solution results whatever the value of p may be. For integer values n of the order, the functional values are all real and (17) gives very simply

$$N_{-n}(x) = (-1)^n N_n(x) = N_n(-x) \tag{18}$$

The *general* solution of the Bessel equation (1) is, therefore,

$$R_p(m\rho) = A J_p(m\rho) + B N_p(m\rho) \tag{19}$$

which reduces to the first term if the axis $\rho = 0$ of the cylindrical system is included in the region of the solution, since N_p is not regular for $\rho = 0$.

Bessel functions of the third kind (*Hankel* functions) are really a special combination of the Bessel functions of the first and second kind; how-

---

[2] Jahnke and Emde, *loc. cit.*, p. 132.

ever, for applications in boundary value problems they have particular usefulness. They are given by the definitions

$$H_p^{(1)}(x) = J_p(x) + jN_p(x) \tag{20}$$

$$H_p^{(2)}(x) = J_p(x) - jN_p(x) \tag{21}$$

for any value of $p > 0$ and can be extended to complex argument in the same manner as the two individual functions $J_p(z)$ and $N_p(z)$. For negative values of the argument one has

$$H_{-p}^{(1)}(x) = e^{jp\pi}H_p^{(1)}(x), \qquad H_{-p}^{(2)}(x) = e^{-jp\pi}H_p^{(2)}(x) \tag{22}$$

Both functions are singular at $x = 0$ because of $N_p(x)$; their values for $x \gg p$ are readily given by the complex combination of (4) and (16),

$$\left. \begin{array}{l} H_p^{(1)}(x) \approx \sqrt{\dfrac{2}{\pi x}} \exp\left\{ j\left[x - (p + \tfrac{1}{2})\,\dfrac{\pi}{2} \right] \right\} \\[4mm] H_p^{(2)}(x) \approx \sqrt{\dfrac{2}{\pi x}} \exp\left\{ (-j)\left[x - (p + \tfrac{1}{2})\,\dfrac{\pi}{2} \right] \right\} \end{array} \right\}, \qquad x \gg p \tag{23}$$

The Hankel functions are therefore related to the first and second kind of Bessel functions as the complex exponential to the cosine and sine functions. Indeed, if one expands the differential equation (1), divides by ρ^2, and lets $\rho \to \infty$, it reduces to the differential equation of the trigonometric or complex exponential functions, indicating that the Bessel solutions degenerate into the simpler harmonic series for the plane boundary value problem.

For complex argument, neither $J_p(z)$ nor $N_p(z)$ remains finite as $z \to \infty$ because of the complex trigonometric functions; however, $H_p^{(1)}(z)$ will vanish as $z \to \infty$ if $\mathrm{Im}(z) > 0$, and $H_p^{(2)}(z)$ similarly if $\mathrm{Im}(z) < 0$ as seen from (23). This fact accounts for the use in boundary value problems where vanishing values at infinity are required.

Modified Bessel Functions. In many problems, the differential equation (1) might have $(-m^2)$ replace $(+m^2)$, so that

$$\rho \frac{d}{d\rho}\left(\rho \frac{d\overline{R}}{d\rho} \right) - (m^2\rho^2 + p^2)\overline{R} = 0 \tag{24}$$

The solution is then given by the same group of Bessel functions, but of imaginary argument $jm\rho = jx$. The approximations (4), (16), and (24) for real arguments $x \gg p$ suggest characteristics like the hyperbolic and real exponential functions for imaginary arguments jx, if $|x| \gg p$.

This has prompted the introduction of the "modified" Bessel functions which have real function values.

From (2) one sees that all terms in the brackets remain real for imaginary argument, so that the *modified Bessel function of the first kind*

$$I_p(x) = j^{-p} J_p(jx)$$

$$= \frac{(x/2)^p}{p!}\left\{1 + \frac{(x/2)^2}{1!\,(p+1)} + \frac{(x/2)^4}{2!\,(p+1)(p+2)} + \cdots\right\},$$

$$p > 0 \quad (25)$$

defines a real solution of (24), which, however, can readily be extended into the complex domain as $I_p(z)$ by replacing x in (25) by $z = x + jy$. For small values of the real argument, the approximations hold

$$I_p(x) \approx \frac{(x/2)^p}{p!}, \quad I_0(x) \approx 1; \quad x \ll 1 \quad (26)$$

whereas for large values of x the function grows beyond all limits.

For *negative, non-integer* orders, one can define in analogy to (7) the modified Bessel function

$$I_{-p}(x) = j^p J_{-p}(jx)$$

$$= \frac{1}{(-p)!}\left(\frac{2}{x}\right)^p \left\{1 + \frac{(x/2)^2}{1!\,(p-1)} + \frac{(x/2)^4}{2!\,(p-1)(p-2)} + \cdots\right\} \quad (27)$$

as a real solution of (24) with $(-p)!$ from (8). But, again, for integer orders n this gives no new function, but rather

$$I_{-n}(x) = I_n(x) = (-1)^n I_n(-x), \quad n > 0, \text{integer} \quad (28)$$

It is therefore customary to construct a *modified Bessel function* of the *second kind* in close analogy to (10),

$$K_p(x) = \frac{\pi}{2}\left[\frac{I_{-p}(x) - I_p(x)}{\sin p\pi}\right] \quad (29)$$

which is clearly related to (27) but carries the extra factor $\pi/2$. For integer values n of the order number, one takes as in (11)

$$K_n(x) = \frac{\pi}{2}\lim_{\eta\to 0}\left[\frac{I_{-(n+\eta)}(x) - I_{n+\eta}(x)}{\sin(n+\eta)\pi}\right] \quad (30)$$

which is formally written as (29) with n replacing p and which can be expressed as an unwieldy series expansion by the process of evaluating indeterminate forms.

Introducing (10) into (20) and combining the coefficients of $J_p(x)$, one has for imaginary argument

$$H_p^{(1)}(jx) = \frac{j[e^{-jp\pi}J_p(jx) - J_{-p}(jx)]}{\sin p\pi} = \frac{2}{\pi} j^{-(p+1)} K_p(x) \qquad (31)$$

so that for large arguments x, by use of (23),

$$K_p(x) \approx \sqrt{\frac{\pi}{2x}} e^{-x}, \qquad x \gg p \qquad (32)$$

The *general solution* of the modified Bessel equation (24) is, therefore,

$$\bar{R}_p(m\rho) = \bar{A} I_p(m\rho) + \bar{B} K_p(m\rho) \qquad (33)$$

which reduces to the first term if the axis $\rho = 0$ of the cylindrical system is included in the region of the solution, because K_p is not regular there; and which reduces to the second term if the point $\rho = \infty$ is included in the region of the solution, since I_p is not regular there.

Notation of Bessel Functions. Though the notation for the Bessel functions of the first kind and for the modified Bessel functions has remained rather well standardized since their introduction into the mathematical literature, not even seeming uniformity has been achieved with respect to the Bessel functions of the second kind. Table 5·1 gives the comparative notation as now found in the literature, and Jahnke and Emde's first edition, p. 173 (see below), should be consulted for the notations and definitions of functions used in the earlier literature. It is most unfortunate that very few authors are considerate enough to relate their own notation at least to that of standard works.

The Bessel function of the second kind $N_p(x)$ defined in (10) is frequently designated as $Y_p(x)$; however, this is also the notation introduced by C. Neumann in 1867 for a function defined by

$$\frac{\pi}{2} N_p(x) + J_p(x) \ln \frac{2}{\gamma} \qquad (34)$$

where $\ln \gamma = C = 0.5772$ is the Euler constant. To avoid confusion, some authors use $K_p(x)$ for this function which, however, is the standard designation for the *modified* Bessel function of the second kind. It is, therefore, imperative to ascertain the defining equations for each of the function symbols used before starting comparison of solutions.

The Orthogonal Function System. The most general solution of the Bessel equation can be taken as (19), since the Hankel functions by (20) and (21) are covered by the special constants $B = \pm jA$, and since the modified functions differ only by constants from standard Bessel functions as shown by (25) and (31). One can, therefore, discuss all general relations directly in terms of $R(m\rho) = R(x)$.

TABLE 5·1

COMPARATIVE NOTATION OF BESSEL FUNCTIONS

Bessel Function	This Book	Refs. (1)	Refs. (2)	Refs. (3)	Refs. (4)	Refs. (5)	Refs. (6)
First kind (Bessel, 1824)	$J_p(x)$	$J_p(x)$	$J_p(x)$	$J_p(x)$	$J_p(x)$	$J_p(x)$	$J_p(x)$
Second kind (Weber, 1873)	$N_p(x)$	$Y_p(x)$	$N_p(x)$	—	$Y_p(x)$	$-\dfrac{2}{\pi}G_p(x)$	$Y_p(x)$
Second kind (Neumann, 1867)	—	—	—	$K_p(x)$	—	$Y_p(x)$	$\gamma_p(x)$
Third kind (Hankel, 1869)	$H_p^{(1)}(x),$ $H_p^{(2)}(x)$	—	$H_p^{(1)}(x),$ $H_p^{(2)}(x)$	—	$H_1^{(p)}(x),$ $H_2^{(p)}(x)$	—	$H_p^{(1)}(x),$ $H_p^{(2)}(x)$
Modified first kind (Basset, 1888)	$I_p(x)$	$I_p(x)$	$= j^{-p}J_p(jx)$	—	$I_p(x)$	$I_p(x)$	$I_p(x)$
Modified second kind* (Basset, 1886)	$K_p(x)$	$K_p(x)$	$= \dfrac{\pi}{2}j^{p+1}.H_p^{(1)}(jx)$	—	$K_p(x)$	$K_p(x)$	$K_p(x)$

References (1): Watson (ref. below), Whittaker and Watson,[*D19] Smythe,[A22] and some of the English authors.

References (2): Jahnke and Emde (ref. below), Ollendorff,[A18] Stratton,[A23] and most of the authors referring to Jahnke and Emde for function values.

References (3): Byerly[C2] and Murnaghan.[C13]

References (4): Nielsen (ref. below), who does, however, not use the modified Bessel functions; Bateman.[C1]

References (5): Gray, Matthews, and MacRobert[C7]; MacRobert[C12] also uses $G_p(x)$.

References (6): MacLachlan (ref. below), Karman and Biot (ref. below), who also gives a good table of comparative notation.

* Whittaker and Watson[D19] use $K_p(x) \cdot \cos p\pi$ in order to obtain the same recurrence formula as for $I_n(x)$, but also designate it as $K_p(x)$.

Useful relations are for real arguments $x = m\rho$

$$R_{p-1}(x) + R_{p+1}(x) = \frac{2p}{x} R_p(x) \tag{35}$$

$$\frac{1}{2} R_{p-1}(x) - \frac{1}{2} R_{p+1}(x) = \frac{d}{dx} R_p(x) \tag{36}$$

$$\frac{d}{d\rho} [\rho^{\pm p} R_p(m\rho)] = \pm m\rho^{\pm p} R_{p\pm 1}(m\rho) \tag{37}$$

$$\int \rho^{\pm p+1} R_p(m\rho)\, d\rho = \pm \frac{1}{m} \rho^{\pm p+1} R_{p\pm 1}(m\rho) \tag{38}$$

In the last two relations upper and lower signs have to be taken correspondingly.

Because the Bessel equation (1) is of the Sturm-Liouville type discussed in section 29, namely,

$$\frac{d}{d\rho}\left(\rho \frac{dR}{d\rho}\right) + \left(m^2\rho - \frac{p^2}{\rho}\right) R = 0$$

with characteristic numbers $\lambda = m_\alpha{}^2$, and weight function $p(\rho) = \rho$, the Bessel functions form an orthogonal function system within a range $\rho_1 \leqslant \rho \leqslant \rho_2$ for homogeneous boundary conditions. One finds, then, for the norm with (37) and (38) and integrating by parts

$$N_p{}^{(\alpha)} = \int_{\rho_1}^{\rho_2} \rho[R_p(m_\alpha\rho)]^2\, d\rho = \frac{\rho^2}{2}\left\{[R_p(m_\alpha\rho)]^2 \right.$$
$$\left. - R_{p-1}(m_\alpha\rho) R_{p+1}(m_\alpha\rho)\right\}\bigg|_{\rho_1}^{\rho_2} \tag{39}$$

which reduces for the homogeneous first boundary value problem with (35) to

$$N_p{}^{(\alpha)} = \frac{\rho_2{}^2}{2} [R_{p+1}(m_\alpha\rho_2)]^2 - \frac{\rho_1{}^2}{2} [R_{p+1}(m_\alpha\rho_1)]^2$$

if

$$R_p(m_\alpha\rho_2) = R_p(m_\alpha\rho_1) = 0 \tag{40}$$

and for the homogeneous second boundary value problem with (35) and (00) to

$$N_p{}^{(\alpha)} = \frac{1}{2m_\alpha{}^2}\left\{[(m_\alpha\rho_2)^2 - p^2][R_p(m_\alpha\rho_2)]^2 \right.$$
$$\left. - [(m_\alpha\rho_1)^2 - p^2][R_p(m_\alpha\rho_1)]^2\right\} \tag{41}$$

if

$$\left[\frac{d}{d\rho} R_p(m_\alpha\rho)\right]_{\rho_2} = \left[\frac{d}{d\rho} R_p(m_\alpha\rho)\right]_{\rho_1} = 0$$

Any integrable function $G(\rho)$ can then be analyzed in terms of the Fourier-Bessel series

$$G(\rho) = \sum_{\alpha=1}^{\infty} A_\alpha R_p(m_\alpha \rho) \qquad (42)$$

where the coefficients A_α have to be determined by the integral

$$N_p{}^{(\alpha)} A_\alpha = \int_{\rho_1}^{\rho_2} \rho G(\rho) R_p(m_\alpha \rho)\, d\rho \qquad (43)$$

Unfortunately, these integrations can be performed in closed form for very few functions $G(\rho)$; see Watson (ref. below) for the most complete collection of integral relations.

References. Most texts on advanced calculus have a chapter devoted to Bessel functions; they are usually restricted to the first kind, however, as for example Churchill,[C3] Reddick and Miller,[D7] and Woods (see 6 below). More complete relations are given in Smythe,[A22] and other references cited in table 5·1, as well as in the following books:

1. E. Jahnke and F. Emde: *Tables of Functions;* reprinted by Dover Publications, New York, 1943; originally published by B. G. Teubner, Leipzig, 1909 (First Edition); 1938 (Third Edition).
2. Th. v. Karman and M. A. Biot: *Mathematical Methods in Engineering,* Chapter II; McGraw-Hill, New York, 1940.
3. N. W. McLachlan: *Bessel Functions for Engineers;* Oxford University Press, 1934.
4. N. Nielsen: *Zylinderfunktionen;* B. G. Teubner, Leipzig, 1904.
5. G. N. Watson: *Bessel Functions;* Cambridge University Press, 1922.
6. F. S. Woods: *Advanced Calculus;* Ginn, Boston, 1926.

As a convenient collection of references to tabulated values of the Bessel functions see A. Fletcher, J. C. P. Miller, and L. Rosenhead: *An Index of Mathematical Tables;* McGraw-Hill, New York, 1946, p. 244.

Appendix 6

ON LEGENDRE FUNCTIONS

The Legendre differential equation

$$\frac{1}{\sin \theta} \frac{d}{d\theta}\left(\sin \theta \frac{dT}{d\theta}\right) + n(n + 1)T = 0, \qquad n = \text{integer} \qquad (1)$$

can be solved most readily in terms of a power series in $\cos \theta = \mu$. With the introduction of μ into (1), the equation transforms into

$$\frac{d}{d\mu}\left[(1 - \mu^2)\frac{dT}{d\mu}\right] + n(n + 1)T = 0, \qquad \mu = \cos \theta \qquad (2)$$

and for integer values of n, as assumed, the solutions actually become polynomials

$$P_n(\mu) = \frac{1 \cdot 3 \cdot 5 \cdots (2n - 1)}{n!}\left\{\mu^n - \frac{n(n - 1)}{2(2n - 1)}\mu^{n-2}\right.$$
$$\left. + \frac{n(n - 1)(n - 2)(n - 3)}{2 \cdot 4 \cdot (2n - 1)(2n - 3)}\mu^{n-4} - \cdots\right\} \qquad (3)$$

of which the first few have the explicit forms

$$P_0(\mu) = 1 \qquad\qquad P_1(\mu) = \mu$$
$$P_2(\mu) = \tfrac{1}{2}(3\mu^2 - 1) \qquad P_3(\mu) = \tfrac{1}{2}(5\mu^3 - 3\mu) \qquad (4)$$

These are variously called *Legendre's coefficients, Legendre's polynomials,* or *Legendre functions of the first kind.* Because of their polynomial nature, these functions actually exist in the complex domain as $P_n(z)$ by replacing μ in (4) by the complex variable $z = x + jy$; they are regular in the entire z-plane with the exception of $z = \infty$, where they have a pole of the order n. One readily has

$$\left.\begin{array}{l} P_{2n}(0) = (-1)^n \dfrac{1 \cdot 3 \cdot 5 \cdots (2n - 1)}{2 \cdot 4 \cdot 6 \cdots 2n}, \qquad P_{2n+1}(0) = 0 \\[2ex] P_n(1) = 1 \end{array}\right\} \qquad (5)$$

as well as

$$P_n(-z) = (-1)^n P_n(z) \qquad (6)$$

Legendre Functions of the Second Kind. A second and linearly independent solution of the differential equation (2) for integer values of n is given by the *second kind* of Legendre functions

$$Q_n(\mu) = \frac{1}{2} P_n(\mu) \ln \frac{1 + \mu}{1 - \mu} - W_{n-1}(\mu), \qquad \mu = \cos \theta \qquad (7)$$

where

$$W_{n-1}(\mu) = \sum_{m=1}^{n} \frac{1}{m} P_{m-1}(\mu) P_{n-m}(\mu) \qquad (8)$$

is a polynomial of the $(n - 1)$st degree; the first term in (7), however, has logarithmic singularities at $\mu = \pm 1$. The *general* solution of the Legendre equation is then

$$T_n(\mu) = A P_n(\mu) + B Q_n(\mu) \qquad (9)$$

which reduces to the first term if the axis $\mu = \pm 1$ of the spherical problem is included in the region of the solution because of the logarithmic singularities of $Q_n(\mu)$.

The functions of the first few orders are explicitly defined as

$$Q_0(\mu) = \frac{1}{2} \ln \frac{1 + \mu}{1 - \mu} \qquad\qquad Q_1(\mu) = P_1(\mu) Q_0(\mu) - 1$$

$$(10)$$

$$Q_2(\mu) = P_2(\mu) Q_0(\mu) - \frac{3}{2} \mu \qquad Q_3(\mu) = P_3(\mu) Q_0(\mu) - \frac{5}{2} \mu^2 + \frac{2}{3}$$

showing the even order functions to be odd in μ, and conversely; one also has for this reason

$$\left. \begin{array}{c} Q_{2n}(0) = 0, \qquad Q_{2n+1}(0) = (-1)^{n+1} \dfrac{2 \cdot 4 \cdot 6 \cdots 2n}{1 \cdot 3 \cdot 5 \cdots (2n - 1)} \\[2mm] Q_n(-\mu) = (-1)^{n+1} Q_n(\mu) \end{array} \right\} \quad (11)$$

Because of the logarithmic term,

$$Q_n(1) = \infty \qquad (12)$$

Extension of the solution (7) into the complex domain as well as to real values $x > 1$ requires a modification in the logarithmic term, namely,

$$\overline{Q}_n(z) = \frac{1}{2} P_n(z) \ln \frac{z + 1}{z - 1} - W_{n-1}(z) \qquad (13)$$

so that for real values $x > 1$ the function remains real. Expanding (13) into a power series, one obtains

$$\overline{Q}_n(z) = \frac{n!}{1 \cdot 3 \cdot 5 \cdots (2n+1)} \left\{ \frac{1}{z^{n+1}} + \frac{(n+1)(n+2)}{2(2n+3)} \frac{1}{z^{n+3}} \right.$$
$$\left. + \frac{(n+1)(n+2)(n+3)(n+4)}{2 \cdot 4 \cdot (2n+3)(2n+5)} \frac{1}{z^{n+5}} + \cdots \right\} \qquad (14)$$

Since in the complex domain $z = \pm 1$ represents branch points of the function (13), one must introduce a branch cut or barrier along the real axis connecting $z = +1$ and $z = -1$ in order to make the logarithmic term in $\overline{Q}_n(z)$ one-valued. One defines, then,

$$z + 1 = \rho_1 e^{j\phi_1}, \qquad z - 1 = \rho_2 e^{j\phi_2}$$

with $0 < \phi_1 < 2\pi$, $-\pi < \phi_2 < +\pi$; this gives different values just above and just below the branch cut and actually defines $Q_n(\mu)$ in (7) as half the sum of the values $\overline{Q}_n(\mu + j0)$ and $\overline{Q}_n(\mu - j0)$.

For values $|z| \gg 1$, one can approximate (14) by the first term,

$$\overline{Q}_n(z) \approx \frac{n!}{1 \cdot 3 \cdot 5 \cdots (2n+1)} \frac{1}{z^{n+1}} \qquad (15)$$

Since $W_{n-1}(z)$ is obtained from (8) by replacing μ by the complex variable $z = x + jy$, one can use the explicit forms (10) with the appropriate change for $\overline{Q}_0(z)$, so that

$$\left. \begin{array}{ll} \overline{Q}_0(z) = \dfrac{1}{2} \ln \dfrac{z+1}{z-1} & \overline{Q}_1(z) = P_1(z) \cdot \overline{Q}_0(z) - 1 \\[3mm] \overline{Q}_2(z) = P_2(z) \overline{Q}_0(z) - \dfrac{3}{2} z & \overline{Q}_3(z) = P_3(z) \cdot \overline{Q}_0(z) - \dfrac{5}{2} z^2 + \dfrac{2}{3} \end{array} \right\} \qquad (16)$$

For purely imaginary arguments one can also use the identity

$$\overline{Q}_0(jy) = \frac{1}{2} \ln \frac{jy+1}{jy-1} = -j \cot^{-1} y$$

The Orthogonal Function System for Integer Values n. The differential equation (2) is definitely of the Sturm-Liouville type with the characteristic numbers $\lambda = n(n+1)$ which are integer because n is integer, and with weight function $p(\mu) = 1$. For the real variable $\mu = \cos\theta$ and $|\mu| \leqslant 1$, the general solution is given by (9); for the complex variable $z \neq \mu$ the general solution is given by

$$\overline{T}_n(z) = \overline{A} P_n(z) + \overline{B} \overline{Q}_n(z) \qquad (17)$$

since the definition (3) of P_n can be directly extended into the complex domain.

Several useful relations are

$$(n + 1)T_n(\mu) + nT_{n-1}(\mu) = (2n + 1)\,\mu T_n(\mu) \tag{18}$$

$$\frac{d}{d\mu}\,T_{n+1}(\mu) - \frac{d}{d\mu}\,T_{n-1}(\mu) = (2n + 1)T_n(\mu) \tag{19}$$

$$(1 - \mu^2)\frac{d}{d\mu}\,T_n(\mu) = (n + 1)[\mu T_n(\mu) - T_{n+1}(\mu)] \tag{20}$$

$$(2n + 1)\int T_n(\mu)\,d\mu = T_{n+1}(\mu) - T_{n-1}(\mu) \tag{21}$$

which also hold for $\overline{T}_n(z)$ if μ is consistently replaced by z.

If one now writes the equation (2) for two different values of n, say, $n = \alpha$ and $n = \beta$, multiplies the first by T_β and the second by T_α and subtracts them, one has

$$\frac{d}{d\mu}\left[(1 - \mu^2)\left(T_\beta\frac{dT_\alpha}{d\mu} - T_\alpha\frac{dT_\beta}{d\mu}\right)\right]$$
$$= [-\alpha(\alpha + 1) + \beta(\beta + 1)]T_\alpha T_\beta$$

Integration between μ_1 and μ_2 gives on the right-hand side the form

$$\int_{\mu_1}^{\mu_2} T_\alpha(\mu)T_\beta(\mu)\,d\mu$$

with a factor that can vanish only for $\alpha = \beta$; the left-hand side is directly

$$(1 - \mu^2)\left(T_\beta\frac{dT_\alpha}{d\mu} - T_\alpha\frac{dT_\beta}{d\mu}\right)\Big]_{\mu_1}^{\mu_2}$$

But no two functions of the series P_n or Q_n or their derivatives can vanish at the same value of the argument $\mu \neq 0$ (observe that in the Bessel functions an adjustable parameter m was available); even at $\mu = 0$ only even-ordered P_n and odd-ordered Q_n vanish. It is therefore not possible to construct an orthogonal system of functions satisfying the first or second boundary value problem, except in the interval $\mu_1 = -1$ to $\mu_2 = +1$. However, at those values $Q_n(\mu)$ possesses logarithmic singularities, so it has to be excluded also. *Only $P_n(\mu)$ can form an orthogonal function system and only in the interval $-1 \leqslant \mu \leqslant +1$*; i.e.,

$$\int_{-1}^{+1} P_\alpha(\mu)P_\beta(\mu)\,d\mu = \begin{cases} 0 \text{ for } \alpha \neq \beta \\ N_n \text{ for } \alpha = \beta = n \end{cases} \tag{22}$$

where the norm N_n is found by integration by parts and use of (20), (21) as

$$N_n = \frac{2}{2n + 1} \tag{23}$$

The same consideration shows that $\overline{T}_n(z)$ cannot form any orthogonal system, not even for the real variable $1 \leqslant x \leqslant \infty$, since $P_n(x) \to \infty$ as $x \to \infty$, and $Q_n(x) \to \infty$ as $x \to 1$.

In order to expand any bounded function $G(\mu)$ with at most a finite number of discontinuities into the orthogonal Legendre series,

$$G(\mu) = \sum_{n=0}^{\infty} A_n P_n(\mu) \tag{24}$$

one determines the coefficients in accordance with (29·12) and (23) above

$$A_n = \frac{2n + 1}{2} \int_{-1}^{+1} G(\mu) P_n(\mu) \, d\mu \tag{25}$$

If the function to be expanded is given in terms of the colatitude θ, then

$$G(\theta) = \sum_{n=0}^{\infty} A_n P_n(\cos \theta) \tag{26}$$

and the Legendre functions (4) can be converted into functions of multiples of the angle θ, namely,

$$P_0(\cos \theta) = 1 \qquad\qquad P_1(\cos \theta) = \cos \theta$$
$$P_2(\cos \theta) = \tfrac{1}{4}(3 \cos 2\theta + 1) \quad P_3(\cos \theta) = \tfrac{1}{8}(5 \cos 3\theta + 3 \cos \theta) \tag{27}$$

The coefficients in (26) are then best determined by

$$A_n = \frac{2n + 1}{2} \int_{\theta=0}^{\pi} G(\theta) P_n(\cos \theta) \sin \theta \, d\theta \tag{28}$$

Associated Legendre Functions of the First Kind. The more general Legendre differential equation for integer values n and m

$$\frac{1}{\sin \theta} \frac{d}{d\theta}\left(\sin \theta \frac{dT}{d\theta} \right) + \left[n(n + 1) - \frac{m^2}{\sin^2 \theta} \right] T = 0,$$
$$(n, m) = \text{integer} \tag{29}$$

can also be solved most readily in terms of a power series in $\mu = \cos \theta$. Introducing μ into (29), this transforms to

$$\frac{d}{d\mu}\left[(1 - \mu^2) \frac{dT}{d\mu} \right] + \left[n(n + 1) - \frac{m^2}{1 - \mu^2} \right] T = 0, \quad \mu = \cos \theta \tag{30}$$

and for integer values of n and m as assumed, the solutions are related to the Legendre polynomials, namely,

$$P_n{}^m(\mu) = (1 - \mu^2)^{m/2} \frac{d^m}{d\mu^m} P_n(\mu), \qquad \mu = \cos\theta \tag{31}$$

which are called *associated Legendre functions of the first kind*, of order n and degree m. Because of (3) it is seen that these associated functions exist only for $m \leqslant n$ as long as both n and m are integer. For the first few values n, m (31) gives the explicit forms

$$
\begin{aligned}
&P_1{}^1(\mu) = (1-\mu^2)^{1/2} \\
&P_2{}^1(\mu) = 3\mu(1-\mu^2)^{1/2} \qquad\quad P_2{}^2(\mu) = 3(1-\mu^2) \\
&P_3{}^1(\mu) = \tfrac{3}{2}(5\mu^2-1)(1-\mu^2)^{1/2} \quad P_3{}^2(\mu) = 15\mu(1-\mu^2) \qquad\quad P_3{}^3(\mu) = 15(1-\mu^2)^{3/2} \\
&P_4{}^1(\mu) = \tfrac{5}{2}(7\mu^3-3\mu)(1-\mu^2)^{1/2} \quad P_4{}^2(\mu) = 1\tfrac{5}{2}(7\mu^2-1)(1-\mu^2) \quad P_4{}^3(\mu) = 105\mu(1-\mu^2)^{3/2}
\end{aligned}
\tag{32}
$$

which are valid for $|\mu| \leqslant 1$ and real values of μ.

The extension to real values $x > 1$ and to general complex values $z = x + jy$ is customarily done by defining the modified functions

$$\overline{P}_n{}^m(z) = (z^2 - 1)^{m/2} \frac{d^m}{dz^m} P_n(z) \tag{33}$$

which are regular polynomials in the entire z-plane for m even, but have branch points at $z = \pm 1$ for m odd. It is therefore necessary to introduce a branch cut or barrier from $z = -1$ to $z = +1$ along the real axis in order to make $P_n{}^m(z)$ single-valued in the z-plane. Actually, then, the value $P_n{}^m(\cos\theta)$ in (31) will be one half the sum of the values just above and just below the real axis, adjusted by $(-1)^{m/2}$ as comparison of (33) and (31) indicates,

$$P_n{}^m(\cos\theta) = \tfrac{1}{2}[j^{-m}\overline{P}_n{}^m(\cos\theta + j0) + j^{+m}\overline{P}_n{}^m(\cos\theta - j0)] \tag{34}$$

One readily verifies that

$$
\left.
\begin{aligned}
&P_n{}^m(0) = 0 \qquad\qquad\qquad\qquad \text{for } (n+m) = \text{odd} \\
&P_n{}^m(0) = (-1)^{\frac{1}{2}(n-m)} \frac{1\cdot3\cdot5\cdots(n+m-1)}{2\cdot4\cdot6\cdots(n-m)} \\
&\qquad\qquad\qquad\qquad\qquad\qquad \text{for } (n+m) = \text{even} \\
&P_n{}^m(1) = 0
\end{aligned}
\right\}
\tag{35}
$$

whereas

$$P_n{}^m(-\mu) = (-1)^{n+m} P_n{}^m(\mu) \tag{36}$$

which also holds for the modified function $\overline{P}_n{}^m(z)$.

Associated Legendre Functions of the Second Kind. A second and linearly independent solution of the differential equation (30) is given by

$$Q_n{}^m(\mu) = (1 - \mu^2)^{m/2} \frac{d^m}{d\mu^m} Q_n(\mu), \qquad \mu = \cos\theta \qquad (37)$$

where $Q_n(\mu)$ is the Legendre function of the second kind defined in (7). Since the logarithmic term remains in $Q_n{}^m$, its characteristics will be essentially dictated by those of Q_n. For the first two values of n, m one has explicitly

$$Q_1{}^1(\mu) = \left[Q_0(\mu) + \frac{\mu}{1 - \mu^2} \right] (1 - \mu^2)^{1/2}$$

$$Q_2{}^1(\mu) = \left[3\mu Q_0(\mu) + \frac{3\mu^2 - 2}{1 - \mu^2} \right] (1 - \mu^2)^{1/2} \qquad (38)$$

$$Q_2{}^2(\mu) = \left[3 Q_0(\mu) - \frac{3\mu^3 - 5\mu}{(1 - \mu^2)^2} \right] (1 - \mu^2)$$

where $Q_0(\mu)$ is taken from (10).

The extension to real values $x > 1$ and to general complex values $z = x + jy$ is customarily done by defining modified functions related to (13), namely,

$$\overline{Q}_n{}^m(z) = (z^2 - 1)^{m/2} \frac{d^m}{dz^m} \overline{Q}_n(z) \qquad (39)$$

which decrease to zero as $z \to \infty$, so that they can be used for potential solutions outside of a closed surface. As in the case of $\overline{Q}_n(z)$, one must introduce a branch cut or barrier between $z = -1$ and $z = +1$ in order to render the function one-valued. Actually, then, the relation (34) can be used for $\overline{Q}_n{}^m$ in identical manner.

One readily verifies that

$$Q_n{}^m(0) = 0 \qquad \qquad \text{for } (n + m) = \text{even}$$

$$Q_n{}^m(0) = (-1)^{\frac{1}{2}(n - m + 1)} \frac{2 \cdot 4 \cdot 6 \cdots (n + m - 1)}{1 \cdot 3 \cdot 5 \cdots (n + m)}$$

$$\text{for } (n + m) = \text{odd} \qquad (40)$$

whereas

$$Q_n{}^m(-\mu) = (-1)^{n + m + 1} Q_n{}^m(\mu) \qquad (41)$$

which also holds for the modified functions $\overline{Q}_n{}^m(z)$.

The Orthogonal Function System for Integer Values n and m. The differential equation (30) is again of the Sturm-Liouville type with two possible sets of characteristic numbers and weight functions (see section 29):

$$\lambda = n(n+1), \quad p(\mu) = 1, \qquad q(\mu) = -\frac{m^2}{1-\mu^2} \tag{42}$$

or

$$\lambda = -m^2, \qquad p(\mu) = \frac{1}{1-\mu^2}, \quad q(\mu) = n(n+1)$$

For each real variable $\mu = \cos\theta$, the general solution is given by

$$T_n{}^m(\mu) = A P_n{}^m(\mu) + B Q_n{}^m(\mu) \tag{43}$$

which can be extended to the complex plane by using the modified functions

$$\bar{T}_n{}^m(z) = \bar{A}\,\bar{P}_n{}^m(z) + \bar{B}\,\bar{Q}_n{}^m(z) \tag{44}$$

Some generally useful relations are

$$(n-m+1)T_{n+1}{}^m(\mu) + (n+m)T_{n-1}{}^m(\mu)$$
$$= (2n+1)\mu T_n{}^m(\mu) \tag{45}$$

$$-(n-m+1)T_{n+1}{}^m(\mu) + (n+1)\mu T_n{}^m(\mu)$$
$$= (1-\mu^2)\frac{d}{d\mu}\,T_n{}^m(\mu) \tag{46}$$

which also hold for $\bar{T}_n{}^m(z)$ if μ is consistently replaced by z.

If one writes equation (30) for two pairs of values n and m, say, $n=\alpha$, $m=r$; $n=\beta$, $m=s$; multiplies the first one by $T_\beta{}^s$ and the second one by $T_\alpha{}^r$, and subtracts them, one has for the case $r=s=m$,

$$\frac{d}{d\mu}\left[(1-\mu^2)\left(T_\beta{}^m\frac{dT_\alpha{}^m}{d\mu} - T_\alpha{}^m\frac{dT_\beta{}^m}{d\mu}\right)\right]$$
$$= [-\alpha(\alpha+1) + \beta(\beta+1)]T_\alpha{}^m T_\beta{}^m$$

By the same reasoning as for the Legendre functions one finds at once that *only* the associated functions of the first kind can form an orthogonal system and *only* in the interval $-1 \leqslant \mu \leqslant +1$; i.e.,

$$\int_{\mu=-1}^{\mu=+1} P_\alpha{}^m(\mu)P_\beta{}^m(\mu)\,d\mu = \begin{cases} 0 & \text{for } \alpha \neq \beta \\ N_n(m) & \text{for } \alpha = \beta = n \end{cases} \tag{47}$$

where the norm $N_n(m)$ pertains to a fixed degree m and variable order n and is found as

$$N_n(m) = \frac{2}{2n+1}\frac{(n+m)!}{(n-m)!} \tag{48}$$

For the second case $\alpha = \beta = n$, one has

$$\frac{d}{d\mu}\left[(1-\mu^2)\left(T_n{}^s \frac{dT_n{}^r}{d\mu} - T_n{}^r \frac{dT_n{}^s}{d\mu}\right)\right] = \frac{r^2-s^2}{1-\mu^2} T_n{}^r T_n{}^s$$

Repeating the reasoning but now pertaining to the degrees r and s, one finds that again *only* the associated functions of the first kind can form an orthogonal system and *only* in the interval $-1 \leqslant \mu \leqslant +1$; i.e.,

$$\int_{\mu=-1}^{\mu=+1} P_n{}^r(\mu)P_n{}^s(\mu)\, \frac{d\mu}{1-\mu^2} = \begin{cases} 0 & \text{for } r \neq s \\ N^m(n) & \text{for } r = s = m \end{cases} \qquad (49)$$

where the norm $N^m(n)$ pertains to a fixed order n and variable degree m and is found as

$$N^m(n) = \frac{1}{m}\frac{(n+m)!}{(n-m)!} \qquad (50)$$

Which of the two alternatives arises in applications depends on the nature of the problem; however, the orthogonalization (47) and (48) with respect to order for fixed degrees is the natural one for spherical coordinates. If for example a distribution function on a spherical surface is given as $G(\theta, \phi)$, where θ is the colatitude and ϕ the longitude, then this function can be represented as

$$G(\theta, \phi) = \sum_{n=0}^{\infty}\{A_n P_n(\cos\theta)$$
$$+ \sum_{m=1}^{m=n}\lfloor A_n{}^m \cos m\phi + B_n{}^m \sin m\phi\rfloor P_n{}^m(\cos\theta)\} \qquad (51)$$

where the coefficients A_n pertain to an axially symmetrical part of the distribution function and are determined by (25), if one defines

$$G(\mu) = \frac{1}{2\pi}\int_0^{2\pi} G(\theta, \phi)\, d\phi \qquad (52)$$

as the average value of $G(\theta, \phi)$. The coefficients $A_n{}^m$ and $B_n{}^m$ are found, respectively, by the combination of the pertinent Fourier series coefficient integration and the integration corresponding to (28) but with the norm (48), namely,

$$\left.\begin{array}{c} A_n{}^m \\ B_n{}^m \end{array}\right\} = \frac{1}{\pi}\cdot\frac{2n+1}{2}\frac{(n-m)!}{(n+m)!}$$
$$\int_{\phi=0}^{2\pi} d\phi \int_{\theta=0}^{\pi} G(\theta, \phi)P_n{}^m(\cos\theta)\begin{Bmatrix}\cos m\phi \\ \sin m\phi\end{Bmatrix}\sin\theta\, d\theta \qquad (53)$$

Non-integral Legendre Functions. Both the Legendre polynomials and the associated Legendre functions of the first kind could be made orthogonal function systems over an interval $\mu_1 \leqslant \mu \leqslant 1$ if one could assure either $P_n(\mu_1) = 0$, or $P_n{}^m(\mu_1) = 0$. This means, however, selecting an order number n such that a zero is made to occur at $\mu = \mu_1$; this requires definitions of Legendre functions for non-integral orders. Though this has been done by relating these generalized Legendre functions to the hypergeometric functions (see particularly Hobson [C9]), the lack of adequate tables makes their use more formal than practical.

Notation of Legendre Functions. Though the Legendre functions have generally been less subject to confusing notation, there is enough variety to make the comparative table 6·1 desirable. The most difficult feature is the fact that a number of authors use the same symbol for the functions of real argument $|\mu| \leqslant 1$ and complex argument z, even though the functional forms and therefore some of the recursion formulas differ. Certainly, one can remember these if one deals frequently with these functions; for study purposes it is not convenient.

References. Many texts on advanced calculus and advanced electromagnetic theory have at least brief chapters on the Legendre polynomials; Churchill[C3] and Murnaghan[C13] also deal with the Legendre functions of the second kind and real argument $|\mu| \leqslant 1$; extension to the associated Legendre functions of the first kind with real argument $|\mu| \leqslant 1$ is shown in Kellogg,[C10] Stratton,[A23] and Webster[C16]. The generalized treatment is found in the references cited in table 6·1, in particular also in the following references:

1. N. M. Ferrers: *Spherical Harmonics*, London, 1877.
2. E. Jahnke and F. Emde: *Tables of Functions*, Third Edition; reprinted by Dover Publications, New York, 1943; originally published by B. G. Teubner, Leipzig, 1938.
3. C. Snow: *The Hypergeometric and Legendre Functions with Applications to Integral Equations and Potential Theory;* National Bureau of Standards, Washington, D.C., 1942.
4. W. J. Sternberg and T. L. Smith: *The Theory of Potential and Spherical Harmonics;* University of Toronto Press, Canada, 1946.
5. A. Wangerin: *Theorie des Potentiales und der Kugelfunktionen;* B. G. Teubner, Leipzig, 1909.

As a convenient collection of references to tabulated values of the Legendre functions see A. Fletcher, J. C. P. Miller, and L. Rosenhead: *An Index of Mathematical Tables;* McGraw-Hill, New York, 1946, p. 232.

TABLE 6·1

COMPARATIVE NOTATION OF LEGENDRE FUNCTIONS

Type of Legendre Function	Range of Variable	Defining Equation	This Book	Refs. (1)	Refs. (2)	Refs. (3)	Refs. (4)
Legendre, first kind	μ real, $\lvert\mu\rvert \leqslant 1$	(3)	$P_n(\mu)$	$P_n(x)$	$P_n(\mu)$	$P_n(z)$	$P_n(\mu)$
Legendre, first kind	z real or complex, $z \neq \mu$	(3)	$P_n(z)$	$P_n(z)$	$P_n(z)$	$P_n(z)$	$P_n(\mu)$
Legendre, second kind	μ real, $\lvert\mu\rvert \leqslant 1$	(7)	$Q_n(\mu)$	$Q_n(x)$	$Q_n(\mu)$	$q_n(z)$	$Q_n(\mu)$
Legendre, second kind	z real or complex, $z \neq \mu$	(13)	$\bar{Q}_n(z)$	$\mathfrak{Q}_n(z)$	$Q_n(z)$	$Q_n(z)$	$Q_n(\mu)$
Associated Legendre, first kind	μ real, $\lvert\mu\rvert \leqslant 1$	(31)	$P_n{}^m(\mu)$	$P_n{}^m(x)$	$P_n{}^m(\mu)$	$T_n{}^m(z)$*	$T_n{}^m(\mu)$*
Associated Legendre, first kind	z real or complex, $z \neq \mu$	(33)	$\bar{P}_n{}^m(z)$	$\mathfrak{P}_n{}^m(z)$	$P_n{}^m(z)$	$P_n{}^m(z)$	$P_n{}^m(\mu)$
Associated Legendre, second kind	μ real, $\lvert\mu\rvert \leqslant 1$	(37)	$Q_n{}^m(\mu)$	$Q_n{}^m(x)$	$Q_n{}^m(\mu)$	$q_n{}^m(z)$	—†
Associated Legendre, second kind	z real or complex, $z \neq \mu$	(39)	$\bar{Q}_n{}^m(z)$	$\mathfrak{Q}_n{}^m(z)$	$Q_n{}^m(z)$	$Q_n{}^m(z)$	$Q_n{}^m(\mu)$

References (1): Jahnke and Emde (ref. p. 574); Heine[C8] used the same symbols for associated Legendre functions with interchange of n and m and with extra factors; since some relations are not quite correctly stated, consult Hobson.[C9]

References (2): Bateman[C1]; Smythe[A22] uses μ throughout for the variable; MacRobert [C12] uses x throughout for the variable, occasionally replacing it by $\mu = \cos\theta$, and also uses $T_n{}^m(x)$ for (31); Whittaker and Watson[D19] use z throughout for the variable, occasionally replacing it by $\cos\theta$ for z real and $\lvert z\rvert \leqslant 1$.

References (3); Snow (ref. p. 574); (*) this symbol was first used by Ferrers (ref. p. 574).

References (4): Hobson[C9]; (*) he uses, however, $(-1)^m T_n{}^m(\mu)$ and calls that also $P_n{}^m(\mu)$); (†) he uses $(-1)^m Q_n{}^m(\mu)$ from first column and also calls it $Q_n{}^m(\mu)$.

INDEX

CATALOGUE OF DOVER BOOKS

BOOKS EXPLAINING SCIENCE AND MATHEMATICS

General

WHAT IS SCIENCE?, Norman Campbell. This excellent introduction explains scientific method, role of mathematics, types of scientific laws. Contents: 2 aspects of science, science & nature, laws of science, discovery of laws, explanation of laws, measurement & numerical laws, applications of science. 192pp. 5⅜ x 8.   S43 Paperbound **$1.25**

THE COMMON SENSE OF THE EXACT SCIENCES, W. K. Clifford. Introduction by James Newman, edited by Karl Pearson. For 70 years this has been a guide to classical scientific and mathematical thought. Explains with unusual clarity basic concepts, such as extension of meaning of symbols, characteristics of surface boundaries, properties of plane figures, vectors, Cartesian method of determining position, etc. Long preface by Bertrand Russell. Bibliography of Clifford. Corrected, 130 diagrams redrawn. 249pp. 5⅜ x 8.
T61 Paperbound **$1.60**

SCIENCE THEORY AND MAN, Erwin Schrödinger. This is a complete and unabridged reissue of SCIENCE AND THE HUMAN TEMPERAMENT plus an additional essay: "What is an Elementary Particle?" Nobel laureate Schrödinger discusses such topics as nature of scientific method, the nature of science, chance and determinism, science and society, conceptual models for physical entities, elementary particles and wave mechanics. Presentation is popular and may be followed by most people with little or no scientific training. "Fine practical preparation for a time when laws of nature, human institutions . . . are undergoing a critical examination without parallel," Waldemar Kaempffert, N. Y. TIMES. 192pp. 5⅜ x 8.
T428 Paperbound **$1.35**

FADS AND FALLACIES IN THE NAME OF SCIENCE, Martin Gardner. Examines various cults, quack systems, frauds, delusions which at various times have masqueraded as science. Accounts of hollow-earth fanatics like Symmes; Velikovsky and wandering planets; Hoerbiger; Bellamy and the theory of multiple moons; Charles Fort; dowsing, pseudoscientific methods for finding water, ores, oil. Sections on naturopathy, iridiagnosis, zone therapy, food fads, etc. Analytical accounts of Wilhelm Reich and orgone sex energy; L. Ron Hubbard and Dianetics; A. Korzybski and General Semantics; many others. Brought up to date to include Bridey Murphy, others. Not just a collection of anecdotes, but a fair, reasoned appraisal of eccentric theory. Formerly titled IN THE NAME OF SCIENCE. Preface. Index. x + 384pp. 5⅜ x 8.   T394 Paperbound **$1.50**

A DOVER SCIENCE SAMPLER, edited by George Barkin. 64-page book, sturdily bound, containing excerpts from over 20 Dover books, explaining science. Edwin Hubble, George Sarton, Ernst Mach, A. d'Abro, Galileo, Newton, others, discussing island universes, scientific truth, biological phenomena, stability in bridges, etc. Copies limited; no more than 1 to a customer,
FREE

POPULAR SCIENTIFIC LECTURES, Hermann von Helmholtz. Helmholtz was a superb expositor as well as a scientist of genius in many areas. The seven essays in this volume are models of clarity, and even today they rank among the best general descriptions of their subjects ever written. "The Physiological Causes of Harmony in Music" was the first significant physiological explanation of musical consonance and dissonance. Two essays, "On the Interaction of Natural Forces" and "On the Conservation of Force," were of great importance in the history of science, for they firmly established the principle of the conservation of energy. Other lectures include "On the Relation of Optics to Painting," "On Recent Progress in the Theory of Vision," "On Goethe's Scientific Researches," and "On the Origin and Significance of Geometrical Axioms." Selected and edited with an introduction by Professor Morris Kline. xii + 286pp. 5⅜ x 8½.   T799 Paperbound **$1.45**

BOOKS EXPLAINING SCIENCE AND MATHEMATICS

Physics

CONCERNING THE NATURE OF THINGS, Sir William Bragg. Christmas lectures delivered at the Royal Society by Nobel laureate. Why a spinning ball travels in a curved track; how uranium is transmuted to lead, etc. Partial contents: atoms, gases, liquids, crystals, metals, etc. No scientific background needed; wonderful for intelligent child. 32pp. of photos, 57 figures. xii + 232pp. 5⅜ x 8.   T31 Paperbound **$1.50**

THE RESTLESS UNIVERSE, Max Born. New enlarged version of this remarkably readable account by a Nobel laureate. Moving from sub-atomic particles to universe, the author explains in very simple terms the latest theories of wave mechanics. Partial contents: air and its relatives, electrons & ions, waves & particles, electronic structure of the atom, nuclear physics. Nearly 1000 illustrations, including 7 animated sequences. 325pp. 6 x 9.
T412 Paperbound **$2.00**

FROM EUCLID TO EDDINGTON: A STUDY OF THE CONCEPTIONS OF THE EXTERNAL WORLD, Sir Edmund Whittaker. A foremost British scientist traces the development of theories of natural philosophy from the western rediscovery of Euclid to Eddington, Einstein, Dirac, etc. The inadequacy of classical physics is contrasted with present day attempts to understand the physical world through relativity, non-Euclidean geometry, space curvature, wave mechanics, etc. 5 major divisions of examination: Space; Time and Movement; the Concepts of Classical Physics; the Concepts of Quantum Mechanics; the Eddington Universe. 212pp. 5⅜ x 8.   T491 Paperbound **$1.35**

PHYSICS, THE PIONEER SCIENCE, L. W. Taylor. First thorough text to place all important physical phenomena in cultural-historical framework; remains best work of its kind. Exposition of physical laws, theories developed chronologically, with great historical, illustrative experiments diagrammed, described, worked out mathematically. Excellent physics text for self-study as well as class work. Vol. 1: Heat, Sound: motion, acceleration, gravitation, conservation of energy, heat engines, rotation, heat, mechanical energy, etc. 211 illus. 407pp. 5⅜ x 8. Vol. 2: Light, Electricity: images, lenses, prisms, magnetism, Ohm's law, dynamos, telegraph, quantum theory, decline of mechanical view of nature, etc. Bibliography. 13 table appendix. Index. 551 illus. 2 color plates. 508pp. 5⅜ x 8.

Vol. 1 S565 Paperbound **$2.00**
Vol. 2 S566 Paperbound **$2.00**
The set **$4.00**

A SURVEY OF PHYSICAL THEORY, Max Planck. One of the greatest scientists of all time, creator of the quantum revolution in physics, writes in non-technical terms of his own discoveries and those of other outstanding creators of modern physics. Planck wrote this book when science had just crossed the threshold of the new physics, and he communicates the excitement felt then as he discusses electromagnetic theories, statistical methods, evolution of the concept of light, a step-by-step description of how he developed his own momentous theory, and many more of the basic ideas behind modern physics. Formerly "A Survey of Physics." Bibliography. Index. 128pp. 5⅜ x 8.   S650 Paperbound **$1.15**

THE ATOMIC NUCLEUS, M. Korsunsky. The only non-technical comprehensive account of the atomic nucleus in English. For college physics students, etc. Chapters cover: Radioactivity, the Nuclear Model of the Atom, the Mass of Atomic Nuclei, the Disintegration of Atomic Nuclei, the Discovery of the Positron, the Artificial Transformation of Atomic Nuclei, Artificial Radioactivity, Mesons, the Neutrino, the Structure of Atomic Nuclei and Forces Acting Between Nuclear Particles, Nuclear Fission, Chain Reaction, Peaceful Uses, Thermonuclear Reactions. Slightly abridged edition. Translated by G. Yankovsky. 65 figures. Appendix includes 45 photographic illustrations. 413 pp. 5⅜ x 8.   S1052 Paperbound **$2.00**

PRINCIPLES OF MECHANICS SIMPLY EXPLAINED, Morton Mott-Smith. Excellent, highly readable introduction to the theories and discoveries of classical physics. Ideal for the layman who desires a foundation which will enable him to understand and appreciate contemporary developments in the physical sciences. Discusses: Density, The Law of Gravitation, Mass and Weight, Action and Reaction, Kinetic and Potential Energy, The Law of Inertia, Effects of Acceleration, The Independence of Motions, Galileo and the New Science of Dynamics, Newton and the New Cosmos, The Conservation of Momentum, and other topics. Revised edition of "This Mechanical World." Illustrated by E. Kosa, Jr. Bibliography and Chronology. Index. xiv + 171pp. 5⅜ x 8½.   T1067 Paperbound **$1.00**

THE CONCEPT OF ENERGY SIMPLY EXPLAINED, Morton Mott-Smith. Elementary, non-technical exposition which traces the story of man's conquest of energy, with particular emphasis on the developments during the nineteenth century and the first three decades of our own century. Discusses man's earlier efforts to harness energy, more recent experiments and discoveries relating to the steam engine, the engine indicator, the motive power of heat, the principle of excluded perpetual motion, the bases of the conservation of energy, the concept of entropy, the internal combustion engine, mechanical refrigeration, and many other related topics. Also much biographical material. Index. Bibliography. 33 illustrations. ix + 215pp. 5⅜ x 8½.   T1071 Paperbound **$1.25**

HEAT AND ITS WORKINGS, Morton Mott-Smith. One of the best elementary introductions to the theory and attributes of heat, covering such matters as the laws governing the effect of heat on solids, liquids and gases, the methods by which heat is measured, the conversion of a substance from one form to another through heating and cooling, evaporation, the effects of pressure on boiling and freezing points, and the three ways in which heat is transmitted (conduction, convection, radiation). Also brief notes on major experiments and discoveries. Concise, but complete, it presents all the essential facts about the subject in readable style. Will give the layman and beginning student a first-rate background in this major topic in physics. Index. Bibliography. 50 illustrations. x + 165pp. 5⅜ x 8½. T978 Paperbound **$1.00**

THE STORY OF ATOMIC THEORY AND ATOMIC ENERGY, J. G. Feinberg. Wider range of facts on physical theory, cultural implications, than any other similar source. Completely non-technical. Begins with first atomic theory, 600 B.C., goes through A-bomb, developments to 1959. Avogadro, Rutherford, Bohr, Einstein, radioactive decay, binding energy, radiation danger, future benefits of nuclear power, dozens of other topics, told in lively, related, informal manner. Particular stress on European atomic research. "Deserves special mention . . . authoritative," Saturday Review. Formerly "The Atom Story." New chapter to 1959. Index. 34 illustrations. 251pp. 5⅜ x 8.   T625 Paperbound **$1.60**

THE STRANGE STORY OF THE QUANTUM, AN ACCOUNT FOR THE GENERAL READER OF THE GROWTH OF IDEAS UNDERLYING OUR PRESENT ATOMIC KNOWLEDGE, B. Hoffmann. Presents lucidly and expertly, with barest amount of mathematics, the problems and theories which led to modern quantum physics. Dr. Hoffmann begins with the closing years of the 19th century, when certain trifling discrepancies were noticed, and with illuminating analogies and examples takes you through the brilliant concepts of Planck, Einstein, Pauli, de Broglie, Bohr, Schroedinger, Heisenberg, Dirac, Sommerfeld, Feynman, etc. This edition includes a new, long postscript carrying the story through 1958. "Of the books attempting an account of the history and contents of our modern atomic physics which have come to my attention, this is the best," H. Margenau, Yale University, in "American Journal of Physics." 32 tables and line illustrations. Index. 275pp. 5⅜ x 8. **T518 Paperbound $1.50**

THE EVOLUTION OF SCIENTIFIC THOUGHT FROM NEWTON TO EINSTEIN, A. d'Abro. Einstein's special and general theories of relativity, with their historical implications, are analyzed in non-technical terms. Excellent accounts of the contributions of Newton, Riemann, Weyl, Planck, Eddington, Maxwell, Lorentz and others are treated in terms of space and time, equations of electromagnetics, finiteness of the universe, methodology of science. 21 diagrams. 482pp. 5⅜ x 8. **T2 Paperound $2.25**

THE RISE OF THE NEW PHYSICS, A. d'Abro. A half-million word exposition, formerly titled THE DECLINE OF MECHANISM, for readers not versed in higher mathematics. The only thorough explanation, in everyday language, of the central core of modern mathematical physical theory, treating both classical and modern theoretical physics, and presenting in terms almost anyone can understand the equivalent of 5 years of study of mathematical physics. Scientifically impeccable coverage of mathematical-physical thought from the Newtonian system up through the electronic theories of Dirac and Heisenberg and Fermi's statistics. Combines both history and exposition; provides a broad yet unified and detailed view, with constant comparison of classical and modern views on phenomena and theories. "A must for anyone doing serious study in the physical sciences," JOURNAL OF THE FRANKLIN INSTITUTE. "Extraordinary faculty . . . to explain ideas and theories of theoretical physics in the language of daily life," ISIS. First part of set covers philosophy of science, drawing upon the practice of Newton, Maxwell, Poincaré, Einstein, others, discussing modes of thought, experiment, interpretations of causality, etc. In the second part, 100 pages explain grammar and vocabulary of mathematics, with discussions of functions, groups, series, Fourier series, etc. The remainder is devoted to concrete, detailed coverage of both classical and quantum physics, explaining such topics as analytic mechanics, Hamilton's principle, wave theory of light, electromagnetic waves, groups of transformations, thermodynamics, phase rule, Brownian movement, kinetics, special relativity, Planck's original quantum theory, Bohr's atom, Zeeman effect, Broglie's wave mechanics, Heisenberg's uncertainty, Eigen-values, matrices, scores of other important topics. Discoveries and theories are covered for such men as Alembert, Born, Cantor, Debye, Euler, Foucault, Galois, Gauss, Hadamard, Kelvin, Kepler, Laplace, Maxwell, Pauli, Rayleigh, Volterra, Weyl, Young, more than 180 others. Indexed. 97 illustrations. ix + 982pp. 5⅜ x 8. **T3 Volume 1, Paperbound $2.00**
T4 Volume 2, Paperbound $2.00

SPINNING TOPS AND GYROSCOPIC MOTION, John Perry. Well-known classic of science still unsurpassed for lucid, accurate, delightful exposition. How quasi-rigidity is induced in flexible and fluid bodies by rapid motions; why gyrostat falls, top rises; nature and effect on climatic conditions of earth's precessional movement; effect of internal fluidity on rotating bodies, etc. Appendixes describe practical uses to which gyroscopes have been put in ships, compasses, monorail transportation. 62 figures. 128pp. 5⅜ x 8. **T416 Paperbound $1.00**

THE UNIVERSE OF LIGHT, Sir William Bragg. No scientific training needed to read Nobel Prize winner's expansion of his Royal Institute Christmas Lectures. Insight into nature of light, methods and philosophy of science. Explains lenses, reflection, color, resonance, polarization, x-rays, the spectrum, Newton's work with prisms, Huygens' with polarization, Crookes' with cathode ray, etc. Leads into clear statement of 2 major historical theories of light, corpuscle and wave. Dozens of experiments you can do. 199 illus., including 2 full-page color plates. 293pp. 5⅜ x 8. **S538 Paperbound $1.85**

THE STORY OF X-RAYS FROM RÖNTGEN TO ISOTOPES, A. R. Bleich. Non-technical history of x-rays, their scientific explanation, their applications in medicine, industry, research, and art, and their effect on the individual and his descendants. Includes amusing early reactions to Röntgen's discovery, cancer therapy, detections of art and stamp forgeries, potential risks to patient and operator, etc. Illustrations show x-rays of flower structure, the gall bladder, gears with hidden defects, etc. Original Dover publication. Glossary. Bibliography. Index. 55 photos and figures. xiv + 186pp. 5⅜ x 8. **T662 Paperbound $1.35**

ELECTRONS, ATOMS, METALS AND ALLOYS, Wm. Hume-Rothery. An introductory-level explanation of the application of the electronic theory to the structure and properties of metals and alloys, taking into account the new theoretical work done by mathematical physicists. Material presented in dialogue-form between an "Old Metallurgist" and a "Young Scientist." Their discussion falls into 4 main parts: the nature of an atom, the nature of a metal, the nature of an alloy, and the structure of the nucleus. They cover such topics as the hydrogen atom, electron waves, wave mechanics, Brillouin zones, co-valent bonds, radio-activity and natural disintegration, fundamental particles, structure and fission of the nucleus, etc. Revised, enlarged edition. 177 illustrations. Subject and name indexes. 407pp. 5⅜ x 8½. **S1046 Paperbound $2.25**

OUT OF THE SKY, H. H. Nininger. A non-technical but comprehensive introduction to "meteoritics", the young science concerned with all aspects of the arrival of matter from outer space. Written by one of the world's experts on meteorites, this work shows how, despite difficulties of observation and sparseness of data, a considerable body of knowledge has arisen. It defines meteors and meteorites; studies fireball clusters and processions, meteorite composition, size, distribution, showers, explosions, origins, craters, and much more. A true connecting link between astronomy and geology. More than 175 photos, 22 other illustrations. References. Bibliography of author's publications on meteorites. Index. viii + 336pp. 5⅜ x 8. T519 Paperbound **$1.85**

SATELLITES AND SCIENTIFIC RESEARCH, D. King-Hele. Non-technical account of the manmade satellites and the discoveries they have yielded up to the autumn of 1961. Brings together information hitherto published only in hard-to-get scientific journals. Includes the life history of a typical satellite, methods of tracking, new information on the shape of the earth, zones of radiation, etc. Over 60 diagrams and 6 photographs. Mathematical appendix. Bibliography of over 100 items. Index. xii + 180pp. 5⅜ x 8½. T703 Paperbound **$2.00**

BOOKS EXPLAINING SCIENCE AND MATHEMATICS

Mathematics

CHANCE, LUCK AND STATISTICS: THE SCIENCE OF CHANCE, Horace C. Levinson. Theory of probability and science of statistics in simple, non-technical language. Part I deals with theory of probability, covering odd superstitions in regard to "luck," the meaning of betting odds, the law of mathematical expectation, gambling, and applications in poker, roulette, lotteries, dice, bridge, and other games of chance. Part II discusses the misuse of statistics, the concept of statistical probabilities, normal and skew frequency distributions, and statistics applied to various fields—birth rates, stock speculation, insurance rates, advertising, etc. "Presented in an easy humorous style which I consider the best kind of expository writing," Prof. A. C. Cohen, Industry Quality Control. Enlarged revised edition. Formerly titled "The Science of Chance." Preface and two new appendices by the author. Index. xiv + 365pp. 5⅜ x 8. T1007 Paperbound **$1.85**

PROBABILITIES AND LIFE, Emile Borel. Translated by M. Baudin. Non-technical, highly readable introduction to the results of probability as applied to everyday situations. Partial contents: Fallacies About Probabilities Concerning Life After Death; Negligible Probabilities and the Probabilities of Everyday Life; Events of Small Probability; Application of Probabilities to Certain Problems of Heredity; Probabilities of Deaths, Diseases, and Accidents; On Poisson's Formula. Index. 3 Appendices of statistical studies and tables. vi + 87pp. 5⅜ x 8½. T121 Paperbound **$1.00**

GREAT IDEAS OF MODERN MATHEMATICS: THEIR NATURE AND USE, Jagjit Singh. Reader with only high school math will understand main mathematical ideas of modern physics, astronomy, genetics, psychology, evolution, etc., better than many who use them as tools, but comprehend little of their basic structure. Author uses his wide knowledge of non-mathematical fields in brilliant exposition of differential equations, matrices, group theory, logic, statistics, problems of mathematical foundations, imaginary numbers, vectors, etc. Original publication. 2 appendices. 2 indexes. 65 illustr. 322pp. 5⅜ x 8. S587 Paperbound **$1.75**

MATHEMATICS IN ACTION, O. G. Sutton. Everyone with a command of high school algebra will find this book one of the finest possible introductions to the application of mathematics to physical theory. Ballistics, numerical analysis, waves and wavelike phenomena, Fourier series, group concepts, fluid flow and aerodynamics, statistical measures, and meteorology are discussed with unusual clarity. Some calculus and differential equations theory is developed by the author for the reader's help in the more difficult sections. 88 figures. Index. viii + 236pp. 5⅜ x 8. T440 Clothbound **$3.50**

THE FOURTH DIMENSION SIMPLY EXPLAINED, edited by H. P. Manning. 22 essays, originally Scientific American contest entries, that use a minimum of mathematics to explain aspects of 4-dimensional geometry: analogues to 3-dimensional space, 4-dimensional absurdities and curiosities (such as removing the contents of an egg without puncturing its shell), possible measurements and forms, etc. Introduction by the editor. Only book of its sort on a truly elementary level, excellent introduction to advanced works. 82 figures. 251pp. 5⅜ x 8. T711 Paperbound **$1.35**

MATHEMATICS—INTERMEDIATE TO ADVANCED

General

INTRODUCTION TO APPLIED MATHEMATICS, Francis D. Murnaghan. A practical and thoroughly sound introduction to a number of advanced branches of higher mathematics. Among the selected topics covered in detail are: vector and matrix analysis, partial and differential equations, integral equations, calculus of variations, Laplace transform theory, the vector triple product, linear vector functions, quadratic and bilinear forms, Fourier series, spherical harmonics, Bessel functions, the Heaviside expansion formula, and many others. Extremely useful book for graduate students in physics, engineering, chemistry, and mathematics. Index. 111 study exercises with answers. 41 illustrations. ix + 389pp. 5⅜ x 8½.
S1042 Paperbound **$2.00**

OPERATIONAL METHODS IN APPLIED MATHEMATICS, H. S. Carslaw and J. C. Jaeger. Explanation of the application of the Laplace Transformation to differential equations, a simple and effective substitute for more difficult and obscure operational methods. Of great practical value to engineers and to all workers in applied mathematics. Chapters on: Ordinary Linear Differential Equations with Constant Coefficients;; Electric Circuit Theory; Dynamical Applications; The Inversion Theorem for the Laplace Transformation; Conduction of Heat; Vibrations of Continuous Mechanical Systems; Hydrodynamics; Impulsive Functions; Chains of Differential Equations; and other related matters. 3 appendices. 153 problems, many with answers. 22 figures. xvi + 359pp. 5⅜ x 8½.
S1011 Paperbound **$2.25**

APPLIED MATHEMATICS FOR RADIO AND COMMUNICATIONS ENGINEERS, C. E. Smith. No extraneous material here!—only the theories, equations, and operations essential and immediately useful for radio work. Can be used as refresher, as handbook of applications and tables, or as full home-study course. Ranges from simplest arithmetic through calculus, series, and wave forms, hyperbolic trigonometry, simultaneous equations in mesh circuits, etc. Supplies applications right along with each math topic discussed. 22 useful tables of functions, formulas, logs, etc. Index. 166 exercises, 140 examples, all with answers. 95 diagrams. Bibliography. x + 336pp. 5⅜ x 8.
S141 Paperbound **$1.75**

Algebra, group theory, determinants, sets, matrix theory

ALGEBRAS AND THEIR ARITHMETICS, L. E. Dickson. Provides the foundation and background necessary to any advanced undergraduate or graduate student studying abstract algebra. Begins with elementary introduction to linear transformations, matrices, field of complex numbers; proceeds to order, basal units, modulus, quaternions, etc.; develops calculus of linears sets, describes various examples of algebras including invariant, difference, nilpotent, semi-simple. "Makes the reader marvel at his genius for clear and profound analysis," Amer. Mathematical Monthly. Index. xii + 241pp. 5⅜ x 8.
S616 Paperbound **$1.50**

THE THEORY OF EQUATIONS WITH AN INTRODUCTION TO THE THEORY OF BINARY ALGEBRAIC FORMS, W. S. Burnside and A. W. Panton. Extremely thorough and concrete discussion of the theory of equations, with extensive detailed treatment of many topics curtailed in later texts. Covers theory of algebraic equations, properties of polynomials, symmetric functions, derived functions, Horner's process, complex numbers and the complex variable, determinants and methods of elimination, invariant theory (nearly 100 pages), transformations, introduction to Galois theory, Abelian equations, and much more. Invaluable supplementary work for modern students and teachers. 759 examples and exercises. Index in each volume. Two volume set. Total of xxiv + 604pp. 5⅜ x 8.
S714 Vol I Paperbound **$1.85**
S715 Vol II Paperbound **$1.85**
The set **$3.70**

COMPUTATIONAL METHODS OF LINEAR ALGEBRA, V. N. Faddeeva, translated by **C. D. Benster.** First English translation of a unique and valuable work, the only work in English presenting a systematic exposition of the most important methods of linear algebra—classical and contemporary. Shows in detail how to derive numerical solutions of problems in mathematical physics which are frequently connected with those of linear algebra. Theory as well as individual practice. Part I surveys the mathematical background that is indispensable to what follows. Parts II and III, the conclusion, set forth the most important methods of solution, for both exact and iterative groups. One of the most outstanding and valuable features of this work is the 23 tables, double and triple checked for accuracy. These tables will not be found elsewhere. Author's preface. Translator's note. New bibliography and index. x + 252pp. 5⅜ x 8.
S424 Paperbound **$1.95**

ALGEBRAIC EQUATIONS, E. Dehn. Careful and complete presentation of Galois' theory of algebraic equations; theories of Lagrange and Galois developed in logical rather than historical form, with a more thorough exposition than in most modern books. Many concrete applications and fully-worked-out examples. Discusses basic theory (very clear exposition of the symmetric group); isomorphic, transitive, and Abelian groups; applications of Lagrange's and Galois' theories; and much more. Newly revised by the author. Index. List of Theorems. xi + 208pp. 5⅜ x 8.
S697 Paperbound **$1.45**

Differential equations, ordinary and partial; integral equations

INTRODUCTION TO THE DIFFERENTIAL EQUATIONS OF PHYSICS, L. Hopf. Especially valuable to the engineer with no math beyond elementary calculus. Emphasizing intuitive rather than formal aspects of concepts, the author covers an extensive territory. Partial contents: Law of causality, energy theorem, damped oscillations, coupling by friction, cylindrical and spherical coordinates, heat source, etc. Index. 48 figures. 160pp. 5⅜ x 8.
S120 Paperbound **$1.25**

INTRODUCTION TO THE THEORY OF LINEAR DIFFERENTIAL EQUATIONS, E. G. Poole. Authoritative discussions of important topics, with methods of solution more detailed than usual, for students with background of elementary course in differential equations. Studies existence theorems, linearly independent solutions; equations with constant coefficients; with uniform analytic coefficients; regular singularities; the hypergeometric equation; conformal representation; etc. Exercises. Index. 210pp. 5⅜ x 8.
S629 Paperbound **$1.65**

DIFFERENTIAL EQUATIONS FOR ENGINEERS, P. Franklin. Outgrowth of a course given 10 years at M. I. T. Makes most useful branch of pure math accessible for practical work. Theoretical basis of D.E.'s; solution of ordinary D.E.'s and partial derivatives arising from heat flow, steady-state temperature of a plate, wave equations; analytic functions; convergence of Fourier Series. 400 problems on electricity, vibratory systems, other topics. Formerly "Differential Equations for Electrical Engineers." Index 41 illus. 307pp. 5⅜ x 8.
S601 Paperbound **$1.65**

DIFFERENTIAL EQUATIONS, F. R. Moulton. A detailed, rigorous exposition of all the non-elementary processes of solving ordinary differential equations. Several chapters devoted to the treatment of practical problems, especially those of a physical nature, which are far more advanced than problems usually given as illustrations. Includes analytic differential equations; variations of a parameter; integrals of differential equations; analytic implicit functions; problems of elliptic motion; sine-amplitude functions; deviation of formal bodies; Cauchy-Lipschitz process; linear differential equations with periodic coefficients; differential equations in infinitely many variations; much more. Historical notes. 10 figures. 222 problems. Index. xv + 395pp. 5⅜ x 8.
S451 Paperbound **$2.00**

DIFFERENTIAL AND INTEGRAL EQUATIONS OF MECHANICS AND PHYSICS (DIE DIFFERENTIAL-UND INTEGRALGLEICHUNGEN DER MECHANIK UND PHYSIK), edited by P. Frank and R. von Mises. Most comprehensive and authoritative work on the mathematics of mathematical physics available today in the United States: the standard, definitive reference for teachers, physicists, engineers, and mathematicians—now published (in the original German) at a relatively inexpensive price for the first time! Every chapter in this 2,000-page set is by an expert in his field: Carathéodory, Courant, Frank, Mises, and a dozen others. Vol I, on mathematics, gives concise but complete coverages of advanced calculus, differential equations, integral equations and potential, and partial differential equations. Index. xxiii + 916pp. Vol. II (physics): classical mechanics, optics, continuous mechanics, heat conduction and diffusion, the stationary and quasi-stationary electromagnetic field, electromagnetic oscillations, and wave mechanics. Index. xxiv + 1106pp. Two volume set. Each volume available separately. 5⅝ x 8⅜.
S787 Vol I Clothbound **$7.50**
S788 Vol II Clothbound **$7.50**
The set **$15.00**

LECTURES ON CAUCHY'S PROBLEM, J. Hadamard. Based on lectures given at Columbia, Rome, this discusses work of Riemann, Kirchhoff, Volterra, and the author's own research on the hyperbolic case in linear partial differential equations. It extends spherical and cylindrical waves to apply to all (normal) hyperbolic equations. Partial contents: Cauchy's problem, fundamental formula, equations with odd number, with even number of independent variables; method of descent. 32 figures. Index. iii + 316pp. 5⅜ x 8. S105 Paperbound **$1.75**

THEORY OF DIFFERENTIAL EQUATIONS, A. R. Forsyth. Out of print for over a decade, the complete 6 volumes (now bound as 3) of this monumental work represent the most comprehensive treatment of differential equations ever written. Historical presentation includes in 2500 pages every substantial development. Vol. 1, 2: EXACT EQUATIONS, PFAFF'S PROBLEM; ORDINARY EQUATIONS, NOT LINEAR: methods of Grassmann, Clebsch, Lie, Darboux, Cauchy's theorem; branch points; etc. Vol. 3, 4: ORDINARY EQUATIONS, NOT LINEAR; ORDINARY LINEAR EQUATIONS: Zeta Fuchsian functions, general theorems on algebraic integrals, Brun's theorem, equations with uniform periodic coffiecients, etc. Vol. 4, 5: PARTIAL DIFFERENTIAL EQUATIONS: 2 existence-theorems, equations of theoretical dynamics, Laplace transformations, general transformation of equations of the 2nd order, much more. Indexes. Total of 2766pp. 5⅜ x 8. S576-7-8 Clothbound: the set **$15.00**

PARTIAL DIFFERENTIAL EQUATIONS OF MATHEMATICAL PHYSICS, A. G. Webster. A keystone work in the library of every mature physicist, engineer, researcher. Valuable sections on elasticity, compression theory, potential theory, theory of sound, heat conduction, wave propagation, vibration theory. Contents include: deduction of differential equations, vibrations, normal functions, Fourier's series, Cauchy's method, boundary problems, method of Riemann-Volterra. Spherical, cylindrical, ellipsoidal harmonics, applications, etc. 97 figures. vii + 440pp. 5⅜ x 8. S263 Paperbound **$2.00**

CATALOGUE OF DOVER BOOKS

ELEMENTARY CONCEPTS OF TOPOLOGY, P. Alexandroff. First English translation of the famous brief introduction to topology for the beginner or for the mathematician not undertaking extensive study. This unusually useful intuitive approach deals primarily with the concepts of complex, cycle, and homology, and is wholly consistent with current investigations. Ranges from basic concepts of set-theoretic topology to the concept of Betti groups. "Glowing example of harmony between intuition and thought," David Hilbert. Translated by A. E. Farley. Introduction by D. Hilbert. Index. 25 figures. 73pp. 5⅜ x 8. **S747 Paperbound $1.00**

Number theory

INTRODUCTION TO THE THEORY OF NUMBERS, L. E. Dickson. Thorough, comprehensive approach with adequate coverage of classical literature, an introductory volume beginners can follow. Chapters on divisibility, congruences, quadratic residues & reciprocity, Diophantine equations, etc. Full treatment of binary quadratic forms without usual restriction to integral coefficients. Covers infinitude of primes, least residues, Fermat's theorem, Euler's phi function, Legendre's symbol, Gauss's lemma, automorphs, reduced forms, recent theorems of Thue & Siegel, many more. Much material not readily available elsewhere. 239 problems. Index. I figure. viii + 183pp. 5⅜ x 8. **S342 Paperbound $1.65**

ELEMENTS OF NUMBER THEORY, I. M. Vinogradov. Detailed 1st course for persons without advanced mathematics; 95% of this book can be understood by readers who have gone no farther than high school algebra. Partial contents: divisibility theory, important number theoretical functions, congruences, primitive roots and indices, etc. Solutions to both problems and exercises. Tables of primes, indices, etc. Covers almost every essential formula in elementary number theory! Translated from Russian. 233 problems, 104 exercises. viii + 227pp. 5⅜ x 8. **S259 Paperbound $1.60**

THEORY OF NUMBERS and DIOPHANTINE ANALYSIS, R. D. Carmichael. These two complete works in one volume form one of the most lucid introductions to number theory, requiring only a firm foundation in high school mathematics. "Theory of Numbers," partial contents: Eratosthenes' sieve, Euclid's fundamental theorem, G.C.F. and L.C.M. of two or more integers, linear congruences, etc "Diophantine Analysis": rational triangles, Pythagorean triangles, equations of third, fourth, higher degrees, method of functional equations, much more. "Theory of Numbers": 76 problems. Index. 94pp. "Diophantine Analysis": 222 problems. Index. 118pp. 5⅜ x 8. **S529 Paperbound $1.35**

Numerical analysis, tables

MATHEMATICAL TABLES AND FORMULAS, Compiled by Robert D. Carmichael and Edwin R. Smith. Valuable collection for students, etc. Contains all tables necessary in college algebra and trigonometry, such as five-place common logarithms, logarithmic sines and tangents of small angles, logarithmic trigonometric functions, natural trigonometric functions, four-place antilogarithms, tables for changing from sexagesimal to circular and from circular to sexagesimal measure of angles, etc. Also many tables and formulas not ordinarily accessible, including powers, roots, and reciprocals, exponential and hyperbolic functions, ten-place logarithms of prime numbers, and formulas and theorems from analytical and elementary geometry and from calculus. Explanatory introduction. viii + 269pp. 5⅜ x 8½. **S111 Paperbound $1.00**

MATHEMATICAL TABLES, H. B. Dwight. Unique for its coverage in one volume of almost every function of importance in applied mathematics, engineering, and the physical sciences. Three extremely fine tables of the three trig functions and their inverse functions to thousandths of radians; natural and common logarithms; squares, cubes; hyperbolic functions and the inverse hyperbolic functions; $(a^2 + b^2)$ exp. ½a; complete elliptic integrals of the 1st and 2nd kind; sine and cosine integrals; exponential integrals Ei(x) and Ei(−x); binomial coefficients; factorials to 250; surface zonal harmonics and first derivatives; Bernoulli and Euler numbers and their logs to base of 10; Gamma function; normal probability integral; over 60 pages of Bessel functions; the Riemann Zeta function. Each table with formulae generally used, sources of more extensive tables, interpolation data, etc. Over half have columns of differences, to facilitate interpolation. Introduction. Index. viii + 231pp. 5⅜ x 8. **S445 Paperbound $1.75**

TABLES OF FUNCTIONS WITH FORMULAE AND CURVES, E. Jahnke & F. Emde. The world's most comprehensive 1-volume English-text collection of tables, formulae, curves of transcendent functions. 4th corrected edition, new 76-page section giving tables, formulae for elementary functions—not in other English editions. Partial contents: sine, cosine, logarithmic integral; factorial function; error integral; theta functions; elliptic integrals, functions; Legendre, Bessel, Riemann, Mathieu, hypergeometric functions, etc. Supplementary books. Bibliography. Indexed. "Out of the way functions for which we know no other source," SCIENTIFIC COMPUTING SERVICE, Ltd. 212 figures. 400pp. 5⅜ x 8. **S133 Paperbound $2.00**

CHEMISTRY AND PHYSICAL CHEMISTRY

ORGANIC CHEMISTRY, F. C. Whitmore. The entire subject of organic chemistry for the practicing chemist and the advanced student. Storehouse of facts, theories, processes found elsewhere only in specialized journals. Covers aliphatic compounds (500 pages on the properties and synthetic preparation of hydrocarbons, halides, proteins, ketones, etc.), alicyclic compounds, aromatic compounds, heterocyclic compounds, organophosphorus and organometallic compounds. Methods of synthetic preparation analyzed critically throughout. Includes much of biochemical interest. "The scope of this volume is astonishing," INDUSTRIAL AND ENGINEERING CHEMISTRY. 12,000-reference index. 2387-item bibliography. Total of x + 1005pp. 5⅜ x 8. Two volume set.

S700 Vol I Paperbound **$2.25**
S701 Vol II Paperbound **$2.25**
The set **$4.50**

THE MODERN THEORY OF MOLECULAR STRUCTURE, Bernard Pullman. A reasonably popular account of recent developments in atomic and molecular theory. Contents: The Wave Function and Wave Equations (history and bases of present theories of molecular structure); The Electronic Structure of Atoms (Description and classification of atomic wave functions, etc.); Diatomic Molecules; Non-Conjugated Polyatomic Molecules; Conjugated Polyatomic Molecules; The Structure of Complexes. Minimum of mathematical background needed. New translation by David Antin of "La Structure Moleculaire." Index. Bibliography. vii + 87pp. 5⅜ x 8½.

S987 Paperbound **$1.00**

CATALYSIS AND CATALYSTS, Marcel Prettre, Director, Research Institute on Catalysis. This brief book, translated into English for the first time, is the finest summary of the principal modern concepts, methods, and results of catalysis. Ideal introduction for beginning chemistry and physics students. Chapters: Basic Definitions of Catalysis (true catalysis and generalization of the concept of catalysis); The Scientific Bases of Catalysis (Catalysis and chemical thermodynamics, catalysis and chemical kinetics); Homogeneous Catalysis (acid-base catalysis, etc.); Chain Reactions; Contact Masses; Heterogeneous Catalysis (Mechanisms of contact catalyses, etc.); and Industrial Applications (acids and fertilizers, petroleum and petroleum chemistry, rubber, plastics, synthetic resins, and fibers). Translated by David Antin. Index. vi + 88pp. 5⅜ x 8½.

S998 Paperbound **$1.00**

POLAR MOLECULES, Pieter Debye. This work by Nobel laureate Debye offers a complete guide to fundamental electrostatic field relations, polarizability, molecular structure. Partial contents: electric intensity, displacement and force, polarization by orientation, molar polarization and molar refraction, halogen-hydrides, polar liquids, ionic saturation, dielectric constant, etc. Special chapter considers quantum theory. Indexed. 172pp. 5⅜ x 8.

S64 Paperbound **$1.50**

THE ELECTRONIC THEORY OF ACIDS AND BASES, W. F. Luder and Saverio Zuffanti. The first full systematic presentation of the electronic theory of acids and bases treating the theory and its ramifications in an uncomplicated manner. Chapters: Historical Background; Atomic Orbitals and Valence; The Electronic Theory of Acids and Bases; Electrophilic and Electrodotic Reagents; Acidic and Basic Radicals; Neutralization; Titrations with Indicators; Displacement; Catalysis; Acid Catalysis; Base Catalysis; Alkoxides and Catalysts; Conclusion. Required reading for all chemists. Second revised (1961) eidtion, with additional examples and references. 3 figures. 9 tables. Index. Bibliography xii + 165pp. 5⅜ x 8.

S201 Paperbound **$1.50**

KINETIC THEORY OF LIQUIDS, J. Frenkel. Regarding the kinetic theory of liquids as a generalization and extension of the theory of solid bodies, this volume covers all types of arrangements of solids, thermal displacements of atoms, interstitial atoms and ions, orientational and rotational motion of molecules, and transition between states of matter. Mathematical theory is developed close to the physical subject matter. 216 bibliographical footnotes. 55 figures. xi + 485pp. 5⅜ x 8.

S95 Paperbound **$2.55**

THE PRINCIPLES OF ELECTROCHEMISTRY, D. A. MacInnes. Basic equations for almost every subfield of electrochemistry from first principles, referring at all times to the soundest and most recent theories and results; unusually useful as text or as reference. Covers coulometers and Faraday's Law, electrolytic conductance, the Debye-Hueckel method for the theoretical calculation of activity coefficients, concentration cells, standard electrode potentials, thermodynamic ionization constants, pH, potentiometric titrations, irreversible phenomena, Planck's equation, and much more. "Excellent treatise," AMERICAN CHEMICAL SOCIETY JOURNAL. "Highly recommended," CHEMICAL AND METALLURGICAL ENGINEERING. 2 Indices. Appendix. 585-item bibliography. 137 figures. 94 tables. ii + 478pp. 5⅝ x 8⅜.

S52 Paperbound **$2.45**

THE PHASE RULE AND ITS APPLICATION, Alexander Findlay. Covering chemical phenomena of 1, 2, 3, 4, and multiple component systems, this "standard work on the subject" (NATURE, London), has been completely revised and brought up to date by A. N. Campbell and N. O. Smith. Brand new material has been added on such matters as binary, tertiary liquid equilibria, solid solutions in ternary systems, quinary systems of salts and water. Completely revised to triangular coordinates in ternary systems, clarified graphic representation, solid models, etc. 9th revised edition. Author, subject indexes. 236 figures. 505 footnotes, mostly bibliographic. xii + 494pp. 5⅜ x 8.

S91 Paperbound **$2.50**

PHYSICS

General physics

FOUNDATIONS OF PHYSICS, R. B. Lindsay & H. Margenau. Excellent bridge between semi-popular works & technical treatises. A discussion of methods of physical description, construction of theory; valuable for physicist with elementary calculus who is interested in ideas that give meaning to data, tools of modern physics. Contents include symbolism, mathematical equations; space & time foundations of mechanics; probability; physics & continua; electron theory; special & general relativity; quantum mechanics; causality. "Thorough and yet not overdetailed. Unreservedly recommended," NATURE (London). Unabridged, corrected edition. List of recommended readings. 35 illustrations. xi + 537pp. 5⅜ x 8.
S377 Paperbound **$2.75**

FUNDAMENTAL FORMULAS OF PHYSICS, ed. by D. H. Menzel. Highly useful, fully inexpensive reference and study text, ranging from simple to highly sophisticated operations. Mathematics integrated into text—each chapter stands as short textbook of field represented. Vol. 1: Statistics, Physical Constants, Special Theory of Relativity, Hydrodynamics, Aerodynamics, Boundary Value Problems in Math. Physics; Viscosity, Electromagnetic Theory, etc. Vol. 2: Sound, Acoustics, Geometrical Optics, Electron Optics, High-Energy Phenomena, Magnetism, Biophysics, much more. Index. Total of 800pp. 5⅜ x 8.
Vol. 1 S595 Paperbound **$2.00**
Vol. 2 S596 Paperbound **$2.00**

MATHEMATICAL PHYSICS, D. H. Menzel. Thorough one-volume treatment of the mathematical techniques vital for classic mechanics, electromagnetic theory, quantum theory, and relativity. Written by the Harvard Professor of Astrophysics for junior, senior, and graduate courses, it gives clear explanations of all those aspects of function theory, vectors, matrices, dyadics, tensors, partial differential equations, etc., necessary for the understanding of the various physical theories. Electron theory, relativity, and other topics seldom presented appear here in considerable detail. Scores of definitions, conversion factors, dimensional constants, etc. "More detailed than normal for an advanced text . . . excellent set of sections on Dyadics, Matrices, and Tensors," JOURNAL OF THE FRANKLIN INSTITUTE. Index. 193 problems, with answers. x + 412pp. 5⅜ x 8.
S56 Paperbound **$2.00**

THE SCIENTIFIC PAPERS OF J. WILLARD GIBBS. All the published papers of America's outstanding theoretical scientist (except for "Statistical Mechanics" and "Vector Analysis"). Vol I (thermodynamics) contains one of the most brilliant of all 19th-century scientific papers—the 300-page "On the Equilibrium of Heterogeneous Substances," which founded the science of physical chemistry, and clearly stated a number of highly important natural laws for the first time; 8 other papers complete the first volume. Vol II includes 2 papers on dynamics, 8 on vector analysis and multiple algebra, 5 on the electromagnetic theory of light, and 6 miscellaneous papers. Biographical sketch by H. A. Bumstead. Total of xxxvi + 718pp. 5⅝ x 8⅜.
S721 Vol I Paperbound **$2.50**
S722 Vol II Paperbound **$2.00**
The set **$4.50**

BASIC THEORIES OF PHYSICS, Peter Gabriel Bergmann. Two-volume set which presents a critical examination of important topics in the major subdivisions of classical and modern physics. The first volume is concerned with classical mechanics and electrodynamics: mechanics of mass points, analytical mechanics, matter in bulk, electrostatics and magnetostatics, electromagnetic interaction, the field waves, special relativity, and waves. The second volume (Heat and Quanta) contains discussions of the kinetic hypothesis, physics and statistics, stationary ensembles, laws of thermodynamics, early quantum theories, atomic spectra, probability waves, quantization in wave mechanics, approximation methods, and abstract quantum theory. A valuable supplement to any thorough course or text.
Heat and Quanta: Index. 8 figures. x + 300pp. 5⅜ x 8½. S968 Paperbound **$1.75**
Mechanics and Electrodynamics: Index. 14 figures. vii + 280pp. 5⅜ x 8½.
S969 Paperbound **$1.75**

THEORETICAL PHYSICS, A. S. Kompaneyets. One of the very few thorough studies of the subject in this price range. Provides advanced students with a comprehensive theoretical background. Especially strong on recent experimentation and developments in quantum theory. Contents: Mechanics (Generalized Coordinates, Lagrange's Equation, Collision of Particles, etc.), Electrodynamics (Vector Analysis, Maxwell's equations, Transmission of Signals, Theory of Relativity, etc.), Quantum Mechanics (the Inadequacy of Classical Mechanics, the Wave Equation, Motion in a Central Field, Quantum Theory of Radiation, Quantum Theories of Dispersion and Scattering, etc.), and Statistical Physics (Equilibrium Distribution of Molecules in an Ideal Gas, Boltzmann statistics, Bose and Fermi Distribution, Thermodynamic Quantities, etc.). Revised to 1961. Translated by George Yankovsky, authorized by Kompaneyets. 137 exercises. 56 figures. 529pp. 5⅜ x 8½. S972 Paperbound **$2.50**

ANALYTICAL AND CANONICAL FORMALISM IN PHYSICS, André Mercier. A survey, in one volume, of the variational principles (the key principles—in mathematical form—from which the basic laws of any one branch of physics can be derived) of the several branches of physical theory, together with an examination of the relationships among them. Contents: the Lagrangian Formalism, Lagrangian Densities, Canonical Formalism, Canonical Form of Electrodynamics, Hamiltonian Densities, Transformations, and Canonical Form with Vanishing Jacobian Determinant. Numerous examples and exercises. For advanced students, teachers, etc. 6 figures. Index. viii + 222pp. 5⅜ x 8½. S1077 Paperbound **$1.75**

MATHEMATICAL PUZZLES AND RECREATIONS

AMUSEMENTS IN MATHEMATICS, Henry Ernest Dudeney. The foremost British originator of mathematical puzzles is always intriguing, witty, and paradoxical in this classic, one of the largest collections of mathematical amusements. More than 430 puzzles, problems, and paradoxes. Mazes and games, problems on number manipulation, unicursal and other route problems, puzzles on measuring, weighing, packing, age, kinship, chessboards, joining, crossing river, plane figure dissection, and many others. Solutions. More than 450 illustrations. vii + 258pp. 5⅜ x 8.   T473 Paperbound **$1.25**

SYMBOLIC LOGIC and THE GAME OF LOGIC, Lewis Carroll. "Symbolic Logic" is not concerned with modern symbolic logic, but is instead a collection of over 380 problems posed with charm and imagination, using the syllogism, and a fascinating diagrammatic method of drawing conclusions. In "The Game of Logic," Carroll's whimsical imagination devises a logical game played with 2 diagrams and counters (included) to manipulate hundreds of tricky syllogisms. The final section, "Hit or Miss" is a lagniappe of 101 additional puzzles in the delightful Carroll manner. Until this reprint edition, both of these books were rarities costing up to $15 each. Symbolic Logic: Index, xxxi + 199pp. The Game of Logic: 96pp. Two vols. bound as one. 5⅜ x 8.   T492 Paperbound **$1.50**

MAZES AND LABYRINTHS: A BOOK OF PUZZLES, W. Shepherd. Mazes, formerly associated with mystery and ritual, are still among the most intriguing of intellectual puzzles. This is a novel and different collection of 50 amusements that embody the principle of the maze: mazes in the classical tradition; 3-dimensional, ribbon, and Möbius-strip mazes; hidden messages; spatial arrangements; etc.—almost all built on amusing story situations. 84 illustrations. Essay on maze psychology. Solutions. xv + 122pp. 5⅜ x 8.   T731 Paperbound **$1.00**

MATHEMATICAL RECREATIONS, M. Kraitchik. Some 250 puzzles, problems, demonstrations of recreational mathematics for beginners & advanced mathematicians. Unusual historical problems from Greek, Medieval, Arabic, Hindu sources: modern problems based on "mathematics without numbers," geometry, topology, arithmetic, etc. Pastimes derived from figurative numbers, Mersenne numbers, Fermat numbers; fairy chess, latruncles, reversi, many topics. Full solutions. Excellent for insights into special fields of math. 181 illustrations. 330pp. 5⅜ x 8.   T163 Paperbound **$1.75**

MATHEMATICAL PUZZLES OF SAM LOYD, Vol. I, selected and edited by M. Gardner. Puzzles by the greatest puzzle creator and innovator. Selected from his famous "Cyclopedia of Puzzles," they retain the unique style and historical flavor of the originals. There are posers based on arithmetic, algebra, probability, game theory, route tracing, topology, counter, sliding block, operations research, geometrical dissection. Includes his famous "14-15" puzzle which was a national craze, and his "Horse of a Different Color" which sold millions of copies. 117 of his most ingenious puzzles in all, 120 line drawings and diagrams. Solutions. Selected references. xx + 167pp. 5⅜ x 8.   T498 Paperbound **$1.00**

MY BEST PUZZLES IN MATHEMATICS, Hubert Phillips ("Caliban"). Caliban is generally considered the best of the modern problemists. Here are 100 of his best and wittiest puzzles, selected by the author himself from such publications as the London Daily Telegraph, and each puzzle is guaranteed to put even the sharpest puzzle detective through his paces. Perfect for the development of clear thinking and a logical mind. Complete solutions are provided for every puzzle. x + 107pp. 5⅜ x 8½.   T91 Paperbound **$1.00**

MY BEST PUZZLES IN LOGIC AND REASONING, H. Phillips ("Caliban"). 100 choice, hitherto unavailable puzzles by England's best-known problemist. No special knowledge needed to solve these logical or inferential problems, just an unclouded mind, nerves of steel, and fast reflexes. Data presented are both necessary and just sufficient to allow one unambiguous answer. More than 30 different types of puzzles, all ingenious and varied, many one of a kind, that will challenge the expert, please the beginner. Original publication. 100 puzzles, full solutions. x + 107pp. 5⅜ x 8½.   T119 Paperbound **$1.00**

MATHEMATICAL PUZZLES FOR BEGINNERS AND ENTHUSIASTS, G. Mott-Smith. 188 mathematical puzzles to test mental agility. Inference, interpretation, algebra, dissection of plane figures, geometry, properties of numbers, decimation, permutations, probability, all enter these delightful problems. Puzzles like the Odic Force, How to Draw an Ellipse, Spider's Cousin, more than 180 others. Detailed solutions. Appendix with square roots, triangular numbers, primes, etc. 135 illustrations. 2nd revised edition. 248pp. 5⅜ x 8.   T198 Paperbound **$1.00**

MATHEMATICS, MAGIC AND MYSTERY, Martin Gardner. Card tricks, feats of mental mathematics, stage mind-reading, other "magic" explained as applications of probability, sets, theory of numbers, topology, various branches of mathematics. Creative examination of laws and their applications with scores of new tricks and insights. 115 sections discuss tricks with cards, dice, coins; geometrical vanishing tricks, dozens of others. No sleight of hand needed; mathematics guarantees success. 115 illustrations. xii + 174pp. 5⅜ x 8.   T335 Paperbound **$1.00**

RECREATIONS IN THE THEORY OF NUMBERS: THE QUEEN OF MATHEMATICS ENTERTAINS, Albert H. Beiler. The theory of numbers is often referred to as the "Queen of Mathematics." In this book Mr. Beiler has compiled the first English volume to deal exclusively with the recreational aspects of number theory, an inherently recreational branch of mathematics. The author's clear style makes for enjoyable reading as he deals with such topics as: perfect numbers, amicable numbers, Fermat's theorem, Wilson's theorem, interesting properties of digits, methods of factoring, primitive roots, Euler's function, polygonal and figurate numbers, Mersenne numbers, congruence, repeating decimals, etc. Countless puzzle problems, with full answers and explanations. For mathematicians and mathematically-inclined laymen, etc. New publication. 28 figures. 9 illustrations. 103 tables. Bibliography at chapter ends. vi + 247pp. 5⅜ x 8½. T1096 Paperbound **$1.85**

PAPER FOLDING FOR BEGINNERS, W. D. Murray and F. J. Rigney. A delightful introduction to the varied and entertaining Japanese art of origami (paper folding), with a full crystal-clear text that anticipates every difficulty; over 275 clearly labeled diagrams of all important stages in creation. You get results at each stage, since complex figures are logically developed from simpler ones. 43 different pieces are explained: place mats, drinking cups, bonbon boxes, sailboats, frogs, roosters, etc. 6 photographic plates. 279 diagrams. 95pp. 5⅜ x 8⅜. T713 Paperbound **$1.00**

1800 RIDDLES, ENIGMAS AND CONUNDRUMS, Darwin A. Hindman. Entertaining collection ranging from hilarious gags to outrageous puns to sheer nonsense—a welcome respite from sophisticated humor. Children, toastmasters, and practically anyone with a funny bone will find these zany riddles tickling and eminently repeatable. Sample: "Why does Santa Claus always go down the chimney?" "Because it soots him." Some old, some new—covering a wide variety of subjects. New publication. iii + 154pp. 5⅜ x 8½. T1059 Paperbound **$1.00**

EASY-TO-DO ENTERTAINMENTS AND DIVERSIONS WITH CARDS, STRING, COINS, PAPER AND MATCHES, R. M. Abraham. Over 300 entertaining games, tricks, puzzles, and pastimes for children and adults. Invaluable to anyone in charge of groups of youngsters, for party givers, etc. Contains sections on card tricks and games, making things by paperfolding—toys, decorations, and the like; tricks with coins, matches, and pieces of string; descriptions of games; toys that can be made from common household objects; mathematical recreations; word games; and 50 miscellaneous entertainments. Formerly "Winter Nights Entertainments." Introduction by Lord Baden Powell. 329 illustrations. v + 186pp. 5⅜ x 8. T921 Paperbound **$1.00**

DIVERSIONS AND PASTIMES WITH CARDS, STRING, PAPER AND MATCHES, R. M. Abraham. Another collection of amusements and diversion for game and puzzle fans of all ages. Many new paperfolding ideas and tricks, an extensive section on amusements with knots and splices, two chapters of easy and not-so-easy problems, coin and match tricks, and lots of other parlor pastimes from the agile mind of the late British problemist and gamester. Corrected and revised version. Illustrations. 160pp. 5⅜ x 8½. T1127 Paperbound **$1.00**

STRING FIGURES AND HOW TO MAKE THEM: A STUDY OF CAT'S-CRADLE IN MANY LANDS, Caroline Furness Jayne. In a simple and easy-to-follow manner, this book describes how to make 107 different string figures. Not only is looping and crossing string between the fingers a common youthful diversion, but it is an ancient form of amusement practiced in all parts of the globe, especially popular among primitive tribes. These games are fun for all ages and offer an excellent means for developing manual dexterity and coordination. Much insight also for the anthropological observer on games and diversions in many different cultures. Index. Bibliography. Introduction by A. C. Haddon, Cambridge University. 17 full-page plates. 950 illustrations. xxiii + 407pp. 5⅜ x 8½. T152 Paperbound **$2.00**

CRYPTANALYSIS, Helen F. Gaines. (Formerly ELEMENTARY CRYPTANALYSIS.) A standard elementary and intermediate text for serious students. It does not confine itself to old material, but contains much that is not generally known, except to experts. Concealment, Transposition, Substitution ciphers; Vigenere, Kasiski, Playfair, multafid, dozens of other techniques. Appendix with sequence charts, letter frequencies in English, 5 other languages, English word frequencies. Bibliography. 167 codes. New to this edition: solution to codes. vi + 230pp. 5⅜ x 8. T97 Paperbound **$2.00**

MAGIC SQUARES AND CUBES, W. S. Andrews. Only book-length treatment in English, a thorough non-technical description and analysis. Here are nasik, overlapping, pandiagonal, serrated squares; magic circles, cubes, spheres, rhombuses. Try your hand at 4-dimensional magical figures! Much unusual folklore and tradition included. High school algebra is sufficient. 754 diagrams and illustrations. viii + 419pp. 5⅜ x 8. T658 Paperbound **$1.85**

CALIBAN'S PROBLEM BOOK: MATHEMATICAL, INFERENTIAL, AND CRYPTOGRAPHIC PUZZLES, H. Phillips ("Caliban"), S. T. Shovelton, G. S. Marshall. 105 ingenious problems by the greatest living creator of puzzles based on logic and inference. Rigorous, modern, piquant, and reflecting their author's unusual personality, these intermediate and advanced puzzles all involve the ability to reason clearly through complex situations; some call for mathematical knowledge, ranging from algebra to number theory. Solutions. xi + 180pp. 5⅜ x 8. T736 Paperbound **$1.25**

FICTION

THE LAND THAT TIME FORGOT and THE MOON MAID, Edgar Rice Burroughs. In the opinion of many, Burroughs' best work. The first concerns a strange island where evolution is individual rather than phylogenetic. Speechless anthropoids develop into intelligent human beings within a single generation. The second projects the reader far into the future and describes the first voyage to the Moon (in the year 2025), the conquest of the Earth by the Moon, and years of violence and adventure as the enslaved Earthmen try to regain possession of their planet. "An imaginative tour de force that keeps the reader keyed up and expectant," NEW YORK TIMES. Complete, unabridged text of the original two novels (three parts in each). 5 illustrations by J. Allen St. John. vi + 552pp. 5⅜ x 8½.

T1020 Clothbound **$3.75**
T358 Paperbound **$2.00**

AT THE EARTH'S CORE, PELLUCIDAR, TANAR OF PELLUCIDAR: THREE SCIENCE FICTION NOVELS BY EDGAR RICE BURROUGHS. Complete, unabridged texts of the first three Pellucidar novels. Tales of derring-do by the famous master of science fiction. The locale for these three related stories is the inner surface of the hollow Earth where we discover the world of Pellucidar, complete with all types of bizarre, menacing creatures, strange peoples, and alluring maidens—guaranteed to delight all Burroughs fans and a wide circle of adventure lovers. Illustrated by J. Allen St. John and P. F. Berdanier. vi + 433pp. 5⅜ x 8½.

T1051 Paperbound **$2.00**

THE PIRATES OF VENUS and LOST ON VENUS: TWO VENUS NOVELS BY EDGAR RICE BURROUGHS. Two related novels, complete and unabridged. Exciting adventure on the planet Venus with Earthman Carson Napier broken-field running through one dangerous episode after another. All lovers of swashbuckling science fiction will enjoy these two stories set in a world of fascinating societies, fierce beasts, 5000-ft. trees, lush vegetation, and wide seas. Illustrations by Fortunino Matania. Total of vi + 340pp. 5⅜ x 8½. T1053 Paperbound **$1.75**

A PRINCESS OF MARS and A FIGHTING MAN OF MARS: TWO MARTIAN NOVELS BY EDGAR RICE BURROUGHS. "Princess of Mars" is the very first of the great Martian novels written by Burroughs, and it is probably the best of them all; it set the pattern for all of his later fantasy novels and contains a thrilling cast of strange peoples and creatures and the formula of Olympian heroism amidst ever-fluctuating fortunes which Burroughs carries off so successfully. "Fighting Man" returns to the same scenes and cities—many years later. A mad scientist, a degenerate dictator, and an indomitable defender of the right clash—with the fate of the Red Planet at stake! Complete, unabridged reprinting of original editions. Illustrations by F. E. Schoonover and Hugh Hutton. v + 356pp. 5⅜ x 8½.

T1140 Paperbound **$1.75**

THREE MARTIAN NOVELS, Edgar Rice Burroughs Contains: Thuvia, Maid of Mars; The Chessmen of Mars; and The Master Mind of Mars. High adventure out in an imaginative and intricate conception of the Red Planet. Mars is peopled with an intelligent, heroic human race which lives in densely populated cities and with fierce barbarians who inhabit dead sea bottoms. Other exciting creatures abound amidst an inventive framework of Martian history and geography. Complete unabridged reprintings of the first edition. 16 illustrations by J. Allen St. John. vi + 499pp. 5⅜ x 8½. T39 Paperbound **$1.85**

THREE PROPHETIC NOVELS BY H. G. WELLS, edited by E. F. Bleiler. Complete texts of "When the Sleeper Wakes" (1st book printing in 50 years), "A Story of the Days to Come," "The Time Machine" (1st complete printing in book form). Exciting adventures in the future are as enjoyable today as 50 years ago when first printed. Predict TV, movies, intercontinental airplanes, prefabricated houses, air-conditioned cities, etc. First important author to foresee problems of mind control, technological dictatorships. "Absolute best of imaginative fiction," N. Y. Times. Introduction. 335pp. 5⅜ x 8. T605 Paperbound **$1.50**

28 SCIENCE FICTION STORIES OF H. G. WELLS. Two full unabridged novels, MEN LIKE GODS and STAR BEGOTTEN, plus 26 short stories by the master science-fiction writer of all time. Stories of space, time, invention, exploration, future adventure—an indispensable part of the library of everyone interested in science and adventure. PARTIAL CONTENTS: Men Like Gods, The Country of the Blind, In the Abyss, The Crystal Egg, The Man Who Could Work Miracles, A Story of the Days to Come, The Valley of Spiders, and 21 more! 928pp. 5⅜ x 8.

T265 Clothbound **$4.50**

THE WAR IN THE AIR, IN THE DAYS OF THE COMET, THE FOOD OF THE GODS: THREE SCIENCE FICTION NOVELS BY H. G. WELLS. Three exciting Wells offerings bearing on vital social and philosophical issues of his and our own day. Here are tales of air power, strategic bombing, East vs. West, the potential miracles of science, the potential disasters from outer space, the relationship between scientific advancement and moral progress, etc. First reprinting of "War in the Air" in almost 50 years. An excellent sampling of Wells at his storytelling best. Complete, unabridged reprintings. 16 illustrations. 645pp. 5⅜ x 8½.

T1135 Paperbound **$2.00**

SEVEN SCIENCE FICTION NOVELS, H. G. Wells. Full unabridged texts of 7 science-fiction novels of the master. Ranging from biology, physics, chemistry, astronomy to sociology and other studies, Mr. Wells extrapolates whole worlds of strange and intriguing character. "One will have to go far to match this for entertainment, excitement, and sheer pleasure . . . ," NEW YORK TIMES. Contents: The Time Machine, The Island of Dr. Moreau, First Men in the Moon, The Invisible Man, The War of the Worlds, The Food of the Gods, In the Days of the Comet. 1015pp. 5⅜ x 8.   T264 Clothbound **$4.50**

BEST GHOST STORIES OF J. S. LE FANU, Selected and introduced by E. F. Bleiler. LeFanu is deemed the greatest name in Victorian supernatural fiction. Here are 16 of his best horror stories, including 2 nouvelles: "Carmilla," a classic vampire tale couched in a perverse eroticism, and "The Haunted Baronet." Also: "Sir Toby's Will," "Green Tea," "Schalken the Painter," "Ultor de Lacy," "The Familiar," etc. The first American publication of about half of this material: a long-overdue opportunity to get a choice sampling of LeFanu's work. New selection (1964). 8 illustrations. 5⅜ x 8⅜.   T415 Paperbound **$1.85**

THE WONDERFUL WIZARD OF OZ, L. F. Baum. Only edition in print with all the original W. W. Denslow illustrations in full color—as much a part of "The Wizard" as Tenniel's drawings are for "Alice in Wonderland." "The Wizard" is still America's best-loved fairy tale, in which, as the author expresses it, "The wonderment and joy are retained and the heartaches and nightmares left out." Now today's young readers can enjoy every word and wonderful picture of the original book. New introduction by Martin Gardner. A Baum bibliography. 23 full-page color plates. viii + 268pp. 5⅜ x 8.   T691 Paperbound **$1.50**

GHOST AND HORROR STORIES OF AMBROSE BIERCE, Selected and introduced by E. F. Bleiler. 24 morbid, eerie tales—the cream of Bierce's fiction output. Contains such memorable pieces as "The Moonlit Road," "The Damned Thing," "An Inhabitant of Carcosa," "The Eyes of the Panther," "The Famous Gilson Bequest," "The Middle Toe of the Right Foot," and other chilling stories, plus the essay, "Visions of the Night" in which Bierce gives us a kind of rationale for his aesthetic of horror. New collection (1964). xxii + 199pp. 5⅜ x 8⅜.   T767 Paperbound **$1.00**

HUMOR

MR. DOOLEY ON IVRYTHING AND IVRYBODY, Finley Peter Dunne. Since the time of his appearance in 1893, "Mr. Dooley," the fictitious Chicago bartender, has been recognized as America's most humorous social and political commentator. Collected in this volume are 102 of the best Dooley pieces—all written around the turn of the century, the height of his popularity. Mr. Dooley's Irish brogue is employed wittily and penetratingly on subjects which are just as fresh and relevant today as they were then: corruption and hypocrisy of politicans, war preparations and chauvinism, automation, Latin American affairs, superbombs, etc. Other articles range from Rudyard Kipling to football. Selected with an introduction by Robert Hutchinson. xii + 244pp. 5⅜ x 8½.   T626 Paperbound **$1.00**

RUTHLESS RHYMES FOR HEARTLESS HOMES and MORE RUTHLESS RHYMES FOR HEARTLESS HOMES, Harry Graham ("Col. D. Streamer"). A collection of Little Willy and 48 other poetic "disasters." Graham's funniest and most disrespectful verse, accompanied by original illustrations. Nonsensical, wry humor which employs stern parents, careless nurses, uninhibited children, practical jokers, single-minded golfers, Scottish lairds, etc. in the leading roles. A precursor of the "sick joke" school of today. This volume contains, bound together for the first time, two of the most perennially popular books of humor in England and America. Index. vi + 69pp. 5⅜ x 8.   T930 Paperbound **75¢**

A WHIMSEY ANTHOLOGY, Collected by Carolyn Wells. 250 of the most amusing rhymes ever written. Acrostics, anagrams, palindromes, alphabetical jingles, tongue twisters, echo verses, alliterative verses, riddles, mnemonic rhymes, interior rhymes, over 40 limericks, etc. by Lewis Carroll, Edward Lear, Joseph Addison, W. S. Gilbert, Christina Rossetti, Chas. Lamb, James Boswell, Hood, Dickens, Swinburne, Leigh Hunt, Harry Graham, Poe, Eugene Field, and many others. xiv + 221pp. 5⅜ x 8½.   T195 Paperbound **$1.25**

MY PIOUS FRIENDS AND DRUNKEN COMPANIONS and MORE PIOUS FRIENDS AND DRUNKEN COMPANIONS, Songs and ballads of Conviviality Collected by Frank Shay. Magnificently illuminated by John Held, Jr. 132 ballads, blues, vaudeville numbers, drinking songs, cowboy songs, sea chanties, comedy songs, etc. of the Naughty Nineties and early 20th century. Over a third are reprinted with music. Many perennial favorites such as: The Band Played On, Frankie and Johnnie, The Old Grey Mare, The Face on the Bar-room Floor, etc. Many others unlocatable elsewhere: The Dog-Catcher's Child, The Cannibal Maiden, Don't Go in the Lion's Cage Tonight, Mother, etc. Complete verses and introductions to songs. Unabridged republication of first editions, 2 Indexes (song titles and first lines and choruses). Introduction by Frank Shay. 2 volumes bounds as 1. Total of xvi + 235pp. 5⅜ x 8½.   T946 Paperbound **$1.25**

MAX AND MORITZ, Wilhelm Busch. Edited and annotated by H. Arthur Klein. Translated by H. Arthur Klein, M. C. Klein, and others. The mischievous high jinks of Max and Moritz, Peter and Paul, Ker and Plunk, etc. are delightfully captured in sketch and rhyme. (Companion volume to "Hypocritical Helena.") In addition to the title piece, it contians: Ker and Plunk; Two Dogs and Two Boys; The Egghead and the Two Cut-ups of Corinth; Deceitful Henry; The Boys and the Pipe; Cat and Mouse; and others. (Original German text with accompanying English translations.) Afterword by H. A. Klein. vi + 216pp. 5⅜ x 8½.
T181 Paperbound **$1.15**

THROUGH THE ALIMENTARY CANAL WITH GUN AND CAMERA: A FASCINATING TRIP TO THE INTERIOR, Personally Conducted by George S. Chappell. In mock-travelogue style, the amusing account of an imaginative journey down the alimentary canal. The "explorers" enter the esophagus, round the Adam's Apple, narrowly escape from a fierce Amoeba, struggle through the impenetrable Nerve Forests of the Lumbar Region, etc. Illustrated by the famous cartoonist, Otto Soglow, the book is as much a brilliant satire of academic pomposity and professional travel literature as it is a clever use of the facts of physiology for supremely comic purposes. Preface by Robert Benchley. Author's Foreword. 1 Photograph. 17 illustrations by O. Soglow. xii + 114pp. 5⅜ x 8½.
T376 Paperbound **$1.00**

THE BAD CHILD'S BOOK OF BEASTS, MORE BEASTS FOR WORSE CHILDREN, and A MORAL ALPHABET, H. Belloc. Hardly an anthology of humorous verse has appeared in the last 50 years without at least a couple of these famous nonsense verses. But one must see the entire volumes—with all the delightful original illustrations by Sir Basil Blackwood—to appreciate fully Belloc's charming and witty verses that play so subacidly on the platitudes of life and morals that beset his day—and ours. A great humor classic. Three books in one. Total of 157pp. 5⅜ x 8.
T749 Paperbound **$1.00**

THE DEVIL'S DICTIONARY, Ambrose Bierce. Sardonic and irreverent barbs puncturing the pomposities and absurdities of American politics, business, religion, literature, and arts, by the country's greatest satirist in the classic tradition. Epigrammatic as Shaw, piercing as Swift, American as Mark Twain, Will Rogers, and Fred Allen. Bierce will always remain the favorite of a small coterie of enthusiasts, and of writers and speakers whom he supplies with "some of the most gorgeous witticisms of the English language." (H. L. Mencken) Over 1000 entries in alphabetical order. 144pp. 5⅜ x 8.
T487 Paperbound **$1.00**

THE COMPLETE NONSENSE OF EDWARD LEAR. This is the only complete edition of this master of gentle madness available at a popular price. A BOOK OF NONSENSE, NONSENSE SONGS, MORE NONSENSE SONGS AND STORIES in their entirety with all the old favorites that have delighted children and adults for years. The Dong With A Luminous Nose, The Jumblies, The Owl and the Pussycat, and hundreds of other bits of wonderful nonsense. 214 limericks, 3 sets of Nonsense Botany, 5 Nonsense Alphabets. 546 drawings by Lear himself, and much more. 320pp. 5⅜ x 8.
T167 Paperbound **$1.00**

SINGULAR TRAVELS, CAMPAIGNS, AND ADVENTURES OF BARON MUNCHAUSEN, R. E. Raspe, with 90 illustrations by Gustave Doré. The first edition in over 150 years to reestablish the deeds of the Prince of Liars exactly as Raspe first recorded them in 1785—the genuine Baron Munchausen, one of the most popular personalities in English literature. Included also are the best of the many sequels, written by other hands. Introduction on Raspe by J. Carswell. Bibliography of early editions. xliv + 192pp. 5⅜ x 8. T698 Paperbound **$1.00**

HOW TO TELL THE BIRDS FROM THE FLOWERS, R. W. Wood. How not to confuse a carrot with a parrot, a grape with an ape, a puffin with nuffin. Delightful drawings, clever puns, absurd little poems point out farfetched resemblances in nature. The author was a leading physicist. Introduction by Margaret Wood White. 106 illus. 60pp. 5⅜ x 8.
T523 Paperbound **75¢**

JOE MILLER'S JESTS OR, THE WITS VADE-MECUM. The original Joe Miller jest book. Gives a keen and pungent impression of life in 18th-century England. Many are somewhat on the bawdy side and they are still capable of provoking amusement and good fun. This volume is a facsimile of the original "Joe Miller" first published in 1739. It remains the most popular and influential humor book of all time. New introduction by Robert Hutchinson. xxi + 70pp. 5⅜ x 8½.
T423 Paperbound **$1.00**

Prices subject to change without notice.

Dover publishes books on art, music, philosophy, literature, languages, history, social sciences, psychology, handcrafts, orientalia, puzzles and entertainments, chess, pets and gardens, books explaining science, intermediate and higher mathematics, mathematical physics, engineering, biological sciences, earth sciences, classics of science, etc. Write to:

Dept. catrr.
Dover Publications, Inc.
180 Varick Street, N.Y. 14, N.Y.